FRAMINGHAM STATE COLLEGE
3 3014 00054 3993

D1289362

L. C. YOUNG

Distinguished Research Professor of Mathematics
University of Wisconsin
Former Fellow of Trinity College
Cambridge University

Lectures on the
CALCULUS OF VARIATIONS AND OPTIMAL CONTROL THEORY

W. B. SAUNDERS COMPANY
Philadelphia London Toronto 1969

W. B. Saunders Company: West Washington Square
Philadelphia, Pa. 19105

12 Dyott Street
London, W.C. 1

1835 Yonge Street
Toronto 7, Ontario

Lectures on the Calculus of Variations and Optimal Control Theory

 Press of W. B. Saunders Company. Library of Congress catalog card number 69-11201.

FOREWORD

The calculus of variations is a subject with a long history, and one in which a great deal of interest has recently been rekindled. The impetus has come partly from such related branches of mathematics as differential geometry and partial differential equations which have vigorously developed, and partly from the success of variational methods in new applied fields, such as control engineering and mathematical economics.

Among the ideas which have had a decisive impact on recent developments in calculus of variations are those in L. C. Young's work on generalized curves and surfaces. Beginning with his papers on generalized curves (1933 to 1938), Young introduced what were then quite novel viewpoints; for example, a curve or surface should be determined by the way it acts on variational integrands. This provided a link between calculus of variations and the ideas of weak solutions of differential equations, Schwartz's distributions, and De Rham's currents. Eventually it led to deep and beautiful results on the many dimensional Plateau problem, and to analysis in the large in the setting of integral currents and varifolds. (For a short introduction to these latter topics see F. J. Almgren: Plateau's Problem: an Invitation to Varifold Geometry. Benjamin, New York, 1966.) From Young's viewpoint the "obvious" topologies on the space of curves were wrong. He introduced another, which is better suited to calculus of variations. In this topology, the space of ordinary curves is not complete; its completion contains objects that Young called generalized curves. These provide solutions to variational problems, which have no solutions in the ordinary sense. For this reason, generalized curves, or their equivalents, are widespread in current control theory literature. They appear under such names as sliding regimes, chattering controls, and relaxed controls.

These *Lectures* progress from classical topics in calculus of variations, at the beginning of Volume I, to quite recent work on optimal control theory in Volume II. They do not represent merely a compilation of useful theorems and their proofs; the *Lectures* are also a welcome account, in the author's highly personal style, of his view of the field to which he has contributed so much.

WENDELL H. FLEMING
Brown University

PREFACE

These lectures are intended for a wide range of readers.

The subject matter is directed toward the most modern developments and even includes some as yet unpublished work; it goes deep into applications of functional analysis. In addition the whole Hamiltonian theory has been completely recast in the spirit of modern convexity concepts. We also give an introduction to the Morse theory. Further, even the preamble leads the reader to the modern theory of distributions, whereas the classical theory, developed in Chapters I and II, and in the unicity part of Chapter V, is given nowhere else with the same completeness except in the masterly work of Carathéodory. Finally, the entire volume is designed to prepare the reader for contemporary researches in optimal control, which will be treated in a second volume.†

Under the circumstances, it might be thought that the lectures would be unreadable except by a select few who happen to be fully conversant with the most advanced concepts and methods of the rest of modern analysis. We firmly believe that this is not the case. On the contrary, the lectures were delivered to students of rather varied backgrounds, and they have been written for readers with only a minimum of mathematical preparation. Apart from this, the only prerequisite to reading this book is an intense desire to learn, and this we do our best to encourage and to foster. We do not by any means subscribe to the arrogant Pythagorean exclusiveness, according to which none may enter save a professional in the field. The lectures are intended, partly, for specialists in other fields, such as engineers, astronomers, and computer scientists, who need the material in space science. Above all, they are planned for the talented young persons now emerging from the high schools, who will soon be taking over from the rest of us. Naturally, they will need time and effort to study the book, but we give them all the help we can.

To be writing for such a varied audience without detracting from the interest of the mathematical specialist may sound impossibly optimistic, but it has been done before. To illustrate this we need only refer to the famous book, *Inequalities*, by Hardy, Littlewood and Polya,‡ which we strongly commend to the reader. Similarly, those who are partial to astronomy will point to the inspiring books of Eddington. In our case we have had already some evidence of success; the preamble, while still in typescript, has been in great demand among colleagues to provide light reading after a hard week's work. This is partly because we have tried to stress suitably the

† For the reader's convenience the two volumes have been bound together. For those mainly interested in a practical knowledge of optimal control, we suggest confining their reading of Volume I to the Preamble, Chapter I and the duality part of Chapter II before passing to the initial parts of Volume II.

‡ New York, Cambridge University Press, 1952.

historical aspects, which few people know nowadays, and the philosophical trends, which few people realize. In this respect, the author has had the advantage of a long acquaintance with great mathematicians, known to most people today only as famous names. Above all, we have tried by every means to stimulate and develop the reader's insight and understanding, in accordance with the imaginative tradition of W. H. and G. C. Young, the author's late parents.

With regard to the many asides, which reflect opinions held by the author as the result of his long experience with mathematicians and with mathematical research, the reader who disagrees with them should bear in mind that we are not really trying to convert him or anyone else, but only to promote a healthy atmosphere of discussion. If we do convince him, so much the better, but this must only be on the basis of his own convictions. An atmosphere of free discussion and criticism is quite essential in mathematics, although it is extremely difficult to build up with mathematics only. What is really vital is that the reader should take no piece of mathematics on trust if he is ever to grasp it.

Generally, our main object in these lectures is to stimulate the reader's interest, enthusiasm and, especially, his desire to learn and to find things out for himself. In particular, we take every opportunity to urge him to read and study the great books (listed in the references at the end of this book), where he will find this stimulus too.†

My thanks are due to the many students and friends who have helped in removing minor inaccuracies and obscurities, and, especially, to Dr. M. H. Vasavada who read all the proofs.

L. C. Young

† A good way to treat these lectures is to regard them as being delivered orally and to take notes. These notes should be comprised of what the reader considers important, and they should be supplemented by material from reference books when he considers this helpful.

CONTENTS

Volume I- Lectures on the Calculus of Variations

Preamble

GENERALITIES AND TYPICAL PROBLEMS 2

1. Introduction 2
2. The Place of the Calculus of Variations in Relation to the Rest of Mathematics and to Space Science 3
3. Statement of the Simplest Problem and Some Cognate Matters 4
4. Extremals in Some Classical Problems 7
5. Solutions of the Preceding Problems (a), (b), (c) 9
6. The Euler-Lagrange Lemma and Schwartz Distributions 16
7. Alternative Forms of the Lemma 18
8. Proof of the Main Form of the Lemma 19
9. First Variation, Euler Equation, Transversality 21
10. Perron's Paradox 22

Chapter I

THE METHOD OF GEODESIC COVERINGS 24

11. Introduction 24
12. The Variational Algorithm of Huygens 25
13. A Link with Elementary Convexity 27
14. Reappearance of the Euler Equation 30
15. The Theorem of Malus 32
16. Sufficient Conditions for Independence of the Hilbert Integral 34
17. Invariance Properties and an Envelope Theorem 35
18. General Comments and the Applications to Plane Problems 38
19. Background on Fix-Points and on Existence Theorems for Differential Equations and Implicit Functions 40

Chapter II

DUALITY AND LOCAL EMBEDDING 46

20. Introduction 46
21. The Legendre Transformation 46

22. The Hamiltonian and its Properties . . . 47
23. Cauchy Characteristics . . . 49
24. Duality and the Standard Hamiltonian in the Parametric Case . . . 50
25. Other Admissible Parametric Hamiltonians . . . 53
26. Local Passage from Parametric to Nonparametric Case . . . 55
27. The Embedding of Small Extremals in Small Tubes . . . 56
28. Local Existence Theory for Nonparametric Variational Problems and for Ordinary Second Order Differential Equations . . . 58
29. Local Parametric Existence Theory for the Elliptic Case . . . 64

Chapter III

EMBEDDING IN THE LARGE . . . 70

30. Introduction . . . 70
31. First and Second Variations and Transversality . . . 71
32. The Second Variation Fallacy . . . 73
33. The Secondary Hamiltonian . . . 74
34. Geometrical Interpretation of Exactness . . . 76
35. Distinguished Families . . . 78
36. Canonical Embeddings and Focal Points . . . 81
37. The Jacobi Theory of Conjugate Points . . . 83
38. The Index of Stability of an Extremal . . . 88
39. The Second Stage of the Morse Theory . . . 92

Chapter IV

HAMILTONIANS IN THE LARGE, CONVEXITY, INEQUALITIES AND FUNCTIONAL ANALYSIS . . . 94

40. Introduction . . . 94
41. Center of Gravity and Dispersal Zone . . . 95
42. Convexity and the Hahn-Banach Theorem . . . 98
43. The Conceptual Heritage of Georg Cantor . . . 101
44. Duality of Convex Figures . . . 105
45. Duality of Convex Functions . . . 108
46. Hamiltonians in the Large and Reformulated Variational Theory . . . 110
47. Remarks on Classical Inequalities . . . 112
48. The Dual Unit Ball of a Functional Space . . . 113
49. The Riesz Representation . . . 118

Chapter V

EXISTENCE THEORY AND ITS CONSEQUENCES . . . 122

50. Introduction . . . 122
51. The Hilbert Construction and Some of its Consequences in the Standard Parametric Case . . . 123

52. The Parametric Theory of Conjugate Points and the Parametric Jacobi Condition 128
53. The Tonelli-Carathéodory Unicity Theorem 133
54. Absolute and Homotopic Minima on $B \cdot \cdot i$-Compact Domains and Manifolds 143
55. Toward an Automatic Existence Theory 147
56. First Stage of an Abstract Approach: Semicontinuity in a $B \cdot \cdot i$-Compact Set 151
57, 58, 59 154

Chapter VI

GENERALIZED CURVES AND FLOWS 155

60. Introduction 155
61. Intuitive Background 156
62. A Question of Semantics 160
63. Parametric Curves in the Calculus of Variations 161
64. Admissible Curves as Elements of a Dual Space 163
65. A Human Analogy 165
66. Generalized Curves and Flows, and Their Boundaries 166
67. Parametric Representation of Generalized Curves 171
68. Existence of a Minimum 178
69. The Nature of the Generalized Solutions 179

Appendix I

SOME FURTHER BASIC NOTIONS OF CONVEXITY AND INTEGRATION 184

70. Introduction 184
71. Separation Theorem for a Convex Cone in $\mathscr{C}_0(A)$ 184
72. The Lemma of the Insufficient Radius 185
73. The Dual Separation Theorem 187
74. A Localization Lemma for a $B \cdot \cdot i$-Compact Set 188
75. Riesz Measures 189
76. Euclidean Approximation to a Banach Vector Function 190
77. An Elementary Norm Estimate 190
78. Vector Integration 191
79. Closure of a Convex Hull 192

Appendix II

THE VARIATIONAL SIGNIFICANCE AND STRUCTURE OF GENERALIZED FLOWS 194

80. Introduction 194
81. Polygonal Flows 195

82. The Basis of Modern Duality in the Calculus of Variations 197
83. The Variational Convexity Principle in its Elementary Form 197
84. A First Extension 198
85. The Enlargement Principle and the First Closure Theorem for Generalized Flows 199
86. The Extension to Consistent Flows and Boundaries 200
87. Preliminary Information on Mixtures and on the Lagrange Representation 202
88. Further Comments on Measures, Mixtures, and Consistent Flows ...204
89. The Lagrange Representation of a Consistent Flow 209

Volume II-Optimal Control Theory

Preamble

THE NATURE OF CONTROL PROBLEMS........................214

1. Introduction 214
2. The Multiplier Rule..215
3. Optimal Control and the Lagrange Problem 217
4. The Sad Facts of Life..218
5. A First Revision of the Euler Equation and of the Multiplier Rule ..220
6. The Weierstrass Condition, Transversality, Hamiltonians and a Strong Revised Euler Recipe 222
7. The Classical Constrained Hamiltonians........................224
8. Controls and the Maximum Principle 228
9. The Maximum Principle and Its Special Cases as Definitions.......231
10. Solutions of Two Elementary Time-Optimal Problems 233

Chapter I

NAIVE OPTIMAL CONTROL THEORY........................243

11. Introduction 243
12. Discrete Time and Programming 244
13. Some Basic Remarks on Linear Differential Equations.............247
14. Suspected Solutions of the Simplest Time-Optimal Problems 250
15. Unicity and Optimality 251
16. Two Dimensional Problems: Switching Times and Basic Constructions 253
17. Discussion of Case (a) 256
18. Discussion of Case (b_1) 257
19. Discussion of Case (b_2) 259

Chapter II

THE APPLICATION OF STANDARD VARIATIONAL METHODS TO OPTIMAL CONTROL 261

20. Introduction 261
21. Trajectories and Lines of Flight 263
22. The Synchronization Condition and the Notions of Standard Projection and Descriptive Map 266
23. The Notion of a Spray of Flights 267
24. The Hilbert Independence Integral 269
25. Preliminary Lemmas 272
26. The Theorem of Malus 274
27. Chains of Flights 275
28. Piecing Together Fragments of Curves 276
29. The Fundamental Theorem and Its Consequences 279

Chapter III

GENERALIZED OPTIMAL CONTROL 282

30. Introduction 282
31. The Preproblem 285
32. More Semantics 287
33. Conventional and Chattering Controls in Differential Equations 289
34. The Halfway Principle and the Filippov Lemma 292
35. Unicity and a Key Lemma for Approximations 297
36. Control Measures 300
37. A Proper Setting for Optimal Control Problems 304
38. Hilbert's Principle of Minimum 307
39. Pontrjagin's Maximum Principle 308
39A. The Perturbation 312
39B. Reduction to a Separation Theorem 316
39C. An Equivalent Form of the Separation 318
39D. Proof of the Maximum Principle 319
39E. Epilogue 321

REFERENCES 323

INDEX 327

Lectures on the Calculus of Variations and Optimal Control Theory

---

Volume I

LECTURES ON THE CALCULUS OF VARIATIONS

Preamble

GENERALITIES AND TYPICAL PROBLEMS

§1. INTRODUCTION

The general plan of these lectures and the way to study them will perhaps be made clearer by some preliminary remarks. The plan has been affected by several causes.

In the first place, not everyone realizes that the present space-age upsurge of interest in real mathematics is having a profound effect on mathematical teaching, at all levels and in all countries. The mathematical public is wider, and lectures can no longer be properly designed only for persons with a certain specific clearly marked out background of previous mathematical courses. The present lectures are not *reserved* for graduate students in mathematics, and of course professionals, although a good deal of the material will be found nowhere else but in original papers. The lectures are equally intended for engineers and others who may desperately need this type of work as a rigorous basis for space science. The lectures were actually delivered to an audience consisting partly of engineers, and we consider them suitable to anyone, young or old, who possesses a background of at least elementary calculus (with, as is fairly usual, a little about differential equations, matrices, and determinants thrown in), together with a really compelling desire to learn. However, at times such readers may need to rush to the library to study certain reference books if they are to follow all details.

In the second place, the outlook in mathematics itself is changing a great deal, and many teachers of long experience are now somewhat lost. It is now many years since church bells were rung for a Senior Wrangler,† and there is each year less reason for the use of mathematics as a barrier consisting largely of a collection of examination problems whose answers must be written very fast, and exactly as the teacher wishes. To select mathematicians on this basis is as reasonable as picking a poet in a spelling contest.

At any rate, it should be clear that under the circumstances these lectures could not possibly consist of short sections of unintelligible text, followed by long strings of illustrative examples. A valid criticism of such a teaching method is provided by the child of nine, a perfect lady, who wrote, after doing only one sum in her homework:

---

† This name was given to the highest male scorer in an examination known as the Cambridge Mathematical Tripos, prior to 1910.

"The others are done in the same way." In any case, however, even a single problem in our subject needs a considerable study, and cannot be dismissed in a few lines. Therefore, generally speaking, the lectures will not help those who only wish to solve examination problems fast, but rather those who wish to acquire a real understanding of the basic concepts.

Such an understanding comes only gradually, and we do not therefore rush through the text, but we try to include a proper motivation and to induce a proper attitude of mind in the reader, or simply try to provide a more relaxed atmosphere and stimulate the reader's imagination by interspersing material which may even consist of anecdotes. What is mainly important is that the reader whose reaction time is slower should not feel at a disadvantage. Real ability must on no account be confused with mere quickness; speed is for parrots and machines; human beings work better at a more deliberate pace.

§2. THE PLACE OF THE CALCULUS OF VARIATIONS IN RELATION TO THE REST OF MATHEMATICS AND TO SPACE SCIENCE

The study of particular problems of the calculus of variations, or, as we shall say, particular variational problems, is extremely old. It arises from the fact that for human beings, in many instances, only the best can be good enough. We are therefore led to optimization problems, i.e., to problems of maximum or minimum. Some of these have been met in the elementary calculus, but most often they need more complicated methods.

In fact, these problems require not only methods, but, what is more important, they require concepts. They are not problems to tackle with one's bare hands, but only when one is properly equipped. The necessary concepts have been evolved rather slowly, although today they occur all through modern mathematics, and many students do not realize that they originated in our subject. This is partly because an old-fashioned terminology is at times retained in the calculus of variations.

Already the title of our subject is a purely historical one; it refers to a particular method, due to Euler and based on so-called variations, that was at one time important in the subject, but which is of very secondary interest today. Actually the calculus of variations is simply part of functional analysis and plays in it the same role as the theory of maxima and minima in elementary calculus.

This being so, it is only natural that concepts that are now attached to or derived from functional analysis should have appeared first in a less polished form in the calculus of variations. In this way, a number of basic tools of contemporary mathematics, such as Schwartz distributions, Young's inequality and convex figures and their duals, are to be found in germ in classical methods within our subject.

This means that the calculus of variations plays a part not only as a branch of mathematics, but also *as a record of the history of mathematical concepts*. In this respect, since so much of the advance of mathematics is now conceptual, our subject provides a much needed guide to future research, and this is a role that no other branch of mathematics possesses to an equal extent.

In regard to the direct relation of the calculus of variations to the rest of mathematics, the reader will soon be aware of the role in it of basic questions of pure logic, while the Morse theory of Chapter III has overtones of homology, which link it with both algebra and topology. Topologists are, moreover, aware of important applications of the Morse theory or of methods based on cognate ideas to their subject. The main applications of the calculus of variations are, however, in analysis and geometry, either in connection with definite inequalities or estimates, as in the theory of partial differential equations, or else qualitatively and conceptually, as in Riemann's use of the Dirichlet principle of minimum in conformal mapping and in potential theory, a principle later established by a famous paper of Hilbert.

From what we have just said, it might be imagined, in spite of our references to the needs of engineers, that the calculus of variations is very "pure" and has little relation to applied mathematics. Actually the opposite is the case. Not only do particular problems of the calculus of variations play a fundamental part in our everyday life and in such topics as economics, engineering, and so forth (because, as indicated previously, mankind strives to do the best with the means available), but, also, whole developments of the theory have arisen directly from the needs of optics and, lately, from those of space science and cognate matters.

The developments related to space science are here separated from the rest and attached to the title Optimal Control. This is not to imply that they are in any way independent of the rest, but rather that they are more complicated, and therefore best treated later when the basic methods and concepts have been presented in a simpler context. Actually, they constitute equally a study of the variational problems known as those of Lagrange and Bolza.

A typical problem of space science is that of getting a controlled projectile to the moon. A corresponding variational problem, or, as we say here, a problem of optimal control, could be the transfer of a controlled particle to the moon in the least time or at the least expense. Optimization enters naturally into the problem, and our subject really plays a central part in space science.

§3. STATEMENT OF THE SIMPLEST PROBLEM AND SOME COGNATE MATTERS

Although all problems of maxima and minima of functional analysis properly belong to the calculus of variations, only a few rather special types have so far been studied in detail. The simplest of these may be formulated as follows, in a notation that, we emphasize, is provisional and will be discarded after this chapter.

Suppose given a function of three variables f. We consider in the x, y plane, for curves C which join two given points and which have the form $y = y(x)$, where $y(x)$ has a derivative $y'(x)$, the problem of the minimum of the integral

$$\mathscr{I}(C) = \int f(x, y, y')\, dx \tag{3.1}$$

where, in the function f under the integral sign, we suppose substituted, for y, y', the functions $y(x), y'(x)$. In this problem, the function f is, as stated, a given one, while the function y is to be determined if possible by the condition of minimum. Here $\mathscr{I}(C)$ is thus dependent on an unknown function $y = y(x)$, so that we have a problem of minimum in functional analysis.

The same problem can be given a slightly more geometrical form, in terms of curves defined by a parametric representation $x(t), y(t)$ on corresponding t intervals, where $x(t)$, $y(t)$ have derivatives $\dot{x}(t)$, $\dot{y}(t)$. In that case the integral $\mathscr{I}(C)$ to be minimized has the form

(3.2) $$\mathscr{I}(C) = \int F(x, y, \dot{x}, \dot{y})\, dt,$$

where we suppose substituted for $x, y, \dot{x}, \dot{y}$ the functions $x(t), y(t)$ defining C and their derivatives. The curves C are again supposed to have given endpoints, and integration is on the corresponding t-interval. The function F is again supposed given; however it is now subject to a homogeneity condition

(3.3) $$F(x, y, \sigma\dot{x}, \sigma\dot{y}) = \sigma F(x, y, \dot{x}, \dot{y}),$$

for $\sigma \geq 0$. This is to ensure that the integral (3.2) depends on the curve C, rather than on the choice of the particular representation $x(t), y(t)$ of C.

In practice, the function f or F is usually a rather simple function: for instance, if

$$f = \sqrt{1 + y'^2}, \quad \text{or} \quad F = \sqrt{\dot{x}^2 + \dot{y}^2},$$

the integral $\mathscr{I}(C)$ represents the length of C. For the present we shall suppose f, F differentiable as often as may be required. We recall from elementary calculus that (3.3) implies

(3.4) $$\dot{x}F_{\dot{x}} + \dot{y}F_{\dot{y}} = F,$$

by Euler's formula on homogeneous functions. In the sequel, it will be convenient to pass from the function f to the function F, or vice versa, by setting $f(x, y, y') = F(x, y, 1, y')$, i.e., by identifying the parameter t with x. In that case the partial derivative $F_{\dot{y}}$, for the same variables, can be identified with $f_{y'}$, while $F_{\dot{x}}$ can be evaluated by (3.4). We find, for the same variables,

(3.5) $$F_{\dot{x}} = f - y'f_{y'}.$$

This last expression is rather important, and (3.5) accounts for the fact that it keeps cropping up.

Of course, the problem with f and that with F are not equivalent. The former concerns the minimum for only those C that possess representations of the form $y(x)$, and this is equivalent to the restriction $\dot{x}(t) > 0$.

Our problem in either case is to nail down a particular curve C that provides our minimum, just as in a detective story the reader is expected to nail down the culprit if he can. However, in the latter case the reader is sometimes warned of the identity of the most likely suspect: "Beware of a seafaring man with one leg." And, sure enough, in time this individual reveals himself as the villain.

In this chapter, we shall similarly provide the reader with a rather simple recipe for producing curves C that are to be provisionally suspected. This recipe is due to Euler, and it provides for us a mysterious connection with a certain differential equation or pair of differential equations, namely (3.6) and (3.7) below. In fact Euler thought, quite wrongly as it happened, that he had solved the problem with his recipe. We shall have more to say about this, but at this stage we would like to remind the reader that every lawyer knows the difference between having a suspect arrested and actually convicting him.

Euler's recipe is as follows: Look for the suspected curves among the solutions of the differential equation

(3.6) $$\frac{d}{dx}(f_{y'}) = f_y,$$

or of the pair of differential equations

$$\textbf{(3.7)} \qquad \frac{d}{dt}(F_{\dot{x}}) = F_x, \qquad \frac{d}{dt}(F_{\dot{y}}) = F_y.$$

We observe that (3.6) corresponds to the second of the equations (3.7); it may be verified, however, that (3.6) can be written (after multiplication by y') in the alternative form

$$\textbf{(3.8)} \qquad \frac{d}{dx}(f - y'f_{y'}) = f_x,$$

which corresponds to the former of the equations (3.7). Thus, the two equations (3.7) are not independent. A curve C that satisfies Euler's equation (3.6) or his equations (3.7) is termed, in the calculus of variations, an *extremal*. Euler's recipe is that the curves to be suspected are the extremals.

We shall give, at this stage, absolutely no grounds for this suspicion; in fact, we shall shortly subject it to the most careful criticism. Nevertheless, if we do succeed in proving that a particular suspected curve actually provides the desired minimum, it will no longer matter how flimsy the original grounds for suspicion in fact were. In the same way, a criminal who is actually convicted, can hardly base an appeal on having originally been arrested on insufficient evidence. However, there is this difference: everyone can conceive how it may help a prosecuting lawyer to have the right criminal under arrest, but it is not at all clear how we can use our suspicions in a variational problem.

Suppose, in fact, that we suspect just one curve C_0 with the given extremities A, B. To verify the desired minimum property we still have to compare it with every other curve C with these extremities and show that

$$\mathscr{I}(C) \geq \mathscr{I}(C_0),$$

i.e., that

$$\int f(x, y, y')\,dx \geq \int f(x, y_0, y_0')\,dx$$

where y, y_0 are the functions defining C and C_0, and we suppose the representations given in the nonparametric form for simplicity. It is hard to see how this problem of minimum in function space is made easier by our suspicions.

The reader will undoubtedly interpose at this point, quite rightly, that there is at least one case where the desired verification is easy, namely the case in which, for each x, and for every y, y', we have

$$f(x, y, y') \geq f(x, y_0, y_0').$$

Unfortunately, this last inequality is practically never satisfied in a given variational problem. Thus if f is the function $\sqrt{1 + y'^2}$, the inequality holds only when $y_0' = 0$, i.e., when y_0 is a constant and C_0 is parallel to the x-axis.

This being so, we can only repeat our original question: of what possible use is a mere suspicion such as is provided by Euler's recipe? Let us not dismiss this too lightly. We have so far failed here to find such a use, but this is a type of situation which occurs many times in mathematical research. Virtually every mathematician meets it at some stage of his career: he has a difficult problem but he has a hunch as to what its solution is; the question is how to use this hunch.

In our case a positive answer can actually be given, and is rather instructive. The idea on which it is based is extremely old, and occurred to several mathematicians independently. It was then forgotten for a couple of centuries. It will play a particularly important part later, in optimal control.

We consider not a single minimum problem, but the various minimum problems that arise when we give to the second extremity B different positions in the (x, y)-plane. The integrand f and the first extremity A will be kept fixed. Suppose now that, on the basis of Euler's recipe, or for some other reason, we suspect, for each B, a corresponding curve C_0 depending on B, and of course terminating there. The value of $\mathscr{I}(C_0)$ now becomes a function of B, which we shall term the corresponding suspected minimum, and denote by $S(B)$. Evidently it vanishes at A, so that it can also be written as the difference $S(B) - S(A)$.

We shall write $S(x, y)$ for $S(B)$ when B is the point (x, y), and $\varphi(x, y, y')$ for the exact derivative $S_x + y'S_y$. Then $S(B) - S(A)$ is, along any C joining A, B, the integral of φ. It follows that the inequality $\mathscr{I}(C) \geq \mathscr{I}(C_0)$, that we wish to verify, may be written

$$\int_C \{f(x, y, y') - \varphi(x, y, y')\}\, dx \geq 0.$$

This inequality is certainly true if it happens that, for all x, y, y',

$$f(x, y, y') \geq \varphi(x, y, y'). \tag{3.9}$$

Here φ is, as stated, the exact expression $S_x + y'S_y$. Moreover, in the parametric form a similar discussion applies, with (3.9) replaced by

$$F(x, y, \dot{x}, \dot{y}) \geq \Phi(x, y, \dot{x}, \dot{y}),$$

where Φ is $\dot{x}S_x + \dot{y}S_y$.

At this stage the reader is not in a position to judge whether (3.9) and its parametric analogue are at all likely to be true in a particular problem, or whether this is too much to expect. We shall therefore test this in some classical problems.

Our discussion conforms to a general principle that applies equally in a criminal court: in order to use a hunch to help solve a case, try to replace it by a more easily tested bigger hunch.

§4. EXTREMALS IN SOME CLASSICAL PROBLEMS

We shall consider three problems, given in the first instance in the nonparametric form, and for fixed, but unspecified, ends. In this section we merely round up possible suspects according to Euler's recipe; i.e., we determine the extremals. This means that we integrate certain elementary differential equations, and, since this is not a course on solving such equations, and we wish to avoid unpleasant calculations, we shall simply try to obtain, rather shortly, solutions that we knew beforehand. Usually this involves some kind of a substitution. Once the extremals are known, we shall be ready to test our bigger hunch, but we leave this to Section 5.

(a) "Shortest distance": $f = \sqrt{1 + y'^2}$.

Here, by (3.6) and (3.8), each of the quantities $f_{y'}, f - y'f_{y'}$ is constant along an extremal, i.e., y'/f, $1/f$ are constant, so that y' is constant. The extremals are thus nonvertical straight lines. In the parametric form they are arbitrary straight lines: for then $F = \sqrt{\dot{x}^2 + \dot{y}^2}$, and $F_{\dot{x}}$, $F_{\dot{y}}$ are constant by (3.7). Thus Euler's recipe here agrees with elementary geometry.

(b) "Brachistochrone": $f = \dfrac{\sqrt{1 + y'^2}}{\sqrt{x}}$.

The problem arises from the search for the shape of a wire along which a ring falls in least time from a given point to another, under gravity. We restrict of course the curves to lie in the half-plane $x \geq 0$, and, for convenience of interpretation, the x-axis is drawn vertically downward. We note that here $F = \sqrt{\dot{x}^2 + \dot{y}^2}/\sqrt{x}$.

Along an extremal we find that $f_{y'}$, or $F_{\dot{y}}$, is constant, so that in terms of the arc length s, we get, if c is the constant in question,

$$\frac{dy}{ds} = c\sqrt{x} = \sin u \text{ (say)},$$

where u is the angle the tangent makes with the x-axis, so that $\cos u = dx/ds$. It follows that

$$\frac{dy}{du} = \tan u \frac{dx}{du} = \tan u \frac{d}{du}\left(\frac{\sin^2 u}{c^2}\right) = 2\frac{\sin^2 u}{c^2} = 2x.$$

Hence, writing $a = \frac{1}{2}c^{-2}$, $t = 2u$, we find that our extremals are the cycloids

$$x = 2a \sin^2 u = a(1 - \cos t)$$

$$y = 2a(u - \tfrac{1}{2}\sin 2u) + b = a(t - \sin t) + b.$$

Our calculation, however, leaves out the case $c = 0$, which clearly gives $y = \text{const.}$, and these vertical lines must thus also be counted as extremals.

(c) "Minimal surface of revolution": $f = y\sqrt{1 + y'^2}$.

This problem arises as a special case from the famous least area problem, or problem of Plateau, which is the two-dimensional analogue of (a). In its general form, Plateau's problem is still the subject of deep contemporary research. It is also of interest to physicists because its solutions can be realized by soap films. The special case that is relevant here is that of a minimal surface of revolution, and it is the profile of such a surface that we seek. This form of the problem has quite an extensive literature, not much of which has special significance today, except as an illustration of the possible complications that variational methods have to contend with.

Here $f - y'f_{y'}$ is constant by (3.8), so that we may write

$$\frac{y}{\sqrt{1 + y'^2}} = a.$$

From this it follows, by setting $y = a \cosh u$ and so $y' = u'a \sinh u$, that

$$\cosh u = \frac{y}{a} = \sqrt{1 + y'^2},$$

and therefore that $\sinh u = \pm y'$, and hence that $u'a = \pm 1$. By integrating this, we obtain

$$u = \pm(x - x_0)/a,$$

and therefore $y = a \cosh (x - x_0)/a$. The extremals are catenaries.

Our calculation ignores the case $y' = 0$, $u = 0$, which leaves $u'a$ indeterminate (or rather 0), and which appears to yield as additional solution $y =$ const. This additional solution is spurious; it arises from the additional factor y' in (3.8), and it fails to satisfy (3.6) unless it reduces to $y = 0$. This line, the x-axis is bounding our half-plane, is an obvious further suspect with area of revolution 0.

In the parametric form, $F = y\sqrt{\dot{x}^2 + \dot{y}^2}$, we obtain the additional solutions $x =$ const., which satisfy both equations (3.7).

We have now rounded up the suspects in all three problems, and the real task begins.

The reader may perhaps interpose at this point, isn't there a simpler way of doing this? Couldn't we perhaps, instead of having merely "suspects," instead of taking Euler's recipe for granted, as it were, save ourselves some trouble by actually proving the recipe? He might even add: "It isn't difficult, you know; I have seen the proof in another book."

Actually, we shall see that things are by no means so simple, and that Euler's recipe has serious limitations, both in theory and in practice. The calculations that we shall perform are unpleasant, but we shall learn much from them. We shall see the need to go much deeper. In mathematics today, and perhaps even more in its applications, the superficial and the plausible have no place. In space science it is too risky and too costly; everything must be tested and retested to the last detail. Some teachers may be satisfied with a quick answer, but nature is a harder taskmaster.

It would be, of course, very nice if we could point to a simple connection between our subject and the solving of certain elementary differential equations, if we could say, in effect: "See how useful this simple connection is! You recognize in the shortest distance problem the solutions that we all know; however, the same method also solves much harder problems such as (b) and (c), which occupied distinguished mathematicians for long periods in the past." Euler, perhaps, may have had some such feelings of elation. However, today we are more critical.

§5. SOLUTIONS OF THE PRECEDING PROBLEMS (a), (b), (c)

We shall solve (a) and (b); however, we shall solve (c) only subject to a certain restriction. Further, we shall not seek interesting pieces of side information, and generally we shall reduce as much as possible the rather unpleasant calculations to be carried out, just as we did in finding the extremals.

In (a) and (b), the initial point is taken to be the origin, while in (c) it is the point (0, 1). This is no real loss of generality. The functions S and φ are as before, and we shall write Φ for $\dot{x}S_x + \dot{y}S_y$. Our object is to verify, if possible, an inequality of the type $f \geq \varphi$, or $F \geq \Phi$. In (b) and (c) a direct verification does not prove feasible, but we can there adopt an equivalent procedure. In each case, by the remarks of the preceding section, the inequality arrived at completes the verification of the minimum property.

(a) In this problem, since the suspects are the lines through the origin, we find $S = \sqrt{x^2 + y^2}$, and therefore $\varphi = (x + yy')/S$. The desired inequality $f \geq \varphi$ is here

$$x + yy' \leq \sqrt{x^2 + y^2} \cdot \sqrt{1 + y'^2},$$

which is a form of Schwarz's inequality. Similarly we verify $F \geq \Phi$.

(b) In order to define our function $S(x, y)$, we must have exactly one suspect ending at the point (x, y). However, our cycloids through the origin may intersect one another. For this reason we must somehow reduce the number of suspects provided by Euler's recipe. Any way of doing this is good enough, provided (and this is the rub) that we do verify in the end that the suspects retained are the culprits. We therefore arbitrarily retain only arcs of the first arch of each cycloid, starting from the origin. Further, in order to include the half-line $y = 0$, as a limiting case, we write the arch of cycloid in the form

$$x = \frac{1 - \cos \alpha\tau}{\alpha^2}, \qquad y = \frac{\alpha\tau - \sin \alpha\tau}{\alpha^2}, \tag{5.1}$$

where $\tau > 0$, $|\alpha|\,\tau < 2\pi$, and we understand this to mean, for $\alpha = 0$, that $x = \frac{1}{2}\tau^2$, $y = 0$. Our suspects are the initial arcs of the arches of cycloids given by setting $\alpha = \text{const.}$

In order to determine the suspect that ends at a given point (x, y), we would have to solve the equations (5.1). This would give the constant value of α for the suspected curve, and the arc $(0, \tau)$ on which it is representable. We would then be in a position to evaluate S and the further quantities needed.

Since we wish to be able to solve the equations (5.1), we shall consider the map $(\alpha, \tau) \to (x, y)$ which they define. We term it the map (5.1). The functions that

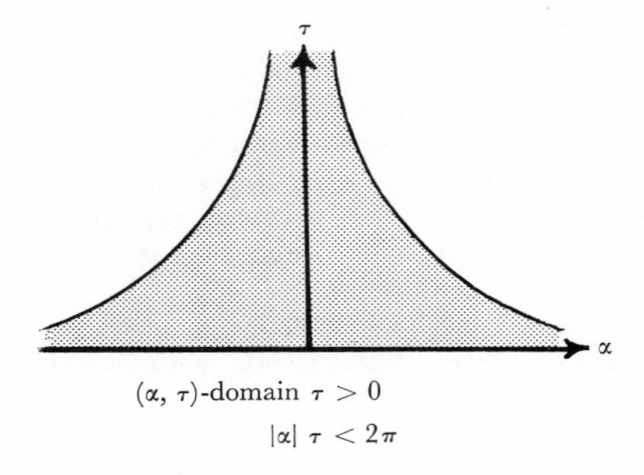

(α, τ)-domain $\tau > 0$
$|\alpha|\,\tau < 2\pi$

define this map are, by Taylor's theorem, expandable in powers of α and τ, and the negative powers cancel. We then verify that they are continuous and have continuous derivatives of all orders, in the (α, τ)-domain, including of course the line $\alpha = 0$. We shall show further that the transformation (5.1) is one-to-one, and that its Jacobian does not vanish. This means that the inverse map $(x, y) \to (\alpha, \tau)$ also has derivatives of all orders, which we can calculate by the chain rule.

To this effect, we write $a = \alpha^{-2}$, $t = \alpha\tau$, and we first suppose $\alpha \neq 0$. We clearly have a one-to-one map of each half of the (α, τ)-domain onto a half-strip $a > 0$, $0 < t < 2\pi$. The Jacobian of this map is $-2\alpha^{-2}$. We have to combine this with the further map $(a, t) \to (x, y)$, given by

$$x = a(1 - \cos t), \qquad y = a(t - \sin t),$$

whose Jacobian is $aq(t)$, where

$$q(t) = 2(1 - \cos t) - t \sin t = 2(1 - \cos t)\left(1 - \frac{\frac{1}{2}t}{\tan \frac{1}{2}t}\right).$$

Here $q(t)$ does not vanish for $0 < |t| < 2\pi$, since $|\tan \frac{1}{2}t| > |\frac{1}{2}t|$. Moreover, for small t we find that $q(t) \sim t^4/12$. It follows that the Jacobian of (5.1) is $-2q(\alpha\tau)/\alpha^4$, which tends to $-\tau^4/6$ as $\alpha \to 0$, and which therefore does not vanish. Finally we observe that the map $(a, t) \to (x, y)$ is one-to-one from the strip $0 < t < 2\pi$ to the positive (x, y) quadrant: in fact the straight line from the origin through a point (x, y) of the quadrant meets the first arch of a fixed cycloid in just one point P, and,

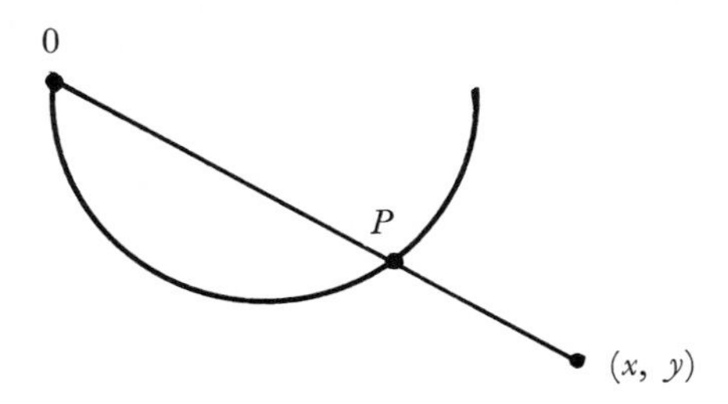

by magnification, just one of our cycloids contains (x, y) on its first arch, so that a, t are uniquely determined by (x, y). [This property of an arch of cycloid could be derived from its convexity, or simply by observing that, along it, the ratio

$$\frac{y}{x} = \frac{t - \sin t}{1 - \cos t} = g(t)$$

is an increasing continuous function of t for $0 < \frac{1}{2}t < \pi$, since its derivative is

$$\frac{d}{dt}\{\tfrac{1}{2}t(1 + \cot^2 \tfrac{1}{2}t) - \cot \tfrac{1}{2}t\} = (1 - \tfrac{1}{2}t \cot \tfrac{1}{2}t)(1 + \cot^2 \tfrac{1}{2}t),$$

which is positive.] Similarly the map is one-to-one from the strip $0 < -t < 2\pi$ to the symmetrical quadrant, so that our combined map is one-to-one from the (α, τ)-domain to the half-plane.

We thus see that the map (5.1) is not only a nice map, with nice derivatives, but also that it has an equally nice inverse. Unfortunately, this does not help us to solve the equations (5.1) in practice. It is thus not practicable to calculate $S(x, y)$ directly.

We shall avoid this difficulty by using the nice transformation (5.1) to shift our whole problem to the (α, τ)-domain. Since we shall partly do this via the intermediate (a, t) variables, dots will now, when relevant, refer to differentiation with respect to a parameter not denoted by t. Under the substitution induced by $(a, t) \to (x, y)$, we then have

$$\dot{x}^2 + \dot{y}^2 = \lambda \dot{a}^2 + 2\mu a\dot{a}\dot{t} + \nu a^2\dot{t}^2,$$

where $\lambda = (1 - \cos t)^2 + (t - \sin t)^2$, $\mu = t(1 - \cos t)$, $\nu = \sin^2 t + (1 - \cos t)^2 = 2(1 - \cos t)$. Dividing by x, we find that F^2 becomes

$$\frac{\Lambda}{a}\dot{a}^2 + 2(t\dot{a} + a\dot{t})\dot{t},$$

where now $\Lambda = \lambda/(1 - \cos t)$. In terms of $\dot{\alpha}$, $\dot{\tau}$ this takes the form

$$4Q\alpha^{-4}\dot{\alpha}^2 + 2\dot{\tau}^2,$$

where $Q(t) = \Lambda - \frac{1}{2}t^2$. Direct calculation gives

$$2Q = \frac{4 - 4\cos t - 4t\sin t + 2t^2}{1 - \cos t} = 4 - \frac{4t\sin t}{1 - \cos t} + t^2\frac{1 + \cos t}{1 - \cos t}$$

$$= 4 - \frac{4t\sin t}{1 - \cos t} + \frac{t^2\sin^2 t}{(1 - \cos t)^2} = \left(2 - \frac{t\sin t}{1 - \cos t}\right)^2$$

$$= 4(1 - \tfrac{1}{2}t\cot\tfrac{1}{2}t)^2 \sim t^4/36 \text{ for small } t.$$

Thus F becomes a function $F^*(\alpha, \tau, \dot\alpha, \dot\tau)$ of the form $\sqrt{2\rho^2\dot\alpha^2 + 2\dot\tau^2}$, where ρ is a nice function of (α, τ).

In formulating our problem in terms of F^* in the variables α, τ, we observe that the map (5.1) extends by continuity to the bounding line $\tau = 0$, and that this line is transformed into the point $x = y = 0$. This means that a curve C issuing from this point is the image of an (α, τ) curve C^*, which need not start from a definite point,

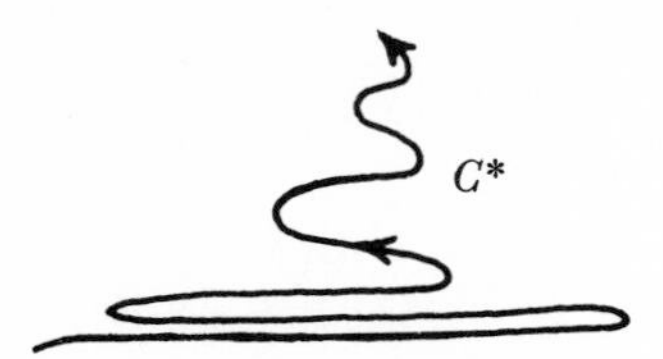

but which approaches the line $\tau = 0$ when we describe it backward—it may, for instance, approach a whole segment of that line. The integral $\mathscr{I}(C)$ of F on C is then expressible as the integral $\mathscr{I}^*(C^*)$ of F^* on this "half open" path C^*.

As suspects we now take the curves $\alpha =$ const. The suspected minimum of $\mathscr{I}^*(C^*)$, for the C^* that terminate at a given point (α, τ) of our domain, is a function $S^*(\alpha, \tau)$. We calculate S^* by inspection, since on a curve $\alpha =$ const. we have $F^* = \sqrt{2}\,\dot\tau$. We find simply $S^* = \sqrt{2}\,\tau$. Thus the total derivative Φ^* is $\sqrt{2}\,\dot\tau$. Clearly,

$$F^* \geq \Phi^*.$$

Therefore $\mathscr{I}^*(C^*) \geq S^*$, or, what amounts to the same, $\mathscr{I}(C) \geq S$. The possible lack of an initial point on C^* nowhere affects the argument.

The length of our discussion is rather typical. The reader must not expect short solutions to problems not specially dished up for examination purposes.

In this problem, we not only see that our suspects are the actual culprits, but also that there are no other culprits. This is because the coefficient $2\rho^2$ does not vanish in the (α, τ)-domain, so that actually $F^* > \Phi^*$ unless $\dot\alpha = 0$. In particular, the excluded extremals, which contain more than one arch, do not provide the minimum since they correspond, in our (α, τ)-domain, to curves on part of which α is not constant. This shows quite clearly that we do not solve a problem simply by finding the extremals; we still have then at least to exclude those extremals that do not provide a minimum. However, we shall see later that there are problems in which the extremal joining two points is unique but still does not provide the desired minimum.

(c) This problem is partly similar to (b), but there are further complications. We shall first find that the catenaries obtained as extremals through (0, 1) cover only part of the half-plane $y > 0$, and then that they cover this part twice. We write these catenaries after renaming the constant x_0 as αa, and using the condition that the catenary passes through (0, 1) to find that then $a = \cosh \alpha$,

(5.2) $$x = \xi(u, \alpha), \qquad y = \eta(u, \alpha)$$

where u, α range over all reals, and where

$$\xi = \frac{u - \alpha}{\cosh \alpha}, \qquad \eta = \frac{\cosh u}{\cosh \alpha}.$$

On each catenary, α is constant and u is the parameter. The common point (0, 1) is given by $u = \alpha$, the lowest point by $u = 0$. This lowest point is in the positive quadrant for $\alpha < 0$ and is in the quadrant $x < 0$ for $\alpha > 0$.

As in (b), we need to regard (5.2) as defining a transformation $(u, \alpha) \to (x, y)$, with a Jacobian $J = \xi_u\eta_\alpha - \xi_\alpha\eta_u$, and a line element given by

$$\dot{x}^2 + \dot{y}^2 = \lambda\dot{\alpha}^2 + 2\mu\dot{\alpha}\dot{u} + \nu\dot{u}^2,$$

whose coefficients $\lambda = \xi_\alpha^2 + \eta_\alpha^2$, $\mu = \xi_\alpha\xi_u + \eta_\alpha\eta_u$, and

$$\nu = \xi_u^2 + \eta_u^2 = \frac{1}{\cosh^2 \alpha} + \frac{\sinh^2 u}{\cosh^2 \alpha} = \frac{\cosh^2 u}{\cosh^2 \alpha} = \eta^2,$$

satisfy, of course, the identity $\lambda\nu - \mu^2 = J^2$. We shall need the explicit value of J, and for this we set $U = J \cosh^3 \alpha$, so that

$$\begin{aligned} U &= (\cosh \alpha \cdot \xi_u)(\cosh^2 \alpha \cdot \eta_\alpha) - (\cosh^2 \alpha \cdot \xi_\alpha)(\cosh \alpha \cdot \eta_u) \\ &= (1)(-\cosh u \sinh \alpha) - (-\cosh \alpha - [u - \alpha] \sinh \alpha)(\sinh u) \\ &= \sinh u \sinh \alpha\{-\coth u + \coth \alpha + u - \alpha\} \\ &= \sinh u \sinh \alpha\{g(u) - g(\alpha)\}, \end{aligned}$$

where $g(t)$ denotes the function $t - \coth t$.

Our catenaries cut a vertical $x =$ const. when $u = \alpha + x \cosh \alpha$, and we then have

$$y = \frac{\cosh(\alpha + x \cosh \alpha)}{\cosh \alpha} = \varphi(\alpha),$$

where for each fixed $x \neq 0$, $\varphi(\alpha)$ is positive and tends to $+\infty$ with $|\alpha|$, and so has a positive minimum. To locate this minimum we set $\varphi'(\alpha) = 0$. The expression $\varphi'(\alpha) \cosh^2 \alpha$ may be written

$$\begin{aligned} &\cosh \alpha \sinh u(1 + x \sinh \alpha) - \cosh u \sinh \alpha \\ &\qquad = \sinh u \sinh \alpha\{(\coth \alpha + u - \alpha) - \coth u\} = U. \end{aligned}$$

The minimum in question does not occur at $u = 0$, since there $U = -\sinh \alpha$, which is $\neq 0$ when $x \neq 0$. Thus it can only occur when $g(u) = g(\alpha)$, $u \neq 0$; and here $g(t) = t - \coth t$ has the derivative

$$g'(t) = 1 - (1 - \coth^2 t) = \coth^2 t > 0,$$

so that g clearly increases from $-\infty$ to $+\infty$ in each of the ranges $(-\infty, 0)$ and $(0, +\infty)$, and is asymptotic to t at $\pm\infty$, from above for negative t, and from below for positive t. The equation $g(t) = g(\alpha)$ is thus satisfied by two values $t = \alpha$, $t = \alpha^*$ of t; and here α^* may be regarded as a function $\alpha^*(\alpha)$, which then increases from $-\infty$ to 0 when $0 < \alpha < +\infty$, and from 0 to $+\infty$ when $-\infty < \alpha < 0$. It follows that in the (u, α)-plane, the locus $g(u) = g(\alpha)$ consists, in addition to the line $u = \alpha$, of two further branches, with the axes as asymptotes, situated in the second and fourth

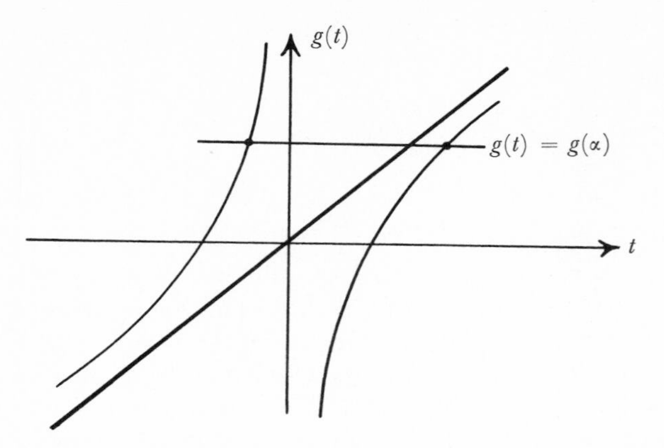

quadrants. We denote by D^* the (u, α)-domain bounded by these two branches, and by D the (x, y)-domain which is its image under the map (5.2). Further let Γ be the image of the pair of bounding curves of D^*.

Clearly Γ consists of the lowest points of verticals $x =$ const. through which there is a catenary (5.2). Thus D is the domain above Γ; and each catenary, except the one for which $\alpha = 0$, has just one point in common with Γ, the one for which $u = \alpha^*(\alpha)$, but remains above Γ. Hence Γ is the envelope of our catenaries (5.2).

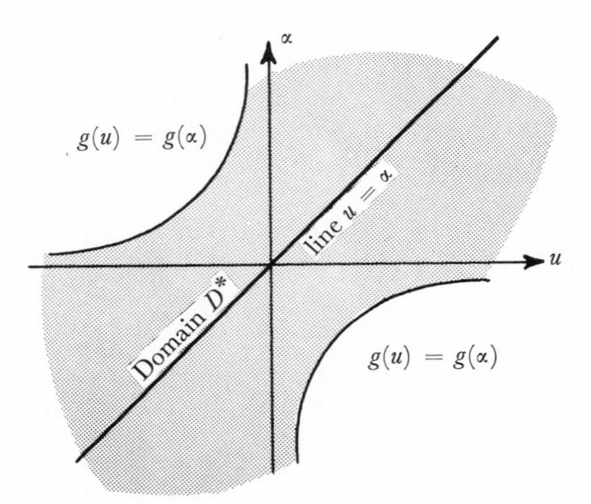

The domain D is covered twice by the catenaries (5.2). It is therefore covered just once by the arcs of these catenaries, which correspond to the parts of horizontals $\alpha =$ const. in the domain D^*. We must except, however, the vertical $x = 0$, of which only the point (0, 1) is covered, and by all the catenaries.

This already shows that, by means of our catenaries, we cannot possibly solve (c) unless the second extremity of our curves is a point of D, or of its boundary Γ. Thus, since we want to see to what use we can put Euler's recipe, we shall modify (c) by stipulating that all curves considered, and also their second extremities, are to lie in D. This is perhaps stronger than is necessary for our purpose; however, it has the advantage of excluding one of the two catenaries through each point of D, namely the one which touches the envelope Γ between the point in question and the point (0, 1). We have therefore, for each point (x, y) of D not on the y-axis, exactly one suspect joining it to (0, 1). Moreover (5.2) now maps one-to-one D^* less the line $u = \alpha$, onto D less the y-axis.

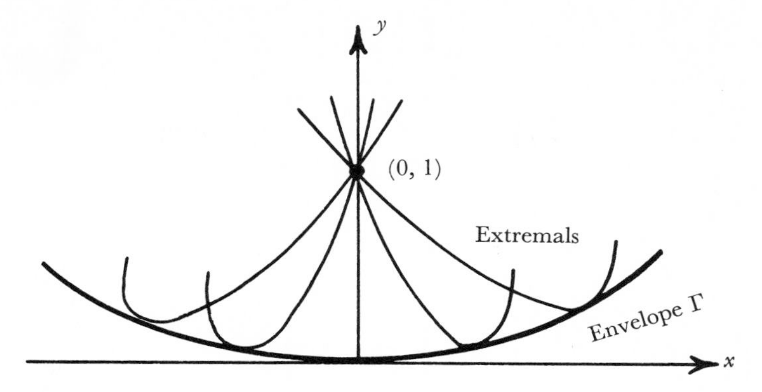

This being so, we now proceed, as in (b), to calculate, not the suspected minimum $S(x, y)$ and its total derivative Φ, but relevant quantities in the variables (u, α). The integrand will be $F^*(u, \alpha, \dot{u}, \dot{\alpha})$; the suspected minimum $S^*(u, \alpha)$; its total derivative $\Phi^* = S^*_u \dot{u} + S^*_u \dot{\alpha}$. Further, our suspects are the lines $\alpha =$ const., described from $u = \alpha$ to the relevant points of D^*. We have

$$F^* = \eta \cdot \sqrt{\lambda \dot{\alpha}^2 + 2\mu \dot{\alpha} \dot{t} + \nu \dot{t}^2},$$

$$S^* = \int_\alpha^u \eta(t, \alpha) \sqrt{\nu(t, \alpha)}\, dt.$$

Since $\nu = \eta^2$, it follows that $S^*_u = \nu$. (This is coincidence number one.) We need also S^*_α, and we shall find that it is μ (coincidence number two). In fact, we have

$$\frac{\partial}{\partial \alpha} \int_0^\alpha \frac{\cosh^2 t}{\cosh^2 \alpha}\, dt = \frac{1}{\cosh \alpha} \frac{\partial}{\partial \alpha} \int_0^\alpha \frac{dt}{\cosh \alpha}\,; \quad \dagger$$

by subtracting this from the evident relation

$$\frac{\partial}{\partial \alpha} \int_0^u \frac{\cosh^2 t}{\cosh^2 \alpha}\, dt = \frac{1}{\cosh \alpha} \frac{\partial}{\partial \alpha} \int_0^u \frac{2 \cosh^2 t}{\cosh \alpha}\, dt,$$

we find that the expression

$$S^*_\alpha = \frac{\partial}{\partial \alpha} \int_\alpha^u \eta^2(t, \alpha)\, dt = \frac{\partial}{\partial \alpha} \int_\alpha^u \frac{\cosh^2 t}{\cosh^2 \alpha}\, dt$$

has the value

$$\frac{1}{\cosh \alpha} \frac{\partial}{\partial \alpha} \left\{ \frac{u - \alpha + \sinh u \cosh u}{\cosh \alpha} \right\}$$

$$= \frac{1}{\cosh \alpha} \frac{\partial}{\partial \alpha} \left(\frac{u - \alpha}{\cosh \alpha} \right) + \frac{\sinh u}{\cosh \alpha} \frac{\partial}{\partial \alpha} \left(\frac{\cosh u}{\cosh \alpha} \right)$$

$$= \xi_u \xi_\alpha + \eta_u \eta_\alpha = \mu.$$

It now follows that, because of $\nu = \eta^2$,

$$F^{*2} - \Phi^{*2} = F^{*2} - (\mu \dot{\alpha} + \nu \dot{u})^2 = (\lambda \nu - \mu^2) \dot{\alpha}^2 = J^2 \dot{\alpha}^2 \geq 0,$$

and hence that $F^* \geq \Phi^*$, where, moreover, equality can only hold in D^* on the line $u = \alpha$, unless $\dot{\alpha} = 0$. By arguing as in (b), it follows that in each of the two

† Or $1 + (\int \cosh^2 t\, dt)(\cosh^{-2} \alpha)' = \cosh^{-2} \alpha + (\int dt) \cdot \frac{1}{2} (\cosh^{-2} \alpha)'$.

halves of D determined by the y-axis, our catenaries provide the minimum of $\mathscr{I}(C)$ for curves C situated in the half in question and joining $(0, 1)$ to a given (x, y). (Of course, just as in (b), each C may here be the image of a curve C^* in D^*, which has not necessarily an initial point, but approaches asymptotically a part of the line $u = \alpha$.)

At the same time we see that the second catenary, the one that touches the envelope between $(0, 1)$ and (x, y), cannot provide the minimum, since we can express it, on account of the one-to-one map provided by (5.2) in each half of D^*,

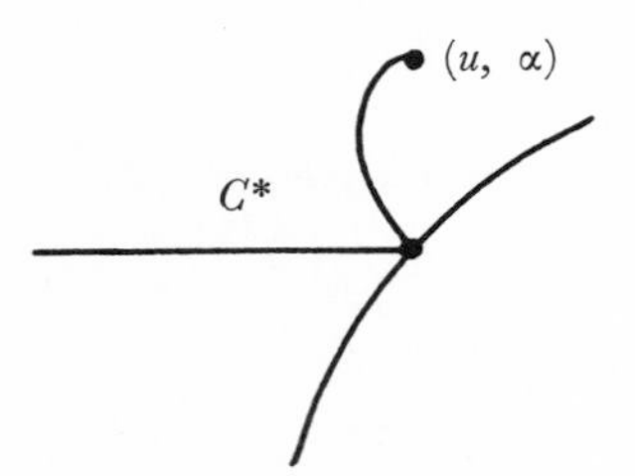

as the image of a curve C^*, which consists of a horizontal part at the level α^* [terminating on the locus $g(u) = g(\alpha)$] together with a nonhorizontal part ending at (u, α), and on which, therefore, $\dot{\alpha}$ cannot constantly vanish, since $\alpha \neq \alpha^*$.

The restriction to curves C that lie in half of D can be relaxed so as to allow curves that cross the y-axis, but the proof is more elaborate. (In (b) the corresponding difficulty was met by incorporating the relevant axis into our family of extremals.) If, however, we remove the restriction to curves situated in D and also allow the second extremity to lie outside D, then Euler's recipe will fail to provide a suspect. The solution, however, still exists, at any rate in the parametric form; it consists of a broken line formed by two vertical segments joined by part of the x-axis. In this case, the minimal surface of revolution, generated by this solution, splits into two circular discs. As it turns out, this broken line also provides the minimum when the second extremity is in D, but rather close to Γ. The proofs of these matters are simple enough in principle, but we must pass over them since there is a limit to what should be tackled with bare hands.

§6. THE EULER-LAGRANGE LEMMA AND SCHWARTZ DISTRIBUTIONS

This is mainly a historical digression. However, it will help to satisfy the reader who asked for a proof of Euler's recipe. Of course, in this book there is no need for Schwartz distributions, and we shall not use them. Historical matters are never necessary, not even when, as in these lectures, they refer to stages in the evolution of concepts.

As already stated, we do not need a proof of Euler's recipe; our solutions are in no way made more complete by such a proof. Moreover, in Chapter II we shall develop a theory where there are no longer suspicions and strange coincidences. Still it is nice to possess a proof and so to motivate better the guesses that we made in solving problems (a), (b), and (c), the last of these only partially. After all, we are not strictly utilitarian.

The Euler-Lagrange lemma, which is basic in the derivation of Euler's differential equation (3.6), amounts to the first use of what we now call Schwartz distributions.

What are Schwartz distributions?

We shall give here only a partial reply, which is limited to the interval (0, 1) instead of to Euclidean space. Actually there seem to be almost as many replies as there are mathematicians, and the importance of the topic is evidenced by the fact that sooner or later almost every mathematician lays claim to a kind of title of nobility, which consists in belonging to at least one of the following (not necessarily mutually exclusive) classes: "those who knew it all before," and "those who have done it much better." A third interesting class is comprised of only one member, the original reviewer of Laurent Schwartz's work in Mathematical Reviews; his review should on no account be missed. The value of the work is not hinted at!

The place to find out what Schwartz distributions are is nonetheless not one of these later accounts, but the actual book by Laurent Schwartz. In mathematics, new concepts and new theories should be studied in the original source, which is nearly always much richer in ideas. Subsequent accounts may be simpler or may go further, but where they are simpler they lack the rich background of ideas, and where they are elaborate they lack the original directness. Of course, there is much to be learned by studying them as well.

Schwartz distributions may be said to arise from the realization that a function $f(x)$ is not so important in itself as by its effect on others. In this respect, a function is very human. The effect of a function $f(x)$, defined on the interval (0, 1) say, on another such function $\eta(x)$, may be thought of as measured by the expression

$$\int_0^1 f(x)\eta(x)\,dx = T_f(\eta).$$

Here, just as in the human case, we are interested in the effect of the given individual f, not on all other individuals, but only on "civilized" individuals η. A function η will be regarded as civilized if it is infinitely differentiable and vanishes identically in some neighborhood of each of the ends 0 and 1. This sounds like asking a great deal of an individual; it seems to imply such a high degree of smoothness and polish that human beings could not achieve it, and perhaps the only civilized function would be identically zero everywhere. Fortunately we shall see that the search for our civilized functions is not so hopeless as that for a perfect woman or perfect man.

The operation T_f, thus applied to a variable civilized function η, is termed the Schwartz distribution attached to the function f. There will also be derived distributions, and the latter are defined as follows: we term n-th derivative of T_f the operation $D^n T_f$ whose effect on a civilized η is given by the quantity

$$(-)^n T_f(D^n\eta) = (-)^n \int_0^1 f(x)\eta^{(n)}(x)\,dx,$$

where $\eta^{(n)}$ is the n-th derivative of η, and is thus itself also a civilized function.

In the theory of Schwartz distributions, a key position is attached to the following lemma:

(6.1) The Euler-Lagrange Lemma. *Let f, g be integrable functions and suppose that $T_f = DT_g$. Then $f = Dg$.*

Equality in this conclusion must, of course, be understood as equality almost everywhere, and this is the modern formulation of the lemma. However, the reader who is not familiar with these terms may, in various places in these lectures, substitute an older interpretation, such as equality everywhere, or except at a finite set of points, if the functions are understood to be continuous, or to be bounded and to have at most a finite number of discontinuities.

The Euler-Lagrange lemma not only shows that derivatives of Schwartz distributions behave like those of functions, but also that the distribution T_f uniquely defines the function f. For if we set $g = 0, f = f_1 - f_2$, the lemma ensures that $T_{f_1} = T_{f_2}$ implies $f_1 = f_2$.

§7. ALTERNATIVE FORMS OF THE LEMMA

Several slightly different forms of the Euler-Lagrange lemma can be used interchangeably to reach the Euler equation (3.6). They correspond to various choices of a class of functions, termed "test functions," which are used in place of the civilized functions of the preceding section. These classes can be the following: (a) the previous class of civilized functions η; (b) a larger class consisting of infinitely differentiable functions ζ which vanish at the two ends; (c) the subclass of (b), consisting of the functions $\sin(2\pi nx)$, $1 - \cos(2\pi nx)$, $(n = 1, 2, \ldots)$; (d) a totally different class consisting of the continuous piecewise linear functions ξ which vanish identically in neighborhoods of the two ends; and (e) the subclass of (c), consisting of what we shall term "stump-shaped" functions, which we define below.

For each of these classes of test functions we have:

(7.1) Alternative Form of Euler-Lagrange Lemma. *Let $\lambda(x)$, $\mu(x)$ denote integrable functions on the interval* $(0, 1)$, *and suppose that*

$$\int_0^1 (\lambda(x)\tau(x) + \mu(x)\tau'(x))\, dx = 0$$

for every test function τ. Then $\lambda = \mu'$.

We shall denote by (7.1)(a), (7.1)(b), and so on, the forms of (7.1) obtained by choosing the test functions as in (a), (b), and so on. The form (7.1)(b) is more properly the Euler-Lagrange lemma, while (7.1)(d) is a convenient modification introduced by du Bois Reymond. In all these forms, it is no loss of generality to suppose that $\lambda = 0$, and we shall do this. The change merely amounts to writing $\mu + \Lambda$ in place of μ in the general case, where Λ denotes the indefinite integral of λ; for we clearly have, by integration by parts,

$$\int_0^1 (\lambda\tau + (\mu + \Lambda)\tau')\, dx = \int_0^1 \mu\tau'\, dx.$$

PROOF OF (7.1)(b) AND (7.1)(c). Clearly, it is enough to prove (7.1)(c). Since now $\lambda = 0$, our hypotheses readily give, for $n = 1, 2, \ldots$

$$\int_0^1 \lambda(x) \cos(2\pi nx)\, dx = \int_0^1 \lambda(x) \sin(2\pi nx)\, dx = 0,$$

so that the Fourier coefficients of λ all vanish except for the constant term. Thus (7.1)(c) reduces to the unicity theorem for Fourier series.

Alternatively, if the reader is unfamiliar with this last theorem, the argument shows that it is equivalent to (7.1)(c), but we shall not use the latter in the sequel.

PROOF OF (7.1)(d) AND (7.1)(e). It is enough to prove (7.1)(e). However, we must first define a stump-shaped function: we mean by this a function $\sigma(x)$,

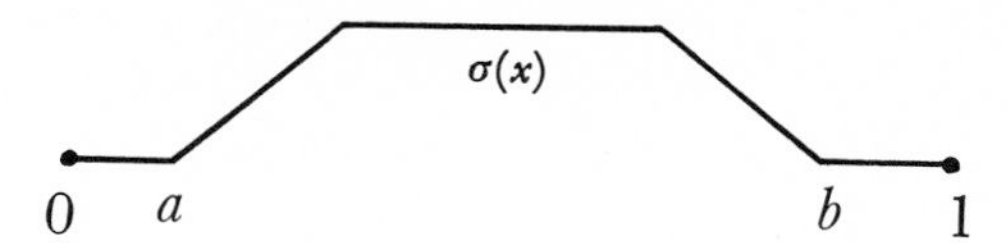

which is linear, with slope 1 and -1 respectively, in two mutually exclusive closed intervals of equal length $(a, a + h)$, $(b - h, b)$, interior to $(0, 1)$, and which is constant in the closed interval $(a + h, b - h)$ and vanishes outside the open interval (a, b). Thus σ depends on the choice of a, b, h. We have to show (since $\lambda = 0$) that the hypothesis

(7.2) $$\int_0^1 \mu(x)\sigma'(x)\,dx = 0 \quad \text{for each} \quad \sigma$$

implies that μ is constant almost everywhere. Now (7.2) may be written

$$\int_a^{a+h} \mu(x)\,dx - \int_{b-h}^{b} \mu(x)\,dx = 0,$$

from which it follows by dividing by h and making $h \to 0$, that for any two points a, b at which $\mu(x)$ is the derivative of its indefinite integral, we must have $\mu(a) = \mu(b)$. This completes the proof.

It now only remains to prove (7.1)(a), which is a restatement of (6.1). This is the modern form of the lemma and we devote the next section to it. Of course the reader may skip it. [See however, the remarks following (8.4)].

§8. PROOF OF THE MAIN FORM OF THE LEMMA

We shall derive (7.1)(a) from (7.1)(e). It is clearly enough to establish the following approximation lemma:

(8.1) Lemma. *Let μ be integrable in* (0, 1), *and let σ be stump-shaped. Then there exists, for each $\varepsilon > 0$, a civilized function η, such that*

(8.2) $$\left|\int_0^1 \mu(x)\{\sigma'(x) - \eta'(x)\}\,dx\right| < \varepsilon.$$

In fact, with the hypotheses of (7.1)(a), where we again suppose $\lambda = 0$, the term in η' in (8.2) vanishes, and the conclusion is equivalent to (7.2).

Proof of (8.1). We recall that τ depends on the previous constants a, b, h. We shall construct a civilized η which mimics suitably the behavior of σ. The desired η will be made to depend on a further constant $\delta > 0$, which will be sufficiently small. For definiteness, we suppose $\delta < h/2$, and further that for all intervals Δ of length δ, we have

(8.3) $$\int_\Delta |\mu(x)|\,dx < \varepsilon/4.$$

Continuity of the indefinite integral of $|\mu|$ ensures that (8.3) will hold for all small δ.

The actual construction of an appropriate η is again related to key facts in the Schwartz theory of distributions, and the key to the construction is, in its turn, a simple observation about the function

(8.4) $$\exp(-1/x^2).$$

This same observation is also the theme of a recurring question in minor examinations in mathematics for prospective doctors in various sciences, since it helps to correct their intuitive ideas by a hard and fast counterexample. The observation is to the effect that if we complete the function (8.4) by making it vanish at the origin, then not only is it continuous, with the value 0 at this point, but it also has at the origin derivatives of all orders, with the same value 0 there. It follows that a function is not uniquely determined by its Taylor series, and that a number of different functions may have the Taylor series 0 at the origin.

We shall denote one such function by $e(x)$, namely the one that coincides with (8.4) for $x > 0$ and with the constant 0 for $x \leq 0$. We write further, for $\alpha < \beta$,

$$\eta_{\alpha\beta}(x) = e(x - \alpha)e(\beta - x), \qquad e_{\alpha\beta}(x) = \int_0^x \eta_{\alpha\beta}(t)\, dt.$$

Thus $e(x)$, $\eta_{\alpha\beta}(x)$, $e_{\alpha\beta}(x)$ are infinitely differentiable. The function $\eta_{\alpha\beta}$ is positive for $\alpha < x < \beta$ and 0 otherwise, and is thus our first example here of a civilized

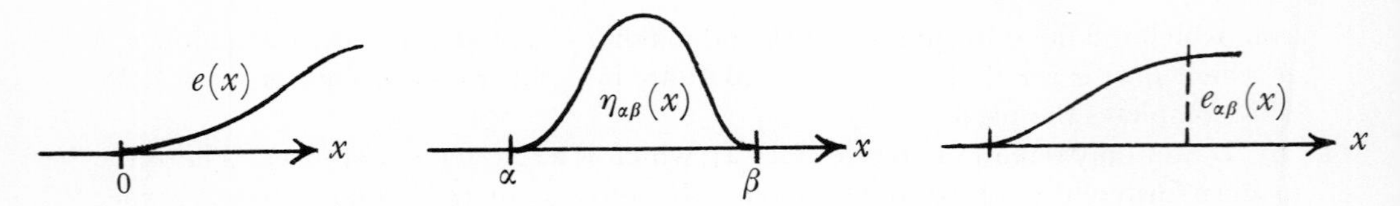

function other than the constant 0, if we restrict it to the interval (0, 1) and suppose $0 < \alpha, \beta < 1$. The function $e_{\alpha\beta}$ is increasing for $\alpha < x < \beta$, and takes the constant values 0, $e_{\alpha\beta}(\beta)$ for $x \leq \alpha$, $x \geq \beta$, respectively.

In terms of our previous numbers h, δ, we now define further

$$\eta_\alpha(x) = e_{\alpha,\alpha+\delta}(x)e_{1-\alpha-h,1+\delta-\alpha-h}(1-x),$$

$$e_\alpha(x) = \int_0^x \eta_\alpha(t)\, dt.$$

These functions are again infinitely differentiable, and we see that η_α vanishes for $x \leq \alpha$ and for $x \geq \alpha + h$, and takes a constant positive value for $\alpha \leq x \leq \alpha + h$, except when x lies within δ of either end, in which case $\eta_\alpha(x)$ takes intermediate

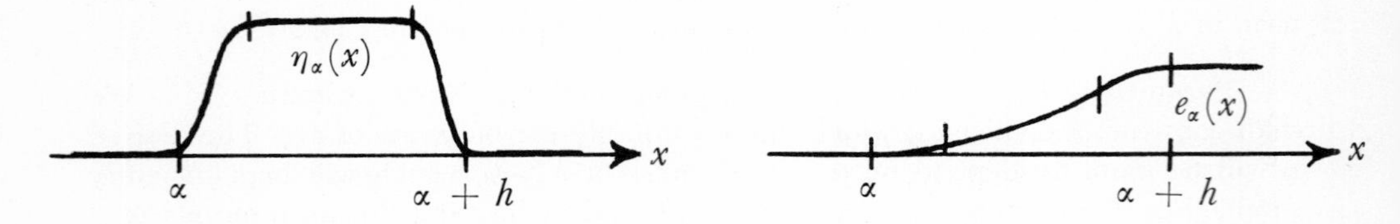

values. Hence e_α vanishes for $x \leq \alpha$, takes a constant positive value for $x \geq \alpha + h$ and is increasing for $\alpha \leq x \leq \alpha + h$; in fact it is linear as well in that interval, except when x lies within δ of either end. We have indicated these things in the figures, and we see that, to some extent, e_α "mimics" a corresponding piecewise linear function.

In order to obtain the desired civilized function $\eta(x)$ $(0 \leq x \leq 1)$, we now simply multiply by a suitable positive constant the restriction to $(0 \leq x \leq 1)$ of the product

$$e_a(x)e_{-b}(-x).$$

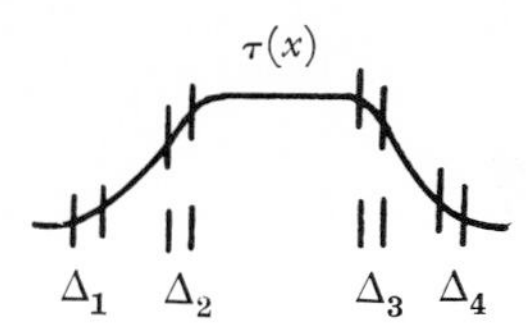

Clearly η now "mimics" the trapezoidal function τ. In fact it differs from τ only in four small intervals Δ_i $i = 1, \ldots, 4$. If Δ is any one of these, we see that in it

$$|\sigma'(x) - \eta'(x)| \leq 1$$

and therefore that

$$\left|\int_0^1 \mu\{\sigma' - \eta'\}\, dx\right| = \left|\sum_{i=1}^{4} \int_{\Delta_i}\right| < 4(\tfrac{1}{4}\varepsilon)$$

by (8.3). This completes the proof of (8.1) and so of (7.1)(a).

§9. FIRST VARIATION, EULER EQUATION, TRANSVERSALITY

We now come to the connection of all this with Euler's recipe, as we called it, for rounding up our suspects. The order of the preceding sections was deliberate. It is only now, after first seeing from actual examples, in which conditions were rather favorable, that the recipe has serious limitations, and, on the other hand, after seeing the conceptual importance of the Euler-Lagrange lemma, which bridges a gap of two centuries in our outlook on mathematics, that we are ready to tackle the recipe by means of the lemma.

For simplicity we consider a nonparametric problem with the integrand $f(x, y, y')$. Our notation, as in the rest of this Chapter, will be provisional, and the definitions of this section will be revised in Chapter III. We suppose given a minimizing curve C of the form $y(x)$ $(a \leq x \leq b)$, and we set, without loss of generality, $a = 0$, $b = 1$.

We embed C in a family of curves C_α of the form $y(x) + \alpha\eta(x)$, where α is a real parameter whose range includes 0 in its interior, and where η is any one of our test functions—for definiteness, say a civilized one. We term first variation of $\mathscr{I}(C)$, and denote by $\delta\mathscr{I}$, the value at $\alpha = 0$ of the derivative $(d/d\alpha)\mathscr{I}(C_\alpha)$. By the elementary rules for differentiating under the integral sign, we see that

(9.1) $$\delta\mathscr{I} = \int_0^1 (\eta f_y + \eta' f_{y'})\, dx,$$

since the integrand in (9.1) is $(\partial/\partial\alpha)f(x, y + \alpha\eta, y' + \alpha\eta')$. Further, since C is minimizing and the C_α have the same ends, $\mathscr{I}(C_\alpha)$, as function of α, attains its minimum for $\alpha = 0$, so that, by the elementary theory of maxima and minima, $\delta\mathscr{I} = 0$. This must, of course, hold for each test function η, and hence, by (7.1), we must have the Euler equation (3.6).

(The assumption that the range of α includes 0 in its interior indicates that the conclusion need not hold for a curve C containing boundary points of the domain in which admissible curves are to lie. We note that in two of the three problems of Sections 4 and 5 this domain was a half-plane, so that such boundary points on C may well exist.)

We remark that the Euler equation, which we have established for a curve that minimizes $\mathscr{I}(C)$ among those joining two fixed points P, Q, holds *a fortiori* for a curve that minimizes in a wider class, for which the ends P, Q are allowed to vary in some way. In that case, however, a new condition becomes necessary; it is termed a transversality condition.

We shall describe this condition here without proving it. However, we observe that in many such problems with variable ends the whole setting is inadequate. Thus, in our examples (b) and (c) of Sections 4 and 5, we effected a map under which the initial point became a line, and we then needed a minimum in a wider class than that of curves issuing from definite points of this line.

It is convenient to use some of the imagery of mechanics. We denote by M the vector $f - y'f_{y'}$, $f_{y'}$ corresponding to a slope y' at (x, y) and term it momentum vector. M_P, M_Q will be its values at P, Q. We denote by δP, δQ the derivatives for $\alpha = 0$ of two continuously differentiable functions $P(\alpha)$, $Q(\alpha)$, where α is a real parameter whose range includes 0 in its interior, and where $P(0) = P$, $Q(0) = Q$. We term δP, δQ virtual displacements of P, Q. The transversality condition is a kind of virtual work condition, which states that

$$M_P\,\delta P - M_Q\,\delta Q = 0,$$

i.e., that the system of two particles at P, Q subject to the constraints, which restrict the variability of these two points, is in equilibrium under forces M_P at P, $-M_Q$ at Q.

The preceding proof that a minimizing curve satisfies the Euler equation occupied for a long time a central position in the calculus of variations. It has behind it today not only the great authority of Euler and Lagrange, but also the fact that their basic lemma anticipated, to some extent, one of the main developments of contemporary analysis. This is undoubtedly the place at which someone making a movie version of these lectures would interpolate an alleged episode in technicolor from the life of Euler or Lagrange—perhaps even misspelled LaGrange for faked antiquity—or at least show a monkish librarian, venerable in his makeup, fetching down from a high shelf of paste and cardboard no mere printed volume, but a great illuminated folio of Euler.

Unfortunately there are a few things that do not quite fit.

§10. PERRON'S PARADOX

In the Middle Ages, an important part was played by the jester: a little joke that seemed so harmless could, as its real meaning began to sink in, topple kingdoms. It is just such little jokes that play havoc today with a mathematical theory: we call them paradoxes.

Perron's paradox runs as follows: "Let N be the largest positive integer. Then for $N \neq 1$ we have $N^2 > N$ contrary to the definition of N as largest. Therefore $N = 1$."

The implications of this paradox are devastating. In seeking the solution to a problem, we can no longer assume that this solution exists. Yet this assumption has been made from time immemorial, right back in the beginnings of elementary algebra, where problems are solved by starting off with the phrase: "Let x be the desired quantity."

In the calculus of variations, the Euler equation and the transversality conditions are among the so-called necessary conditions. They are derived by exactly the same pattern of argument as in Perron's paradox; they assume the existence of a solution. This basic assumption is made explicitly, and it is then used to calculate the solutions whose existence was postulated. In the class of problems in which the basic assumption is valid, there is nothing wrong with doing this. But what precisely *is* this class of problems? How do we know that a particular problem belongs to this class? The so-called necessary conditions do not answer this. Therefore a "solution" derived by necessary conditions only is simply no valid solution at all.

It it strange that so elementary a point of logic should have passed unnoticed for so long! The first to criticize the Euler-Lagrange method was Weierstrass, almost a century later. Even Riemann made the same unjustified assumption in his famous Dirichlet principle. Yet in one of the three classical problems studied in Sections 4 and 5, such an assumption shows itself to be false, if solutions are restricted to be smooth, as at that time they were. We shall meet, in these lectures, still more conclusive examples of even greater simplicity.

The main trouble is that, as Perron's paradox shows, the fact that a "solution" has actually been calculated in no way disposes of the logical objection to the original assumption.

A reader may here interpose that, in practice, surely this is not serious and would lead no half competent person to false results; was not Euler at times logically incorrect by today's standards, but nonetheless correct in his actual conclusions? Do not the necessary corrections amount to no more than a sprinkling of definitions, which his insight perhaps took into account, without explicit formulation?

Actually this legend of infallibility applies neither to the greatest mathematicians nor to competent or half competent persons, and the young candidate with an error in his thesis does not disgrace his calling. At such a time he should not think of suicide, but of rescuing what is good and valid in his work. (When two pupils shot themselves, Hilbert, in pouring rain, pronounced a funeral oration of one hour, in which he showed that their theses could be put right.) Newton formulated a variational problem of a solid of revolution of least resistance, in which the law of resistance assumed is physically absurd and ensures that the problem has no solution—the more jagged the profile, the less the assumed resistance—and this is close to Perron's paradox. If this had been even approximately correct, after removing absurdities, there would be no need today for costly wind tunnel experiments. Lagrange made many mistakes. Cauchy made one tragic error of judgment in rejecting Galois's work. The list is long. Greatness is not measured negatively, by absence of error, but by methods and concepts which guide future generations.

Chapter I

The Method of Geodesic Coverings

§11. INTRODUCTION

The preceding material is now just background and we make a fresh start. We have so far discussed a few problems with insufficient theory, and we have done well under the circumstances. However, this is a wasteful procedure, depending on hunches and coincidences, and on rather unpleasant calculations. Moreover, before spending time and energy in this way one would like to know whether it is likely to succeed in providing a solution. In these respects the Euler-Lagrange method did not really help; it merely explained our hunches without even justifying them, and it did not enable us to avoid any of the work we carried out. We need a different approach. In fact what we really need, and for highly practical reasons, is a theory.

The approach that we shall develop in the present Chapter is obtained roughly by ignoring any special features of the problems that we treated, and by retaining the pattern of our argument and formalizing it into a theory. This approach is classical; in fact its origins are even older than the Euler-Lagrange method, which temporarily superseded it. It was designed precisely to treat classical problems such as those we have encountered, and it is not affected by Perron's paradox.

From the point of view of contemporary mathematics it has, like every classical theory, one drawback (serious here from the practical point of view as well): it assumes too much smoothness in the data. However, this drawback will be largely overcome in Volume II.

Our task at the moment is thus to transform into a coherent theory the method of solution used in a few special problems. In other words, we have to carry out, basically, an exercise in abstraction, which should not be too difficult. Such an exercise constitutes good material for theses, which are usually not of the highest order, but as we shall see they can be very useful as a start. Of course, the really great conceptual advances, such as those furnished by the notion of complex number, or of group, do not usually arise in such a simple-minded way.

It is convenient to develop the theory for problems in n-space, rather than in the plane, and we shall, of course, limit ourselves to variational problems for curves. The latter can here be either parametric or nonparametric, and we shall indicate any differences of treatment that this may necessitate. Apart from this, the level of generality of our curves could be specified in several ways without affecting our arguments, since we shall simply need, for the present, to perform on them certain elementary operations of classical analysis. The reader can therefore be left to make an appropriate choice.

§12. THE VARIATIONAL ALGORITHM OF HUYGENS

We shall follow closely, for the moment, the treatment in Carathéodory's book and papers. Moreover, we quite discard the notation of the previous Chapter. The independent variable, and also the parameter along a curve when we deal with the parametric case, will be denoted by t, while the letter x is now a point of Euclidean n-space. For an integrand of a variational problem, we shall use the traditional term Lagrangian, and we mean by it a function $L(t, x, \dot{x})$ of the scalar t and two vectors x, $\dot{x}$ in n-space. We say that L is a parametric Lagrangian, if t is absent, and if in addition L satisfies the homogeneity condition

$$L(x, \sigma\dot{x}) = \sigma L(x, \dot{x}) \quad \text{for} \quad \sigma \geq 0;$$

this condition implies another that we shall frequently use: by differentiating in σ and setting $\sigma = 1$, we deduce

$$\dot{x}L_{\dot{x}} = L.$$

In the parametric case we term relative unitary vector, a vector $\dot{x}$, for which, at a given point x, we have

$$L(x, \dot{x}) = 1;$$

moreover, along a parametric curve, we term geodesic parameter, or Finsler arc length, a parameter t, in terms of which the function $x(t)$, representing the movable point along the curve, and its derivative $\dot{x}(t)$, satisfy the relation $L[x(t), \dot{x}(t)] = 1$. We then speak of the function $x(t)$ as providing the geodesic representation of the curve. The geodesic parameter reduces to ordinary arc length when L is the function $|\dot{x}|$.

We then suppose that the Lagrangian of a problem is a sufficiently smooth function of its variables. The precise degree of smoothness is difficult to state because we really need the smoothness of certain other functions that are defined by means of L. Continuous five-times differentiability is assumed in some accounts, and is rather generous (twice should really suffice). However, some additional assumptions on L will be needed later to make our theory work in its classical setting, and they are not just assumptions of smoothness. It would be nice to do completely without smoothness, and indeed already in geometrical optics one deals with a problem where the Lagrangian is discontinuous at the surface of a lens or other optical instrument, and generally at the interface of two media of different refractive index. We shall comment further on this as we proceed.

Our problem is now the following: given a Lagrangian L and a suitable class of curves C, for instance smooth, or other, curves with given endpoints, we ask for the minimum of the quantity

$$\mathscr{I}(C),$$

which consists of the integral of L along C, i.e., of the expression

$$\int L(t, x(t), \dot{x}(t))\, dt,$$

where $x(t)$ is the (or a) representation of C, further $\dot{x}(t)$ is its derivative and the range of integration is the relevant interval of definition of $x(t)$.

We shall now reformulate the very obvious remark on which we based the solution of special problems in the preceding Chapter.

(12.1) The Basic Algorithm. *Let M be a class of curves with given endpoints A, B and let C_0 be a member of that class. Suppose further that there exists an exact integrand Φ_0, such that $L = \Phi_0$ along C_0 and that $L \geq \Phi_0$ along all curves of M. Then $\mathscr{I}(C_0)$ is the minimum of $\mathscr{I}(C)$ for $C \in M$.*

The term exact integrand is here used to mean, as in the corresponding part of the preamble, a function $\varphi(t, x, \dot{x})$ of the form $S_t + \dot{x}S_x$, where S is a function of (t, x). Of course t will be absent in the parametric case. Alternatively, an exact integrand is one whose integral along a curve C depends only on the end points.

The proof of (12.1) is immediate: $\mathscr{I}(C)$ is, for $C \in M$, not less than the corresponding integral of Φ_0, and we can take the latter along C_0 without altering its value, which is then $\mathscr{I}(C_0)$.

It may be added that (12.1) actually has a converse; if $\mathscr{I}(C_0)$ is indeed the minimum of $\mathscr{I}(C)$ in the class of curves C with the same end points, then there exists an exact Φ_0 with the stated properties, provided, however, that we extend slightly the notion of an exact integrand by omitting smoothness. In some cases, the relevant exact integrand may have to be discontinuous, even in quite simple problems, such as (c) of Chapter I. This general converse can be reached in various ways, but it requires tools from modern analysis or from functional analysis. In principle, it is one of the forms of a theorem about convex functions and the existence of linear function that touches a given convex function from below, and it is related to the so-called Hahn-Banach theorem. We shall not need the converse here, but we want to draw attention now to the way in which theorems about convexity are interwoven with the material of our subject.

We shall use, in what follows, a slightly modified form of (12.1). Let $p(t, x)$ denote a vector-valued function with values in n-space, and suppose it defined in a domain of the $(n + 1)$-dimensional (t, x)-space; alternatively, in the parametric case, let $p(x)$ be such a vector-valued function defined in a domain of x alone, and suppose that $L(x, p) = 1$. We term p a geodesic slope if there is an exact integrand

$$\Phi_0 = S_t + \dot{x}S_x,$$

or in the parametric case $\Phi_0 = \dot{x}S_x$, such that for all $(t, x, \dot{x})$, or in the parametric case for all $(x, \dot{x})$, we have, whenever (t, x) or x lies in the domain of definition of p,

$$\textbf{(12.2)} \qquad L \geq \Phi_0, \qquad \text{with equality when} \quad \dot{x} = p.$$

In the preamble we started from the function S, which of course determines Φ_0. Conversely Φ_0 determines S except for an additive constant. We wish to remark now that when Φ_0 exists it is also completely determined by p. To this effect we observe that the difference $L - \Phi_0$, regarded as function of $\dot{x}$ only, attains its minimum 0 at $\dot{x} = p$ and so vanishes together with its derivative in $\dot{x}$ at this value of $\dot{x}$. This requires that

$$\textbf{(12.3)} \qquad \begin{cases} S_x = L_{\dot{x}} \\ S_t = L - \dot{x}L_{\dot{x}} \end{cases} \qquad \text{at} \quad \dot{x} = p$$

In the parametric case, the second equation falls away; by homogeneity of L, it reduces to $S_t = 0$, and t does not appear in S.

We shall term geodesic levels, or just levels, the sets of points P on which $S(P)$ is constant. The terms "transversals" and "geodesic parallels" occur also in the literature. The levels are determined by Φ_0 rather than S, since Φ_0 is unique for given p, while S is only determined up to an additive constant.

If p is the geodesic slope, we term curves of geodesic slope the curves that are solutions of the vector differential equation $\dot{x} = p$, where $p = p(t, x)$, or $p = p(x)$.

The family of such curves will be termed a geodesic family. We shall term it a geodesic covering, or a geodesic flow, if it covers the domain of definition of p simply. Since two curves of geodesic slope cannot intersect without touching, which is then equivalent to their being two solutions with a same initial value, the existence of a geodesic covering means that in the domain in question the solutions of the differential equation $\dot{x} = p$ are determined by initial values.

The curves of a geodesic covering will be termed, for brevity, flow curves. Older accounts use the word "field" in place of "flow," but it is best left to algebraists.

With Carathéodory, we regard (12.3) as the fundamental equations of the calculus of variations. We may express them by saying that, for curves C in our domain, the integral

(12.4) $$\int_C \{L(t, x, p) + (\dot{x} - p)L_p(t, x, p)\}\, dt$$

depends only on the endpoints of C. This expression is termed Hilbert's independence integral: its value, on account of (12.3), is clearly $S(B) - S(A)$, where A, B are the end points. Its integrand, incidentally, is our Φ_0.

The relations (12.3), of course, are still only part of the information furnished by (12.2), since we there have an inequality. If we rewrite the latter $L - \Phi_0 \geq 0$, and substitute for Φ_0 its expression as the integrand of (12.4), we obtain the Weierstrass condition

(12.5) $$E \geq 0,$$

where $E = E(t, x, p, \dot{x})$ is the expression

$$L(t, x, \dot{x}) - L(t, x, p) - (\dot{x} - p)L_p(t, x, p).$$

Clearly (12.5), together with (12.3), is equivalent to (12.2). The expression E defined above, as a function of four arguments, is known as the excess function of Weierstrass. In terms of it, when we take for p the geodesic slope, we have $L = \Phi_0 + E$, and therefore, for any curve C which joins in the domain two levels $S = S_1$ and $S = S_2$,

(12.6) $$\mathscr{I}(C) = S_2 - S_1 + \int_C E\, dt.$$

This is the famous formula of Weierstrass, which revolutionized the calculus of variations. We may also write

(12.7) $$\mathscr{I}(C) = \mathscr{I}(C_0) + \int_C E\, dt,$$

where C_0 is a flow curve and C is any curve that joins in our domain the levels of the end points of C_0 in the proper order.

§13. A LINK WITH ELEMENTARY CONVEXITY

One object of a mathematical theory is to reduce computation in individual problems. In this respect we find that the calculations in problems (a), (b), (c) of the preceding Chapter were partly devoted to verifying an inequality of the type $F \geq \Phi$, or $F^* \geq \Phi^*$, and that this can now be replaced by the Weierstrass condition (12.5). We shall see that this verification, which even seemed to require strange coincidences, can now be made quite obvious. For this we only need to understand the true geometrical significance of the Weierstrass condition.

If we regard $L(t, x, \dot{x})$ for fixed (t, x) as a function $f(\xi)$ of the vector $\dot{x} = \xi$, then (12.5) states that $f(\xi) \geq l(\xi)$ where $l(\xi)$ is the linear function that agrees with f at $\xi = p$ and whose graph touches that of f at this point.

This statement is merely one of a number of equivalent definitions of convexity, the "arc above tangent" definition. We term f convex at $\xi = p$ if there is a linear

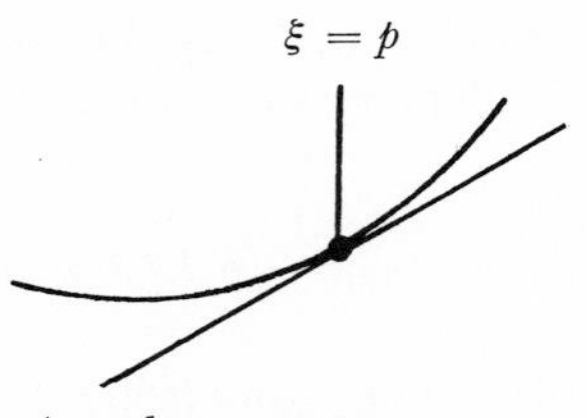

Arc above tangent

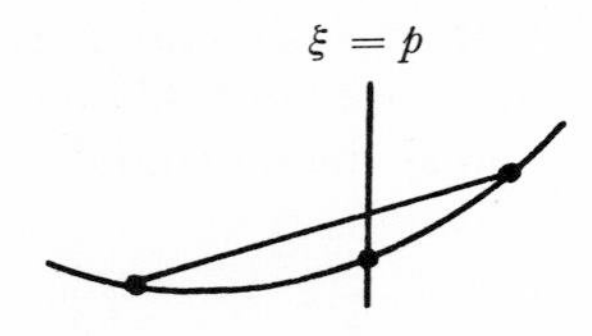

Arc below chord

function l such that $l(\xi) \leq f(\xi)$ for all ξ with equality at $\xi = p$. If f is differentiable, then l is necessarily tangent at this point, as in our case. This is virtually what our argument verified in passing from (12.2) to (12.3).

The more usual definition of convexity corresponds rather to the state of affairs described by the second diagram ("arc below chord" definition). According to it, f is convex at $\xi = p$ if for every chord of the graph of f which meets the line $\xi = p$, the linear function defined by this chord is $\geq f$ at $\xi = p$. (This linear function is defined on the projection of the chord in the space of ξ.) We shall return to these matters in a later Chapter.

What is important here is that the very definitions of convexity are directly related to the Weierstrass condition. Clearly one of these definitions is really implicit in the condition, although Weierstrass formulated the condition many years before anyone introduced the concept of convex function. We can simply say, instead of (12.5), that L is convex in $\dot{x}$ at $\dot{x} = p$.

In the parametric case there is an alternative, even simpler connection between the Weierstrass condition and convexity, provided that we assume L to be positive definite, i.e., to be strictly positive for $\dot{x} \neq 0$. This can often be arranged by passing to an equivalent problem. For this purpose we regard as equivalent two problems whose Lagrangians differ by an exact integrand, since it is clear that after one problem has been solved the other becomes trivial.

In the nonparametric case, of course, we see at once that when (12.2) holds we can arrange for the Lagrangian to be strictly positive by passing to an equivalent problem; in place of L it is sufficient to take the Lagrangian $L - \Phi_0 + 1$.

In the parametric case we can do something similar, provided (12.2) holds in a stronger sense, according to which equality in it holds at most for vectors $\dot{x}$ which lie, except for $\dot{x} = 0$, in a certain open half-space $a\dot{x} > 0$, for some value x_0 of x, and provided the domain of x is a small enough neighborhood of x_0. For $x = x_0$ it then follows, from our assumption, that there exists a small positive constant α, such that, for $x = x_0$, $|\dot{x}| = 1$, the equality $L = \Phi_0$ implies that $a\dot{x} > \alpha$. If we now denote by ε the minimum of $L - \Phi_0$ for $x = x_0$, $|\dot{x}| = 1$, $a\dot{x} \leq \alpha$, and we write $c = \varepsilon/(2\,|a|)$, we find that, for $x = x_0$, $|\dot{x}| = 1$, the equivalent Lagrangian

$$\hat{L} = L - \Phi_0 + ca\dot{x}$$

is $>c\alpha$ for $a\dot{x} > \alpha$, and is $\geq \varepsilon - c\,|a| \geq \varepsilon/2$ for $-|a| \leq a\dot{x} \leq \alpha$. Hence $\hat{L}$ is positive definite near $x = x_0$.

From now on we shall generally suppose that a parametric Lagrangian L is positive definite. This makes it possible, along a curve, to choose for t the geodesic parameter, or Finsler arc length. The set of vectors $\dot{x}$ which satisfy, for given x, the relation

$$L(x, \dot{x}) = 1,$$

(i.e., the set of relative unitary vectors $\dot{x}$) is termed the indicatrix of L at the point x, or sometimes the Finsler unit sphere. We shall be more concerned with the set of $\dot{x}$ for which $L \leq 1$; it is similarly termed the Finsler unit ball at the point x, and we shall denote it by K. We shall moreover write $F(\xi)$, in place of $f(\xi)$, for the function $L(x, \dot{x})$ of the vector $\dot{x} = \xi$, for fixed x.

From what has been said, the Weierstrass condition is a convexity condition for F at $\xi = p$. We shall express it as a convexity condition for K. (The notions of convex function and convex set are, as we shall see in a later Chapter, closely related.) Now the Weierstrass excess function may be written

$$E = F(\xi) - F(p) - (\xi - p)F_p.$$

Suppose now ξ and p on the indicatrix. Then

$$1 = F(\xi) = F(p) = pF_p$$

by homogeneity, and therefore

$$E = \frac{(p - \xi)F_p}{pF_p}.$$

The numerator is here a linear function of ξ, and it is proportional to the perpendicular distance from ξ to the tangent at p. The denominator is its value for $\xi = 0$. Thus E is the ratio of the distances from ξ and from the origin to the tangent at p.

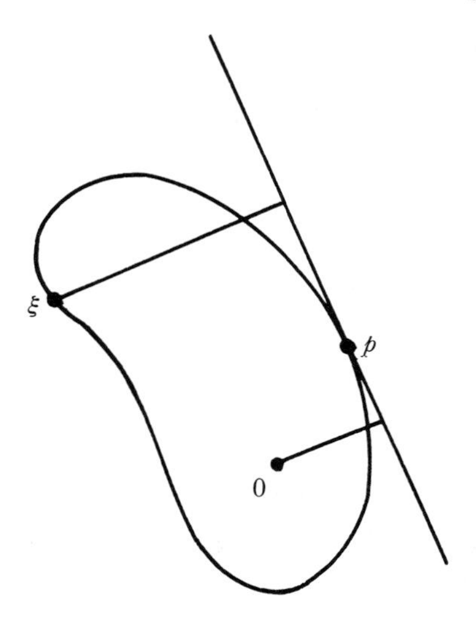

It is positive if ξ lies on the same side as the origin. The condition

$$E \geq 0$$

is equivalent to stipulating that the indicatrix lies on one side of the tangent (or tangent subspace) at p. This is again a convexity condition on K, and again of the same general type as the "arc above tangent" definition in the case of a function.

In problems (a), (b), and (c) of the preceding Chapter this convexity condition is evidently fulfilled, since we see at once that the indicatrix in each problem is a circle. Had we known this at the time, we could have spared ourselves not only some calculations, but also the eerie feeling of living in a world of coincidences.

What we have said makes clear the fundamental part played by convexity in the calculus of variations at the very outset of the theory. Still deeper links with convexity will appear in due course. Yet, strange to relate, the word convexity hardly appears in some quite respectable treatises. The reason for this is partly a matter of dates and time lag, and partly because the less usual definitions of convexity are the relevant ones in our subject. However, according to Carathéodory, Minkowski did give at Munich a summer course on the calculus of variations in which convexity was extensively used (as it naturally would be by the originator of that concept), and the lecture notes are carefully preserved there. They should make most interesting reading.

§14. REAPPEARANCE OF THE EULER EQUATION

So far the smoothness of our Lagrangian has not been used very much, but it will now be rather crucial. Unfortunately the classical arguments that we shall use do not apply very well to Schwartz distributions, for they are nonlinear arguments in which either products or maps are made use of. For this reason, it is not easy to see how to be more economical in smoothness at this point, although economy is rather desirable from the point of view of applications.

The success of the method exposed in Section 12 requires three conditions to be satisfied. One of these is the Weierstrass condition, which has just been given a geometrical interpretation. Another is that the covering by the solutions of the differential equation $\dot{x} = p(t, x)$ be simple, and this will prove to be a thorn in our flesh later on. The third is the exactness condition, which is expressed by the fundamental equations (12.3), or, what amounts to the same, by Hilbert's independence integral. We wish to study this third condition.

We write for short

$$y = L_{\dot{x}}, \qquad -H = L - y\dot{x},$$

for the right hand sides of (12.3). The quantities y and $-H$ are sometimes referred to as space and time momenta, and for the present they are to be treated as functions of $(t, x, \dot{x})$. (Later we shall assign to them different meanings, or more precisely we shall treat them as quantities which are no longer functions of this particular set of variables. However, the new interpretations will not affect our results.)

The exactness condition that we have to study is that the expression

$$\textbf{(14.1)} \qquad y\,dx - H\,dt$$

reduce to an exact differential dS in the variables (t, x) when we substitute $\dot{x} = p(t, x)$. We wish to find out when this occurs.

It is convenient to formulate the question a little more generally because this actually clarifies the analysis and because it will save doing the same work a second time. To this effect we shall enlarge our setting by using a preliminary map. In applications these maps play an important part, as we saw in problems (b) and (c) of the preceding Chapter. Maps also can be used to make the theory work for curves situated, not in Euclidean space, but on a manifold, given in terms of local coordinates.

In this section, we shall not use the most general maps of triples into triples $(t, x, \dot{x})$. Instead we restrict ourselves to spatial transformations

(14.2) $$(t, u) \rightarrow (t, x)$$

in which the time t is unchanged. This means that x is replaced by a function $x(t, u)$, where u is a point of some other Euclidean space, not necessarily of the same dimension, and where $x(t, u)$ is defined in a suitable (t, u)-domain. We then enlarge (14.2) to a map of triples

(14.3) $$(t, u, \dot{u}) \rightarrow (t, x, \dot{x})$$

by setting $\dot{x} = x_t + x_u\dot{u}$. We thus substitute for the variable $\dot{x}$ the total derivative of $x(t, u)$. More generally, if φ is a function of (t, u), we write similarly $\dot{\varphi}$ for the total derivative $\varphi_t + \varphi_u\dot{u}$. The function $x(t, u)$ defining (14.3), will, for good measure, be supposed twice continuously differentiable. We write Ξ for the rectangular Jacobian matrix x_u of partial derivatives, so that now $\dot{x} = x_t + \Xi\dot{u}$. In addition, we shall use α, or α^*, to denote any component of the vector u; a derivative in such a component will generally be indicated by a capital, or by one with a *, for instance X^* will be the partial derivative of x in α^*.

This being so, we ask ourselves under what circumstances a family of curves given by a differential equation

(14.4) $$\dot{u} = p(t, u)$$

is such that our map (14.3), derived as stated from the spatial transformation (14.2), turns the expression (14.1) into an exact differential dS in the variables (t, u). When this is the case, the family of curves given by the differential equation (14.4) will be termed an induced exact family. The integral of the expression (14.1) on an arbitrary curve of (t, u)-space then depends only on the end points; we term it the corresponding Hilbert independence integral.

We shall suppose the function $p(t, u)$ twice continuously differentiable. Moreover, the (t, u)-domain will be supposed (and this is essential to our argument) simply connected.

In that case, a necessary and sufficient condition for the existence of $S(t, u)$ is to be found in various textbooks on such topics as the calculus, vector analysis, differential equations and advanced calculus. The condition is the one derived in the natural way from inversion of order in the mixed second partial derivatives of S, i.e., from the relations $S_{\alpha\alpha^*} = S_{\alpha^*\alpha}$, $S_{\alpha t} = S_{t\alpha}$.

Thus induced exactness is now equivalent to a set of relations of the form

$$[\alpha, \alpha^*] = [\alpha, t] = 0,$$

where the square brackets are abbreviations introduced long ago (oddly enough, by Lagrange, whose approach to the calculus of variations was so different). These square brackets, written in full, are as follows:

$$[\alpha, \alpha^*] = \frac{\partial}{\partial\alpha^*}(yX) - \frac{\partial}{\partial\alpha}(yX^*) = XY^* - YX^*,$$

$$[\alpha, t] = \frac{\partial}{\partial t}(yX) - \frac{\partial}{\partial\alpha}(yx_t - H).$$

The whole setup is actually a special case of one to be found in the theory of first order partial differential equations and their Cauchy characteristics, and the following calculation is more standard, and its result less surprising, than might appear. We write

$$\frac{\partial}{\partial t}(yX) = yX_t + Xy_t = X\dot{y} + yX_t + R$$

$$\frac{\partial}{\partial\alpha}(yx_t) = Yx_t + yX_t = Y\dot{x} + yX_t + Q$$

where $R = X(y_t - \dot{y})$, $Q = Y(x_t - \dot{x})$, so that

$$R - Q = -\textstyle\sum_{\alpha^*}(XY^* - YX^*)\dot{\alpha}^*,$$

which last may be written $-[\alpha, u]\dot{u}$, where $[\alpha, u]$ is the vector with the components $[\alpha, \alpha^*]$ for fixed α. We note also that, since $y = L_{\dot{x}}$,

$$\frac{\partial H}{\partial\alpha} = \frac{\partial}{\partial\alpha}(y\dot{x} - L) = \dot{x}\frac{\partial y}{\partial\alpha} - L_x\frac{\partial x}{\partial\alpha} = Y\dot{x} - XL_x.$$

By substituting these various expressions in the definition of $[\alpha, t]$, we find that

$$[\alpha, t] = X(\dot{y} - L_x) - \dot{u}[\alpha, u],$$

so that

$$X(\dot{y} - L_x) = [\alpha, t] + \dot{u}[\alpha, u]. \tag{14.5}$$

Here, in the case of induced exactness, all the Lagrange brackets vanish, and therefore so do, for each α, both sides of (14.5). If we change the order of the two factors on the left, the resulting set of equations, obtained from the vanishing of the left hand side for the various components α, may now be written as the single vector equation

$$(\dot{y} - L_x)\Xi = 0. \tag{14.6}$$

We term (14.6) the induced Euler equation and its solutions induced extremals. If (14.2) is the identity map, so that Ξ is the identity matrix, we have the Euler equation

$$\dot{y} - L_x = 0. \tag{14.7}$$

§15. THE THEOREM OF MALUS

We continue with our analysis of induced exactness, and from now on we can, and shall, suppose that the curves of our family, given by the differential equation $\dot{u} = p(t, u)$, satisfy the induced Euler equation (14.6). We have to find just what further conditions are needed. The answer is provided by a famous theorem of Malus.

It is significant that Malus stated the theorem for geometrical optics, which, on account of Fermat's principle of least time, can be regarded as a variational problem with a certain type of discontinuous Lagrangian. Huygens also developed his theory, on which this Chapter is based, for geometrical optics, and a similar remark applies to a large extent to Hamilton, whose contribution will occupy us later. In this respect, these authors are closer to today's problems than the classical theory that came later, which assumes a high degree of smoothness.

Because of (14.5), we now have

$$[\alpha, t] + \dot{u}[\alpha, u] = 0. \tag{15.1}$$

Besides this, the Lagrange brackets satisfy an identity, obtained by Lagrange, that we shall refer to as the double curl identity, which is expressed by the vector relation

$$\frac{\partial}{\partial u}[\alpha, \alpha^*] + \frac{\partial}{\partial \alpha^*}[u, \alpha] + \frac{\partial}{\partial \alpha}[\alpha^*, u] = 0,$$

together with the similar scalar identity, in which t replaces u, and in which, of course, $[t, \alpha] = -[\alpha, t]$. To verify the scalar identity we need only write it in the form

$$\begin{vmatrix} \dfrac{\partial}{\partial t} & \dfrac{\partial}{\partial \alpha^*} & \dfrac{\partial}{\partial \alpha} \\ \dfrac{\partial}{\partial t} & \dfrac{\partial}{\partial \alpha^*} & \dfrac{\partial}{\partial \alpha} \\ A & B & C \end{vmatrix} = 0, \tag{15.2}$$

where A, B, C are the coefficients of dt, $d\alpha^*$, $d\alpha$ in the expression derived from (14.1) by substituting for dx the appropriate differential in (t, u)-space. The relation (15.2) is valid if A, B, C are twice continuously differentiable. Similarly we verify the vector double curl identity also.

This being so, we now apply to the function

$$\varphi = [\alpha, \alpha^*]$$

our previous definition of $\dot{\varphi}$. We find that

$$\dot{\varphi} = \frac{\partial}{\partial t}[\alpha, \alpha^*] + \dot{u}\frac{\partial}{\partial u}[\alpha, \alpha^*],$$

and we may use the scalar and vector double curl identities to transform these two terms. The right hand side becomes

$$\frac{\partial}{\partial \alpha^*}[\alpha, t] + \dot{u}\frac{\partial}{\partial \alpha^*}[\alpha, u] - \frac{\partial}{\partial \alpha}[\alpha^*, t] - \dot{u}\frac{\partial}{\partial \alpha}[\alpha^*, u];$$

here, we compare the first two terms with the result of differentiating (15.1) partially in α^*, and the other two terms with the similar result in which α and α^* are interchanged; in either case there is a missing term and hence we find that

$$\dot{\varphi} = -[\alpha, u]\frac{\partial \dot{u}}{\partial \alpha^*} + [\alpha^*, u]\frac{\partial \dot{u}}{\partial \alpha}.$$

Thus, setting $\dot{u} = p$, and denoting, as previously, partial derivatives by capitals, we obtain

$$[\alpha, \alpha^*]^{\cdot} = P[\alpha^*, u] - P^*[\alpha, u]. \tag{15.3}$$

In particular, in the case $p = 0$ (i.e., if our induced family is $u =$ const.) we have a result of Lagrange much used in celestial mechanics, namely that on each curve of the family the quantities $[\alpha, \alpha^*]$ are constant.

Here, however, we are concerned with the general case. Then (15.3) shows that the Lagrange brackets $[\alpha, \alpha^*]$ satisfy a system of homogeneous linear differential equations; moreover the $[\alpha, t]$ are, by (15.1), homogeneous linear combinations of the $[\alpha, \alpha^*]$.

By a unicity theorem for solutions of such differential equations, which we shall recall and prove briefly at the end of this chapter, all our Lagrange brackets will vanish identically if the $[\alpha, \alpha^*]$ vanish at some point of each curve of our family. This is the theorem of Malus.

§16. SUFFICIENT CONDITIONS FOR INDEPENDENCE OF THE HILBERT INTEGRAL

We denote by M the family of curves $\dot{u} = p(t, u)$, which covers our (t, u)-domain, and by N the family of their images in (t, x)-space. We suppose, as before, the (t, u)-domain simply connected. The vanishing of the Lagrange brackets then ensures the existence of $S(t, u)$, which means that the Hilbert integral

$$\int y\, dx - H\, dt \tag{16.1}$$

is independent of the (t, u)-path of integration for given ends.

For this independence the conditions found in the preceding section are then necessary and sufficient. They are that in M each member curve be an induced extremal, at some point of which the Lagrange brackets in the variables u vanish. It only remains to reformulate this last condition in cases of interest. We shall suppose that M consists of induced extremals.

(16.2) Trivial Cases. *The condition is satisfied* (a) *for all plane problems, and* (b) *whenever, for some* $t = t_0$, *the member curves of* N *all pass through a same point* (t_0, x_0), *or else all have the same momenta* $y = y_0$.

(16.3) The Standard Case. *The condition is satisfied if the Hilbert differential* $y\, dx - H\, dt$ *is exact in* u *on some smooth locus of the form* $t = t(u)$, *which meets each member curve of* M *but is not tangent to it.*

We remark that (16.2) makes the exactness trivial in two different ways in our discussion of the problems of the preceding section.

In regard to (16.3), the nontangency hypothesis concerns only the (t, u) situation, not necessarily the situation in (t, x)-space. The hypothesis will be used in our proof, but it is not clear to what extent it is indispensable. The envelope theorem of the next section is of a rather different type, and we give it there, moreover, in the parametric form.

Proof of (16.2). (*a*) In the nonparametric case u is here a scalar, so that $\alpha = \alpha^* = u$ and $[\alpha, \alpha^*] = 0$. In the parametric case the map $u \to x$ and the slope $\dot{u} = p$ do not depend on t. Then $H = 0$ by homogeneity, so that the Hilbert differential is $y\, dx$ and the brackets of the type $[\alpha, t]$, $[\alpha^*, t]$ vanish. Thus in a plane parametric problem there is only one Lagrange bracket to consider. It has the form $[\alpha, \alpha^*]$ with $\alpha \neq \alpha^*$, and it vanishes by (15.1), since the vector p is here supposed $\neq 0$.

(b) Clearly, in either case we have, at $t = t_0$, one of the pairs of relations $X = X^* = 0$, $Y = Y^* = 0$, and so, evidently, $XY^* - YX^* = 0$.

PROOF OF (16.3). We shall make use of a simple identity. By antisymmetry, the sum over α, α^* of the expression $\dot{\alpha}[\alpha, \alpha^*]\dot{\alpha}^*$ vanishes, and by (15.1) this result may be written

$$\dot{u}[u, t] = 0. \tag{16.4}$$

We observe further that when $\dot{u} = p(t, u)$, $t = t(u)$, the quantity $\lambda = t_u \dot{u}$ is $\neq 1$. This is because, by our nontangency condition, the differential relations $dt = t_u\, du$, $du = \dot{u}\, dt$ are not compatible, as they would be if $t_u \dot{u} = 1$.

In terms of (t, u) we write our Hilbert differential in the form

$$v(t, u)\, du - K(t, u)\, dt,$$

and we set

$$\hat{v}(u) = v(t(u), u), \qquad \hat{K}(u) = K(t(u), u).$$

We denote by v_1, v_2 and by $\hat{v}_1$, $\hat{v}_2$ the components of v along the α, α^* axes and those of $\hat{v}$. Further, in accordance with our conventions, T, T^* will stand for t_α, t_{α^*}. On the locus $t = t(u)$, exactness concerns the differential expression

$$(v - \hat{K}t_u)\, du, \tag{16.5}$$

and in it the terms in $d\alpha$, $d\alpha^*$ will be

$$(\hat{v}_1 - T\hat{K})\, d\alpha + (\hat{v}_2 - T^*\hat{K})\, d\alpha^*.$$

Since (16.5) is exact by hypothesis, we must have

$$0 = \frac{\partial}{\partial \alpha^*}(v_1 - T\hat{K}) - \frac{\partial}{\partial \alpha}(\hat{v}_2 - T^*\hat{K}).$$

Here the right hand side is the value for $t = t(u)$ of the expression

$$\left(\frac{\partial}{\partial \alpha^*} + T^* \frac{\partial}{\partial t}\right)(v_1 - TK) - \left(\frac{\partial}{\partial \alpha} + T\frac{\partial}{\partial t}\right)(v_2 - T^*K),$$

which reduces to

$$\left(\frac{\partial v_1}{\partial \alpha^*} - \frac{\partial v_2}{\partial \alpha}\right) + T^*\left(\frac{\partial v_1}{\partial t} + \frac{\partial K}{\partial \alpha}\right) - T\left(\frac{\partial v_2}{\partial t} + \frac{\partial K}{\partial \alpha^*}\right)$$

and which may be written $[\alpha, \alpha^*] + T^*[\alpha, t] - T[\alpha^*, t]$. It follows that for $t = t(u)$ this vanishes, so that if we fix α and take for α^* the various components of u, we obtain the vector equation

$$[\alpha, u] + t_u[\alpha, t] = T[u, t]. \tag{16.6}$$

By multiplying scalarwise by $\dot{u}$ and using (15.1), the definition of λ and (16.4) we find that

$$(-1 + \lambda)[\alpha, t] = 0,$$

whence $[\alpha, t] = 0$ and so $[u, t] = 0$, so that (16.6) reduces to $[\alpha, u] = 0$. This shows that, for $t = t(u)$, the Lagrange brackets $[\alpha, \alpha^*]$ all vanish, and so this completes the proof.

§17. INVARIANCE PROPERTIES AND AN ENVELOPE THEOREM

We can avoid the map $(t, u) \to (t, x)$ by considering the Lagrangian $F(t, u, \dot{u})$ obtained by substitution from $L(t, x, \dot{x})$. For we shall verify the following:

(17.1) Invariance Theorem for a Map $(t, u) \to (t, x)$. *The induced extremals and Lagrange brackets for L reduce to the extremals and Lagrange brackets for F.*

To this effect, we set $v = F_{\dot u}$, $K = uv - F$. Since $\dot x = x_t + x_u \dot u$, we have, when the variables are t, u, $\dot u$

$$\frac{\partial \dot x}{\partial \dot u} = x_u = \Xi \quad \text{and} \quad \frac{\partial \dot x}{\partial \alpha} = X_t + X_u \dot u = \dot X.$$

We thus find that

$$F_\alpha = L_x x_\alpha + L_{\dot x}\frac{\partial \dot x}{\partial \alpha} = L_x X + y\dot X,$$

so that $F_u = L_x \Xi + y\dot\Xi$, and that further

$$v = F_{\dot u} = L_{\dot x}\frac{\partial \dot x}{\partial \dot u} = y\Xi.$$

Hence

$$\textbf{(17.2)} \qquad \dot v - F_u = (\dot y - L_x)\,\Xi,$$

so that the Euler equation for F is the induced Euler equation for L. Further, since $v = yx_u$, we find that $V = Yx_u + yX_u$; hence, remembering that U^* is the unit vector along the axis of α^*, we see that

$$VU^* = Yx_{\alpha^*} + yX_{\alpha^*} = YX^* + yx_{\alpha\alpha^*}.$$

On subtracting this from the similar formula for V^*U, we find that

$$UV^* - U^*V = XY^* - X^*Y.$$

This establishes the invariance of $[\alpha, \alpha^*]$, and, by (14.5) and (17.2), that of $[\alpha, t]$.

We pass on to discuss the relationship between the parametric and nonparametric forms. So far, we have mainly stated our results for a nonparametric Lagrangian $L(t, x, \dot x)$, and have regarded a parametric one as a special case of the form $L(x, \dot x)$ subject to the homogeneity relation of Section 12. We now wish to proceed in the opposite direction, and for this it is convenient to write x_0, x_1, x_1' in place of t, x, $\dot x$, and L_0 in place of L, in the nonparametric case. (We do this only temporarily.) The pair (x_0, x_1) will now be denoted by x, and we denote by $L(x, \dot x)$ a parametric Lagrangian which then agrees with L_0 when $\dot x = (1, x_1')$.

This passage from L_0 to L raises a number of questions. In the first instance L is defined only when $\dot x$ has a certain form, and we then extend the definition by homogeneity. This still only defines L for vectors $\dot x = (\dot x_0, \dot x_1)$ such that $\dot x_0 > 0$ and for the vector $\dot x = 0$. The smooth extension of the definition of L to all vectors $\dot x \neq 0$ may be impossible, or it may be capable of being effected in a number of different ways. Thus, in the plane, if $L_0(x_0, x_1, x_1') = (x_1')^2$, we find that L takes the value $1/\varepsilon$ when $\dot x = (\varepsilon, 1)$, where $\varepsilon > 0$, so that there is no smooth extension to $\dot x = (0, 1)$. On the other hand, if L_0 vanishes for $|x_1'| \geq 1$, there are many smooth extensions of L to vectors $\dot x \neq 0$. We must exclude $\dot x = 0$, because only a parametric Lagrangian, which happens to be linear in $\dot x$, can be smooth at this value of $\dot x$. For $L_{\dot x}$ is positively homogeneous in $\dot x$ of degree 0, so that its continuity at $\dot x = 0$ would require $L_{\dot x}(x, \dot x) = L_{\dot x}(x, 0)$, independent of $\dot x$.

Actually, in this section we shall not need an extension of the definition of L. We need L only near certain sets of $(x, \dot x)$ along particular curves or families of curves, and in their vicinity. When L arises from L_0, these sets arise from corresponding relevant sets for the nonparametric problem, so that L is defined there. Along an arbitrary curve we shall need, not the Lagrangian L, but only the Hilbert differential, in which $\dot x$ does not appear except as a vector derived from p.

(17.3) Invariance Theorem for the Passage to the Parametric Form. *In passing from L_0 to L the Hilbert differential is unaltered and induced extremals remain induced extremals.*

Since $H = 0$ in the parametric form, the new Hilbert differential is $y\,dx$, while the old one is now to be written $y_1\,dx_1 - H_0\,dx_0$. To verify their identity (for the same family of curves) we must set $\dot{x} = (1, x_1')$ and show that $y = (y_0, y_1)$ where $y_0 = -H_0$. This is so because, on the one hand,

$$y = L_{\dot{x}} = (L_{\dot{x}_0}, L_{\dot{x}_1}),$$

where clearly

$$L_{\dot{x}_1} = \frac{\partial L_0}{\partial x_1'} = y_1;$$

and, on the other hand, by homogeneity,

$$L = \dot{x}L_{\dot{x}} = L_{\dot{x}_0} + x_1'y_1,$$

which requires that

$$L_{\dot{x}_0} = L - x_1'y_1 = L_0 - x_1'y_1 = -H_0.$$

From the homogeneity relation $L = \dot{x}y$ we derive further, by differentiation along a curve,

$$L_x\dot{x} + L_{\dot{x}}\ddot{x} = \ddot{x}y + \dot{x}\dot{y},$$

which reduces to

(17.4)
$$(L_x - \dot{y})\dot{x} = 0.$$

On the other hand, the induced Euler equations for the parametric integrand L, and for a map $(u_0, u_1) \to (x_0, x_1)$ where $x_0 = u_0$ and $x_1 = x_1(u_0, u_1)$, are given by

(17.5)
$$(L_x - \dot{y})\,\frac{\partial(x_0, x_1)}{\partial(u_0, u_1)} = 0.$$

When the parameter t along a relevant curve is identified with x_0 and u_0, we have $\dot{x} = (\partial x/\partial u_0) + (\partial x/\partial u_1)u_1'$, so that, by (17.4), the first component of the vector equation (17.5) is a consequence of the others, which may be combined into the equation

$$(L_x - \dot{y})\,\frac{\partial x}{\partial u_1} = 0.$$

Here the first component of $L_x - \dot{y}$ plays no part, since $\partial x_0/\partial u_1 = 0$. Thus (17.5) reduces to

$$\{(L_0)_{x_1} - y_1'\}\,\frac{\partial x_1}{\partial u_1} = 0,$$

i.e., to the induced Euler equation for L_0. This completes the proof.

(17.6) Exactness Theorem, in a Particularly Smooth Case, for a Family with Envelope. *Suppose a simply connected domain covered by a family $x(t, u)$ of parametric extremals, on each of which u is constant and t is the parameter along the curve. Further, suppose given a second family N of curves, situated on a parametric variety $x = \xi(u)$, where N is the image under the map $u \to x$ defined by ξ, of a family M of u-curves, given by $\dot{u} = p(u)$. Suppose, moreover, that for $t = 0$,*

(17.7)
$$x(0, u) = \xi(u), \qquad \dot{x}(0, u) = \xi_u p(u).$$

Then if all the functions concerned are smooth, the family $x(t, u)$ *is exact, if and only if* M *is an induced exact family.*

Here (17.7) means that the given extremals $x(t, u)$ touch, for $t = 0$, the variety $x = \xi(u)$, along the line elements of N, and that the parameter t has been, if necessary, suitably translated and magnified. Smoothness of all functions concerned is here an essential stipulation, and this does not follow from smoothness of $x(t, u)$, since nice families may have quite unpleasant envelopes.

We pass on to the proof of (17.6), which is easier than the statement. By what we saw in connection with (17.1), the initial values for $t = 0$ of the quantities $y(t, u) = L_{\dot{x}}$ are related to the corresponding quantities $v(u) = F_{\dot{u}}$ for the induced problem, by

$$v = y(0, u)\,\Xi(u),$$

where $\Xi = \xi_u$. Since $dx = \Xi(u)\,du$ on $x = \xi(u)$, this may be written

$$v(u)\,du = y(0, u)\,dx(0, u). \tag{17.8}$$

This shows that, for $t = dt = 0$, the Hilbert differential $y(t, u)\,dx(t, u)$ reduces to that of the induced problem on $x = \xi(u)$. By Malus's theorem, we see that the family $x(t, u)$ is exact, if and only if the right hand side of (17.8) is exact, and so, if and only if the left hand side is exact, i.e., if and only if M is an induced exact family.

§18. GENERAL COMMENTS AND THE APPLICATIONS TO PLANE PROBLEMS

The reader now has enough background and equipment to take a fresh look at particular problems. For instance, he can now appreciate those to be found in the beautiful chapter on the calculus of variations in Hardy, Littlewood and Polya's *Inequalities*. Or, if he is interested in an old problem or in historical matters, he can now study, from a more modern point of view, some of the old books and papers in our subject. This is somewhat like reading old newspapers, since we know what they could only guess.

In a concrete problem a complete solution may be very long, although finding the extremals may be a matter of only a few lines or pages. One is then certainly tempted to make some short cuts. Moreover, some applications are not really variational problems at all, but problems of mechanics or of differential equations in which one only wants to determine extremals. When actual variational problems occur and are treated in detail, they are nearly always confined to the plane so as to be reasonably manageable, and we saw in (16.2) that exactness is then trivial. This rather indicates that while the study of particular problems may be valuable, the experience so gained is liable to be rather one-sided. Thus even for problems in 3-space, the envelope theorem of the preceding section does not arise; an envelope is then at most two-dimensional, and in two dimensions all extremal families are exact. This means that to get a family of extremals which is not exact, but which has a nice envelope, we have to go at least to 4-space. The rather special nature of variational problems in the plane is also illustrated by the following result, in which the envelope in question is a curve, as necessarily happens if the problem is in the plane.

(18.1) The Envelope Theorem of Jacobi. *Suppose that in* (17.6) *the variety* $x = \xi(u)$ *is a curve, and that the extremals* $x(t, u)$ *all issue from a same point* P_0. *Further let* $\mathscr{I}(u_1)$, $\mathscr{I}(u_2)$ *denote the integrals of* L *from* P_0 *along* $x(t, u_1)$, $x(t, u_2)$, *respectively, as far as the points of contact* u_1, u_2 *with the envelope* $x = \xi(u)$, *and let* $\mathscr{I}(u_1, u_2)$ *be the integral from* u_1 *to* u_2 *of* L *on this envelope. Then for* $u_2 \geq u_1$ *we have*

$$\mathscr{I}(u_2) = \mathscr{I}(u_1) + \mathscr{I}(u_1, u_2). \tag{18.2}$$

This follows at once from the method of proof of (17.6), for on the one hand $v(u)\,du$ is clearly exact, and hence the family $x(t, u)$ is exact by (17.6), and on the other hand the relation

$y(t, u)\, dx(t, u) = dS(t, u)$ then implies $v(u)\, du = dS(0, u)$. Here we can take $S(t, u)$ to be the integral, from P_0 to the point $x(t, u)$, of the Lagrangian L along the extremal of parameter u, and we find that the difference of $S(0, u)$ is the corresponding integral of $v(u)\, du$. This is expressed by (18.2).

The theorem is restricted by our rather strong smoothness assumptions and, in addition, the assumption that the envelope is a curve, which in effect means that it does not apply directly for problems that are not in the plane. However, it is historically the origin of the theory of conjugate points, which we treat more satisfactorily later in this book (Chapter IV). In practice, (18.1) is rather rarely applicable because an envelope usually has a cusp.

Jacobi's envelope theorem can be given a more general form by allowing the extremals $x(t, u_1)$, $x(t, u_2)$ to have different initial points Q_1, Q_2. In that case, the difference of the two

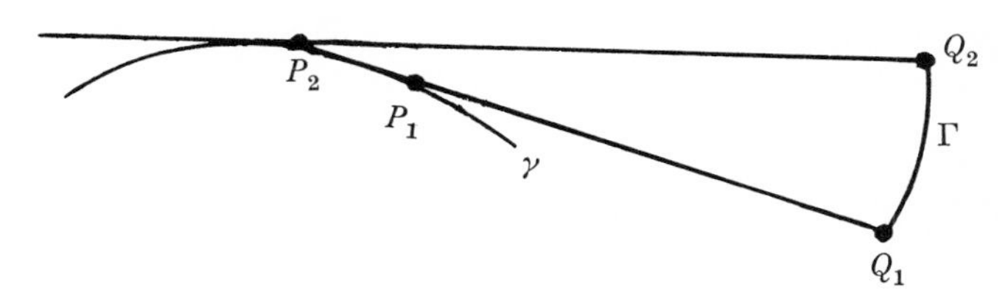

sides of (18.2) is $S(Q_1) - S(Q_2)$. The best known special case is a result of plane differential geometry, which corresponds to the shortest distance problem; it asserts that the difference of the lengths of two normals

$$Q_2P_2, \qquad Q_1P_1$$

of a plane curve Γ is the length of the arc from P_1 to P_2 of the evolute γ of Γ, i.e., of the envelope of the normals to Γ. In this case, by orthogonality, the function S is constant on Γ.

One case to which Jacobi's envelope theorem applies is the minimal surface of revolution problem (c) of the preceding Chapter, with for P_0 the point (0, 1) of the plane. In this case,

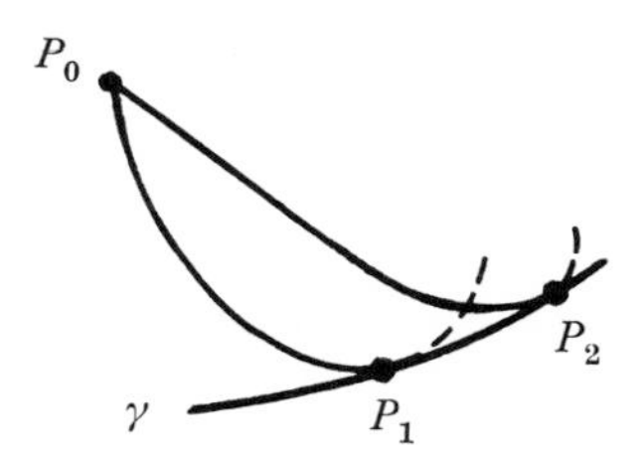

an arc of the envelope γ is not an extremal arc, and therefore the curve consisting of the extremal P_0P_1 and the envelope arc P_1P_2 cannot be minimal. However, by (18.2), the integral for this curve is the same as for the extremal from P_0 to P_2. Hence the extremal from P_0 to P_2 does not provide the minimum between these two points.

The same conclusion can also be derived from an interesting geometrical property of this extremal, due to L. Lindeloef (1861); the tangents to the extremal arc P_0P_2 at the two extremities meet on the axis. (This property can actually be established without any calculation

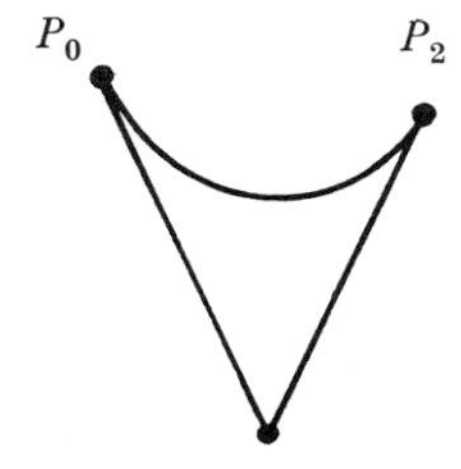

by the theory of conjugate points, as is shown in Carathéodory's book §341.) Lindeloef showed further that the integral from P_0 to P_2 along the broken line, formed by the two tangents, is equal to that along the extremal itself. (Carathéodory shows in his book §365 how this can be derived quite simply, without calculation, from the above property.) Since neither of these tangents is an extremal, the corresponding value of the integral is clearly not minimal.

PROBLEMS. 1. Show that in the same problem the extremal from P_0 to P_2 does provide the minimum for curves with the same ends, which do not cross γ.

2. Show similarly that for Q above γ the extremal from P_0 to Q, which touches γ on the way, provides the minimum for curves with the same ends, which meet γ without crossing it.

3. Show that there exist points Q above γ for which the minimum between P_0 and Q is not provided by a catenary.

(These problems require no computation.)

We see that a comparatively uncomplicated problem really comprises a number of further questions, and when all is said and done it may be simpler to build a theory. This is what we are doing, but we are not finished yet. We shall need some tools.

§19. BACKGROUND ON FIX-POINTS AND ON EXISTENCE THEOREMS FOR DIFFERENTIAL EQUATIONS AND IMPLICIT FUNCTIONS

We shall need a few standard results and methods from other subjects. These can mainly be classed as fix-point theorems, and our purpose is partly to stress this, without demanding an undue effort from the reader. But first, let us review our plan of campaign and explain our needs.

We are in a position to simplify the solutions in the preceding Chapter and avoid dep ending on certain apparently crucial coincidences. However, we have yet to discuss two stages of these solutions: the finding of extremals and the verifying of one-to-one coverings. These stages we cannot simplify, but we can show that the results could not have been negative. We shall do so quite generally in the next chapter by establishing local variational existence theorems. We can also see this in the problems we have studied by using the tools introduced in this section, and these will be needed also in the general case.

The determination of extremals, short though it was in the problems concerned, really requires an existence theorem for the initial value problem of a first order differential equation

$$\dot{x} = p(t, x). \tag{19.1}$$

Actually the Euler equation is a second order one, but we can clearly write z for $\dot{x}$ and regard the pair x, z as a single vector that can be written simply x. In that case the Euler equation is easily put in the form (19.1).

Actually we also need this existence theorem for (19.1) in connection with the theory of the present Chapter, and we must be assured of the unicity and smoothness of the solution in its dependence on the initial values. We have assumed something of the kind in speaking of families of curves defined by an equation of the type (19.1), and we explicitly used unicity in the proof of the theorem of Malus.

In regard to the second stage, referred to previously, the relevant tool is similarly an implicit function theorem. In our problems, after obtaining a family of curves by giving the coordinates as functions of variables α, t, we needed a domain in which these variables could be uniquely expressed in terms of the original coordinates. The relevant implicit function theorem can be stated and proved in several ways.

Both the existence theorem concerning (19.1) and that concerning implicit functions can be formulated as fix-point theorems. In the former case, this is partly brought out by the proof that we shall give, although this proof is quite old. The importance of general fix-point theorems in many questions of analysis is such that the reader should certainly plan to study them. Here we shall use just one further fix-point theorem, the now classical one of Brouwer. We shall derive from it a "small distortion" theorem, which plays an important part in our next Chapter and which is highly intuitive.

The differential equation (19.1) may be thought of as describing a fluid motion by the fluid velocity $\dot{x}$ at each (t, x); this is Euler's description, while that of Lagrange provides the actual streamlines $x = x(t, c)$ where c is constant on each streamline. In fluid mechanics one finds beautiful drawings of such families of curves. The two descriptions are shown to be equivalent, subject to classical smoothness assumptions. The curves $x(t, c)$ are the integral curves of (19.1), and the constant c can be taken to be the value of x for $t = 0$. This is why we speak of an initial value problem, but such a problem may make no sense without smoothness, and later, in optimal control, we shall have to face this. More generally, we can allow c to be just a label that fixes a particular curve of the family. This may be necessary when there is not enough smoothness. The figure illustrates two curves C_1, C_2 that touch at their initial and final

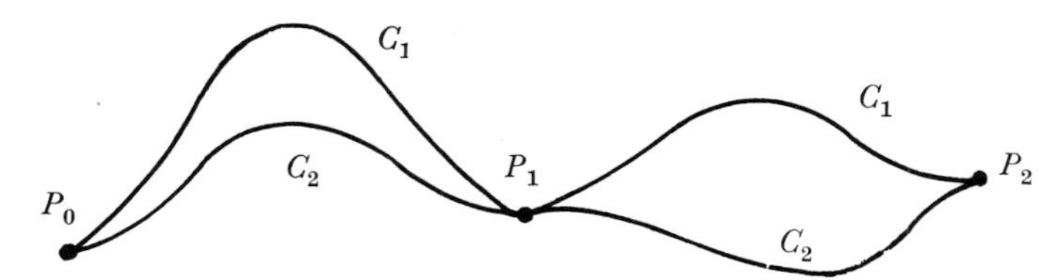

points P_0, P_2 and at an intermediate point P_1. They can be made to satisfy a same differential equation (19.1) with a continuous $p(t, x)$. Among its solutions, they are not even determined by their whole portions from P_0 to P_1, since we can interchange their final portions.

For simplicity, we shall suppose in the first instance that $p(t, x)$ is defined in the whole (t, x)-space, and is subject to the conditions

(19.2) $$|p(t, x)| \leq 1, \qquad |p(t, x + h) - p(t, x)| \leq |h|,$$

for all vectors h. We write, for a function $g(t)$,

$$T_g = x_0 + \int_0^t p(\tau, g(\tau))\, d\tau.$$

To ask for a solution $x = g(t)$ of (19.1) subject to the initial condition $g(0) = x_0$ is equivalent to determining a function g for which $g = T_g$. In the function-space with the elements g, we ask for the "fix-points" of the transformation T. The idea of the method of solution is one which is natural in fix-point theory. We take a particular element g_0 and we look for a limit of $T^\nu g_0$. If such a limit g exists as $\nu \to \infty$, it is also the limit of $T^{\nu+1} g_0$, and we find that $g = T \cdot \lim T^\nu g_0 = T_g$. In the differential equations context, where the method is known as the iteration method of Picard, the functions concerned are continuous and the existence of a limit, uniform in any finite interval $|t| \leq N$, is established by a crude estimate, which also gives unicity of the solution.

To this effect we write, for a pair of functions, g_1, g_2, $M = \text{Sup}\,(|g_1 - g_2|)$ for $|t| \leq N$. Then for t in this interval we have by (19.2)

$$|T_{g_1} - T_{g_2}| \leq \int |g_1(\tau) - g_2(\tau)|\, d\tau,$$

where the integral extends over the interval $0 \leq \tau \leq t$ or $t \leq \tau \leq 0$. Hence by an easy induction

$$|T^\nu g_1 - T^\nu g_2| \leq M\, |t|^\nu / \nu!$$

This is the crude estimate. If g_1, g_2 are both fix-points of T, and so of T^ν, it follows by taking the Sup in t that $M \leq MN^\nu/\nu! < M$ if ν is large, provided $M \neq 0$. This is contradictory unless $M = 0$, which gives unicity. Again, if we choose $g_1 = g_0$, $g_2 = Tg_0$, the same crude estimate shows that the series

$$\sum_{\nu=0}^{\infty} (T^{\nu+1} g_0 - T^\nu g_0)$$

is dominated by the Taylor series in $|t|$ of $Me^{|t|}$. This implies its convergence uniformly in $|t| \leq N$, and so the existence of $g = \lim_\nu T^\nu g_0$, uniformly also in any finite t-interval, and so the existence of a fix-point.

The argument needs to be slightly modified; when we suppose $p(t, x)$ defined only in the closure of a bounded domain G, and continuously differentiable, in place of (19.2), we find that p and its difference ratio are bounded; i.e., (19.2) is weakened by a constant factor $K > 0$ on the right hand sides. However, we can set $K = 1$ without loss of generality by a change of scale in x. Our crude estimates and the argument based on them then apply as long as our operations do not lead the successive $T^\nu g_0$ and their limit out of G, and they must therefore be limited to a suitable t-interval, which we shall term a sojourn interval. We see at once that if $(0, x_0) \in G$, then any small interval $|t| \leq \delta$ is a sojourn interval. For in it, if we choose for g_0 the constant x_0, we have

$$|Tg_0 - g_0| = \left|\int p(\tau, x_0)\, d\tau\right| \leq |t| \leq \delta,$$

so that, by our estimates, $|T^\nu g_0 - g_0| \leq \delta e^{|t|} \leq \delta e^\delta$; if δ is small, all the points $(t, T^\nu g_0)$ are in G. Again we note that if I is a sojourn interval when the initial value x_0 is a certain c_0, then the same is true when x_0 is a constant c near to c_0. We take in this case g_0 to be the fix-point corresponding to c_0, so that for $t \in I$

$$|Tg_0 - g_0| = |(c - c_0) + (T_0 g_0 - g_0)| = |c - c_0|,$$

where we have written T_0 for our transformation T, when the value c of x_0 is replaced by c_0. Thus again we find that $|T^\nu g_0 - g_0| \leq |c - c_0|\, e^{|t|} \leq |c - c_0|\, e^{|I|}$, where $|I|$ is the length of I. Since $c - c_0$ is small we can argue as before, and incidentally we see that our solution g depends continuously on the initial value x_0.

These results apply also when there are additional parameters; *i.e.*, p is a continuously differentiable function of (t, x, u) in a domain G of (t, x, u), and we keep u constant along a solution. To see this we need only add the equations $\dot{u} = 0$ and consider the pair (x, u) as a single vector. In particular, from (19.1) we derive a corresponding differential equation for a finite difference ratio, depending on a parameter h, and the continuity of solutions as functions of h ensures, if $p(t, x)$ is $(r + 1)$-times continuously differentiable, that the solutions of (19.1) considered previously be r-times continuously differentiable as functions of t and of the initial conditions.

We pass on to the discussion of implicit functions. We denote by f a vector-valued function of a pair (x, u) where x is a vector of the same dimension, and u is a point of a parameter space. We suppose f continuously differentiable, $f(0, 0) = 0$ and the determinant of the matrix f_x different from 0. We assert that in some neighborhood of $u = 0$ there exists one and only one function $\xi(u)$, whose graph lies in a sufficiently small neighborhood of the origin, such that $f(\xi(u), u) = 0$; moreover ξ and its Jacobian matrix ξ_u are continuous, and the latter satisfies the relation

$$f_x \xi_u + f_u = 0 \tag{19.3}$$

when $x = \xi(u)$.

This implicit function theorem is entirely equivalent to a corresponding theorem on the local reversal of a map $x \to u$. It is enough to write $f(x, u) = u - u(x)$ to reduce the latter to the implicit form; conversely the map $(x, u) \to (f, u)$, if it is reversible, allows us to solve for x in terms of (f, u) and then to set $f = 0$. The conditions for local reversal correspond to those of the implicit function case. The implicit function theorem can also be stated as a fix-point theorem in the space of functions $\xi(u)$: we denote by $T\xi$ the function $\xi(u) + f(\xi(u), u)$. An element ξ for which $T\xi = \xi$ is then simply a solution $x = \xi(u)$ of the equation $f(x, u) = 0$. However, the proof of the theorem, which is again old, does not use fix-points. It is taken from Kowalewski's book on determinants. There are other equally well known proofs. Moreover, the corresponding direct proof of the local reversal of a map involves only minor changes in the Kowalewski argument, and is reproduced in Rudin's Analysis.

We denote by f_i the i-th component of f, and by F_i the gradient in x of f_i, taken at a point (x, u). By hypothesis, if u and each of the vectors x_i are small enough, the determinant $F = F(x_1, \ldots, x_n, u)$ of the vectors F_i is different from 0, since it does not vanish for $x_1 = x_2 = \cdots = x_n = 0$, $u = 0$.

Suppose now, if possible, that for a same value of u there exist two vectors x', x'' at which $f(x, u) = 0$. Then, since $f_i(x', u) - f_i(x'', u) = 0$ for $i = 1, 2, \ldots, n$, there would exist, by the mean-value theorem, a point x_i on the segment joining x', x'', such that

$$F_i \cdot (x' - x'') = 0 \qquad (i = 1, 2, \ldots, n).$$

This is only possible if the determinant F vanishes or if $x' = x''$. Hence we have unicity near the origin.

In particular, if we fix a sufficiently small $r > 0$, we have, on the circle $|x| = r, f(x, 0) \neq 0$. The continuous function $|f(x, 0)|^2$ therefore attains a minimum $\mu > 0$ for $|x| = r$. Thus

$$|f(x, 0)|^2 \geq \mu > 0 \quad \text{when} \quad |x| = r,$$
$$|f(x, 0)|^2 = 0 \quad \text{when} \quad |x| = 0.$$

It follows by continuity that there exists $\sigma > 0$ so that, whenever $|u| < \sigma$

$$|f(x, u)|^2 \geq \tfrac{1}{2}\mu \quad \text{when} \quad |x| = r,$$
$$|f(x, u)|^2 < \tfrac{1}{2}\mu \quad \text{when} \quad |x| = 0.$$

Hence for any u subject to $|u| < \sigma$, the minimum of $|f(x, u)|^2$ in the disc $|x| \leq r$ is attained at an interior point $x = \xi(u)$. At such a point we have

$$0 = \text{grad}\,(|f(x, u)|^2) = 2f \cdot f_x$$

(where the gradient is in x). Since the determinant of f_x is $\neq 0$ this requires $f = 0$. This establishes the existence of a solution.

Finally, if we write $\Delta\xi$ for $\xi(u + \Delta u) - \xi(u)$ and F_i^*, G_i^* for the gradients in x and in u of f_i at some point, depending on i on the segment from (ξ, u) to $(\xi + \Delta\xi, u + \Delta u)$, we can write the relations $f_i(\xi + \Delta\xi, u + \Delta u) - f_i(\xi, u) = 0$ in the form

$$F_i^* \,\Delta\xi + G_i^* \,\Delta u = 0. \tag{19.4}$$

As before, the determinant of the F_i^* will not vanish, and by solving for $\Delta\xi$ the equations (19.4), regarded as linear equations, we express $\Delta\xi$ as a linear form in Δu; here the coefficients remain bounded as $\Delta u \to 0$, and hence we deduce that ξ is continuous. The same argument shows also the existence of partial derivatives: each of these is a limit of a ratio $\Delta\xi/h$ when we choose for Δu the product of a small scalar $h \neq 0$ and a unit vector along an axis of u, and, by dividing our equations by h and solving as before, we express these ratios as linear forms in the $\Delta u/h$, whose coefficients now have appropriate limits because of the continuity of ξ, as $h \to 0$; this clearly ensures the existence of the limit of $\Delta\xi/h$. At the same time we see that the equations (19.4), after division by h, tend to the corresponding rows of the matrix equations (19.3), and therefore they are continuous.

The two results discussed so far in this section are local theorems; they ensure the existence of a solution near a certain point or curve. The standard machinery for passing from a local to a global theorem is Borel's covering theorem: if a family of neighborhoods covers a bounded closed set E in Euclidean space, then some finite selection covers E. In the next Chapters this will similarly be used to pass from theorems which are local in $(t, x, \dot{x})$ or in $(x, \dot{x})$ to theorems local in (t, x) or in x. For the proof of Borel's covering theorem, see any real variable text.

Another way to free oneself of local restrictions is often to state the theorem concerned as a fix-point theorem. We have shown that both existence theorems discussed above are expressible as fix-point theorems. In Euclidean space, the basic fix-point theorem, from which more general forms have since been adapted to other spaces, is Brouwer's fix-point theorem for the n-dimensional closed ball U: let T be a continuous map of U into itself, then there exists a point $x \in U$ for which $Tx = x$. For the proof see a book on topology.

The following highly intuitive proposition is a typical application of Brouwer's fix-point theorem:

(19.5) Lemma. *Let T be a continuous map of U into a set E of the same space, and suppose that the distance of a point x to its image Tx never exceeds the radius ρ of U. Then E must contain the center of U.*

Strictly, (19.5) is obtained by combining Brouwer's fix-point theorem with a result in the other direction, which concerns the boundary Σ of U; the map T_0 of Σ into itself, which associates to each point $x \in \Sigma$ the antipodal point, which is the second extremity of the diameter through x, has no fix-point—in fact, the distance of each point $x \in \Sigma$ to its image $T_0 x$ is the diameter 2ρ.

We prove (19.5) by showing that if it were false we could construct, quite simply, a fix-point-free map of U into itself. By combining T with projection, from the center of U, of E into Σ, we would obtain a map of U into Σ such that no point of Σ is distant more than $\rho\sqrt{2}$ from its image. By combining this with the map T_0, which moves each point of Σ a distance 2ρ, we would thus have a map of U into Σ which has no fix-point on Σ, and so no fix-point in U. Since this map is continuous, this contradicts Brouwer's fix-point theorem.

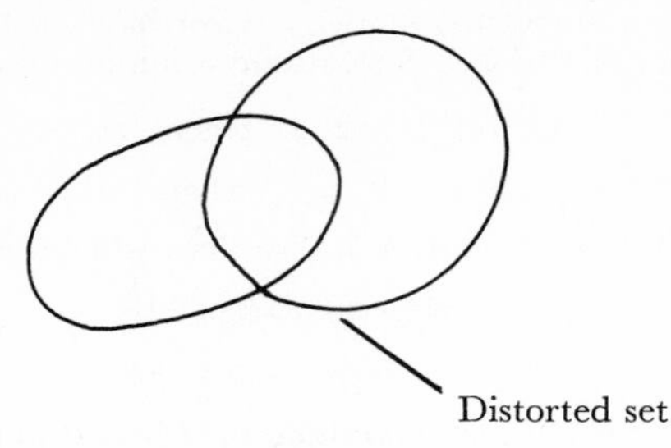

We shall term distortion a continuous map of a set into another in the same space, such that no point is moved by more than a certain $\rho > 0$. Thus (19.5) is a lemma about distortions of the unit ball. We shall derive from it the following general distortion theorem:

(19.6) Theorem. *Let Q be a bounded set in Euclidean n-space, and let H be a subset of Q whose boundary is distant at least ρ from the boundary of Q; further suppose either that Q is closed*

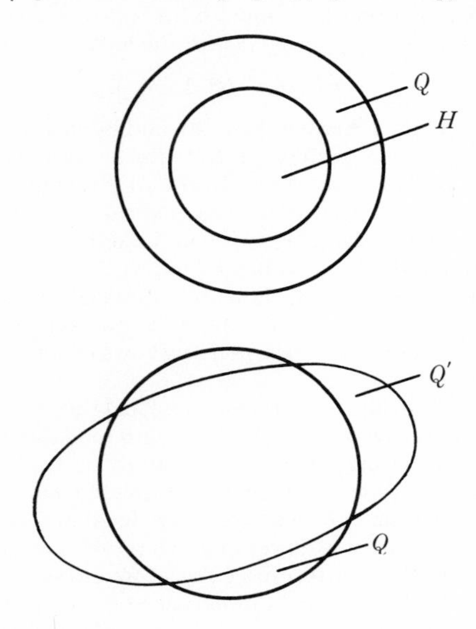

or that H is open. Finally, let T denote a continuous map of Q into a set Q' in the same space, such that the distance of each point $x \in Q$ to its image $Tx \in Q'$ is $\leq \rho$. Then $H \subset Q'$.

This (again highly intuitive) distortion theorem will be required in the next Chapter in a special case, to which we shall refer as Carathéodory's distortion lemma. It differs from (19.6) only by the additional assumptions:

(i) H, Q, Q' are domains,
(ii) T maps Q onto Q',
(iii) H contains at least one point of Q'.

With these additional assumptions, we shall give a second proof, which is direct and elementary. Thus we can avoid appealing to Brouwer's fix-point theorem.

Proof of (19.6) as Stated. If we join by a segment any point $A \in H$ to any point R of the boundary of Q, then this segment must contain a point S of the boundary of H, and by

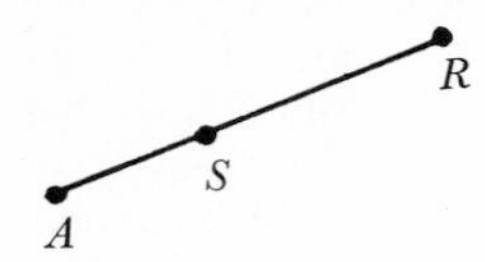

hypothesis the distance SR is at least ρ. It follows, since Q is closed, or H open, that the closed ball U of center A and radius ρ is contained in Q. Hence T restricted to U is a continuous map into Q' to which (19.5) applies, and therefore $A \in Q'$. Thus every point of H lies in Q'.

Direct Proof Subject to (i), (ii), (iii) (Carathéodory's Distortion Lemma). Actually in place of (i) we can here suppose merely that H is a domain and that Q' is open. We delete the last sentence of the preceding proof, and continue from there. We show next that A cannot be a boundary point of Q'. For in that case A would be a limit of points $P'_\nu \in Q'$, expressible (in at least one way) as images under T of points $P_\nu \in Q$ distant at most ρ from them. The points P_ν have then at least one limit point P_0, distant at most ρ from A, and therefore in Q. But by continuity we then have $A = TP_0 \in Q'$, so that A is not a boundary point of Q', since Q' is open.

This being so, we can join any two points of H by an arc in H, and this arc cannot then meet the boundary of Q'. Since one point of H is known to lie in Q', this means that every other point of H also lies in Q'.

Remark. In preparing the reader for Chapter II, we have begun to assume familiarity with such notions as uniform convergence, Borel's covering theorem, and the boundary of a domain. Generally, in passing from one Chapter to the next, a higher mathematical level may be needed for a real grasp of the theory developed. The reader who has not reached that level should not let himself be put off: it is an added incentive to acquire what he lacks.

Chapter II

Duality and Local Embedding

§20. INTRODUCTION

We plan, as stated, to show that our method will not lead to negative results, at least not locally. With this highly practical aim in mind, the reader may well be astonished to find that in the very next section we apparently allow ourselves to be sidetracked into formal developments concerning Hamiltonians and canonical coordinates, and perhaps reminiscent of the faded elegance of the *Ancien Régime* and its profusion of formulae. Hamiltonians were then all the rage—together with elliptic functions. Moreover, they were defined implicitly, and in time everything was made local and the theory became replete with implicit functions. Then a reaction set in: Hamiltonians were not mentioned in Tonelli's famous *Fundamenti* nor in Marston Morse's theory "In the Large."

Actually, Hamiltonians are inseparably intertwined with the notion of convexity, and particularly with duality of convex figures. This is basic in a number of parts of analysis today, particularly in functional analysis. Conceptually, the importance of Hamiltonians compares with that of complex numbers. At the same time, and partly because of the new light they throw on our subject and its connection with other fields, they provide a little of the same eerie atmosphere of duality that one first meets with complex numbers, as if we were thrust into a science fiction world with time going backward. No doubt, in a child the transition from the safety of crawling on all fours to the first uncertain steps on two feet produces a similar eerie feeling. In mathematics, it is suddenly no help to have acquired phenomenal skill in solving very rapidly problems of a lower level, just as it is no help to a child to have been able to crawl up a flight of stairs like greased lightning.

In this Chapter, we shall still use the classical approach to Hamiltonians and canonical coordinates, so that the definitions here are local. This is only partly inconvenient, since they apply equally on a manifold given in terms of local coordinates. (Another approach will come later, and we must have it for optimal control.) The definitions will be different in the parametric and nonparametric cases, and so will the local embedding and existence theorems.

§21. THE LEGENDRE TRANSFORMATION

We give this name to the particular case of the ancient transformation of poles and polars that occurs in the classical geometry of conics and quadrics, a subject much in vogue when Hamiltonians were first introduced. We consider a space isomorphic with that of the variables (t, x), in which we now take as variables a scalar s and a vector z. At the same time we consider a second such space, in which the variables are similarly s^* and z^*. We may think of the two spaces as superimposed if we wish.

In the (s^*, z^*)-space, we consider the maps of points into hyperplanes, and vice versa, defined by associating to the point (a, b) the hyperplane with the equation $s + a = bz$, and conversely. In other words, the coordinates of this point become the coefficients of the equation. This transformation is known as that of poles and polars with respect to the paraboloid $2s = z^2$. It is defined by the bilinear relation

$$s + s^* = zz^*,$$

and we term it the Legendre transformation. It is one of a class of maps long used by geometers to illustrate the duality of points and hyperplanes. As is usual, we also associate with a set of points the envelope of the corresponding set of hyperplanes, if it exists.

We shall use the Legendre transformation to define the transform $H(z^*)$ of a smooth function $L(z)$. To this effect, let Γ denote the graph

$$s = L(z).$$

Then Γ is the envelope of the set γ of its tangent hyperplanes. At the point $(L(z_0), z_0) \in \Gamma$, we find that the tangent hyperplane has the equation

$$s = y_0 z - H_0,$$

where $y_0 = L_{z_0}$, $H_0 = y_0 z_0 - L(z_0)$. Thus the Legendre transform Γ^* of Γ, or more precisely of γ, is the variety in (s^*, z^*)-space, given parametrically by

$$\textbf{(21.1)} \qquad s^* = zL_z - L(z), \qquad z^* = L_z,$$

in terms of a parameter z. If this variety is a graph $s^* = H(z^*)$ of a single valued function H, then H is the desired transform of L.

In general Γ^* need not be such a graph. In that case, we can define a local transform $H(z^*)$. To this effect, let y_0, H_0 be as before, in terms of a fixed z_0, and suppose the matrix L_{zz} nonsingular at z_0. By the implicit function theorem we can then solve near z_0 the vector equation $z^* = L_z$ in the form $z = \varphi(z^*)$ where z^* is near y_0. By substituting for z from this equation in the expression (21.1) for s^*, we obtain $s^* = H(z^*)$ where H is the desired local transform.

In the sequel, we shall apply this transformation to a Lagrangian $L(t, x, \dot{x})$ regarded as function of the vector $z = \dot{x}$. The resulting function H will be written $H(t, x, y)$ where y is z^*.

§22. THE HAMILTONIAN AND ITS PROPERTIES

We here confine ourselves to the case in which our Lagrangian $L(t, x, \dot{x})$ satisfies at some $(t_0, x_0, \dot{x}_0)$ the condition that the matrix $L_{\dot{x}\dot{x}}$ of its second partial derivatives in $\dot{x}$ is nonsingular. (We limit ourselves, incidentally, to the nonparametric case, for we shall see that the matrix in question is always singular in parametric problems.) Near (t_0, x_0, y_0), where y_0 is the value of $L_{\dot{x}}$ at $(t_0, x_0, \dot{x}_0)$, we term local Hamiltonian, or simply Hamiltonian, the function

$$\textbf{(22.1)} \qquad H(t, x, y),$$

obtained, as explained in the preceding section, by solving for $\dot{x}$ the equation $y = L_{\dot{x}}$ in the form $\dot{x} = \varphi(t, x, y)$, and then substituting for $\dot{x}$ in the expression

$$\textbf{(22.2)} \qquad H = \dot{x}y - L.$$

The variables (t, x, y), which appear as arguments in the Hamiltonian (22.1), are termed canonical.

As might be expected from the symmetry of the Legendre transformation, the relation of L to H is a symmetrical one, and the solution of $y = L_{\dot{x}}$ is obtained by writing

$$\textbf{(22.3)} \qquad \dot{x} = H_y.$$

We have for constant (t, x), when $\dot{x} = \varphi(t, x, y)$,

$$H_y = (\dot{x}y - L)_y = \dot{x} + y\varphi_y - L_{\dot{x}}\varphi_y = \dot{x}.$$

We note that when $\dot{x}$ is so expressed,

$$\textbf{(22.4)} \qquad H_x = y\varphi_x - L_x - L_{\dot{x}}\varphi_x = -L_x.$$

This means that the Euler equation may be written, subject to (22.3), $\dot{y} = -H_x$, so that our extremals are given by the pair of equations

(22.5) $$\dot{x} = H_y, \qquad \dot{y} = -H_x.$$

We term these the canonical Euler equations.

It is sometimes convenient to write them as a single equation for the $2n$-dimensional point $(x, y) = z$. To this effect we write $z = x + iy$ and regard it as a complex vector. We set further

$$\frac{\partial}{\partial z} = \frac{\partial}{\partial x} + i\frac{\partial}{\partial y},$$

and we term transposed gradient the operation

$$-i\frac{\partial}{\partial z} = \frac{\partial}{\partial y} - i\frac{\partial}{\partial x}.$$

Then (22.5) takes the form

$$\dot{x} + i\dot{y} = -i\left(\frac{\partial}{\partial x} + i\frac{\partial}{\partial y}\right)H,$$

or $\dot{z} = -iH_z$, which we write

(22.6) $$\dot{z} = \text{transp. grad. } H.$$

We note that the quantities y, H agree with the values we assigned to them in the preceding Chapter when we took the variables to be t, x, $\dot{x}$. This means that the Hilbert differential is still $ydx - Hdt$; it will be an exact differential dS in the variables t, x, when y is replaced by some function $q(t, x)$, or, what comes to the same, when $\dot{x}$ is replaced by $p(t, x)$ where $p = H_y$ for $y = q(t, x)$, if and only if we have, for $y = q(t, x)$,

(22.7) $$y = S_x, \qquad -H = S_t.$$

Elimination of y thus leads to the equation

(22.8) $$S_t + H(t, x, S_x) = 0,$$

which is the so-called Hamilton-Jacobi partial differential equation. This is an equation from which S is absent, or more precisely S does not enter into it except through its partial derivatives. It is, moreover, solved with respect to S_t.

From a variational problem concerning a Lagrangian $L(t, x, \dot{x})$, we thus derive a local Hamiltonian $H(t, x, y)$ and the corresponding local partial differential equation (22.8). In the theory of partial differential equations, an equation such as (22.8) is normally given, not only locally, but globally. Conversely, from a local or global partial differential equation of the form (22.8), we derive the corresponding Hamiltonian $H(t, x, y)$, and then, by eliminating y from the equations,

$$\dot{x} = H_y, \qquad L = \dot{x}y - H,$$

the Lagrangian $L(t, x, \dot{x})$. This time, however, L is now local, and we presuppose that the matrix B of the second partial derivatives of H in the y is nonsingular. The roles of L and H are reversed here.

Actually, the matrix product AB is here always the identity matrix: this follows by partial differentiation in $\dot{x}$ from the identity

$$H_y(t, x, L_{\dot{x}}) = \dot{x}.$$

This implies further that for a pair of vectors ξ, η the relations $\eta = A\xi$, $\xi = B\eta$ are equivalent, and that the quadratic form $Q = \xi\eta$ may then be written

$$Q = \sum A_{ik}\xi_i\xi_k = \sum B_{ik}\eta_i\eta_k. \tag{22.9}$$

The Weierstrass excess function can also be expressed in terms of H, when the latter is defined for the appropriate y. If we set $q = L_{\dot{x}}$ for $\dot{x} = p$ and omit for brevity the arguments t, x in our functions, we find that

$$E = L(\dot{x}) - L(p) - (\dot{x} - p)L_p(p) = H(q) - H(y) - (q - y)H_y(y).$$

§23. CAUCHY CHARACTERISTICS

The Hamilton-Jacobi partial differential equation (22.7) is a special case of the more general equation

$$S_t + H(t, x, S_x, S) = 0, \tag{23.1}$$

in which our Hamiltonian is replaced by a function $H(t, x, y, r)$ of an additional scalar r. For this more general function H, we can now carry out a calculation similar to that of the preceding Chapter, which led to the Euler equation. We identify this time u with x, so that Ξ is now the identity matrix, but we use the same notation as before. We give ourselves a family $\dot{u} = p(t, u)$ and we complete the identity map to a map $(t, u) \to (t, x, y, r)$ by means of a pair of functions y, r of (t, u), *i.e.*, of (t, x). We suppose that the differential

$$y\,dx - H\,dt \tag{23.2}$$

then reduces to an exact differential dS in (t, u), where $dS = dr$, and S is smooth.

Exactness then implies the vanishing of the same Lagrange brackets $[\alpha, \alpha^*]$, $[\alpha, t]$ as previously. Further, the identity of dS and dr leads to the vanishing of the further quantities

$$[r, \alpha] = \frac{\partial r}{\partial \alpha} - y\frac{\partial x}{\partial \alpha}, \qquad [r, t] = \frac{\partial r}{\partial t} + H - y\frac{\partial x}{\partial t}.$$

These two relations can then be replaced by the following

$$[r, \alpha] = R - yX, \qquad [r, t] + \dot{u}[r, u] = \dot{r} + H - y\dot{x}. \tag{23.3}$$

Further, we shall have

$$\frac{\partial H}{\partial \alpha} = XH_x + YH_y + RH_r.$$

In our earlier calculation, in Section 14 of the preceding Chapter, the corresponding right hand side was $Y\dot{x} - XL_x$. The change amounts to replacing $-L_x$ by H_x and adding the terms

$$Y(H_y - \dot{x}) + RH_r.$$

Otherwise our calculation can be as before. Previously it led to (14.5); however, taking account of the change, we get instead

$$X(\dot{y} + H_x) + Y(H_y - \dot{x}) + RH_r = [\alpha, t] + \dot{u}[\alpha, u],$$

or, if we make use of the first relation (23.3),

$$X(\dot{y} + yH_r + H_x) + Y(H_y - \dot{x}) = [\alpha, t] + \dot{u}[\alpha, u] - [r, \alpha]H_r. \tag{23.4}$$

Thus, finally, if we choose the family $\dot{u} = p(t, u)$ so that $p = H_y$, and we set $u = x$, we shall have from (23.4) and the second relation (23.3), since all square brackets vanish,

$$\dot{x} - H_y = \dot{y} + yH_r + H_x = \dot{r} + H - yH_y = 0, \tag{23.5}$$

and moreover, from the first relation (23.3), $y = r_x$.

The curves defined by the differential equations (23.5), or, more precisely, the projections in (t, x)-space of the corresponding curves in (t, x, y, r)-space, are termed Cauchy characteristics of the partial differential equation (23.1). In the case in which H is independent of r, the equations (23.5) reduce to the canonical Euler equations (22.5), and the characteristics coincide with the extremals of the problem whose Hamiltonian is H. The mystery of the reappearance in Section 14 of the Euler equation is resolved. The equation results from a standard calculation, by which Cauchy determined, at a much earlier date, his characteristics.

The values of y, r along a characteristic can be regarded as defining a moving surface element in (t, x, r)-space, passing through the points of a curve which projects into our characteristic. We distinguish formally between two characteristics consisting of the same points, but corresponding to different such moving surface elements.

The importance of Cauchy characteristics in the theory of partial differential equations is made clear in many books on the subject. We shall mention here the following well known property, which we shall not use:

(23.6) Theorem. *Let C be a characteristic and let P be a point of C. Further let Σ denote the corresponding surface element at P. Then any two smooth solutions of* (23.1), *that agree at P and both contain Σ, necessarily agree and are tangent to one another, at each point of C.*

In fact, if t_0, x_0, y_0, r_0 are defined by P, Σ, and if $S(t, x)$ is either of our two given solutions, then the quantities $y = S_x$, $r = S$, together with t, x, satisfy (23.5) for the family of curves given by

$$\dot{x} = H_y(t, x, S_x, S) = p(t, x).$$

As functions of t, the quantities t, x, y, r are then determined by the initial values t_0, x_0, y_0, r_0 together with (23.5), and so agree with the values that correspond to the points of C. At these points, therefore, the two solutions and their partial derivatives must agree as asserted (in the case of the partial derivative S_t; this agreement follows from (23.1) and from the agreement of the S_x).

§24. DUALITY AND THE STANDARD HAMILTONIAN IN THE PARAMETRIC CASE

The transformation that leads to the parametric Hamiltonian theory is no longer that of Legendre, but is the simpler transformation of poles and polars with respect to the unit sphere. It appears also, though under a different name, in functional analysis. We merely require it in n dimensions. (It so happens that in the parametric case the matrix $L_{\dot{x}\dot{x}}$ is always singular; we shall see why a little later.)

We consider two Euclidean spaces in which the variable points are y and z, respectively. To the point y of the former of these spaces we associate the hyperplane of z, given by

$$yz = 1. \tag{24.1}$$

The same equation gives also the hyperplane of y-space, which corresponds to the point z. Clearly any hyperplane not passing through the origin is the image of exactly one such point. We term the hyperplane the polar of the point in question; we term the point the pole of the hyperplane. We take for granted in what follows the elementary symmetry properties of our transformation, for instance the fact that the hyperplanes through a point y transform into the points on the polar of y. This statement has to be qualified by conventions in regard to those hyperplanes which pass through the origin; they transform into certain "points at infinity."

Let I be a locus, or set of points, of y-space, at each point of which there is a tangent hyperplane. Polar reciprocation induces for I an image F in z-space, where F is the set of poles of tangent hyperplanes to I. We term F the polar locus associated with I, or the polar transform of I. If we now associate in turn to F its polar locus in y-space, the latter is found to reduce to the original locus I; however, this is only the case if appropriate conventions are made.

Thus if I is the figure consisting of two semicircles joined by two parallel tangent segments, we find that if we take appropriate axes in the plane of y and introduce polar coordinates r, θ

the image F is the set of the points of the form

$$\frac{e^{i\theta}}{1 + a\,|\cos\theta|}$$

where a is a positive constant. In this case F has no tangent at the points $\pm i$, and its polar locus consists of the original locus I without the pair of parallel tangent segments; in order to restore these two segments to the locus we have to agree to count as tangents to F at $\pm i$ the lines through these points that fill the angle between the tangents to the two arcs of F joined at these points.

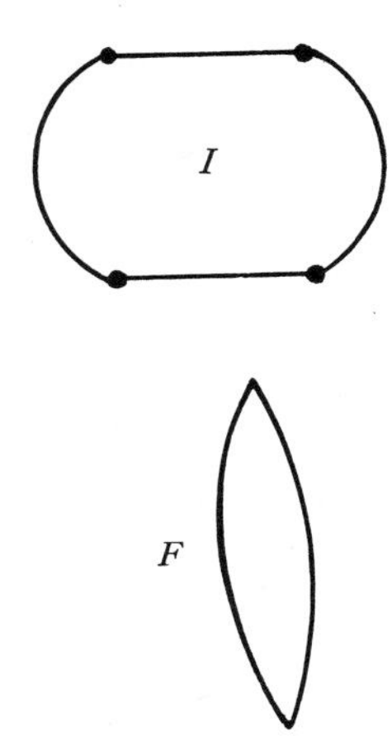

In a parametric variational problem, I will be taken to be the indicatrix at the point x, i.e., the set of z for which $L(x, z) = 1$. More precisely, in the local theory that we shall consider in this section, I is the part of this indicatrix near a particular point p on it. The definitions then apply to the neighborhood of a line element $(x, \dot{x})$ at which $L > 0$ and p is chosen as a positive scalar multiple of the corresponding $\dot{x}$. We could apply them similarly to the case $L < 0$ if we take for I the set $L(x, z) = -1$, or part of it. Line elements at which $L = 0$ must be excluded.

Analytically, we can define the figuratrix F as the locus of the points y which have the form

(24.2) $$y = L_{\dot{x}} \quad \text{where} \quad L(x, \dot{x}) = 1.$$

Here the condition $L(x, \dot{x}) = 1$ can, by homogeneity of order 1 for L and of order 0 for $L_{\dot{x}}$, be replaced by $L(x, \dot{x}) > 0$. Moreover, we shall only be concerned here with the neighborhood of a given line element at which the condition holds. We shall define a standard Hamiltonian H by the condition that $H(x, y) = 1$ for $y \in F$ at the point x, where $H(x, y)$ is to be positively homogeneous in y. This standard Hamiltonian exhibits most symmetry and is the true dual of L. Other admissible Hamiltonians will be defined later. In defining H and establishing its main properties, we could use implicit functions directly, but it is simpler to make use of the non-parametric theory already developed. We cannot apply this theory to L because, as stated, we shall verify below that $L_{\dot{x}\dot{x}}$ is always singular. However, we can apply it to a different Lagrangian, which will serve our purpose.

To this effect we write

(24.3) $$L^*(x, \dot{x}) = \tfrac{1}{2}L^2,$$

and we denote by A^* the matrix of the second derivatives of L^* in $\dot{x}$ at a particular line element (x, p) at which $L(x, p) = 1$. By differentiating in $\dot{x}$ the relation

$$L^*_{\dot{x}} = L \, . \, L_{\dot{x}}$$

and setting $\dot{x} = p$, $L = 1$, we obtain

$$A^* = A + Q, \tag{24.4}$$

where Q is the matrix of products of components of the vector $q = L_p(x, p)$. In order to apply the theory developed for the nonparametric case, we must suppose that A^* is nonsingular, i.e., has rank n.

We shall express this last condition in terms of the matrix A. We first observe that the rank of A is at most $n - 1$, so that A is certainly singular. To see this, we apply to the vector-valued function $L_{\dot{x}} = f(\dot{x})$, Euler's formula on m-th order homogeneous functions, i.e., the formula $\dot{x}f_{\dot{x}} = mf$; by setting $m = 0$, $\dot{x} = p$, we find

$$A\dot{x} = 0 \quad \text{for} \quad \dot{x} = p. \tag{24.5}$$

This shows that A has at most rank $n - 1$.

This being so, we now write any vector in the form

$$\xi = \eta + \lambda p \quad \text{where} \quad \eta q = 0, \tag{24.6}$$

i.e., we set $\lambda = \xi q$, $\eta = \xi - p(\xi q)$. (Here q is, as stated above, the vector L_p.) Clearly $Q\xi = \lambda q$, and, by (24.5), $A\xi = A\eta$. It follows from (24.4) that the relations (24.6) imply

$$A\xi = A^*\eta, \qquad A^*\xi = A\eta + \lambda q, \qquad \xi A^* \xi = \eta A \eta + \lambda^2. \tag{24.7}$$

It is now easy to show that the condition that A^* be nonsingular, i.e., of rank n, is equivalent to supposing A of rank $n - 1$, or, what amounts to the same in view of (24.5), that the relation $A\xi = 0$ implies that ξ is a scalar multiple of p.

By the symmetry of A, (24.5) may be written $pA = 0$, so that the second relation (24.7) leads to $pA^*\xi = \lambda$; hence the relation $A^*\xi = 0$ necessitates both $\lambda = 0$ and $A\eta = 0$. If A has rank $n - 1$, this last relation implies also $\eta = 0$, for η cannot otherwise be a scalar multiple of p since $\eta q = 0, pq = 1$. Thus the relation $A^*\xi = 0$ implies $\xi = 0$ in this case, so that A^* is then nonsingular. Conversely, if A^* is nonsingular, the first part of (24.7) shows that $A\xi = 0$ implies $\xi = \lambda p$, hence that A has rank $n - 1$.

We shall say further that L satisfies the parametric Legendre condition if the quadratic form $\xi A^* \xi$ is positive definite. By the third part of (24.7), this is the case, if and only if

$$\eta A \eta > 0 \quad \text{whenever} \quad \eta q = 0 \quad \text{and} \quad \eta \neq 0. \tag{24.8}$$

We remark that the condition that A^* be nonsingular (or A of rank $n - 1$) is in fact violated in the example illustrated by diagrams of I and F earlier in this section; this occurs in the parts of I consisting of straight segments. The example thus illustrates the difficulties that arise when the condition is violated.

We now denote by x, y and $H^*(x, y)$ the canonical variables and the Hamiltonian, associated with L^* as Lagrangian near $\dot{x} = p$, so that y will be near $q = L_p = L^*_p$. We set

$$H^* = \tfrac{1}{2}H^2$$

so that $H = H(x, y)$. The sign of H will be taken positive, and H will only be considered defined when H^* is positive. However, we shall find that H is defined near $y = q$ and is positively homogeneous of the first order in y; moreover that $H = 1$ whenever, in this neighborhood, y has the form $L_{\dot{x}}$, and, in particular, when $y = q$; and that for $\dot{x}$ near p and y near q the solution of (24.2) is obtained by setting

$$\dot{x} = H_y \quad \text{where} \quad H(x, y) = 1. \tag{24.9}$$

For this purpose, we note that, when (24.2) holds, we have $L^* = \frac{1}{2}$, and

$$y = L^*_x, \qquad \dot{x}y = 1, \qquad H^* = \dot{x}y - L^* = \tfrac{1}{2},$$

and therefore $H = 1$. Also L^* is positively second order homogeneous, so that the map $\dot{x} \to y = L^*_{\dot{x}}$ is positively first order homogeneous, together with its inverse map near $\dot{x} = p, y = q$, by unicity. This makes the expressions L^*, $\dot{x}y$, H^* positively second order homogeneous in either $\dot{x}$ or y, so that H is positively first order homogeneous. Finally, for $H = 1$, (24.9) is clearly equivalent to $\dot{x} = H^*_y$, and this last relation, by the nonparametric theory, solves $y = L^*_x$ uniquely.

This being so, the function H, which is now defined near (x, q), can be clearly extended by homogeneity to all pairs (x, y) for which $(x, \sigma y)$ is near (x, q) for some $\sigma \geq 0$. Thus extended we term $H(x, y)$ the standard Hamiltonian of our parametric problem near (x, q).

From the relation (22.4) for L^* and H^*, we have, when $L = H = 1$ and when H_y is substituted for $\dot{x}$,

$$L_x = -H_x.$$

This means that the Euler equation, which we obtained in Chapter I, Section 14 for both the parametric and the nonparametric case, in the canonical form becomes again the pair

$$\dot{x} = H_y, \qquad \dot{y} = -H_x,$$

provided that t is chosen to be a geodesic parameter, i.e., a parameter such that, along the curves in question, $L(x, \dot{x}) = 1$.

PROBLEM. Show that the matrix B of the second derivatives of H in the variables y, satisfies the relation $Bq = 0$ and that B has rank $n - 1$.

§25. OTHER ADMISSIBLE PARAMETRIC HAMILTONIANS

The device of the preceding section enabled us to obtain, for the parametric case, a satisfactory definition of the notions of Hamiltonian and canonical variables, by deriving it from the nonparametric case. However, there are other ways of passing from the one case to the other, and it is important in the calculus of variations that we should be able to do this as freely as possible. It is therefore convenient to allow more flexibility in the definition of Hamiltonian, and we shall now introduce a whole class of admissible parametric Hamiltonians $H(x, y)$, corresponding to a same Lagrangian $L(x, \dot{x})$. To each such Hamiltonian, we shall attach a corresponding choice of the parameter t on all relevant admissible parametric curves.

We shall limit ourselves here to line elements $(x, \dot{x})$ that lie in a neighborhood N of a certain line element (x_0, p) at which $L \neq 0$ and at which A has rank $n - 1$ (or equivalently A^* is nonsingular, according to the preceding section). Since we deal with the parametric case, we suppose that if $(x, \dot{x}) \in N$, then for every $\sigma > 0$, $(x, \sigma\dot{x}) \in N$.

We consider the class of functions $H(x, y)$ such that, when $y = L_{\dot{x}}$ where $(x, \dot{x}) \in N$, the following two conditions are satisfied:

(25.1) (a) $H(x, y) = \text{const.}$, (b) $\dot{x}H_y \geq 0$.

We term such a function H an admissible local Hamiltonian if it is defined in a neighborhood of the canonical point (x_0, q) where q is the vector $L_{\dot{x}}$ at $(x, \dot{x}) = (x_0, p)$.

The matrix A will, by continuity of the second derivatives of L, be of the same rank near (x_0, p), and we restrict N so that this is the case throughout N. We have now, exactly as in (24.5) $A\dot{x} = 0$, where A is taken at $(x, \dot{x}) \in N$. Also, by partial differentiation in $\dot{x}$, we derive from (25.1)(a) that $H_y A = 0$ when $y = L_{\dot{x}}$. Hence there is a scalar λ such that

$$\textbf{(25.2)} \qquad \dot{x} = \lambda H_y \quad \text{when} \quad y = L_{\dot{x}},$$

and by (25.1)(b) we see that $\lambda \geq 0$, and therefore $\lambda > 0$ in N, since $\dot{x} \neq 0$. From (25.2), by scalar multiplication with $L_{\dot{x}}$, we derive, if $yH_y = 1/\mu$ at $y = L_{\dot{x}}$,

$$\lambda = \mu L(x, \dot{x}).$$

Here y, when regarded as function of $\dot{x}$, is positively homogeneous of order 0, and therefore so is μ. Hence λ is, like L, positively homogeneous of order 1, i.e.,

$$\lambda(x, \sigma\dot{x}) = \sigma\lambda(x, \dot{x}) \quad \text{for} \quad \sigma > 0.$$

Since further $\lambda > 0$, we can always effect, on an admissible parametric curve with line elements in N, a change of parameter, by which λ becomes unity for all line elements of the curve. The parameter t for which this is the case will be termed the canonical parameter associated with H.

We saw in the preceding section that the equations $y = L_{\dot{x}}$, $L(x, \dot{x}) = 1$, have, in terms of the standard Hamiltonian, a unique solution of the form $\dot{x} = f(x, y)$. A similar conclusion, of course, applies to the equations $y = L_{\dot{x}}$, $L(x, \dot{x}) = -1$. Since $\lambda > 0$, and λ is positively homogeneous of order 1, while $L_{\dot{x}}$ is positively homogeneous of order 0, the same conclusion applies to the equations $y = L_{\dot{x}}$, $\lambda(x, \dot{x}) = 1$, and (25.2) then tells us that the solution is $\dot{x} = H_y$ in terms of our admissible local Hamiltonian H.

Further, if M is the matrix of partial derivatives of $L_{\dot{x}}$ in x, we have, when $y = L_{\dot{x}}$, on the one hand,

$$L_x = \dot{x}\frac{\partial}{\partial x} L_{\dot{x}} = M\dot{x} = \lambda M H_y,$$

and on the other hand, by partial differentiation in x applied to (25.1)(a),

$$H_x + MH_y = 0.$$

Thus when $y = L_{\dot{x}}$, we find that $L_x + \lambda H_x = 0$, and therefore that

$$L_x + H_x = 0,$$

when $\lambda = 1$ and either $y = L_{\dot{x}}$ or $\dot{x} = H_y$.

We thus see that, in terms of an admissible local Hamiltonian H and its associated canonical parameter t, the Euler equation for the parametric case takes again the canonical form

$$\dot{x} = H_y, \qquad \dot{y} = -H_x,$$

exactly as in the nonparametric case.

Of course the component equations of the parametric Euler equation are not independent. The combination

$$\dot{x}\left(L_x - \frac{d}{dt}L_{\dot{x}}\right)$$

may be written

$$\dot{x}L_x + L_{\dot{x}}\frac{d}{dt}\dot{x} - \frac{d}{dt}(\dot{x}L_{\dot{x}}),$$

which is simply

$$\frac{d}{dt} L - \frac{d}{dt} (\dot{x} L_{\dot{x}}),$$

and this vanishes by homogeneity. Also the combination

$$\dot{y}(H_y - \dot{x}) + \dot{x}(H_x + \dot{y})$$

is simply

$$\dot{y} H_y + \dot{x} H_x,$$

which is $\frac{d}{dt}(H)$; it vanishes on any curve on which H is constant, and, by (25.1)(a) and (25.2), therefore on any canonical curve on which $\dot{x} = H_y$ and $\lambda = 1$.

§26. LOCAL PASSAGE FROM PARAMETRIC TO NONPARAMETRIC CASE

We consider again a neighborhood N of (x_0, p) subject to our previous conditions. We choose a coordinate axis x_n along which the component of p is not 0, and we direct this axis so that the component is positive. The neighborhood N will now be restricted so that for all $(x, \dot{x}) \in N$, we have a positive component $\dot{x}_n$ of $\dot{x}$ along x_n. This means that on any admissible parametric curve whose line elements lie in N we can choose the parameter t to coincide with x_n.

We shall write ξ for the vector with $n - 1$ components, which are those, other than x_n, of the point x, and we now set $t = x_n$. We reverse the usual order of coordinates and write (t, ξ) for the point x. With t as parameter, $L(x, \dot{x})$ becomes $\hat{L}(t, \xi, \dot{\xi})$, since $\dot{x} = (\dot{t}, \dot{\xi})$ and $\dot{t} = 1$.

From the homogeneity relation $L(x, \dot{x}) = \dot{x} L_{\dot{x}}$, we obtain for this value of $\dot{t}$ the corresponding value of the partial derivative $L_{\dot{t}}$ in terms of $\hat{L}$. It is

$$L_{\dot{t}} = \hat{L} - \dot{\xi} \hat{L}_{\dot{\xi}}.$$

We see that $L_{\dot{t}} = -\hat{H}(t, \xi, \eta)$ for $\eta = \hat{L}_{\dot{\xi}}$, where $\hat{H}$ is the nonparametric Hamiltonian corresponding to the Lagrangian $\hat{L}$, and where ξ, η are the relevant canonical variables.

We now define a parametric Hamiltonian by setting

$$H(x, y) = y_n + \hat{H}(t, \xi, \eta),$$

where y_n is the n-th component of y, and where η is the vector with $n - 1$ components, which are the remaining components of y.

We shall verify that t is the canonical parameter associated with H and that H is an admissible local Hamiltonian corresponding to the Lagrangian L. To this effect we note that $L_{\dot{x}}$ is the vector whose first $n - 1$ components are those of $\hat{L}_{\dot{\xi}}$, while its last component was found to be $-\hat{H}(t, \xi, \hat{L}_{\dot{\xi}})$. We therefore have

$$H(x, L_{\dot{x}}) = 0.$$

We have further, when $y = L_{\dot{x}}$,

$$y H_y = y_n + \eta \hat{H}_\eta = -\hat{H} + \eta \hat{H}_\eta$$

where $\eta = \hat{L}_{\dot{\xi}}$. Hence $y H_y = \hat{L} = L$ and therefore

$$\lambda(x, \dot{x}) = 1.$$

The condition $\dot{x}H_y \geq 0$ is then automatically satisfied by (25.2), so that H is an admissible local Hamiltonian.

We can thus pass from the parametric to the nonparametric case and vice versa. Of course, this would not be true in a global theory of Hamiltonians.

The nonparametric Euler equations coincide with the first $n - 1$ components of the parametric ones. The last parametric component is a consequence of the others: it may be written

$$\textbf{(26.1)} \qquad \frac{d}{dt} \hat{H}(t, \xi, \eta) = \hat{H}_t,$$

or equivalently, if we carry out the differentiation on the left, $\dot{\xi}\hat{H}_\xi + \dot{\eta}\hat{H}_\eta = 0$, which reduces, by the nonparametric canonical Euler equations, to $-\dot{\xi}\dot{\eta} + \dot{\eta}\dot{\xi} = 0$.

The equation (26.1) is of some importance in itself. It is rather useful in those problems where $\hat{H}$ does not contain t explicitly, as it then asserts the constancy of $\hat{H}$ along an extremal (conservation of energy in mechanics). This assertion of constancy applies, for instance, to H^* in Section 24, along any one of its (nonparametric) extremals $x^*(t)$. The constant value of H^* will be near $\frac{1}{2}$ if $x^*(t)$ has line elements in a narrow neighborhood of those of an extremal for which $H^* = \frac{1}{2}$. The corresponding value of H is then a constant near to unity. Since $x^*(t)$ satisfies canonical Euler equations for H^*, we find that, for a suitable constant c near to unity, $x^*(ct)$ satisfies canonical Euler equations for H. Thus the curve $x^*(t)$ is a parametric extremal. We can verify similarly that an exact family of extremals for H^* becomes an exact parametric family of extremals for H. The converses of these remarks go without saying.

Examples. In each of the problems (a), (b), (c) of the Preamble, determine the nonparametric and all the parametric Hamiltonians, together with corresponding neighborhoods of line elements and with the attached canonical parameters.

§27. THE EMBEDDING OF SMALL EXTREMALS IN SMALL TUBES

During all these—seemingly interminable—formal developments of a local character, we have not forgotten our main purpose, and we come to it at last. In a campaign, the actual battles, ideally, are short; William the Conqueror settled the fate of England in one day. However, the period of preparation may have seemed endless. Here the conceptual importance of the notions introduced is not apparent at the local stage, to maintain our interest; all this will now change. We shall prove in this section a single theorem that will be the key to the local existence theorems, both in the parametric and the nonparametric case. This key theorem concerns the nonparametric case.

From now on, we shall be working in several spaces simultaneously, and we may as well distinguish them. A pair (t, x) is, as before, a point; a triple $(t, x, \dot{x})$ is a line element; a triple (t, x, y) is a canonical point. A neighborhood of a point is a wide neighborhood; a neighborhood of a line element is a narrow one; that of a canonical point is a canonical one. Neighborhoods in these spaces, with t omitted or constant, i.e., in the corresponding subspaces, will be spoken of as neighborhoods for constant t. All neighborhoods will be understood to be simply connected open domains in their spaces, and we shall term a neighborhood factorizable when it is expressible as a Cartesian product.

A family of canonical extremals $x(t, u), y(t, u)$, given in terms of a vector-valued parameter u (of the same dimension n as x), where u is constant on each member of the family, will be termed a canonical tube, if, for some t_0, we have $x(t_0, u) = u$ and $y(t_0, u) = y_0$, where y_0 is independent of u. The corresponding family of extremals $x(t, u)$ will be termed a tube of extremals, or simply a tube.

A line element will be termed nonsingular, if the matrix A of the second partial derivatives of L in the $\dot{x}$ is there nonsingular.

(27.1) Theorem (Embedding in a Tube). *Let (t_0, x_0, p_0) be a nonsingular line element. Then there exist*

(i) *a wide neighborhood W of (t_0, x_0),*

(ii) *a narrow neighborhood N of (t_0, x_0, p_0), such that any extremal in W that contains at least one line element in N can be embedded in a tube that covers W simply. Further, given any narrow neighborhood N_0 of (t_0, x_0, p_0) we can arrange that all line elements of the tube lie in N_0.*

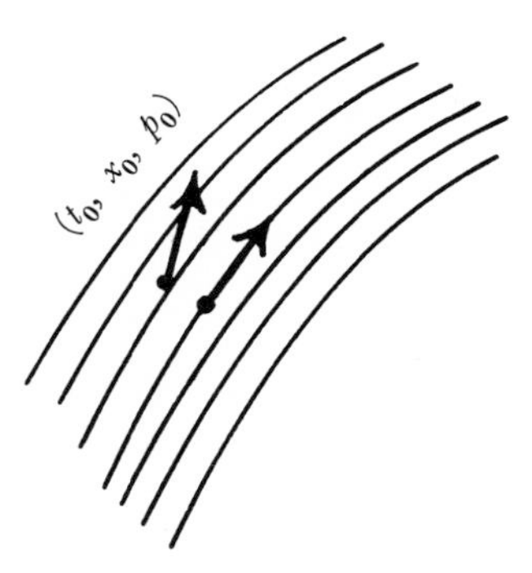

Proof. This is basically a "three map" proof. We construct three separate maps.

Map n^0 1. We write y_0 for $L_{\dot{x}}$ at (t_0, x_0, p_0). Then, as seen in Section 22, in a canonical neighborhood K of (t_0, x_0, y_0) there is just one Hamiltonian $H(t, x, y)$, and K is mapped one-to-one onto a narrow neighborhood N of (t_0, x_0, p_0) by setting $\dot{x} = H_y$. The inverse map is $y = L_{\dot{x}}$. We shall shrink the size of K, N, if necessary in the sequel, without change of notation. In particular, we arrange that $N \subset N_0$.

Our map n^0 1 is thus a map

$$(t, x, y) \rightarrow (t, x, \dot{x}).$$

Map n^0 2. Consider, for a small canonical neighborhood for constant $t = t_0$, of (x_0, y_0), the canonical extremals $x(t, u, v)$ $y(t, u, v)$ with the initial values $x = u$ $y = v$ when $t = t_0$, where (u, v) lies in the neighborhood in question. The canonical, extremals exist and are unique, and they are suitably smooth, by the existence theory for differential equations in the preceding Chapter. At $t = t_0$ the Jacobian in u, v is the identity matrix, and so nonsingular. By the implicit function theory of the preceding Chapter, we can, after shrinking K (and so N) suitably, determine our neighborhood for constant $t = t_0$, so that the equations $t = t$, $x = x(t, u, v)$, $y = y(t, u, v)$, have, for $(t, x, y) \in K$, unique solutions t, u, v.

Our second map, defined by these solutions, is thus of the form

$$(t, u, v) \rightarrow (t, x, y).$$

Map n^0 3. The same argument shows, since the Jacobian in u of $x(t, u, v)$ is, for $t = t_0$, the identity matrix, that we can solve locally in u the equation $x = x(t, u, v)$, when (t, x, v) lies in a suitable canonical neighborhood of (t_0, x_0, y_0). This defines our third map in the form

$$(t, x, v) \rightarrow (t, u, v).$$

The domain of (t, x, v) can be taken to be an interval, and so of the form $W \times W'$ where W, W' are intervals in (t, x) and v.

All three maps are one-to-one. Moreover, if we shrink the initial domain $W \times W'$ sufficiently, the image of each map can be mapped by the previous map, and the final image will be in N. We can then shrink N in its turn, so that the final image coincides with it.

THE COMPOSITE MAP T. We can now arrange the three maps in reverse order, and combine them by writing

$$(t, x, v) \to (t, u, v) \to (t, x, y) \to (t, x, \dot{x}).$$

Their combination clearly defines a composite map T, which is a one-to-one map of $W \times W'$ onto N, of the form

$$(t, x, v) \to (t, x, \dot{x}).$$

This means that it is given by equations of the form

$$t = t, \qquad x = x, \qquad \dot{x} = p(t, x, v),$$

and here, for given $(t, x, \dot{x}) \in N$, there is just one v for which the third equation holds.

This being so, let (t_1, x_1, p_1) be any fixed line element in N, and choose v_1 as just explained, so that $p_1 = p(t_1, x_1, v_1)$. We write $p(t, x)$ for $p(t, x, v_1)$. The restriction of the map T to the set $(t, x) \in W$, $v = v_1$ is then one-to-one onto the set of $(t, x, \dot{x})$ for which $(t, x) \in W$ and $\dot{x} = p(t, x)$.

By its construction, the map T, thus restricted, is a combination of our three original maps. It leads to a line element $(t, x, \dot{x})$ of an extremal $x(t, u, v)$ where $v = v_1$. The family of these extremals is the required tube, and here u is uniquely determined by $(t, x, \dot{x})$ of the form $\big(t, x, p(t, x)\big)$, and so by (t, x). This means that W is simply covered by the family, which completes the proof.

NOTE. In the final shrinking of N, when it becomes the actual image of $W \times W'$ under our composite map, we need to know that it remains a neighborhood. To verify this we can use implicit function theory; each element of the image set N has a neighborhood that is the image of one in $W \times W'$, and hence N is open. Similarly, it is easy to see that N is simply connected. However, mathematics today possesses more efficient tools, and it is not our object in this book to show how to avoid using them.

In the present instance, instead of appealing to an argument based on implicit functions and on the special nature of our maps, we can simply quote directly a famous theorem of topology, namely Brouwer's theorem on the invariance of the notion of domain, under a map that is merely continuous and one-to-one. This theorem has quite a history, and there is nothing to be gained by ignoring it and using less efficient tools. It actually arose from the discovery (at first sight, rather disturbing) that there exist maps of a segment onto a square that are one-to-one (but not continuous), or else continuous—the Peano curve (but not one-to-one). Prior to this, notations such as ∞^2 were much in vogue, in the belief that ∞^2 must be much larger than ∞. These matters are treated in real analysis or point set topology.

This is thus the second time that an important theorem of topology plays a part here. The first occasion concerned the Brouwer fix-point theorem at the end of Chapter I, when we treated the distortion theorem (19.6). The latter plays an important part in our next section, although there too, for our variational applications, a slightly less efficient procedure, based on the special case of Carathéodory's distortion lemma, is adequate.

§28. LOCAL EXISTENCE THEORY FOR NONPARAMETRIC VARIATIONAL PROBLEMS AND FOR ORDINARY SECOND ORDER DIFFERENTIAL EQUATIONS

Our principal local results will here be of two kinds: one asserts that certain "well-directed" small extremals provide a minimum, the other that a suitable pair of points can be joined by a small extremal, or, more generally, by a local solution of a given second order differential equation. The second really concerns the boundary value problem for such an equation, and the key to it will be the distortion theorem (19.6). The first concerns our minimum problem only, and the key to it will be the embedding theorem (27.1).

The reader must not imagine at this stage, particularly if he has skimmed over our later chapters, that the existence of a nonparametric extremal, joining given near points, is a commonplace matter, which concerns the theory of differential equations. In point of fact, there are almost no nonparametric problems in which such an extremal exists without further restrictions. In this respect, as we shall see, problems (a), (b), and (c) of the Preamble are anything but typical.

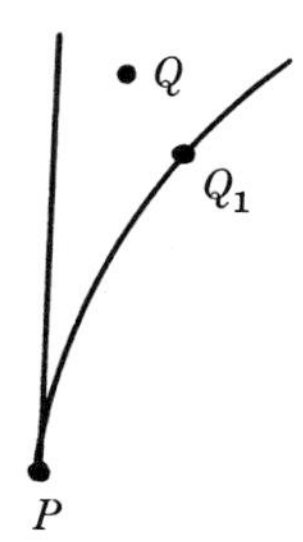

In many plane problems, for instance, there is, at a point P, just one nonparametric extremal with a vertical tangent at P, and for near points Q_1 on it, this is the only extremal joining PQ_1. For a point Q near P, in the space between this extremal and its tangent there can be no extremal joining PQ, for such a second extremal would then, contrary to our assumption, either possess also a vertical tangent at P or else cross the first at some point Q_1, so that both extremals would join PQ_1.

In order to study the existence of an extremal joining two given points, we first consider the more general problem of joining them by a solution of a differential equation

(28.1) $$\ddot{x} = g(t, x, \dot{x}),$$

where g is a continuous function defined in an open set of $(t, x, \dot{x})$. We shall suppose g smooth enough for the existence and unicity of solutions with given initial values of the equivalent system

$$\dot{z} = g(t, x, z), \qquad \dot{x} = z,$$

which is of the type treated at the end of the preceding Chapter, and for the continuity of such solutions in their dependence on the initial values of (t, x, z).

We shall denote by G the open set of definition of g in the space of line elements $(t, x, \dot{x})$, and by E a bounded closed subset of G. We determine further a bounded open set G_- where $E \subset G_- \subset G$, such that the function g is bounded in G_-. This can be done as follows: we write $\hat{g}$ for the function

$$|g(t, x, \dot{x})| + |t| + |x| + |\dot{x}|,$$

which is continuous, and so bounded in E by some constant k, and we define G_- to be the set of line elements $(t, x, \dot{x})$ of G for which $\hat{g} < 2k$.

By a change of scale of the form $(t, x) \to (at, bx)$, where a, b are positive constants, this change of scale being accompanied by the further one $\dot{x} \to b\dot{x}/a$, for consistency with our notation for derivatives, we now arrange that in G_-

(28.2) $$|g| \leq 1, \qquad |\dot{x}| \leq 1.$$

In studying local properties in the arbitrary chosen bounded closed subset E of G, there is no loss of generality in limiting ourselves to G_-, which we may now simply write G, and in using the new scales on our axes, so that (28.2) then holds in G.

This being so, we determine $\delta > 0$ so that, in the space of line elements $(t, x, \dot{x})$, the distance of E to the boundary of G is $>3\delta$. We shall denote by E_+ the set of $(t, x, \dot{x})$ at a distance $\leq 3\delta$ from E. Here and in what follows, we can always reduce the size of δ; in particular, we can replace it by $\delta/2$ when convenient.

We shall term δ-trajectory, or simply trajectory, a solution curve $x(t)$ of (28.1) that corresponds to a t-interval of length $\leq\delta$. Further, given a line element $(t_0, x_0, p_0) \in E$, we shall term local δ-pencil of δ-trajectories, or simply local pencil, the family of trajectories defined on a t-interval of length δ, beginning (or ending) at t_0, and containing corresponding line elements of the form (t_0, x_0, p), where $|p - p_0| \leq \delta$. Finally, in (t, x)-space, we write $P = (x - x_0)/(t - t_0)$, and we term local δ-angle about (t_0, x_0, p_0), or simply local angle, the set of the points (t, x) for which $t_0 < t < t_0 + \delta$ (or else $t_0 - \delta < t < t_0$) and $|P - p_0| < \delta$. When we wish to distinguish the cases $t > t_0$, $t < t_0$ in these definitions, we may speak, in the former case, of a forward pencil or angle, and in the latter of a backward one.

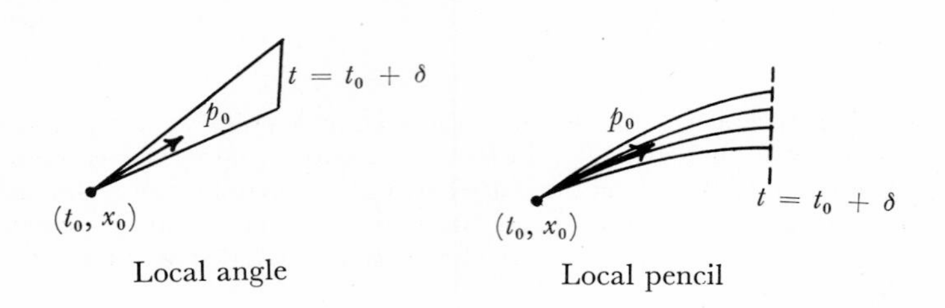

Local angle Local pencil

(28.3) Lemma. *The line elements of the trajectories of each local pencil all lie in E_+.*

Proof. Actually we shall prove that they are interior to E_+. Suppose the contrary. There would be a line element $(t_0, x_0, p_0) \in E$, a value of p such that $|p - p_0| \leq \delta$, and a trajectory $x(t)$ possessing the line element (t_0, x_0, p) as well as a line element not interior to E_+. There would then be a first value of $t > t_0$ (or a last one $< t_0$) at which the trajectory has a line element on the boundary of E_+, and for this value of t, taking (t_0, x_0) as origin, for convenience, we would have

$$|\dot{x} - p| = \left|\int_0^t \ddot{x}\right| \leq |t|, \qquad |x| = \left|\int_0^t \dot{x}\right| \leq |t|,$$

whence $t^2 + x^2 + (\dot{x} - p_0)^2 \leq 2t^2 + (|t| + \delta)^2 < 9\delta^2$, which shows that the line element in question is interior to E_+ and not on its boundary. This completes the proof.

(28.4) Lemma. *On a trajectory Γ, the value of $\dot{x}$ at time t and the gradient P of a chord whose ends correspond to the times t_1, t_2 are subject to*

$$|P - \dot{x}| \leq \frac{|t - t_1| + |t - t_2|}{2}.$$

Proof. We may set $t = 0$, and suppose $x = 0$, $\dot{x} = p$ for the corresponding line-element of Γ. We denote, for $i = 1, 2$, by T_i the triangle $0 < u < v < t_i$, or else $0 > u > v > t_i$, according to the sign of t_i, and by $|T_i|$ its area $\frac{1}{2}t_i^2$. If we now introduce the remainder in Taylor's theorem

$$R_i = x(t_i) - pt_i = \iint_{T_i} \ddot{x}(u)\, du\, dv,$$

we find that $|R_1 - R_2| = |t_1 - t_2| \cdot |P - p|$. Hence, if t_1, t_2 have opposite signs, $|P - p|$ will be at most

$$\frac{|R_1| + |R_2|}{|t_1| + |t_2|} \leq \frac{|T_1| + |T_2|}{|t_1| + |t_2|} \leq \frac{|t_1| + |t_2|}{2}.$$

Otherwise, by renumbering indices and reversing the t-axis, if necessary, we may suppose $0 < t_1 < t_2$, so that

$$|R_1 - R_2| = \left| \iint_{T_2 - T_1} \ddot{x}(u)\, du\, dv \right| \leq |T_2| - |T_1|,$$

and by dividing by $t_2 - t_1$ we get the same estimate. This completes the proof.

Two trajectories Γ_1, Γ_2 will be termed markedly deflected if they possess, respectively, line elements (t_1, x_1, p_1), (t_2, x_2, p_2) such that either $|p_1 - p_2| \geq 2\delta$ or else $(t_1, x_1) = (t_2, x_2)$ and $|p_1 - p_2| > \delta$.

(28.5) Corollary. *Two markedly deflected trajectories cannot intersect in more than one point.*

In fact, if there were two intersections, the gradient P of the common chord would satisfy the inequality of (28.4) for the slopes $\dot{x} = p_1$ and $\dot{x} = p_2$. We would therefore have $|p_1 - p_2| < 2\delta$. This still leaves the possibility that the line elements occurring in the definition of markedly deflected have the form (t_1, x_1, p_1), (t_1, x_1, p_2). In that case we can take one intersection to be (t_1, x_1) and apply the inequality of (28.4) in the case $(t = t_1)$. Arguing as before, we find that $|p_1 - p_2| \leq \delta$, which contradicts the definition.

We are now in a position to establish, for the differential equation (28.1), the existence of a solution of the boundary-value problem in a local angle.

(28.6) Local Angle Theorem. *Let $(t_0, x_0, p_0) \in E$, and let (t_1, x_1) lie in the local $(\delta/3)$-angle about (t_0, x_0, p_0). Then the points (t_0, x_0), (t_1, x_1) can be joined by a trajectory of the local δ-pencil, and by no trajectory not of that pencil.*

For variational purposes, a weaker version of this is sufficient; the same conclusion is then drawn under the further assumption that no trajectories of the local pencil intersect in a second point. The proof of this weaker version is the same as for the stronger one, except that we then verify that the distortion theorem is only used in the form of Carathéodory's lemma.

Proof of (28.6). It will be sufficient to show that the points in question can be joined by a trajectory of the local $(\delta/2)$-pencil, for by (28.5), with $\delta/3$ in place of δ, they cannot be joined by trajectories whose initial slopes $\dot{x}$ differ by more than $\delta/3$.

This being so, we may suppose $t_1 > t_0$, we take (t_0, x_0) as origin, we write $x(t, p)$ for the trajectory $x(t)$ $(0 \leq t \leq \delta)$ satisfying $x(0) = 0$, $\dot{x}(0) = p$, we set $P = P(p) = x(t_1, p)/t_1$, and we denote by Q, H respectively, the sets of vectors p, subject to $|p - p_0| < \delta/2$ and to $|p - p_0| < \delta/3$. In Q, we have, by (28.4),

$$|P - p| \leq t_1/2 \leq \delta/6.$$

By (19.6), the image Q' of Q under the continuous map $p \to P$, defined by the function $P(p)$, satisfies $Q' \supset H$. This implies in particular $(x_1/t_1) \in Q'$, which means that for some $p \in Q$ we have $P = x_1/t_1$, and so $x(t_1, p) = x_1$. This completes the proof.

In the weaker version, we note that Q' is the one-to-one image of Q, and therefore a domain, and further, that the image $P(p_0)$ of p_0 is certainly in H. This means that (19.6) is then only used in the form of Carathéodory's lemma.

We now return to the study of a nonparametric variational problem. The place of (28.1) is taken by the Euler equation; we write the latter in full:

$$L_{\dot{x}\dot{x}}\ddot{x} + L_{\dot{x}x}\dot{x} + L_{\dot{x}t} = L_x,$$

and we confine ourselves to nonsingular line elements, so that the matrix $A = L_{\dot{x}\dot{x}}$ then has an inverse B. By multiplying by B, our Euler equation can be put in the form (28.1), with, for g, the expression

$$B(L_x - L_{\dot{x}t} - L_{\dot{x}x}\dot{x}).$$

A line element (t_0, x_0, p_0) will be termed strong if for all (t, x, p) of some narrow neighborhood of (t_0, x_0, p_0) and for all $\dot{x} \neq p$, the Weierstrass excess function $E(t, x, p, \dot{x})$ satisfies

$$E > 0. \tag{28.7}$$

Given a strong nonsingular line element (t_0, x_0, p_0), an extremal C_0 situated in a sufficiently small, wide neighborhood of (t_0, x_0) will be termed a well directed local extremal, if C_0 contains a sufficiently small narrow neighborhood of (t_0, x_0, p_0).

(28.8) Theorem (Minimum Property of Well Directed Local Extremals). *Let (t_0, x_0, p_0) be a strong nonsingular line element. Then there exist*

(i) *a wide neighborhood W of (t_0, x_0),*
(ii) *a narrow neighborhood N of (t_0, x_0, p_0),*

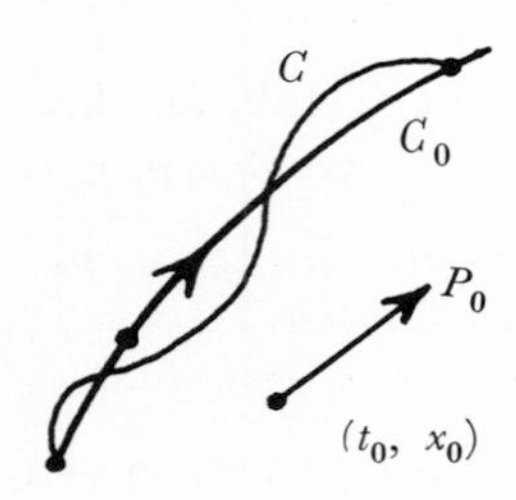

such that for any extremal C_0 in W, with some line element in N, and for any other admissible nonparametric curve C in W with the same ends as C_0, we have

$$\mathscr{I}(C) > \mathscr{I}(C_0).$$

PROOF. We choose for N_0 in (27.1) a narrow neighborhood of (t_0, x_0, p_0) in which (28.1) holds by definition, and we apply the embedding theorem. The tube in which C_0 is then embedded is an exact family of extremals by (16.2), since it consists of extremals $x(t, u, v)$ with a fixed constant v, and since the domain of (t, u), which is mapped one-to-one onto W, is simply connected. Further, the family covers W simply, and the line elements (t, x, p) of its members satisfy (28.1). The relation asserted thus follows from the Weierstrass formula (12.6).

We remark that the neighborhoods W, N for which the conclusion holds retain this property when they are shrunk—this would not apply to (27.1). In the sequel, we shall arrange that N has the form $W \times M$ in this way.

The minimum property established in (28.8) leads at once to a unicity property: two distinct local well-directed extremals can intersect in W in, at most, one point. Otherwise, their arcs γ_1, γ_2 between two intersections could be so ordered that $\mathscr{I}(\gamma_1) \leq \mathscr{I}(\gamma_2)$, and by taking for C_0 the extremal containing γ_2, and for C the admissible curve distinct from C_0 and derived from C_0 by replacing its arc γ_2 by γ_1, we would obtain, contrary to the minimum property, $\mathscr{I}(C) \leq \mathscr{I}(C_0)$. This means that arcs of local well-directed extremals are uniquely determined by their pairs of endpoints.

We shall prove one more theorem in this section; it incorporates the unicity just established and is the variational counterpart of (28.6). We have already found the variational counterpart of the function g of (28.1). Moreover, we shall take as the set G of the line elements for which g is defined, the set of nonsingular line elements. This is easily seen to be an open set. In G we locate as before an open subset G_- in which the "data" (i.e., g, $\dot{x}$, x, t) are bounded. (Alternatively, we can take for G and G_-, the corresponding sets of strong nonsingular line elements.) Finally, it will be convenient to extend the notion of local angle, defined earlier in this section: given an angular neighborhood $N = W \times M$ and a point $(t_1, x_1) \in W$, we term angle of vertex (t_1, x_1) determined by N the set of the points $(t, x) \in W$ for which $t > t_0$ (or $t < t_0$) and $(x - x_0)/(t - t_0) \in M$. (We speak of a forward or backward angle according to the sign of $t - t_0$.)

(28.9) Small Angle Theorem (Nonparametric Variational Version). *Let (t_0, x_0, p_0) be a strong nonsingular line element, and choose G_- (the open set of line elements in which the data are bounded) so that $(t_0, x_0, p_0) \in G_-$; further, let $\hat{N} \subset G_-$ be a narrow neighborhood of (t_0, x_0, p_0). Then there exists an angular neighborhood $N = W \times M \subset \hat{N}$*

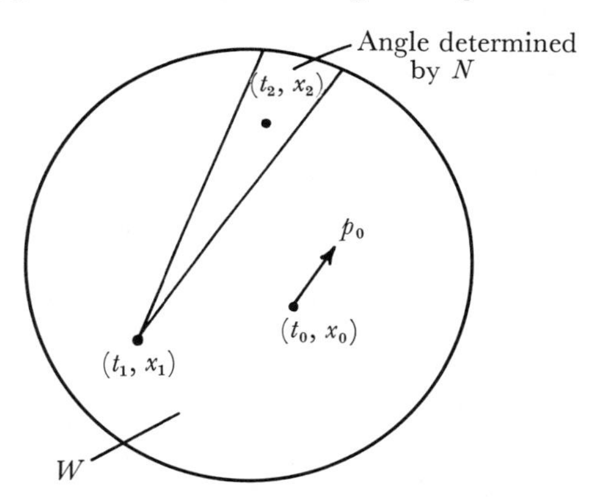

of (t_0, x_0, p_0) such that any point (t_1, x_1) of W can be joined, by an extremal whose line elements lie in $\hat{N}$, to any point (t_2, x_2) situated in the angle of vertex (t_1, x_1) determined by N, and can be so joined by no other extremal in W, all of whose line elements lie in G_-.

PROOF. We first choose an angular neighborhood $N_0 = W_0 \times M_0$ of (t_0, x_0, p_0) such that W_0, N_0 are contained, respectively, in the neighborhoods W, N of theorem (28.8), and that $N_0 \subset \hat{N} \cap G_-$. Moreover, we suppose that the preliminary change of scale, which ensures the validity of (28.2), has been carried out. We then choose in N_0 a bounded closed set E consisting of a closed ball of center (t_0, x_0, p_0). Further, we choose a number $\delta > 0$, less than the radius of E, and so small that N_0 contains the set E_+ of the line elements distant at most 3δ from E. Finally, we denote by $N = W \times M$ the set of line elements $(t, x, \dot{x})$ for which the three differences $|t - t_0|$, $|x - x_0|$, $|\dot{x} - p_0|$ are all $<\delta/6$.

This being so, let (t_1, x_1), (t_2, x_2) be two points of W such that (t_2, x_2) lies in the angle of vertex (t_1, x_1) determined by N. Clearly (t_1, x_1, p_0) lies in E, and (t_2, x_2) lies in its local $(\delta/3)$-angle. Thus theorem (28.6) applies.

Further, extremals in the local δ pencil associated with the element (t_1, x_1, p_0) have line elements in E_+ and so in N_0. Therefore they cannot have a second intersection. This means that the map $p \to P$ used in the proof of theorem (28.6) is one-to-one, so that we can, if we prefer, appeal to the special case of that theorem to which we drew attention there, and which does not depend on the fix-point theorem.

We thus see that the points (t_1, x_1), (t_2, x_2) can be joined by just one extremal of the local pencil, and by no other extremal, whose line elements are in G_-. This completes the proof.

§29. LOCAL PARAMETRIC EXISTENCE THEORY FOR THE ELLIPTIC CASE

We shall prove much stronger results in the parametric form, subject to a condition which we term ellipticity. We shall obtain these as direct consequences of our nonparametric constructions.

The term elliptic will replace here the colorless adjective "regular" used in the literature; as if the latter were not already overworked by appearing in the theory of regular figures, the theory of regular analytic functions, the theory of regular-singular points of ordinary differential equations, and so on.

In applying our nonparametric constructions, we shall again introduce the auxiliary Lagrangian $L^* = \frac{1}{2}L^2$. This will lead rather directly to the desired results. A different procedure for applying the nonparametric machinery will be found in Carathéodory. It consists in a choice of axes, such that one of them can be appropriately labeled locally the t-axis. However, the parametric results thus obtained in the first instance are then merely the analogues of the nonparametric ones, and some further work is needed to derive stronger results.

Some older treatments go to a great deal of trouble to make independent studies of the nonparametric and the parametric problems; it was somehow ungentlemanly to use one field or subdivision to study another. This code of ethics was partly imposed by the tyranny of examinations; of course it is not "cricket" to set questions requiring extraneous knowledge, and of course it may be unwise to submit work outside an examiner's competence—as Galois learned to his cost. Today, however, such artificial barriers are being swept away regardless.

No one hesitates any more to use nonparametric methods in the parametric case, or vice versa, nor to use real methods in complex analysis. This is not just because we are more practical; according to H. Poincaré, the very essence of mathematics lies in transforming a problem. In the same way, a musician may pass to a different key, and the beauty and depth of music results largely from this freedom.

We shall write, as previously, $A = A(x, \dot{x})$ for the matrix $L_{\dot{x}\dot{x}}$, and we recall from Section 24 that $A\dot{x} = 0$. The line element $(x, \dot{x})$ is nonsingular if A has rank $n - 1$, and the point x is nonsingular if this is so for all $\dot{x} \neq 0$. The line element $(x, \dot{x})$ satisfies the parametric Legendre condition if the quadratic form $\xi A \xi$ is positive whenever ξ is not a real multiple of $\dot{x}$. We shall here term the point x elliptic if this condition holds for all $\dot{x} \neq 0$ at the point x. This is equivalent to requiring that for this value of x the expression $\xi A \xi$ have a positive minimum on the bounded closed set of $(\dot{x}, \xi)$ for which $|\dot{x}| = 1$, $\xi^2 - (\xi\dot{x})^2 = 1$. (This follows from positive homogeneity in ξ and in $\dot{x}$, of the relevant orders.) The set of elliptic points is therefore clearly open.

At an elliptic point, we have, by Taylor's remainder,

$$L(x, \dot{x}) - L(x, p) - (\dot{x} - p)L_p(x, p) = \tfrac{1}{2}\xi\tilde{A}\xi,$$

where $\xi = \dot{x} - p$, $\tilde{A} = A(x, \tilde{p})$, $\tilde{p} = p + \theta(\dot{x} - p)$ for some θ subject to $0 < \theta < 1$, provided that $p \neq 0$ and that the set of vectors of the form $\tilde{p}$ does not include 0 (where $\tilde{A}$ would not exist). Hence, if $p \neq 0$, we have $E(x, p, \dot{x}) > 0$ unless $\dot{x}$ is a real multiple of p, in which case, by continuity, $E \geq 0$. Of course, here $E = 0$ if $\dot{x}$ is a positive multiple of p. On the other hand, if $\dot{x}$ is a positive multiple of $-p$, we verify that E is a positive multiple of the expression $L(x, p) + L(x, -p)$. This expression is thus ≥ 0; moreover it cannot vanish for all $p \neq 0$, since we would then obtain, by two differentiations in p, that $A(x, p) + A(x, -p) = 0$, contrary to our assumption about $\xi A \xi$. Hence, for some $p_0 \neq 0$, of which we may suppose $|p_0| = 1$ without loss of generality, we must have

$$E(x, p_0, \dot{x}) > 0,$$

unless $\dot{x}$ is a non-negative multiple of p_0. This relation, if we write q_0 for the value of $L_p(x, p)$ at $p = p_0$ and omit from E the terms $-L(x, p_0) + p_0 q_0$ which cancel, is then, by homogeneity in $\dot{x}$, equivalent to

$$L(x, \dot{x}) - \dot{x} q_0 > 0 \quad \text{for} \quad |\dot{x}| = 1, \qquad \dot{x} p_0 \neq 1.$$

By applying the argument of Chapter I, Section 13, and writing $c = q_0 - \frac{1}{2}\varepsilon p_0$, where ε has the value

$$\operatorname*{Min}_{\dot{x}} \{L(x, \dot{x}) - \dot{x} q_0\} \quad \text{for} \quad |\dot{x}| = 1, \qquad \dot{x} p_0 \leq \tfrac{1}{2},$$

we find that $L - c\dot{x} \geq \frac{1}{2}\varepsilon$ at the point x for all unit vectors $\dot{x}$, and so, for the same constant values of c, ε,

$$L - c\dot{x} > \tfrac{1}{4}\varepsilon$$

for all unit vectors $\dot{x}$ and all near points to x. By restricting ourselves to a neighborhood of an elliptic point, and by replacing L with an equivalent Lagrangian, we can thus suppose not only that all relevant points are elliptic, but also that $L > 0$ for all $\dot{x} \neq 0$ at these points. Since the relation $L(x, p) + L(x, -p) = 0$ can now only hold for $p = 0$ at these points, we find from our earlier discussion that for all such points x,

$$E(x, p, \dot{x}) > 0, \tag{29.1}$$

provided that $p \neq 0$ and that $\dot{x}$ is not a positive multiple of p.

On an admissible curve we shall now choose the parameter t so that the line elements $(x, \dot{x})$ of the curve are subject to $L(x, \dot{x}) = 1$. Further, as in Section 24, we introduce the nonparametric Lagrangian

$$L^*(x, \dot{x}) = \tfrac{1}{2} L^2(x, \dot{x}),$$

in which t does not appear explicitly. We denote by G a domain of line elements $(t, x, \dot{x})$ in which t is small, x near a given elliptic point and $L(x, \dot{x})$ near to 1, and we identify G_- with G.

The excess-function $E^*(x, p, \dot{x})$, associated with L^*, does not contain t explicitly, and is seen to be related to the excess-function E, associated with L, by the simple identity

$$E^* = \tfrac{1}{2}\{L(x, \dot{x}) - L(x, p)\}^2 + E \cdot L(x, p).$$

Hence by (29.1), $E^* > 0$ unless $\dot{x} = p$. Thus all line elements $(t, x, \dot{x}) \in G$ are strong; they are also nonsingular, since the matrix $A^* = L^*_{\dot{x}\dot{x}}$ at any such line element is nonsingular by section 24. We shall suppose this holds in the closure of G without loss of generality. The determinant of A^* is then bounded from 0, so that the function

g in (28.1) is bounded in G. Thus, for the Lagrangian L^*, all the hypotheses of Theorem (28.9) are fulfilled by an arbitrary line element (t_0, x_0, p_0) of G. Finally, we recall from Section 26 that the extremal curves for L^* in (t, x)-space are the curves whose projections in x-space are extremals for L, and for which t then coincides along each such extremal, with a constant multiple of the corresponding standard parameter.

We are now in a position to apply Theorem (28.9) to establish the following:

(29.2) Basic Lemma. *Let x_0 be an elliptic point. Then there exist neighborhoods W, W_0 such that $x_0 \in W \subset W_0$ and that every pair of points x_1, x_2 of W can be joined in W_0 by one and only one extremal.*

Proof. All neighborhoods in $(t, x, \dot{x})$, or (t, x), that occur can here be taken to be Cartesian products of open t, x and $\dot{x}$ sets, or of open t and x sets. In particular we arrange that the set $G = G_{-}$, described above, be a Cartesian product of a neighborhood W_0 of x_0 with a set of $(t, \dot{x})$. We apply Theorem (28.9) for the Lagrangian L^* and the line element $(0, x_0, p_0)$, where p_0 is any vector subject to $L(x_0, p_0) = 1$. We associate by it, to p_0, an angular neighborhood of this line element, with certain properties. This neighborhood has the form $W^* \times M^*$, where M^* is a neighborhood of p_0. By Borel's covering theorem, a finite number of such M^*, associated to corresponding vectors p_0, then cover the set of p for which $L(x_0, p) = 1$. We denote by $T \times W$ a neighborhood of $(0, x_0)$ contained in the intersection of the corresponding W^*, and here T is an open t-interval, while W is a neighborhood of x_0. We may suppose W so small that, for each pair of points x_1, x_2 of W, the interval T contains the number $t = L(x_0, x_2 - x_1)$. This means that we can set $x_2 - x_1 = tp$, where $L(x_0, p) = 1$, so that the vector p lies in one of (the finite number of) M^*.

In that case, (t, x_2) lies in the angle of vertex $(0, x_1)$ determined by $W^* \times M^*$, so that $(0, x_1)$, (t, x_2) can be joined by one and only one extremal for L^*, whose line elements belong to G.

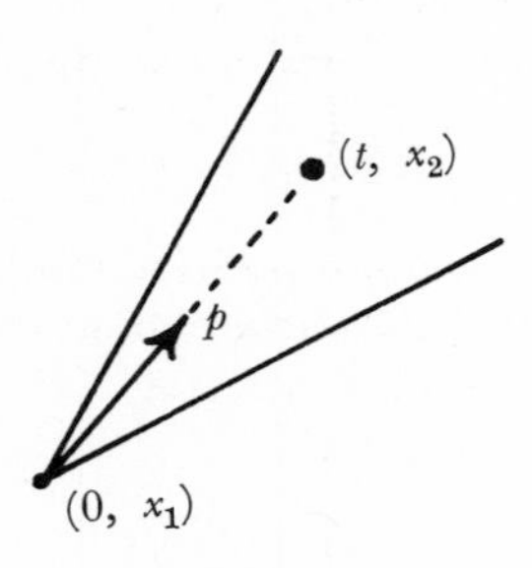

The projection of this extremal for L^* is then an extremal for L, which joins x_1, x_2 in W_0. It is unique, since if there were two, then by choosing on them parameters expressible as suitable constant multiples of standard ones, we could exhibit them as projections of different extremals for L^*, joining $(0, x_1)$, (t, x_2). This completes the proof.

Our main theorem (29.5) will constitute an important refinement of lemma (29.2), the key to which is the following:

(29.3) The Small Sphere Lemma. *Let x_0 be nonsingular. Then there exists a neighborhood U of x_0 such that every sphere Σ with its center in U that meets an extremal Γ situated in U contains at most two points of Γ. Further, the closed ball bounded by Σ meets Γ in a connected arc.*

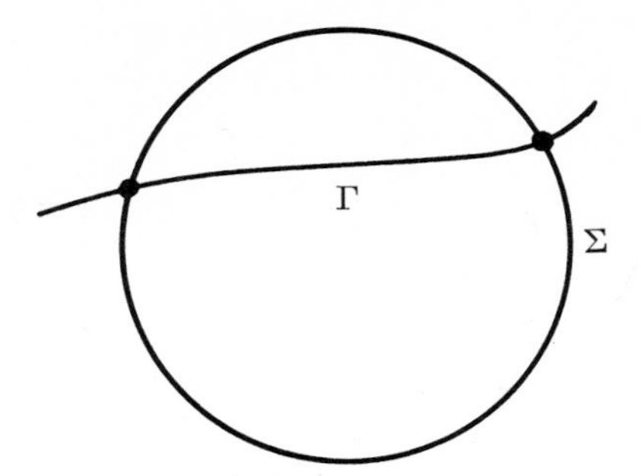

PROOF. Near x_0, the Euler equation takes the form $\ddot{x} = g(x, \dot{x})$. We choose U so that this is the case in it, with g bounded for $|\dot{x}| = 1$, and we shrink U further, if necessary, so as to have small diameter. We then choose in U the center of Σ, which we take as origin, and any extremal Γ, with arc length as parameter, that meets Σ.

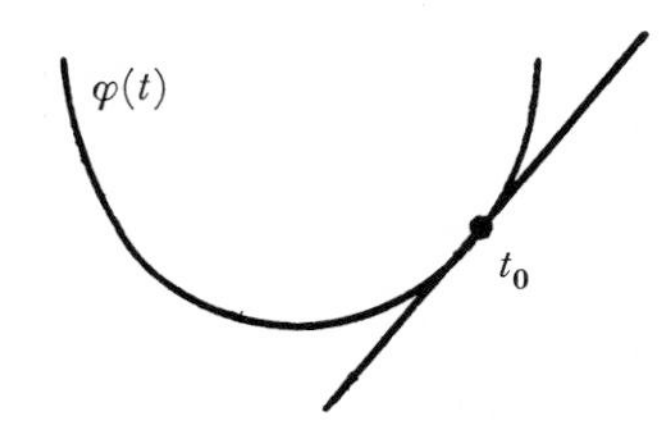

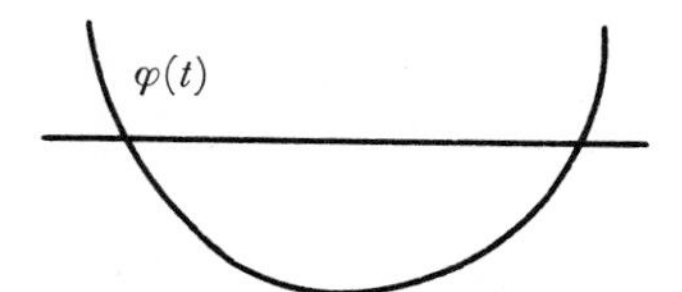

On Γ, since $\dot{x}^2 = 1$, the second derivative of $\varphi = \frac{1}{2}x^2$ is $\ddot{\varphi} = 1 + x\ddot{x}$, which is positive, $\ddot{x}$ being bounded and x small. Thus, by Taylor's remainder, for any pair of distinct abscissae t, t_0, we have

(29.4) $$\varphi(t) > \varphi(t_0) + (t - t_0)\dot{\varphi}(t_0),$$

the difference of the two sides being

$$\tfrac{1}{2}(t - t_0)^2\ddot{\varphi}(\tilde{t}) > 0.$$

Thus φ is convex (tangent below arc definition of Chapter I, Section 13) so that (chord above arc definition, whose equivalence we postpone to Chapter IV) its graph must meet horizontals, either in a whole segment, which is clearly incompatible with (29.4), or else in at most two points, between which φ takes only smaller values. This leads at once to our assertion.

The lemma just proved will enable us to avoid here an unpleasant "geodesic convexity" assumption in Carathéodory's book (Chapter XVI, Section 385: Existence of a certain ρ'). The assumption will reappear, however, in Chapter V.

We are now in a position to establish the main result of this chapter:

(29.5) The Local Parametric Existence Theorem for the Elliptic Case. *Let E be a bounded closed set of elliptic points. Then there exists a number $\rho > 0$, such that*

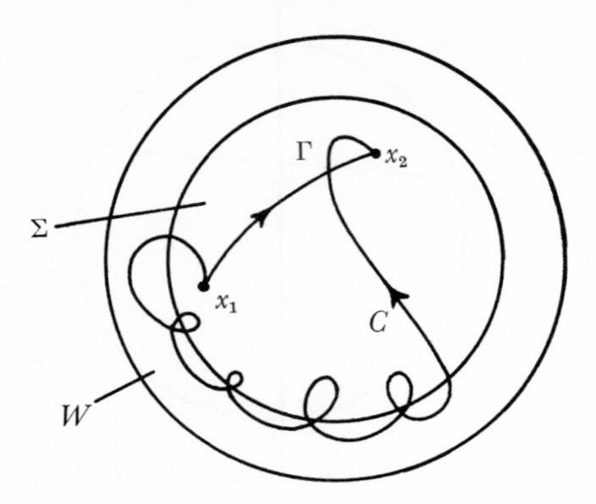

every closed ball Σ of radius $\leq \rho$, which meets E, has the following properties: (i) *each pair of points x_1, x_2 of Σ can be joined by one and only one extremal Γ, interior to Σ except for its ends x_1, x_2;* (ii) *for some domain $W \supset \Sigma$ (alternatively, in the case in which L is positive definite in E, for every domain $W \supset \Sigma$ in which $L \geq 0$), we have, whenever C is an admissible curve in W, distinct from Γ but with the same ends,*

$$\mathscr{I}(\Gamma) < \mathscr{I}(C). \tag{29.6}$$

Proof. We choose a positive number $\theta \leq \frac{1}{3}$. (In the case in which L is positive definite in E, we denote by m, M the minimum and the maximum of $L(x, \dot{x})$ for $x \in E$, $|\dot{x}| = 1$, and we stipulate further that $\theta(m + M) \leq \frac{1}{3}m$). To each point $x_0 \in E$ we attach a ball $|x - x_0| < \rho_0$ so small that it lies in the neighborhoods W and U of lemmas (29.2) and (29.3). (If L is positive definite in E we shrink this ball so that in it, for $|\dot{x}| = 1$, we have $\frac{3}{4}m < L(x, \dot{x}) < \frac{3}{2}M$.) By Borel's covering theorem, a finite number of the concentric open balls of radii $\theta\rho_0$ cover the set E. We denote

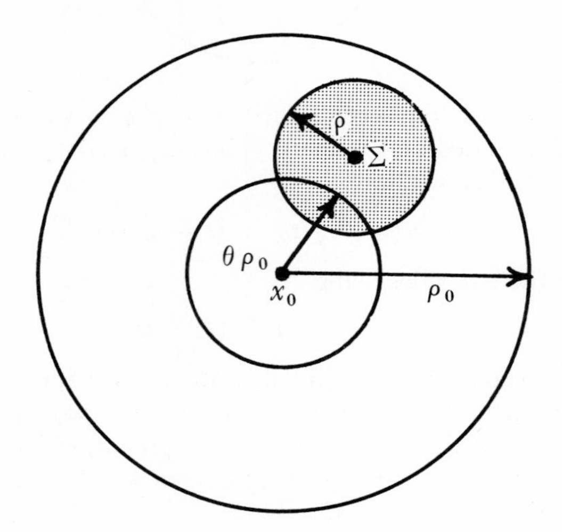

by ρ the smallest of the finite number of such radii $\theta\rho_0$, and we choose any closed ball Σ of radius $\leq\rho$ that meets E. We have to show that Σ has the properties stated. By construction, Σ contains a point of one of the finite number of open balls $|x - x_0| < \theta\rho_0$. Its points are thus all distant from x_0 by $<2\rho + \theta\rho_0 \leq \rho_0$. They thus lie in the neighborhoods W and U of our two lemmas (29.2), (29.3); in particular, the center of Σ is in U. Hence (i) is valid.

In (ii), we can now choose W as in (29.2), and we recall that W was there originally chosen to consist of points at which (29.1) holds. Then (29.6) follows from the Weierstrass formula (12.7) of Chapter I, since the extremals issuing from the initial point of Γ cover simply a domain in W_0, which contains W.

Alternatively, if L is positive definite in E, we take for W any domain including Σ in which $L \geq 0$. Then, first, by the case of (29.6) already disposed of, that inequality is certainly valid for any C situated in the ball $|x - x_0| < \rho_0$. In particular it holds when C is the chord, of length $\leq 2\rho$ of Γ, whence

(29.7) $$\mathscr{I}(\Gamma) < 2M\rho.$$

We shall suppose, therefore, that C contains at least one boundary point of the ball $|x - x_0| < \rho_0$, and so two arcs between Σ and the sphere $|x - x_0| = \rho_0$, whose lengths are clearly at least $\rho_0 - \theta\rho_0 - 2\rho$. Hence

(29.8) $$\mathscr{I}(C) \geq 2m(\rho_0 - \theta\rho_0 - 2\rho).$$

To prove (29.6) it only remains to verify that

(29.9) $$2m(\rho_0 - \theta\rho_0 - 2\rho) - 2M\rho \geq 0.$$

Since $\rho \leq \theta\rho_0$, this is the case if $m(1 - 3\theta) - M\theta \geq 0$, i.e., if $\theta(3m + M) \leq m$, which is true by our choice of θ. Thus (29.9) is valid, and therefore (29.6). This completes the proof.

Chapter III

Embedding in the Large

§30. INTRODUCTION

Various strange coincidences in the solutions of the examples of the Preamble are now accounted for; they are coincidences no longer. Yet one mystery remains. That small extremal arcs issuing from a point were bound to cover a small domain simply, we now know. However, the extremal arcs we selected were not at all small; they were the biggest we could reasonably take. Was it just luck that they provided the desirable simple covering? This would be unbelievable. Nevertheless, this question will take us far afield.

To answer it, we have to bring in a number of so-called "secondary" concepts—a secondary problem with a secondary Lagrangian, a secondary Hamiltonian and secondary extremals. In this respect, secondary matters are not necessarily of secondary importance; here they mean that we enter more deeply into the heart of our subject. Generally, the second look and second thoughts are more penetrating than the first, and depth is what counts in mathematics.

The secondary notions to be described arose from the so-called second variation; thus they are secondary in a second way. In this respect, however, our chronicle of errors is not ended: the second variation was introduced originally on even more flimsy grounds than the first. Everything was based on a simple-minded analogy with minima of functions of one variable. We have found fault with the necessity of a vanishing first variation [Preamble, Section 9]. Even worse is the false assumption, when this condition is fulfilled, of a minimum when the second variation is >0, an assumption bolstered up partly by analogy and partly by a vicious circle taken over from a typical calculus blunder.

Yet it is part of the strangeness of the "queen of the sciences" that concepts born of a blunder may turn out quite basic; it is as if a player in the game of kings, by overlooking that his queen is *en prise*, were to stumble onto one of those incredible beautiful combinations that live a thousand years. In real life, a blunder that leads to success seems less strange; a standing joke has it that a design withdrawn from a $100 prize engineering competition because of a flaw wins a $1000 award as abstract art.

In mathematics many an initial error seems to have proved helpful in the long run. What distinguishes a crank from a mathematician is not his error but his obstinacy. It is no help to keep trying only to advance in the one blocked direction, like the beginning chess player whose pawn can be captured on the eight rank by the enemy king because he thinks it can go no further. So it is that the second variation and the secondary notions connected with it, once we free them from their original mistaken purpose, can and will be given far more effective use when we find out what they really are, just as the chess player's "helpless" pawn can be used when he learns that it has become a queen.

After the introduction of the first and second variations, the formal developments of secondary notions will here be no more than a short exercise in the use of Hamiltonians. The vast literature on these matters can simply be ignored. Further, by an elementary geometrical interpretation of exactness, we are able to reach, almost at once, the Jacobi theory of conjugate points, which clears up our mystery; this leads us on to study the index of stability, which was at one time, and may well be again, considered important in eigenvalue theory in various fields of applied mathematics. From the study of this index, we pass to a brief introduction to the Morse theory, which has applications in widely different fields, and which goes, in many ways, far beyond the calculus of variations itself.

As tools we shall require certain simple results concerning vectors, matrices, quadratic forms, and elementary polyhedra. They will mainly be discussed when we need them. The notion of eigenvalue and the transformation of a quadratic to a diagonal form by an orthogonal transformation will be taken as known. Some books on the calculus of variations provide a review of maxima and minima of functions of several variables, and in particular of quadratic forms, and this gives them an excuse for treating eigenvalues and so forth, but we shall not do this here.

§31. FIRST AND SECOND VARIATIONS AND TRANSVERSALITY

In this Chapter we limit ourselves to the nonparametric case; the Lagrangian is thus $L(t, x, \dot{x})$ and admissible curves have the form $x(t)$ $t_1 < t < t_2$. We shall not yet spell out precise smoothness assumptions. However, these will partly appear later in this Chapter. For the present, all functions are sufficiently smooth for any operations that we carry out.

Consider a one-parameter family of curves

$$x(t, \alpha) \qquad t_1(\alpha) \leq t \leq t_2(\alpha),$$

which reduces to a given curve $x(t)$ when $\alpha = 0$. Here we suppose that α is a real parameter whose range includes 0 in its interior. The values of L, of $y = L_{\dot{x}}$ and of $H = \dot{x}y - L$ can be regarded as functions of (t, α), even when we do not possess a uniquely defined Hamiltonian function $H(t, x, y)$, or we possess one only locally. In the case of L, it will be convenient to distinguish these values from the function $L(t, x, \dot{x})$ itself, and we shall write them $L^*(t, \alpha)$, or simply L^*. We write further $\mathcal{I}$, or $\mathcal{I}(\alpha)$, for the integral in t of L^*, from $t_1(\alpha)$ to $t_2(\alpha)$. In all functions of α, or of (t, α), we shall set $\alpha = 0$ except for the purpose of differentiating in α.

We term first and second variations, $\delta\mathcal{I}$ and $\delta^2\mathcal{I}$, the derivatives in α (for $\alpha = 0$) $\mathcal{I}'(0)$, $\mathcal{I}''(0)$ of $\mathcal{I}(\alpha)$.

We shall begin by giving to these variations a form more convenient for discussion. We write X, Y, $\dot{X}$, $\dot{Y}$, for the derivatives in α of $x, y, \dot{x}, \dot{y}$ as functions of (t, α). We denote further, for the present, by a, b, c the matrices L_{xx}, $L_{x\dot{x}}$, $L_{\dot{x}\dot{x}}$, regarded as functions of t. The matrix c was previously written A, but we wish to reserve that symbol for different uses. We now write $\mathbf{A}$, $\mathbf{B}$, $\mathbf{C}$ for the quadratic forms XaX, $Xb\dot{X}$, $\dot{X}c\dot{X}$, and we term secondary Lagrangian the quantity $\mathbf{L}(t, X, \dot{X})$ defined by setting

$$2\mathbf{L} = \mathbf{A} + 2\mathbf{B} + \mathbf{C}.$$

Now the two partial derivatives L^*_α, $L^*_{\alpha\alpha}$ of L^* are, respectively,

$$XL_x + y\dot{X} \quad \text{and} \quad X_\alpha L_x + \frac{\partial}{\partial\alpha}(y\dot{X}) + \mathbf{A} + \mathbf{B}.$$

We can therefore rewrite them as follows:

$$\text{(31.1)} \qquad \begin{cases} L^*_\alpha = (L_x - \dot{y})X + \dfrac{\partial}{\partial t}(yX), \\[2ex] L^*_{\alpha\alpha} = (L_x - \dot{y})X_\alpha + \dfrac{\partial}{\partial t}(yX_\alpha) + 2\mathbf{L}. \end{cases}$$

In fact, the first of these relations follows by inspection from the expression for L^*_α, while the second follows from that for $L^*_{\alpha\alpha}$ because we have

$$\frac{\partial}{\partial\alpha}(y\dot{X}) = -\dot{y}X_\alpha + \frac{\partial}{\partial t}(yX_\alpha) + Y\dot{X},$$

and here $Y\dot{X} = \dot{X}(\partial L_{\dot{x}}/\partial\alpha) = \mathbf{B} + \mathbf{C}$.

Now by differentiating in α the composite function $\mathscr{I}(\alpha)$, in which the integrand and the limits of integration depend on α, we obtain

$$\mathscr{I}' = \left[L^* \frac{dt}{d\alpha}\right]_{t_1(\alpha)}^{t_2(\alpha)} + \int_{t_1(\alpha)}^{t_2(\alpha)} L^*_\alpha \, dt,$$

$$\mathscr{I}'' = \left[L^* \frac{d^2t}{d\alpha^2} + L^*_t \left(\frac{dt}{d\alpha}\right)^2 + 2L^*_\alpha \frac{dt}{d\alpha}\right]_{t_1(\alpha)}^{t_2(\alpha)} + \int_{t_1(\alpha)}^{t_2(\alpha)} L^*_{\alpha\alpha} \, dt.$$

Hence, setting $\alpha = 0$ and making use of (31.1), we find that if the curve $x(t)$ is an extremal, then

(31.2)
$$\begin{cases} \delta\mathscr{I} = [L^*t' + yX]_{t_1}^{t_2}, \\ \delta^2\mathscr{I} = [L^*t'' + L^*_t(t')^2 + 2L^*_\alpha t' + yX_\alpha]_{t_1}^{t_2} + \displaystyle\int_{t_1}^{t_2} 2\mathbf{L} \, dt. \end{cases}$$

If $x(t)$ is not supposed to be an extremal, we must add to these expressions the integrals of $(L_x - \dot{y})X$ and of $(L_x - \dot{y})X_\alpha$, respectively. In this connection, it is often convenient to retain for $\delta\mathscr{I}$ the expression previously found, using for L^*_α also its first expression rather than the one given in (31.1). In the case of a family $x(t, \alpha)$ with fixed ends, so that $t_1(\alpha) = t_1$, $t_2(\alpha) = t_2$ and $X(t_1) = X(t_2) = 0$, we then have

(31.3)
$$\delta\mathscr{I} = \int_{t_1}^{t_2} (XL_x + y\dot{X}) \, dt.$$

This expression for $\delta\mathscr{I}$ we shall denote by $\delta_I\mathscr{I}$, while that of (31.2) will be written $\delta_{II}\mathscr{I}$.

We regard as definition of extremal, not the Euler relation, but, directly, the relation $\delta_I\mathscr{I} = 0$ for all suitable X which vanish at t_1, t_2. We shall term this the weak definition of extremals; it avoids special commitments as to the precise class of curves admitted, and we shall have occasion to use it later in this Chapter. The proof that it implies the Euler equation, and, indeed, is equivalent to the latter, can be carried out by the arguments in the Preamble, and we need not repeat them here. (A still weaker definition is obtained, as in the Preamble, by restricting X to be, say, infinitely differentiable and to vanish at the ends.)

In regard to $\delta_{II}\mathscr{I}$, we can write it

$$\left[(L^* - y\dot{x}) \frac{dt}{d\alpha} + y\left(X + \dot{x}\frac{dt}{d\alpha}\right)\right]_{t_1}^{t_2}.$$

Here $L^* - y\dot{x} = -H$, and we write δt, δx for $dt/d\alpha$ and $X + \dot{x}\,dt/d\alpha$, respectively. Then $(-H, y)$ is the momentum vector M, while $(\delta t, \delta x)$, at t_1, t_2 respectively, is the virtual displacement, δP or δQ, of the end point, P or Q, of our curve $x(t)$. Thus

(31.4)
$$\delta_{II}\mathscr{I} = M_Q\,\delta Q - M_P\,\delta P,$$

where M_P, M_Q denote the values of M at P, Q. In a variational problem in which the curves admitted have end points P, Q, that are allowed to vary on certain loci, we term transversality condition the condition that (31.4) vanish for all virtual displacements δP, δQ of the end points P, Q on these loci. This is then a "necessary" condition for a minimum in the same sense that the Euler equation is so. The conditions derived from a vanishing first variation thus split into two, which are independent of one another, namely the Euler equation and transversality. This independence will cease in optimal control.

§32. THE SECOND VARIATION FALLACY

A student today is taught to watch out for lack of uniformity, which is responsible for most classical errors. Typical questions affected by it are the following:

(i) Let f be a function of the pair of variables (x, y) in the plane. Suppose we know that for each choice of a line ℓ in the plane the restriction of f to ℓ is continuous on ℓ. Is then f itself continuous in the plane?

(ii) Let f be as before. Suppose that for each choice of the point (x, y) there is an interval of reals t, with center at 0, in which the auxiliary function

$$\varphi(t) = f(tx, ty)$$

can be expressed as the sum of its Taylor series

$$\varphi(0) + t\varphi'(0) + \cdots + \frac{t^k}{k!}\varphi^{(k)}(0) + \cdots.$$

Is then $f(x, y)$ expressible as the sum of its Taylor series in powers of x and y in a neighborhood of $(0, 0)$?

These are routine questions for a graduate student, and the answer is no. If the reader has not already met them, perhaps he should interrupt his reading and think about them for a week. Trying them is useful experience, and there can be no stigma attached to failing a test that Lagrange could not have passed. We give reasons for the answer at the end of this section. Incidentally, these are favorite questions in minor examinations in mathematics for students working for a doctorate in other subjects.

A variation of (ii) is the following: suppose that for each (x, y) the auxiliary function φ satisfies the conditions $\varphi'(0) = 0, \varphi''(0) > 0$. Is it then true that f has a local minimum at the origin? The answer is the same.

Suppose now, with the notation of the preceding section, that with a fixed $x(t)$ embedded in a variable family $x(t, \alpha)$ subject to prescribed end-conditions, we have, for every such family $I'(0) = 0$, $I''(0) > 0$, except in the trivial case where the function $X(t)$ is identically zero. Does it follow that $x(t)$ provides a minimum in the class of curves, subject to the conditions of the problem, that lie in some neighborhood of the set of points of the curve $x(t)$? Lagrange was convinced that the answer must be yes. However, the preceding example strongly suggests that this is not so. A full discussion of the fallacy of Lagrange's argument, together with a counterexample that shows that the answer is no, is given in Hadamard (Sections 38–43). We invite the reader to study this, at first hand, as explained with remarkable clarity by one of the great thinkers of a past era. A broad understanding of mathematical ideas cannot be reached without using library facilities properly to get material at first hand.

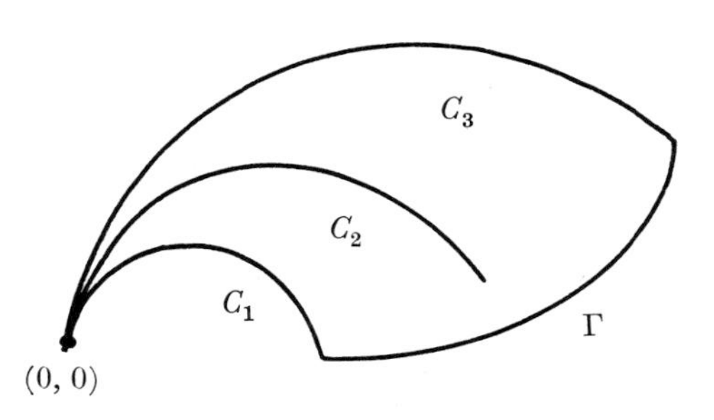

In order to answer (i) and (ii) above, we consider three circular arcs C_1, C_2, C_3 as shown in the figure, which touch at the origin and issue from this point to three points in the first quadrant. We join the second extremities of C_1, C_3 by an arc Γ in the same quadrant, without intersecting C_2. We can now define without difficulty a function $f(x, y)$, which vanishes on the arcs C_1, C_3, Γ and outside the domain bounded by these arcs, and which is continuous in the interior of that domain and takes the constant value 1 on C_2 except at the origin. This function f is discontinuous at the origin. However, it satisfies the conditions of (i) and (ii). Thus the answer to both those questions is no. We can further arrange that $f \geq 0$ in the above construction. In that case the function $x^2 + y^2 - f(x, y)$ satisfies the conditions of the variant of (ii), but does not have a minimum locally at the origin. In defining f in the above construction, we can for instance choose for it a product $f_1 f_2$ where f_2 is continuous, with $f_2 = 1$ on C_2, $f_2 = 0$ on Γ, and where f_1 is such that the lines $f_1 =$ const. in the domain interior to $C_1 + C_3 + \Gamma$ are the circular arcs in it which touch the C_i at the origin. In this interior domain f_1 can be chosen as an elementary function of the radius of such arcs, so as to vanish for the radius of C_1 or C_3, and to take the value 1 on C_2.

§33. THE SECONDARY HAMILTONIAN

We now suppose the line elements of the curve $x(t)$ of Section 31 nonsingular. The matrix now denoted by c is thus nonsingular, and we can take the quantity H to be the Hamiltonian $H(t, x, y)$ defined locally, as in Section 22 of Chapter II. This means that any family $x(t, \alpha)$ in which we embed $x(t)$ will provide vectors x, $\dot{x}$, y locally subject to

$$\textbf{(33.1)} \qquad L_x = -H_x, \qquad L_{\dot{x}} = y, \qquad H_y = \dot{x}.$$

We denote by a', b', c' the matrices whose elements are, along $x(t)$, the second order partial derivatives of H in the components of x, x, those of x, y, and those of y, y. We write $\mathbf{A}'$, $\mathbf{B}'$, $\mathbf{C}'$ for the quadratic forms $Xa'X$, $Xb'Y$, $Yc'Y$, and we term secondary Hamiltonian the function $\mathbf{H} = \mathbf{H}(t, X, Y)$ defined by setting

$$2\mathbf{H} = \mathbf{A}' + 2\mathbf{B}' + \mathbf{C}'.$$

We shall see presently that the choice of a local H does not affect this secondary Hamiltonian.

When the vectors X, $\dot{X}$, Y are functions of t, derived from our family $x(t, \alpha)$ as indicated, they will be in their turn related by equations that we derive from (33.1). By the elementary rules of partial differentiation of composite functions, we find, first, that for $\alpha = 0$,

$$\frac{\partial}{\partial \alpha} H_{y_i} = \Sigma_j (b'_{ji} X_j + c'_{ij} Y_j) = \mathbf{H}_{Y_i},$$

which may be written

$$\frac{\partial}{\partial \alpha} H_y = \mathbf{H}_Y.$$

By entirely similar calculations we see that

$$\frac{\partial}{\partial \alpha} H_x = \mathbf{H}_X, \qquad \frac{\partial}{\partial \alpha} L_x = \mathbf{L}_X, \qquad \frac{\partial}{\partial \alpha} L_{\dot{x}} = \mathbf{L}_{\dot{X}}.$$

Hence, from (33.1) we derive the corresponding relations between X, $\dot{X}$, Y by differentiating in α; they are

$$\textbf{(33.2)} \qquad \mathbf{L}_X = -\mathbf{H}_X, \qquad \mathbf{L}_{\dot{X}} = Y, \qquad \mathbf{H}_Y = \dot{X}.$$

When these are satisfied, it follows further, on the one hand, that

$$\dot{X}Y = Y\mathbf{H}_Y = \dot{X}\mathbf{L}_{\dot{X}},$$

and on the other hand, by applying to the quadratics **L**, **H** the Euler identity for homogeneous functions, that

$$2(\mathbf{L} + \mathbf{H}) = X\mathbf{L}_X + X\mathbf{H}_X + \dot{X}\mathbf{L}_{\dot{X}} + Y\mathbf{H}_Y.$$

Here the first two right hand terms cancel one another, and each of the others equals $\dot{X}Y$. Consequently

$$\mathbf{L} + \mathbf{H} = \dot{X}Y. \tag{33.3}$$

In order to discuss these formulae, we recall that c, c' are inverse matrices, as remarked at the end of Section 22 of Chapter II. Further the relation

$$b + b'c = 0 \tag{33.4}$$

can be derived by differentiating in $\dot{x}$ the identity

$$L_x(t, x, \dot{x}) + H_x(t, x, L_{\dot{x}}) = 0.$$

By multiplying by c', (33.4) can also be written

$$b' + bc' = 0, \tag{33.5}$$

and there follows the equivalence of the vector equations

$$Xb + \dot{X}c = Y \quad \text{and} \quad \dot{X} = Xb' + Yc'. \tag{33.6}$$

This means that the last two relations (33.2) are equivalent.

This being so, we choose an arbitrary triple (t_0, X_0, Y_0) where X_0, Y_0 are vectors and $t_1 < t_0 < t_2$. By the remark just made, there is a unique P_0 for which Y_0 is the value of $\mathbf{L}_{\dot{X}}$ at (t_0, X_0, P_0). We choose as our family

$$x(t, \alpha) = x(t) + \alpha X_0 + \alpha(t - t_0)P_0.$$

At $t = t_0$, we find that $X = X_0$, $\dot{X} = P_0$, $Y = Y_0$ are the appropriate derivatives of x, $\dot{x}$, y. Hence, for the arbitrarily chosen triple $(t, X, Y) = (t_0, X_0, Y_0)$, we have (33.2), (33.3), when $\dot{X}$ is the unique vector satisfying (33.6). Thus $\mathbf{H}(t, X, Y)$ can be defined by (33.3) for all triples, and this shows that **H** is the unique Hamiltonian corresponding to the problem with **L** as its Lagrangian, according to our general definition (Section 22 of Chapter II). Here that definition is no longer local.

We shall term secondary problem, the problem with **L** as Lagrangian; its extremals will be similarly termed secondary extremals, or simply secondaries. Canonical secondary extremals are then given by the further equation

$$\dot{Y} = -\mathbf{H}_X.$$

We remark that this equation results at once from differentiating the relation $\dot{y} = -H_x$ with respect to α. This means that if each $x(t, \alpha)$ is an extremal, then the curve $X(t)$ is a secondary extremal.

This result is worth stressing; from a family of extremals $x(t, \alpha)$ of the original problem, we derive by partial differentiation in α at $\alpha = 0$, a secondary extremal, whose canonical equations are

$$\dot{X} = \mathbf{H}_Y, \qquad \dot{Y} = -\mathbf{H}_X. \tag{33.7}$$

These equations, which are linear and homogeneous in X, Y, with coefficients depending on t, are known as the Jacobi differential equations. Conversely, any solution $X(t)$, $Y(t)$ of (33.7) can be derived by partial differentiation in α at $\alpha = 0$ from the family of extremals $x(t, \alpha)$, $y(t, \alpha)$, determined by the original canonical Euler equations together with the initial conditions $x(t_0) + \alpha X(t_0)$, $y(t_0) + \alpha Y(t_0)$ at $t = t_0$.

Along a secondary extremal, we have, since $\mathbf{H}$ is a homogeneous quadratic in X, Y,

$$2\mathbf{H} = X\mathbf{H}_X + Y\mathbf{H}_Y = -X\dot{Y} + Y\dot{X},$$

and therefore, by (33.3),

$$2\mathbf{L} = \dot{X}Y + \dot{Y}X = \frac{d}{dt}(XY).$$

Hence, by integrating along a secondary $X(t)$, at whose ends t takes the values t_1, t_2, we find that

(33.8)
$$\int_{t_1}^{t_2} 2\mathbf{L}\, dt = X(t_2)Y(t_2) - X(t_1)Y(t_1).$$

This simple way of carrying out the integration explicitly will greatly assist our study.

§34. GEOMETRICAL INTERPRETATION OF EXACTNESS

We need to treat an elementary problem of complex analytic geometry, which provides a simple interpretation of the vanishing of our Lagrange brackets. We consider complex vectors $X + iY$ with n complex numbers as components. We shall term $X + iY$ a pure complex vector if X and Y are real multiples of a same real unit vector e; the latter is unique in that case, unless X and Y both vanish, and we term it the direction of the pure complex vector. A set of pure complex vectors will be said to be independent if their directions are orthogonal. The set of real linear combinations of n independent pure complex vectors will be termed a distinguished hyperplane.

We term enlarged scalar product of two complex vectors $X + iY$ and $X^* + iY^*$, the complex number

(34.1)
$$XX^* + YY^* + i(YX^* - XY^*),$$

where the expressions XX^* and so on denote ordinary scalar products of real vectors. The expression (34.1), which is in general not commutative, is a formal product of $X + iY$ with $X^* - iY^*$, although we find it more convenient not to change the sign of i. The real part of (34.1) is the usual scalar product of vectors (X, Y), (X^*, Y^*) with twice the number of components. Its imaginary part, with the sign changed, is the Lagrange bracket of these two vectors. Clearly (34.1) is only commutative, if the Lagrange bracket vanishes. In that case we term (34.1) the exact scalar product. A set of complex vectors, every pair of which have an exact scalar product, will be termed a set of exactness.

(34.2) Theorem. *In order that a set of complex vectors be a set of exactness, it is necessary and sufficient that it lie in some distinguished hyperplane.*

PROOF. The "sufficiency" follows from four simple remarks: (i) The enlarged scalar product is not altered by a real orthogonal transformation—we may thus take a given distinguished hyperplane to consist of real linear combinations of n pure complex vectors, each of which lies in a complex coordinate plane. (ii) These n pure complex vectors then constitute a set of exactness, since the products (34.1) all vanish. (iii) Exactness of a set of complex vectors is preserved by linear combination, since Lagrange brackets are bilinear—hence a distinguished hyperplane is a set of exactness. (iv) Exactness of a set remains valid for any of its subsets—hence a subset of a distinguished hyperplane is a set of exactness.

We pass on to "necessity." In order to employ induction with respect to n, we first dispose of the case $n = 1$; the distinguished hyperplane through our set of exactness is then simply the line through the origin, given by the equation

$$XY^* - YX^* = 0,$$

where $X^* + iY^*$ is any fixed member of the set other than the origin. We can therefore suppose $n > 1$ and use induction. Let E be a set of exactness in the space C_n of complex vectors with n components. We consider two possibilities:

(a) First suppose that there exists a hyperplane $\Pi \supset E$ through the origin such that Π is a set of exactness and that Π contains at least one pure complex vector

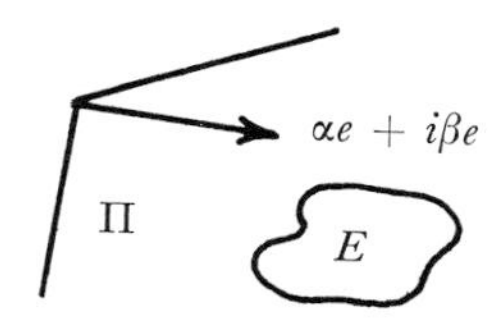

$\alpha e + i\beta e$ where e is a real unit vector, and α, β are real and do not both vanish. We may take e as a coordinate unit vector. Let Π_1 be the subset of Π consisting of vectors $X + iY$ such that $Xe = 0$, and let Π_2 be the subset for which $Ye = 0$. Since Π is a set of exactness, $\beta Xe - \alpha Ye$ vanishes, and therefore in at least one of the sets Π_1, Π_2 we have both $Xe = 0$ and $Ye = 0$. We shall denote this set by E_1.† It is a set of exactness and it lies in C_{n-1}; by the inductive hypothesis, it must lie in a distinguished hyperplane of C_{n-1}. By taking the linear combinations with the vector $\alpha e + i\beta e$, we obtain a distinguished hyperplane of C_n which contains Π and so E.

(b) Now suppose the hypothesis of (a) not fulfilled. We shall arrive at a contradiction. By replacing E by the set of its linear combinations, we may suppose that E is a hyperplane through the origin. Let now R be the set of real vectors X such that $X + iY \in E$. R can only be the whole of n-space. Otherwise it would be orthogonal to some unit vector e, and then the pure complex vector $X^* + iY^* = 0 + ie$ would satisfy $XY^* - YX^* = 0$ for all $X + iY \in E$. The hypothesis of (a) would then be fulfilled by the hyperplane Π of linear combinations of E with $0 + ie$.

This being so, we observe that for each $X \in R$ there can only be one Y such that $X + iY \in E$. Otherwise, contrary to hypothesis again, E would contain the difference of two such vectors, which would have the form of a pure complex vector $0 + iY$.

In particular, taking for X the coordinate unit vectors e_k $k = 1, \ldots, n$, we obtain vectors $Y_k = \Sigma_s a_{ks} e_s$ such that $e_k + iY_k \in E$. From the exactness of E it follows that

$$0 = e_k Y_s - e_s Y_k = a_{sk} - a_{ks}.$$

---

† Either Π_1, Π_2 both coincide with E_1 or one does so and the other is Π.

The matrix $A = (a_{ks})$ is thus symmetric. There is therefore an orthogonal unit matrix T such that

$$TAT^{-1}$$

is a diagonal matrix, with certain diagonal elements λ_k.

If we write (t_{rs}) and (τ_{rs}) for the matrices T and T^{-1}, there will be n orthogonal unit vectors e_r^* for which

$$e_r^* = \sum_s t_{rs} e_s, \qquad e_s = \sum_r \tau_{sr} e_r^*.$$

Then

$$\sum_s t_{rs} Y_s = \sum_{s,k} t_{rs} a_{sk} e_k = \sum_{s,k,\ell} t_{rs} a_{sk} \tau_{k\ell} e_\ell^* = \lambda_r e_r^*.$$

Hence the hyperplane E contains for any r the combination

$$\sum_s t_{rs}(e_s + iY_s) = e_r^* + i\lambda_r e_r^*,$$

which is a pure complex vector, contrary to our assumption.

This completes the proof.

§35. DISTINGUISHED FAMILIES

We now suppose that, for each line element of the original extremal $x(t)$, the Lagrangian L satisfies the Legendre condition that the quadratic form **C** of Section 31 be positive definite. (For its connection with the second variation fallacy, see Hadamard's book Sections 259–262.) For our secondary problem, the condition states that every line element $(t, X, \dot{X})$ is strong (Chapter II, Section 28). It is convenient to express data in terms of the secondary formulation, which will occupy us here, and in which a number of simplifications occur. The Lagrangian is then a quadratic, the Euler equations (now renamed Jacobi's) are linear, the integral of **L** along a curve C, which we shall write $\mathbf{I}(C)$, can be evaluated explicitly when C is a secondary extremal.

In the secondary problem, a point, a line element and a canonical point will still be denoted by symbols such as (t, X), $(t, X, \dot{X})$, (t, X, Y). However, when t is not present, capitals mostly refer to corresponding functions of t. A pair (X, Y) or $(X + iY)$, will thus denote a canonical secondary extremal, possibly one which depends on a further parameter u. The superscript ^{0} then denotes the "initial" value at some $t = t_0$.

Because of the linearity of the Jacobi equations the canonical secondary extremals constitute a $2n$-dimensional linear family, where members are determined by their initial values. This means also that the correspondence between initial values and members preserves linear relations: we express this by saying that our $2n$-dimensional linear family is isomorphic with $2n$-dimensional Euclidean space. Thus any family of canonical secondaries, or as we shall say, any secondary family can be pictured by a subset of this $2n$-dimensional space. To distinguish it from its image we shall sometimes speak of a moving subset. We shall be mainly concerned with linear subfamilies, which are pictured by hyperplanes, and particularly with the case of an n-parameter family, which then consists of members of the form

$$X + iY = \sum_k u_k(X_k + iY_k), \tag{35.1}$$

where the u_k are the components, for $k = 1, \ldots, n$, of an n-dimensional parameter u, and where the (X_k, Y_k) are n canonical secondary extremals, whose initial values, at some $t = t_0$, are linearly independent. We shall write $X(t, u)$, $Y(t, u)$ for the family thus defined by (35.1).

One consequence of this linearity is that any two canonical secondaries (X, Y), (X^*, Y^*) can always be embedded in a family of the form

$$(\alpha X + \alpha^* X^*,\ \alpha Y + \alpha^* Y^*),$$

in which the Lagrange bracket $[\alpha, \alpha^*]$ has, for the secondary problem, the same expression as for the first, namely $XY^* - YX^*$. We shall term this the Lagrange bracket of the two canonical secondaries. We note in this regard that

(35.2) $$\frac{d}{dt}(XY^* - YX^*) = 0.$$

This is a special case of (15.3) of Section 15 of Chapter I (when the slope $\dot{u} = p(t, u)$ vanishes throughout the relevant domain of t, u). Or we may simply observe that

$$\frac{d}{dt}(XY^*) = -X\mathbf{H}_{X^*} + Y^*\mathbf{H}_Y,$$

where the right hand side, in the notation of Section 33, is the bilinear form $-Xa'X^* + Yc'Y^*$, which, by symmetry, must also be the derivative of X^*Y.

From (35.2) it follows that secondary families in which the Lagrange bracket vanishes are isomorphic to sets of exactness of their initial values $X^0 + iY^0$. Such families will be termed families of exactness. A family of exactness will be termed a distinguished family if it is an n-parameter family.

According to (34.2), the set of initial values of a distinguished family is contained in a distinguished hyperplane of complex vectors. Hence it must coincide with the latter for any t_0 at which the set of initial values is n-dimensional, and certainly for some such t_0. In that case, moreover, the family cannot be enlarged without losing exactness, by (34.2). For this reason, if we shift t_0 the set of initial values must remain a distinguished hyperplane of complex vectors; otherwise we could enlarge the new initial value set and so the family.

Thus if F is a distinguished family of canonical secondaries and t_0 is any value of t for which F is defined, there exist orthogonal unit vectors e_k $(k = 1, \ldots, n)$ and corresponding pairs of reals a_k, b_k not both 0, such that the members of F are the linear combinations (35.1) of n canonical secondaries $X_k + iY_k$ whose initial values are

(35.3) $$X_k^0 + iY_k^0 = a_k e_k + i b_k e_k.$$

We shall write $c_k = 0$ when $a_k = 0$ and $c_k = b_k/a_k$ otherwise. We shall have occasion to consider, along with F, a further distinguished family F^* in which members are linear combinations of a second system of n canonical secondaries $X_k^* + iY_k^*$ whose initial values are

(35.4) $$X_k^{*0} + iY_k^{*0} = e_k + i c_k e_k.$$

One important quantity, which takes the same values in F and in F^*, is the initial value at $t = t_0$ of the scalar product XY for members of the families. Its value in F, by (35.3), is

(35.5) $$X^0Y^0 = \textstyle\sum_k a_k b_k (u_k)^2 = \sum_k c_k (X_k^0)^2,$$

where $X_k^0 = (X^0 e_k)$ depends only on X^0 for each k. The families F, F^* will be the same, except for renaming the parameters, in the case where all $a_k \neq 0$; however, they are different, but may have some members in common.

We denote by G, G^* the families of real parts of members $X + iY$ of F, F^*, respectively.

(35.6) Lemma. *There exists $\delta > 0$ such that the strip $|t - t_0| < \delta$ of (t, X)-space is simply covered by G^*.*

PROOF. As solutions of Jacobi equations, which are linear, the members of F^* have the form

$$X^* + iY^* = X^*(t, u) + iY^*(t, u) = u(\Xi(t) + i \vdash\!\dashv (t))$$

where u is as in (35.1) and Ξ, $\vdash\!\dashv$ are $n \times n$ matrices. Further, the initial values are

$$X^{*0} + iY^{*0} = u + i\textstyle\sum_k c_k u_k e_k.$$

The matrix Ξ thus reduces to the unit matrix for $t = t_0$ and is therefore nonsingular in some interval $|t - t_0| < \delta$. In that interval we can solve the equation

$$X^*(t, u) = v$$

for an arbitrary vector v simply by setting

$$u = v\Xi^{-1}.$$

The map is clearly one-to-one for each t, and therefore G^* covers the strip simply.

(35.7) Corollary. *G^* is a geodesic covering of the strip.*

PROOF. We pass from G^* to F^* by setting $Y = \mathbf{L}_X$. Since the Lagrange brackets then vanish, and the (t, u) strip is simply connected, G^* is an induced exact family, and so an exact one in the (t, X) strip, onto which the (t, u) strip is mapped one-to-one.

(35.8) Theorem. *With the same δ as in the lemma, each of the strips $t_0 - \delta < t < t_0$ and $t_0 < t < t_0 + \delta$ of (t, X)-space is simply covered by G.*

PROOF. Since the map provided by G is again linear for each t, we need verify only that no two members can intersect in the strips, or, what comes to the same by subtraction, that in the strips the t-axis does not meet any other member of G. We shall suppose the contrary.

There is then an arc γ of a member of G that joins two points, one of the form (t_0, X^0), the other $(t_1, 0)$ where $|t_1 - t_0| < \delta$, and moreover γ is not a segment of the t-axis. According to (35.5) and (33.8),

$$\mathbf{I}(\gamma) = \tfrac{1}{2}\, \varepsilon \textstyle\sum_k c_k (X^0 e_k)^2,$$

where ε is the sign of $t_0 - t_1$.

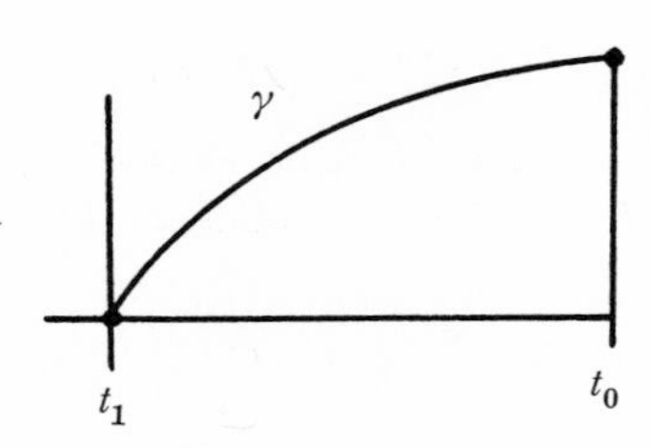

Further, we can define in the strip $|t - t_0| < \delta$, a function $S(t, X)$, vanishing at $(t_0, 0)$, by means of the Hilbert independence integral for the family F^*. For $t = t_0$, by integrating $Y\,dX$ on a straight line from $(t_0, 0)$, we find from (35.4)

$$Y = \sum_k c_k (Xe_k) e_k, \qquad S(t_0, X) = \tfrac{1}{2} \sum_k c_k (Xe_k)^2.$$

Further, on any arc γ^* of a member of G^* in the strip $|t - t_0| < \delta$, the difference of S at the ends is $\mathbf{I}(\gamma^*)$. In particular, by taking γ^* on the t-axis, we find that $S(t_1, 0) = 0$. We can thus calculate the difference ΔS of S at the two ends of our previous arc γ. We find in this way that

$$\Delta S = \mathbf{I}(\gamma).$$

This contradicts the Weierstrass formula (12.6) of Chapter I, Section 12, since of the secondary excess function must have a positive integral on γ, which is not an arc of G^*. This contradiction completes the proof.

(35.9) Corollary. *In the same pair of strips, if $X(t, u) + iY(t, u)$ is the family F, we have $X(t, u) \neq 0$ unless $u = 0$.*

In fact, if $X(t, u) = 0$ for some t, then (35.8) shows that $X(t, u) = 0$ for all t of the segments of the t-axis in the strips. The Jacobi equations then require $Y(t, u) = 0$, and so $u = 0$.

§36. CANONICAL EMBEDDINGS AND FOCAL POINTS

We consider, in the original problem with L as Lagrangian, a canonical extremal Γ along which the Legendre condition is satisfied and an embedding of Γ in a family of canonical extremals

$$x(t, u), \qquad y(t, u) \qquad u = (u_1, \ldots, u_n),$$

given, in an appropriate t-interval, for all sufficiently small constant values of the n-dimensional parameter u, so that Γ is obtained by setting $u = 0$. We suppose that the family is sufficiently smooth, and that it is subject, for some $t = t_0$, to the following initial conditions: the Lagrange brackets vanish, and for $u = 0$ the $2n \times n$ Jacobian matrix (x_u, y_u) has rank n. When these assumptions are verified, we term the embedding canonical.

To a canonical embedding, we associate the family F of canonical secondaries

$$X(t, u) + iY(t, u) = \sum_k u_k (X_k(t) + iY_k(t)),$$

where X_k, Y_k are the partial derivatives in u_k, at $u = 0$, of the functions $x(t, u)$, $y(t, u)$. The Jacobian matrix (x_u, y_u) is thus the matrix whose rows are the vectors (X_k, Y_k). Since the latter are thus linearly independent at t_0 and have vanishing Lagrange brackets there, it follows that F is a distinguished family; hence, further, the initial conditions stated previously for $t = t_0$ remain valid at every relevant t. Any distinguished family defined on the same t-interval as the curve Γ provides, in its turn, a canonical embedding for the secondary problem, of the canonical secondary $X(t) = Y(t) = 0$, which reduces to that interval of the t-axis.

Let now γ denote the extremal which gives rise to Γ as its canonical counterpart; this means that we pass from γ to Γ simply by forming the function $y(t)$ defined along γ by $L_{\dot{x}}$. The extremal γ is then embedded in the family of extremals $x(t, u)$, which similarly give rise to our original family; we term this the real part of our canonical embedding. As previously, we shall frequently use the complex notation $x + iy$ in place of (x, y). For brevity and informality, the family of $x(t, u)$, which defines the real part of a canonical embedding, will be termed a stick of extremals around γ. The real parts $X(t, u)$ of the corresponding members of F will similarly constitute a secondary stick, which is always around the relevant interval of the t-axis.

We term focal point of our canonical embedding a point of γ at which the real Jacobian matrix x_u is singular. The corresponding value of t determines on the t-axis a focal point of the secondary canonical embedding, provided by the family F: this can be defined as a point t at which the determinant of the vectors X_k vanishes, i.e., for which there exists a linear combination

$$X(t, u) = \sum_k u_k X_k(t) \qquad (u \neq 0)$$

such that $X(t, u)$ vanishes at this value of t. Hence, by (35.9), we have:

(36.1) Theorem. *If the Legendre condition holds along γ, then the focal points of each canonical embedding of Γ are isolated.*

(Nevertheless, as shown by an example in Carathéodory Section 328, γ may well contain non-isolated focal points of the embeddings of its sister extremals in the same family; the whole of γ may consist of intersections with sister extremals at their focal points. When an arc of γ is said to be free of focal points, these "extraneous" focal points, if any, are not counted.)

In the sequel, the Legendre condition will be replaced mainly by the more stringent one that γ consist of strong nonsingular line elements, or, as we say, that γ be strong and nonsingular. (By replacing the excess-function by its Taylor remainder, we see rather easily that the matrix $c = L_{\dot{x}\dot{x}}$ cannot then have any negative eigenvalues; nor can it have the eigenvalue 0 since it is nonsingular. This means that the quadratic form **C** is then positive definite, i.e., that the Legendre condition then holds.) We note that this stronger form is automatically valid in the secondary problem, subject to the Legendre condition.

(36.2) Theorem. *Let γ be a strong nonsingular extremal arc, embedded, free of focal points in a stick of extremals, and let Δ denote the strip $t' \leq t \leq t''$ of the values of t for which γ is defined. Then this stick provides a geodesic covering by strong extremal arcs of the part in Δ of an open set $W \supset \gamma$, in which, for every other admissible nonparametric curve $C \subset W$ with the same ends as γ, we have*

$$\mathscr{I}(\gamma) < \mathscr{I}(C).$$

Proof. By shrinking the u-domain if necessary, we may suppose each extremal of the stick strong and nonsingular. Further, since the matrix $x_u(t, 0)$ is nonsingular for each relevant t, we can solve, near $u = 0$, the equation $x(t, u) = x$ uniquely in u. Hence, if we shrink again the u-domain, if necessary, our stick of extremals will cover simply the part in Δ of an open set $W \supset \gamma$. The stick then provides, for this part of W, a geodesic covering, since the Lagrange brackets vanish. The final inequality thus follows from (12.7) of Chapter I, Section 12.

We shall see later (37.6) that the same conclusions can be drawn in the limiting case, in which γ has one extremity at a focal point, but is otherwise free of further focal points.

In the sequel, the most important case of a stick of extremals will be that in which the extremals all pass through a same point (t_0, x_0). In that case we speak of a pencil of extremals and the point (t_0, x_0) will be termed its vertex. We shall mainly be interested in the case in which the vertex is the first, or second, extremity of the extremals concerned, and we then speak of a forward or a backward pencil. The terminology agrees with that of Chapter II, where we restricted ourselves to local pencils (Section 28).

In the canonical form, we shall realize the embedding as follows: Let Γ be again the canonical extremal determined by a given extremal γ which contains the point (t_0, x_0), and suppose the Legendre condition satisfied along γ. We denote by y_0 the initial value, at t_0, of the conjugate canonical vector. We term canonical pencil with vertex (t_0, x_0) the family of canonical extremals

$$x(t, u), \qquad y(t, u)$$

defined on a t-interval containing t_0, and subject at t_0 to the initial conditions

$$x(t_0, u) = x_0, \qquad y(t_0, u) = y_0 + u.$$

We shall limit ourselves here to a sufficiently small u-domain including $u = 0$. We note that the matrix (x_u, y_u) has the required rank n for $u = 0$, and that the Lagrange brackets vanish at t_0. This shows that a canonical pencil always provides a canonical embedding of Γ. The corresponding families of secondaries (and canonical secondaries) will be termed secondary pencil (and secondary canonical pencil). These

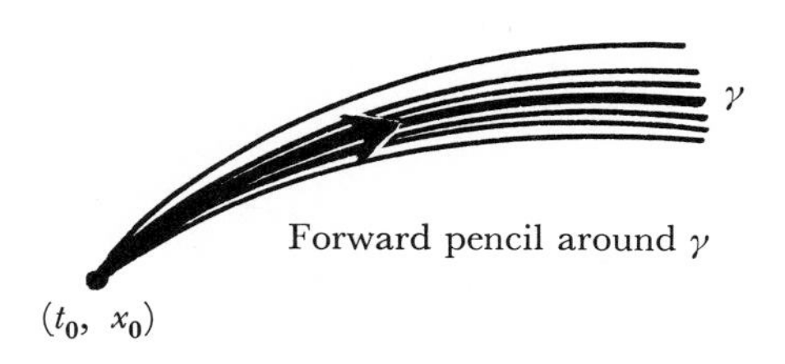

Forward pencil around γ

various pencils depend only on the t-interval, the vertex, and the initial value of y for Γ. The dependence on y_0 does not affect individual members, but does affect the way in which the pencils can be shrunk.

The vertex of a pencil is clearly a focal point of the embedding. The other focal points, if any, on γ, constitute, according to the sign of $t - t_0$, the forward or backward conjugate set of the point (t_0, x_0). The two sets can be considered at the same time on γ, but we shall mainly consider only one of them, since we are concerned mainly with a forward or backward pencil. The nearest points to (t_0, x_0) in the forward (the backward) conjugate set, will be termed the forward (backward) conjugate point of (t_0, x_0) on γ; the corresponding values of t will be denoted by t_1 and t_{-1} and are themselves the forward (backward) conjugate points of t_0 on the t-axis, for the secondary problem. Of course, either or both conjugate sets may be empty.

§37. THE JACOBI THEORY OF CONJUGATE POINTS

With the notion of conjugate point just defined, we shall penetrate furthest into the heart of the classical theory in this section. The classical theory is characterized, as in the theory of analytic functions, by smoothness assumptions, which in our case are supplemented by further so-called regularity assumptions, excluding any but strong nonsingular line elements. As in the theory of analytic functions, such assumptions, from which modern analysis has largely freed itself, then tend to make us notice most the connections with topology, which we have stressed occasionally, and which will appear further in this Chapter in the final sections.

Our aim in the following Chapters is to free ourselves, in part, from the classical body of assumptions, and so to enter again the mainstream of ideas and methods of real analysis and functional analysis, with the object of attacking more general situations, closer to optimal control.

Nevertheless, the main theorem of this section, on which we shall spend some time, already requires a device, due to Tonelli, that is very modern in its conception. The device, in effect, fits together the conclusions drawn from two different geodesic coverings of adjacent domains, and this is similar to an important procedure in optimal control later. The proof of this theorem will be a little long, for we go over it, in a sense, with a microscope.

(37.1) Jacobi's Main Theorem. *Let γ be a strong, nonsingular extremal arc, and let (t_0, x_0) be one of its extremities. Suppose further that γ contains no conjugate point of (t_0, x_0). Then there exists an open set $W_0 \supset \gamma$ such that, for every other admissible nonparametric curve $C \subset W_0$ with the same ends as γ, we have*

$$\mathscr{I}(\gamma) < \mathscr{I}(C).$$

PROOF. We need only consider the case in which (t_0, x_0) is the first extremity. We suppose γ given by $x(t)$ $(t_0 \le t \le t'')$, and we denote by p_0 its initial slope $\dot{x}(t_0)$. We embed γ in a forward pencil and we may suppose, by shrinking the relevant u-domain, if necessary, that all members of the pencil are strong and nonsingular.

The open set W_0 in our assertion will be defined as the set of the points distant from γ by less than a certain $\rho > 0$. The choice of ρ will be made in the following

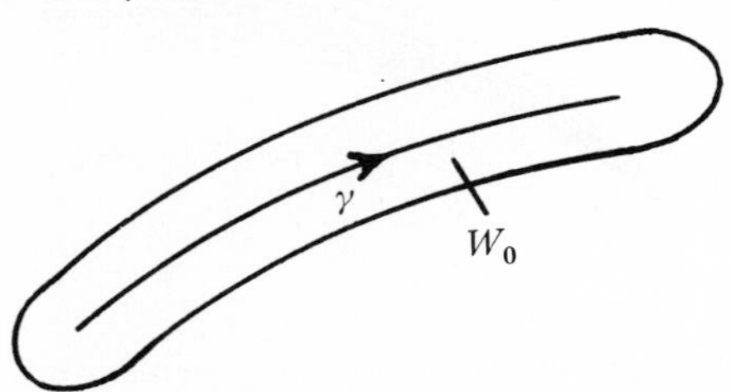

way. We choose a certain t' where $t_0 < t' < t''$, and we denote by Δ', Δ'' and T, the strips $t_0 \le t \le t'$, $t' \le t \le t''$ and the hyperplane $t = t'$. The parts of γ in Δ', Δ'' and the point of γ in T, will be denoted by γ', γ'' and Q. The subsets of W_0, consisting of the points at a distance $<\rho$ from γ', γ'' and Q, respectively, will be denoted

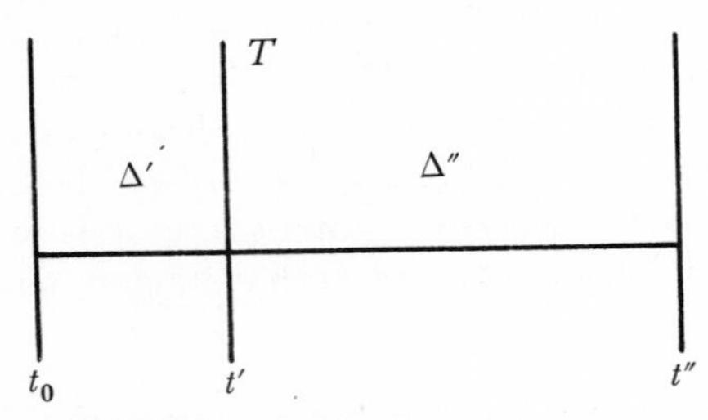

by W_0', W_0'' and V_0. We shall choose for ρ any positive number small enough to satisfy the three conditions that W_0', W_0'' and V_0 lie in three corresponding neighborhoods W', W'' and V of γ', γ'' and Q, respectively, where W', W'' and V will be defined presently.

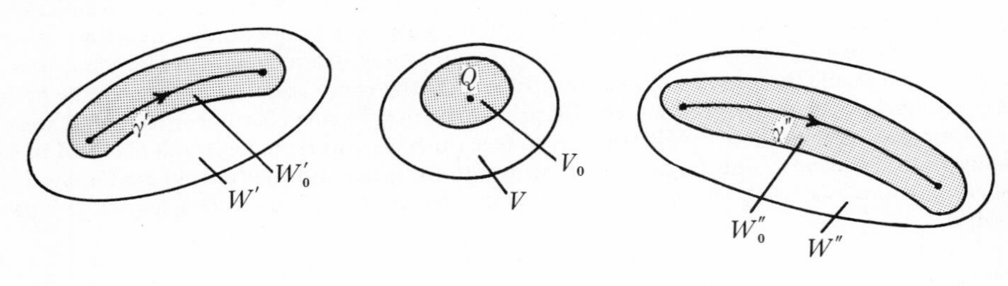

We first choose for W' the neighborhood of (t_0, x_0) that occurs, together with a certain weak neighborhood of the line element (t_0, x_0, p_0), in Theorem (28.8) of Chapter II, Section 28. In order that W' satisfy our requirement of being a neighborhood of γ', it will be sufficient to choose t' close enough to t_0. This will be automatically the case, if we stipulate that t' is to be subject to $t_0 < t' < t_0 + \delta$, where $\delta > 0$ is subject to $t_0 + \delta < t''$, and small enough to ensure that, for every such t', and for every vector $\hat{p}$ such that $|\hat{p} - p_0| < \delta$, the set W' contains the extremal arc $\hat{\gamma}'$, which corresponds to the interval $t_0 \leq t \leq t'$ and which possesses the initial line element $(t_0, x_0, \hat{p})$. For small enough δ, this is certainly the case, by continuity.

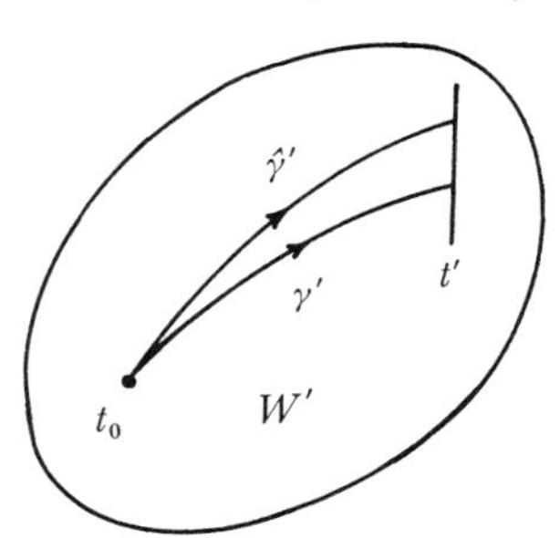

The number δ will be chosen small enough, so that all such initial line elements $(t_0, x_0, \hat{p})$ lie in the weak neighborhood of (t_0, x_0, p_0), which we denoted by N in Theorem (28.8). In that case, that theorem asserts that each of our extremal arcs

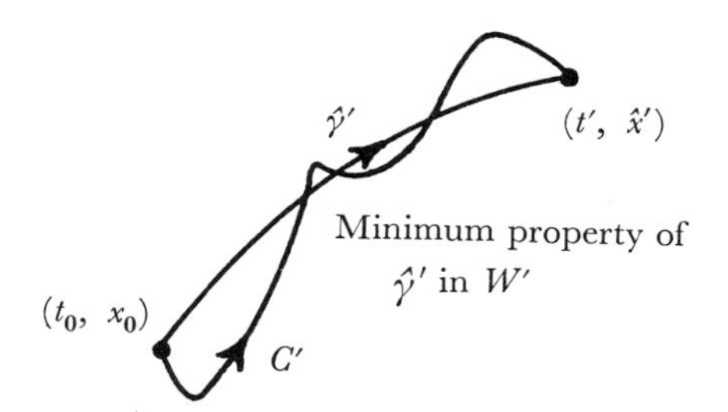

$\hat{\gamma}'$ has the following minimum property: if $(t', \hat{x}')$ denotes the second extremity of $\hat{\gamma}'$, and C' is any admissible nonparametric curve that joins in W' the points (t_0, x_0), $(t', \hat{x}')$, we have

(37.2) $$\mathscr{I}(\hat{\gamma}') < \mathscr{I}(C'),$$

unless C' coincides with $\hat{\gamma}'$.

The number δ will now be further decreased, if necessary, so that, in accordance with the local angle theorem (28.6) of the same Chapter and Section, the extremal $\hat{\gamma}'$ of the local δ-pencil is uniquely determined by its second extremity $(t', \hat{x}')$, instead of by its initial slope $\hat{p}$, provided this extremity lies in the local $(\delta/3)$-angle about (t_0, x_0, p_0). We shall denote the interior of this local angle by V.

Since the initial direction of γ, and those of members of the local $(\delta/6)$-pencil, point inward at the vertex into V, we can choose our t' so close to t_0 that the arcs $t_0 \leq t \leq t'$ lie in V after the initial point. Then γ' certainly lies in V except for its initial point, and therefore V is, as required, a neighborhood of the extremity Q. Further, for any point $\hat{Q} \in T \cap V$, there is exactly one extremal $\hat{\gamma}$ of our pencil which passes through $\hat{Q}$, and the initial arc $\hat{\gamma}'$ in which $\hat{\gamma}$ intersects Δ' has the minimum property (36.4).

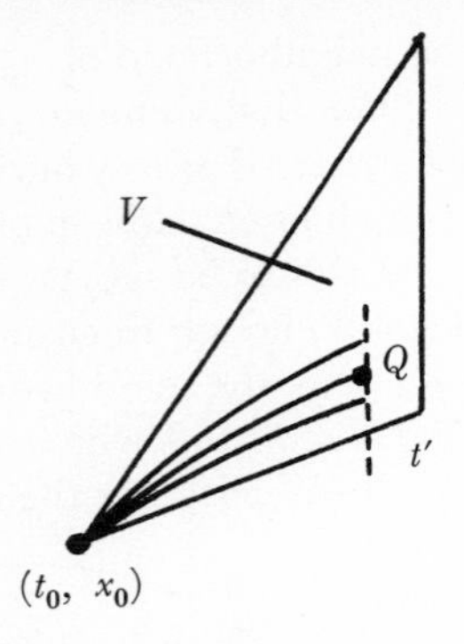

Finally, we consider the arcs $\hat{\gamma}''$ in Δ'' of the extremals $\hat{\gamma}$ of our pencil. We shall consider these only for values of u so small that the initial arcs $\hat{\gamma}'$ of the $\hat{\gamma}$ belong to the local $(\delta/6)$-pencil, and so lie in V. The arcs $\hat{\gamma}''$ form a stick of extremals around γ'', free of focal points. Theorem (36.2) applies, and we denote by W'' the open set containing γ'', whose existence is there asserted.

Accordingly, the arcs $\hat{\gamma}''$ constitute a strong geodesic covering of $W'' \cap \Delta''$. By combining this covering with that of V by the local δ-pencil, issuing from (t_0, x_0), we

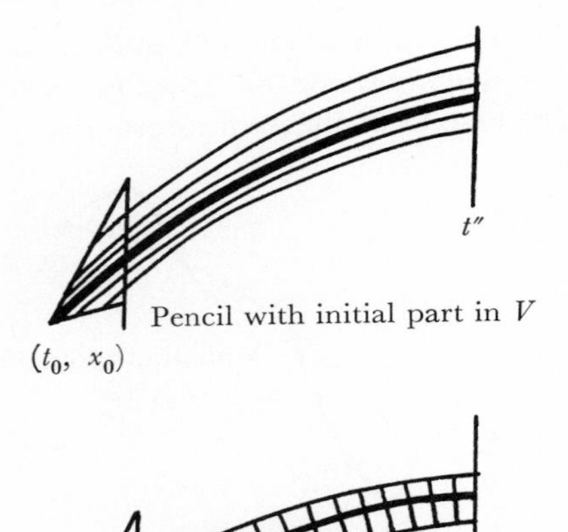

Pencil with initial part in V

Pencil in which S is defined

obtain a covering by arcs of extremals of our pencil of an arrow-shaped set, in which we can define a level function $S(t, x)$, vanishing at the vertex, in terms of the Hilbert independence integral. This function coincides with the integral of L on the extremals $\hat{\gamma}$, which lie wholly in the arrow-shaped set.

This being so, we define the open set W_0 as explained at the beginning of this proof, and we denote by C an arbitrary admissible nonparametric curve in W_0, with the same ends as γ. We write C', C'' for the two arcs of C, which are joined at $t = t'$. By Weierstrass's formula (12.6) of Chapter I, Section 12, we have, unless C'' is γ'',

$$\mathscr{I}(C'') > S_2 - S_1$$

where S_1 and S_2 are the values of S at the ends of C''. On the other hand, S_1 is the value $\mathscr{I}(\hat{\gamma}')$ of the extremal arc joining the vertex to common extremity of C', C'', and

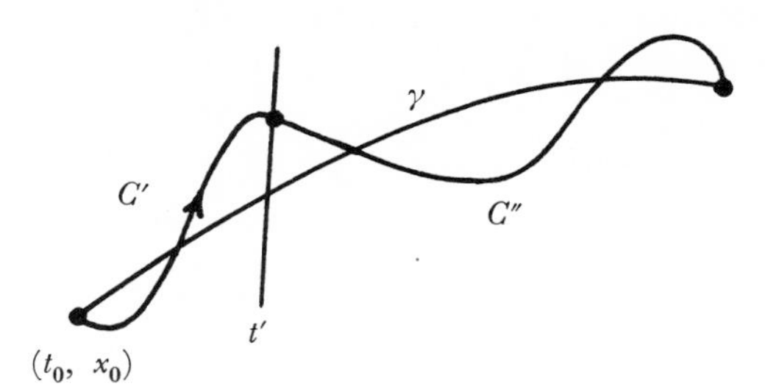

therefore, by (37.2), $\mathscr{I}(C') > S_1$ unless C' coincides with $\hat{\gamma}'$. Since $S_2 = \mathscr{I}(\gamma)$ the assertion of our theorem follows at once.

In (36.2) and (37.1), a weaker conclusion is similarly reached, if the Legendre condition is substituted for the hypothesis that γ be strong. We can then also formulate the conclusion in the strong form as above, but for the secondary problem, when γ becomes a t-interval, $\mathbf{I}(\gamma)$ vanishes, and W_0 becomes, by homogeneity, the whole (t, X)-space. In this secondary version of (37.1), by making t'' tend to a conjugate point, we find that $\mathbf{I}(C) \geq 0$ for any C which joins t_0 with t_1 or t_{-1} of the t-axis. Further, by definition of focal point, there is then one such $C \neq \gamma$ which is a secondary extremal, and $\mathbf{I}(C)$ then vanishes by (33.8).

We can now define t_1, t_{-1}, respectively, as the least $t > t_0$ and the greatest $t < t_0$, such that t and t_0, on the t-axis, can be joined by a C such that $\mathbf{I}(C) = 0$. It follows easily that, subject to the Legendre condition:

(37.3) Theorem. *The point t_0 is the backward conjugate point of t_1, and the two points increase together, strictly and continuously.*

If γ is an interval $t_0 \leq t \leq t''$ of the t-axis, where $t'' > t_1$, there is clearly again a C with the same ends, such that $\mathbf{I}(C) = 0$. We need only prolong our previous C by the t-interval from t_1 to t''. We can, however, reduce the value of $\mathbf{I}(C)$, and so make

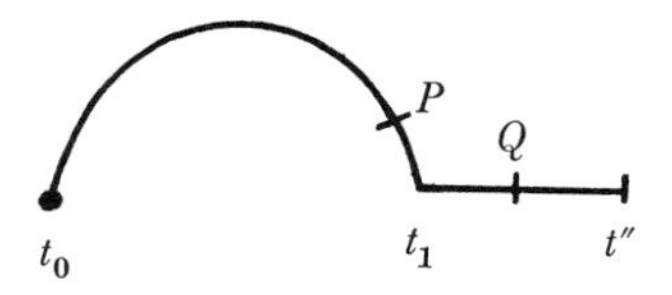

$\mathbf{I}(C) < 0$, by a small modification near t_1, which consists in replacing, by a small secondary extremal arc PQ, the arc of C which joins two points P, Q via t_1. From this secondary result, we deduce, for the original problem:

(37.4) Theorem. *Let γ_0 be a nonparametric extremal arc on which the Legendre condition holds, and whose extremities are A, B. Suppose further that γ_0 contains the forward conjugate point of A, or the backward conjugate point of B. Then there exists, in any narrow neighborhood of γ_0, an admissible curve C joining AB, for which $\mathscr{I}(C) < \mathscr{I}(\gamma_0)$.*

Proof. We consider an embedding of γ_0 of the form

$$x(t, u) = x(t) + uX(t) \qquad (t_0 \leq t \leq t''),$$

where $t'' > t_1$, and where $X(t)$ defines a curve C_1 such as considered above, for which $\mathbf{I}(C_1) < 0$. For small enough u, the curve C defined by $x(t, u)$ then has the stated properties.

(37.5) Corollary. *Let P, Q be two consecutive focal points of a canonical embedding of a nonparametric extremal γ, subject to the Legendre condition. Then no point conjugate to P or Q can be interior to the arc of γ with the extremities P, Q.*

PROOF. If this were false, then on the corresponding t-interval $(t' \leq t \leq t'')$ there would be, by (37.3), a pair of conjugate points t_0, t_1 interior to the interval, belonging to the secondary problem. Since these would lie also in a slightly shrunk t-interval, the assertions of (36.2) and (37.4), applied to the secondary problem, would contradict each other.

(37.6) Further Corollary. *Let γ be a strong nonsingular extremal arc embedded in a stick of extremals. Suppose that the set of focal points on γ is either empty or reduces to a single end point. Then there exists an open set $W_0 \supset \gamma$ such that, for every other admissible nonparametric curve $C \subset W_0$ with the same ends as γ, $\mathscr{I}(\gamma) < \mathscr{I}(C)$.*

This now follows at once from (37.5) and (37.1).

(37.7) Remark. *In two-dimensional space (t, x), consecutive focal points are always conjugate.*

In this case there is only one parameter u, and, for the secondary problem, if $uX(t) = 0$ for some $u \neq 0$, then the same is true for every u at this point t. Thus our remark follows from the alternative definition of conjugate point, given for the secondary problem just before (37.3).

The remark brings out once more the fact that problems in the plane are not representative of the state of affairs in higher space, where there is no such relation between focal points and conjugate points.

Nevertheless we invite the reader to reconsider our solution of problem (c) of the Preamble in the light of the results of this section.

§38. THE INDEX OF STABILITY OF AN EXTREMAL

In the rest of this Chapter we shall allow ourselves to use the term "stability" in a fictitious sense, introduced by the applied mathematician Lichtenstein on the basis of what may have been, partly, wishful thinking. This use of the term superseded, for a decade or two, the older use in the sense of Liapounov, which is again current in the theory of differential equations today. It is not too clear whether our use here of stability is related properly to problems of safety or not. In the calculus of variations, concepts of importance have a way of appearing "for the wrong reason." The real importance of Lichtenstein's version of stability seems to lie in a different direction, followed by Marston Morse.

Let γ be an extremal arc on which the Legendre condition is satisfied. By the forward conjugate set on γ we shall mean the forward conjugate set of its first extremity. Similarly the backward conjugate set will be that of its second extremity. To each point P of the conjugate set we attach in either case a multiplicity $m(t)$ where t is the corresponding point of the t-axis, and $m(t)$ is then also the multiplicity of the point t, regarded as a member of the conjugate set on the t-axis, for the secondary problem on the corresponding t-interval. We define $m(t)$ as the maximal number of linearly independent secondaries of the (forward or backward) pencil, whose vertex is the relevant end of the t-interval. This is equivalent to defining it as the maximal number of linearly independent secondaries which meet the t-axis at the points t, t', where t' is the relevant end. The number $m(t)$ vanishes automatically when t is not in the conjugate set of t'.

For an extremal defined on the interval $t' \leq t \leq t''$, we shall term forward index of stability the sum of the multiplicities $m(t)$ of the points t, interior to the interval of definition, which belong to the forward conjugate set. We may define, similarly, a backward index, which in fact will be seen later to coincide with the forward one.

Various other such equivalent indices of stability can be defined. The first such definition is that of Lichtenstein, and it concerns the number of certain negative eigenvalues associated with a variational problem; some of the relevant material will be found in Hilbert-Courant, and the definition is one of a number given in Morse. We shall not repeat it here; however, we shall give two other definitions due to Morse, which we term the Morse index and the Morse σ-index.

Since the Legendre condition is satisfied, we can determine a positive number ρ, with the help of (35.9), (or else (28.9) of Chapter II, Section 28) such that no secondary extremal other than the t-axis can meet this axis at two distinct points distant less than ρ: this follows from the result quoted, by a simple application of Borel's covering theorem. We may express it by saying that no subinterval of $t' \leq t \leq t''$ of length $<\rho$ can contain a pair of conjugate points.

This being so, we denote by σ any subdivision of $t' \leq t \leq t''$ into meshes of lengths $<\rho$ and we consider the class of curves C_z (henceforth termed broken secondaries), each of which is a continuous arc joining the points t', t'' of the t-axis and made up of a finite number of secondary extremal arcs, which correspond to the various meshes of σ and have their ends, which we term corners of C_z, at the points whose t-coordinates correspond to the points of division of σ.

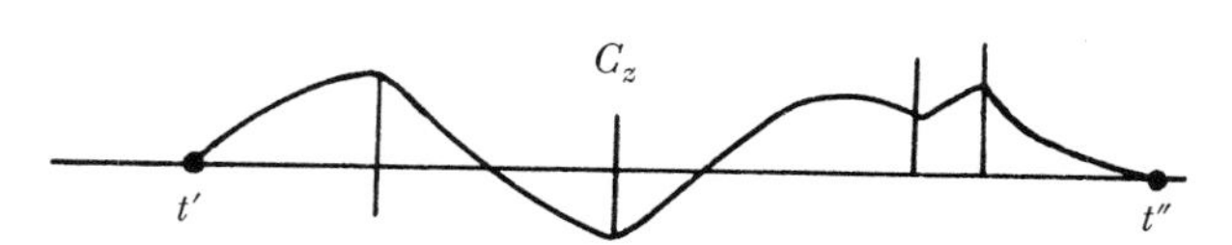

Since no mesh of σ can contain a pair of conjugate points, each secondary extremal arc, for which t describes a mesh of σ is completely determined by its two extremities. Hence C_z will be completely determined by its corners. We shall therefore identify its suffix z with a finite-dimensional vector, whose components are the various X-coordinates of these corners, so that C_z is the broken secondary whose corners are given by z and whose ends are the points t', t'' of the t-axis.

The secondary integral $\mathbf{I}$, extended over the part of C_z between two corners, is clearly a quadratic function of the X-coordinates of these corners. By addition, we may therefore set

$$\mathbf{I}(C_z) = Q(z),$$

where $Q(z)$ is a quadratic form, which depends, of course, on the initial subdivision σ. We term $Q(z)$ the Morse index form associated with the subdivision σ.

We shall denote by M_σ the maximum dimension of the hyperplanes of z-space on which $Q(z)$ is negative definite, i.e., on which $Q(z) < 0$ for $z \neq 0$. We write M_σ^* for the maximum dimension of the hyperplanes on which $Q(z) \leq 0$. The numbers M_σ, M_σ^* will be called, respectively, the Morse σ-index and the augmented σ-index.

We term Morse index M the maximal number of linearly independent continuous, piecewise continuously differentiable, vector functions $X_k(t)$ that vanish at the ends t', t'' and are such that, for every linear combination $X(t, u) = \sum u_k X_k(t)$ with constant coefficients $u = (u_1, \ldots, u_k)$ not all 0, the secondary integral $\mathbf{I}(C)$ on the curve C defined by $X(t, u)$ for $t' \leq t \leq t''$ is <0. If we replace this last inequality by ≤ 0, we define similarly the augmented index M^*. In the language of Morse, the linear combinations generate what he calls, descriptively, a hyperplane of admissible arcs, and M is the maximum dimension of such a hyperplane on which $\mathbf{I}$ is negative definite.

(38.1) Lemma. *We have*

$$\text{(a) } M = M_\sigma, \qquad \text{(b) } M^* = M_\sigma^*, \qquad \text{(c) } M_\sigma^* - M_\sigma = m,$$

where $m = m(t'')$.

Proof. We observe that in a hyperplane of admissible curves on which $\mathbf{I} \leq 0$, there cannot be two distinct members which agree for each point of subdivision of σ. This is because the difference would define a member which would meet the t-axis at each point of division, and for such a curve we would have $\mathbf{I} > 0$ by the secondary version of (37.1).

To each curve that is a member of the hyperplane in question, we can thus attach a unique broken secondary C_z which agrees with it at the corners of the latter. In this way, linearly independent members will correspond to linearly independent broken secondaries C_z, and so to linearly independent vectors z. Clearly, in passing from the member curves to the broken secondaries, $\mathbf{I}$ does not increase. The maximal dimension of a hyperplane on which $\mathbf{I} \leq 0$ is thus attained for a hyperplane of broken accessory extremals C_z. The same is true, similarly, for a hyperplane on which $\mathbf{I}$ is negative definite. These dimensions are therefore those of corresponding maximal hyperplanes of z on which $Q \leq 0$ or on which Q is negative definite, and this disposes of (a) and (b).

We have still to deal with (c). By a rotation in z space, which transforms Q into a sum of squares, we see that the difference $d = M_\sigma^* - M_\sigma$ is the multiplicity of the eigenvalue 0 for Q, and hence that d is the number of linearly independent vectors z that are critical for Q, i.e., such that the partial derivatives of Q all vanish. On the other hand, m is the number of linearly independent secondaries through the points t', t'' of the t-axis, i.e., the number of linearly independent broken secondaries C_z, which reduce to secondary extremals. To establish (c) it is thus sufficient to show that C_z reduces to a secondary extremal, if and only if z is critical for Q.

In doing so, we may interpret the notion of secondary extremal in the wide sense, as in the remark following (31.3), since for piecewise continuously differentiable curves the notion of extremal is the same, in this sense, whenever continuity of $L_{\dot{x}}$ implies that of $\dot{x}$. This is the case in the secondary problem, since $\dot{X}$ is a linear function of X, Y, with continuous coefficients.

Temporarily, we write for brevity $\mathbf{I}(X)$ for $\mathbf{I}(C)$, where C is the curve given by a function X of the form $X(t)$ on $t' \leq t \leq t''$, and we denote by X_z, X_σ the functions defining, respectively, a broken secondary C_z and a piecewise continuously differentiable curve C_σ, where the latter meets the t-axis at each point of division of σ. From a remark made in the proof of (a), (b), we deduce that

$$\mathbf{I}(X_z + \alpha X_\sigma) \geq \mathbf{I}(X_z),$$

and therefore that the derivative in α, at $\alpha = 0$, always vanishes for $(X + \alpha X_\sigma)$ when X is a broken secondary with corners defined by some z_0 in our space of z. It follows at once that the expressions

$$\mathbf{I}[X + \alpha(X_z + X_\sigma)] \quad \text{and} \quad \mathbf{I}(X + \alpha X_z)$$

have the same derivative in α at $\alpha = 0$, and hence that the necessary and sufficient condition, that the given broken secondary X reduce to a secondary extremal, is that $\mathbf{I}(X + \alpha X_z)$ have a vanishing derivative in α at $\alpha = 0$, i.e., that $Q(z_0 + \alpha z)$ have such a vanishing derivative for every z. Since this is clearly equivalent to the condition that z_0 be critical for Q, our proof of (c) is complete.

We pass on to another lemma.

We denote by $\sigma(t)$ a subdivision of the interval (t', t) derived by similarity from the subdivision σ of the interval (t', t''), where we suppose $t' \leq t \leq t''$. The form $Q(z)$ and the integers M, M^*, M_σ, M_σ^* that we obtain by replacing the interval (t', t'') by (t', t) and the subdivision σ by $\sigma(t)$ will be written $Q(z, t)$, $M(t)$, $M^*(t)$, $M_\sigma(t)$, $M_\sigma^*(t)$.

(38.2) Lemma. (a) *$M(t)$, $M^*(t)$ are nondecreasing.* (b) *$M_\sigma(t)$, $M_\sigma^*(t)$ are, respectively, lower and upper semicontinuous.*

PROOF. The hyperplanes of admissible curves which serve to define $M(t)$ or $M^*(t)$ become corresponding hyperplanes of admissible curves for the interval $(t', t + h)$ if we simply add to each curve the segment $(t, t + h)$ of the t-axis. On these hyperplanes, $\mathscr{I}$ clearly remains negative definite (or nonpositive, as the case may be) and hence $M(t + h) \geq M(t)$, $M^*(t + h) \geq M^*(t)$, for $h \geq 0$. This proves (a).

To establish (b), we may suppose $Q(z, t)$ to be, for a particular t, given by a diagonal matrix. The addition of a small quadratic form $Q(z)$ such that $|Q'|$ does not exceed $\varepsilon\, |z|^2$ will not alter the sign of Q on the hyperplane of z determined by the axes for which the diagonal coefficients of the matrix are negative. Hence, the coefficients of $Q(z, t)$ being continuous in t, there is a neighborhood of the point t in which the maximal dimension of a hyperplane, where Q is negative definite, is not less than at t. This shows that $M_\sigma(t)$ is lower semicontinuous. Similarly we show that $M_\sigma^*(t)$ is upper semicontinuous.

(38.3) Morse's First Theorem. *Let E be an extremal on which the Legendre condition is satisfied. Then the forward and backward indices of stability, the Morse index and the Morse σ-index are all equal.*

PROOF. By applying (38.1) to the interval (t', t) in place of (t', t'') and by combining it with (38.2), we find that $M(t)$ agrees with $M_\sigma(t)$ and is lower semicontinuous and nondecreasing, while, similarly, $M^*(t)$ agrees with $M_\sigma^*(t)$ and is upper semicontinuous and nondecreasing. Moreover, by (38.1)(c), $M(t)$, $M^*(t)$ agree except at the forward conjugate set, which consists of isolated points by (36.1). It follows that $M(t)$, $M^*(t)$ are continuous except at isolated points, and therefore that they are step-functions, since they are integer valued. At a discontinuity, we have then $M(t - 0) = M(t)$ and $M(t + 0) = M^*(t)$, so that, by (38.1)(c), with t in place of t'', the jump $M(t + 0) - M(t - 0)$ is $m(t)$.

Since $M(t) = 0$ for values of t near the initial point t', it follows that $M(t)$ is the sum of its jumps between t' and $t - 0$, and hence that the number $M = M(t'')$ agrees with the forward index of stability. By symmetry it also agrees with the backward index. This completes the proof.

Morse's theorem thus reduces the various forms of the index to an elementary algebraic concept, namely to the number of negative characteristic values, or eigenvalues, of a quadratic form. This is analogous to the ordinary maxima and saddle points of a function of several real variables, where the quadratic form is then furnished by the second order terms of the Taylor expansion. However, an entirely new feature of Morse's theory, as compared with the classical elementary treatment of saddle points, is that this algebraic concept is now given a very beautiful geometrical meaning, in terms of the topology of simplicial figures.

Given a nonsingular quadratic form $Q(z)$ in the N variables $z = (z_1, \ldots, z_n)$, the number M of its negative eigenvalues is first characterized by the following system of numbers

$$\textbf{(38.4)} \qquad \begin{cases} M_k = 0 & \text{for} \quad k \neq M, \qquad 1 \leq k \leq N, \\ M_k = 1 & \text{for} \quad k = M. \end{cases}$$

These numbers uniquely determine M, and are, in their turn, determined by it. It is to them, rather than to M itself, that we shall attach a geometrical meaning, in the section that follows.

§39. THE SECOND STAGE OF THE MORSE THEORY

We shall content ourselves, at this stage, with the barest of outlines. A set of z will be termed submerged if it is made up only of points at which $Q(z) < 0$. It will be termed hanging if it comprises, in addition to its submerged part, only the origin $z = 0$. The sets that will concern us will be elementary polytopes, i.e., finite sums of simplices of a given dimension; we speak of polygons and polyhedra when the dimension is one or two. We recall that a k-dimensional simplex is the convex figure, with $k + 1$ linearly independent vertices, and that it can be oriented in just two ways, by fixing the order of its vertices apart from an even permutation. A k-dimensional polytope will thus have a definite orientation attached to each of its simplices, and, moreover, we shall regard it as unaltered by cancellation of two simplices that differ only in orientation.

The boundary of a simplex is then a polytope whose dimension is one lower, and the orientation rule of the face opposite a given vertex is defined by retaining the given order of its vertices if the opposite vertex is of odd order, and by replacing by an odd permutation in the opposite case. The boundary of a polytope is defined by addition, and one finds that the boundary of a boundary always vanishes.

A polytope will be regarded as unchanged by subdividing its simplices into smaller ones, and the orientations will be so adjusted that the boundary is unchanged also.

A polytope whose boundary (after cancellations) is submerged will be termed a relative cycle. A polytope that is the sum of a boundary and a submerged polytope will be termed a relative boundary. Since the boundary of a submerged polytope is submerged and that of a boundary vanishes, we see at once that the boundary of a relative boundary is submerged, and therefore that every relative boundary is a relative cycle.

In the definition of a polytope, there is nothing to prevent our taking a same simplex more than once. It follows that we can form any positive integer multiple of a polytope, the result being still a polytope. Since a change of orientation is equivalent to multiplying by -1, it follows that we can multiply by any integer, and therefore that any finite linear combination, with integer coefficients, of polytopes, is a polytope. It is easily seen that the boundary of such a combination is the combination of the boundaries, and hence that the combination of relative cycles or of relative boundaries is itself a relative cycle or relative boundary.

We term a system of relative cycles independent if no linear combination with integer coefficients not all 0 is a relative boundary. We note that this notion ultimately depends on that of a submerged polytope, and so on the quadratic form $Q(z)$.

We are now in a position to state the geometrical property found by Morse for the numbers M_k of (38.4).

(39.1) Morse's Second Theorem. *The number M_k is the maximum number of independent relative k-dimensional cycles.*

On the basis of (39.1), M_k is termed the k-th type number of $Q(z)$. If we recall the values of the M_k, we can restate (39.1) as follows:

(39.2) Theorem. *Let $Q(z)$ be a nonsingular quadratic form in N variables, with exactly M negative eigenvalues. Then for $k \neq M$ every k-dimensional relative cycle is a relative boundary, while for $k = M$ there is just one independent relative cycle of dimension k.*

We shall content ourselves here with indicating how the proof uses certain basic ideas and methods, which we list under (a) and (b) below, and which are standard in elementary topology. The indications are given in (c) and (d) below.

(a) While ordinary notions in topology are invariant under deformation, our relative notions are invariant for special kinds of deformations, which we term downward deformations, and which transform every submerged set into a submerged set. We term downward deformation a map of the points z of a suitable set into points z^*, or, more precisely, a map $(z, t) \rightarrow z^*$, by which the image z^* depends continuously on z and on a parameter t where $t_0 \leq t \leq t_1$, and which is such that z^* reduces to z for $t = t_0$ and that $Q(z^*)$ becomes, by substitution, a nonincreasing function of t for each fixed z. In our case we shall limit ourselves to piecewise linear downward deformations. They transform polytopes into polytopes, if we ignore the images of simplices which are degenerate images, i.e., for which the vertices are not linearly independent. It is with this understanding that our relative notions are invariant.

(b) If we suppose, without loss of generality, the axes so chosen that $Q(z)$ takes the diagonal form

$$Q(z) = \sum a_k z_k^2,$$

where $a_k < 0$ for $k \leq M$, and $a_k > 0$ for $M < k \leq N$, there exists for any bounded set, in particular for any polytope, an obvious piecewise linear downward deformation, for which the final image, which corresponds to $t = t_1$, is contained in the subspace of the first M variables $z_1, \ldots, z_M$, in which $Q(z)$ is negative definite. In the case $M = 0$, this subspace is understood to consist of the single point $z = 0$.

(c) From (a) and (b) we see that we may suppose $k \leq M = N$. (We may also suppose $M \neq 0$, the case $k = M = 0$ being trivial, if we remember that a single point, wherever situated, has a boundary that is regarded as submerged.) We note that with these hypotheses every polytope is now either hanging or submerged. In the case $k < M$, we easily obtain a piecewise linear downward deformation of a hanging polytope into a submerged one, so that there is no independent relative cycle of dimension k.

(d) There remains only the case $k = M = N$. In this case, no k-dimensional polytype is a boundary unless it is identically 0. If the polytope is a relative hanging cycle, it is certainly no relative boundary. On the other hand, we see at once that two such hanging relative cycles have a linear combination with nonvanishing coefficients, which is not hanging and therefore is submerged. Thus there can only be one independent relative cycle in this case.

This completes the justification of (39.2). For more details we refer the reader to the literature.

Chapter IV

Hamiltonians in the Large, Convexity, Inequalities and Functional Analysis

§40. INTRODUCTION

One of our main objects is to draw attention to basic modern concepts which arose out of the calculus of variations. Most of those treated in this Chapter have grown out of the notion of Hamiltonian. We shall need these concepts in any case, quite apart from their historical origin. A concept is like a public conveyance: it helps a person to reach his destination. Of course some people prefer to walk, but life is then not really long enough.

One of the basic concepts that we shall treat is that of convexity. We briefly mentioned it in Chapter I, Section 13, in order to interpret the Weierstrass condition. We now need to go into it more fully in order to free ourselves from local restrictions in our definition of Hamiltonian. For this purpose we need to discuss duality of convex figures and of convex functions. This duality is expressed by the inequalities of Schwarz and of Young (W. H.), and it takes us at the same time to the heart of modern functional analysis. Thus the various concepts of this Chapter will turn out to be strongly interrelated.

The reader who is familiar with convexity or with functional analysis can, of course, do a good deal of skipping, while the one to whom these matters are new will need to supplement the Chapter by outside reading, in due course of time. Unfortunately, both types of readers need to draw up a dictionary of terms, since we have yielded to the temptation of reforming the overworked terminology. It really was high time, and indeed, if Britain can finally go over to the metric system, reforms do become thinkable in "mathematical officialese," without a Bourbaki. To minimize the inconvenience thus caused, all readers, students, friends and colleagues are hereby urged to appoint themselves as fanatic missionaries for the new terms.

The little excursion that we propose to make into functional analysis may seem a bit tough on a beginner. However, this is partly a matter of preconceived ideas. There is some similarity to mountain climbing: some beginners take to it like a duck takes to water, while others are inclined to get dizzy. In this case, there is nothing to get dizzy about; the work is exactly the same as in Euclidean space for a good part of the way, and the rest can be omitted until the reader has more confidence, or it can be taken at the "slow pace of the men of the hills."

The functional analysis part is, of course, not needed for defining Hamiltonians in the large. To do this we could just as well stay in Euclidean n-space. However, common sense suggests that it is time to begin to place our whole subject in its proper setting. When we treat a variational problem we are not in Euclidean space, but in a space whose elements are curves, that is, the space in which we seek certain minimizing elements out of the relevant sets, or families. Basically, the calculus of variations studies certain problems in this space of curves, and therefore in the functional space defined by the representations $x(t)$ $(t' \leq t \leq t'')$ of such curves. This being so, the sooner we start studying functional space, the better. And as for getting dizzy, all this abstraction is largely a matter of eliminating certain unnecessary assumptions, like ceasing to suppose that the earth is supported by four elephants, and no sensible person need feel dizzy on that account.

In regard to the notion of convexity, even readers fully acquainted with this notion do not always realize the reasons for its importance, and we shall try here to present these in rather simple terms. To this effect, we first recall to mind the fundamental importance, in elementary analysis and later stages, of procedures for studying functions of several variables, rather than only those of one variable. Without them, a mathematician would be as helpless, and as inaccurate as those economists who speak only of "tendencies" and of "other things being equal." In mathematical terms, this amounts to considering a function $f(x, y)$ only for constant y, or for constant x.

The standard procedure in passing from one to several variables is that of seeking the right way to generalize the notions that were important in the case of one variable. In this respect, linearity is the proper generalization of equality, as every algebraist knows full well. Modern analysis works, however, much less with equality than with the relation of inequality $\geq$. The importance of convexity lies in the fact that it constitutes the higher dimensional generalization of this relation.

§41. CENTER OF GRAVITY AND DISPERSAL ZONE

The letter z will denote a variable point, or vector, in a vector space. By a vector space, we here mean a space, or simply a set, in which we can specify, as a point, the sum of an arbitrary linear combination

$$\sum a_i z_i$$

of a finite number of points z_i, with nonvanishing scalars a_i as coefficients.

Scalars will, here, be identified with real numbers. Moreover, we make no restriction as to dimensionality, and nothing whatever is assumed in regard to a metric or a topology. What we do assume is the validity of the usual laws of vector algebra; they depend on one axiom although it is more usual to split it into bits and pieces. This axiom is the rearrangement axiom for a double sum

$$\sum \sum a_{ik} z_k;$$

it states that such a finite double sum represents the same point of our vector space, when we sum first in k and then in i, as when we reverse this order. Besides this, we specify that our scalars are to be arbitrary real numbers. The existence of an origin, $0 = 0z$ for all z, and its unicity, follow at once from the rearrangement axiom.

It is convenient to introduce, besides the notion of a vector space, that of a linear space. The latter is obtained similarly, except that in it we admit only as linear combinations those for which

$$\textbf{(41.1)} \qquad \sum a_i = 1;$$

we term such linear combinations unitary. We pass from a linear space to a vector space simply by a choice of an arbitrary point as origin. This means that we agree to omit the corresponding term from any unitary linear combination, and therefore that we attach a meaning to an arbitrary linear combination, so that we are back in the previously discussed case of a vector space.

In a linear space (and, in particular, in a vector space), we term linear subspace a set G such that, for vectors $z_i \in G$, the unitary linear combinations $\sum a_i z_i$ have points of G as their sums. We term linear a function $\ell(z)$ $z \in G$, where G is a linear subspace and where the values of $\ell(z)$ are either real numbers or vectors (in some vector space), if

$$\textbf{(41.2)} \qquad \ell(\sum a_i z_i) = \sum a_i \ell(z_i)$$

for all unitary linear combinations $\sum a_i z_i$ of points of G.

In the sequel, the underlying space will be taken to be a vector space, rather than a linear space. This is, of course, immaterial, except where the choice of origin plays a part. However, the linear subspaces considered will not necessarily be vector subspaces, i.e., they need not pass through the origin. A linear function ℓ will, moreover, be termed homogeneous if it is defined in a vector subspace G, and if it vanishes at the origin. This agrees with the notion of homogeneity, which we define more generally in the next section, for a function which need not be linear. In the case of a homogeneous linear function ℓ, the relation (41.2) clearly holds for all linear combinations $\sum a_i z_i$ of points of G, and not merely for unitary ones.

We term convex combination, or center of gravity (barycenter for those who prefer Greek) a unitary linear combination $\sum a_i z_i$ with positive coefficients a_i, termed weights. Further, given a set E in our vector space, we denote by $\tilde{E}$ and term

convex hull of E the set of the points expressible by convex combinations $\sum a_i z_i$ of points $z_i \in E$. We denote, similarly, by $\hat{E}$, and term linear hull of E the set of the points expressible by unitary linear combinations of points of E. Clearly $E \subset \tilde{E} \subset \hat{E}$.

The notion of linear hull will also be defined for more than one set; for instance we term linear hull of the pair of sets A, B, and denote by $\langle A, B\rangle$, the linear hull of their union. For this purpose we shall not distinguish between a single point and the set consisting of a single point, so that if p is a point and A a set, the symbols $\langle A, p\rangle$ and $\langle p, A\rangle$ denote the linear hull of A and of the set consisting of the single point p. The latter is then termed simply the linear hull of the set A and the point p.

In this connection, we shall require later the following remark: if G is any vector subspace and z_0 is any point outside G, then $\langle z_0, G\rangle$ is a vector space each of whose points has exactly one representation of the form $z + tz_0$, where $z \in G$ and where t is real. (We shall refer to this as the standard representation of a point of $\langle z_0, G\rangle$.) Such a representation clearly exists, and it is unique, since the equality $z + tz_0 = z' + t'z_0$ is equivalent to the relation $z - z' = (t' - t)z_0$, where the left hand side is in G and the right hand side is not, unless the latter reduces to the origin. Hence $t = t'$ and $z = z'$.

In our discussion of the main definitions of the next section, a further notion, that of dispersal zone, which is given here for the first time, and which is somehow reciprocal to that of convex hull, will play an important part. Let E be a set in our vector space, and let p denote either a point or a set of points of the same space. (We shall mainly be interested in the case in which p is either a point or a linear subspace.) We term a point z, of our vector space, compensated in E relative to p, if there exists a convex combination $\sum a_i z_i$ of sum p, or of sum in p, such that z is one of the z_i and that all the other z_i belong to E. The subset of E, consisting of points of E that are compensated in E relative to p, will be termed the dispersal zone of p in E, and will be written $E(\text{mod } p)$. The linear hull of p and $E(\text{mod } p)$ will be termed the dispersal space of p generated by E.

(In the diagram, the dispersal zone is the empty set when p is a point in the position p_1, outside $\tilde{E}$; it is the whole of E when p is a point in the position p_2. If p is

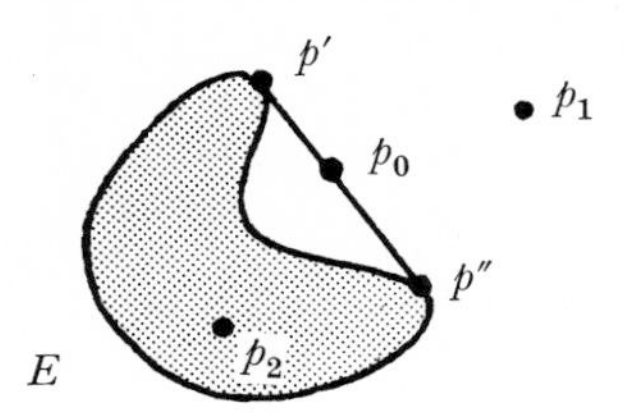

in the position p_0, the dispersal zone of p in E consists of the pair of points p', p'' indicated.)

(41.3) Lemma. *In our vector space, let p be any point, or any nonempty linear subspace, and let E be any set. Further, let*

$$M = E(\text{mod } p), \qquad p^* = \langle p, M \rangle, \qquad M^* = E(\text{mod } p^*).$$

Then, relative to p, each point $q \in p^*$ is compensated in M, and each point $r \in M^*$ is compensated in E.

(We may verify this in the preceding diagram with $p = p_0$; then p^* is the line through p', p'' and q is on this line, M^* is the pair p', p'', and r is one of p', p''. In this case, both q and r are compensated in M, and so in E, relative to p.)

Proof. We may suppose M not empty and the origin shifted to a point of p. For suitable $p_0 \in p$, $m_i \in M$ and real coefficients c_i, a point of the form

$$p_0 + \sum c_i m_i$$

then coincides with q, or again with a point of the form $r + \sum a_k z_k$, where $z_k \in E$ and $a_k > 0$. In both cases, by subtracting a number of corresponding expressions that vanish and have positive coefficients, we can arrange for all c_i to be negative, since each m_i occurs in a convex combination of points of M, whose sum is in p. It follows that some convex combination of q with points of M, or of r with points of E, is a multiple of p_0, and so in p, and this is our assertion.

(41.4) Corollary. $M(\text{mod } p) = E \cap p^* = M^* = M.$

Proof. We apply (41.3) to an arbitrary $q \in E \cap p^*$ and to an arbitrary $r \in M^*$. Then r is a point of E compensated in E, so that $r \in M$; while q is a point of E compensated in $M \subset E$, so that $q \in M$ and so further $q \in M(\text{mod } p)$. By varying q, r, we thus find that

$$E \cap p^* \subset M(\text{mod } p), \qquad M^* \subset M.$$

Our assertion now follows by combining these with the obvious inclusions

$$E \cap p^* \supset M \supset M(\text{mod } p), \qquad M^* \supset M.$$

(41.5) Lemma. *With the notation of* (41.3), *let N be the dispersal zone $\tilde{E}(\text{mod } p)$ of p in $\tilde{E}$. Then $N \subset \tilde{M}$.*

Proof. Each point $z \in N$ lies in $\tilde{E}$, and is thus the center of gravity of certain $z_i \in E$; moreover z is compensated in $\tilde{E}$, and so in E. It follows that each z_i is likewise compensated in E, and therefore that $z_i \in M$, and hence that $z \in \tilde{M}$.

(41.6) Corollary. $\tilde{M}(\text{mod } p) = N = \tilde{M}$, moreover $\langle p, N \rangle = \langle p, M \rangle$.

Proof. We first observe that the set $\tilde{M}(\text{mod } p)$ is convex; in fact, since it is a subset of the convex set $\tilde{M}$, the latter contains any center of gravity z of points z_i of this subset. By forming a suitable combination of equations that express the fact that each z_i is compensated in $\tilde{M}$, we see that z is so, and hence that $z \in \tilde{M}(\text{mod}\, p)$. The set $\tilde{M}(\text{mod}\, p)$ is thus convex, and it is clearly subject to

$$M = M(\text{mod}\, p) \subset \tilde{M}(\text{mod}\, p) \subset \tilde{E}(\text{mod}\, p) = N,$$

where $N \subset \tilde{M}$ by (41.5); it must therefore coincide with the convex hull $\tilde{M}$, and also with N. The final assertion is now obvious too, since it becomes $\langle p, \tilde{M}\rangle = \langle p, M\rangle$.

Recapitulating, we have

(41.7) Theorem (The Dispersal Identities). *In our vector space, let p be any point, or non-empty linear subspace, and E any set. Further let*

$$M = E(\text{mod}\, p), \qquad p^* = \langle p, M\rangle, \qquad N = \tilde{E}(\text{mod}\, p).$$

Then

$$p^* = \langle p, N\rangle, \qquad N = \tilde{M}, \qquad M = E \cap p^* = E(\text{mod}\, p^*).$$

§42. CONVEXITY AND THE HAHN-BANACH THEOREM

We shall give two definitions of convexity: the first of these, the more usual one, which we adopt until the equivalence is proved, is the so-called center of gravity definition; the second is its dual. Both are due in substance to Minkowski, but their equivalence, one of the powerful tools of analysis, is substantially what is now called the Hahn-Banach theorem, or continuation principle, in the new "officialese." Unfortunately, the proof of this principle just fails to be elementary: it needs a substitute for finite mathematical induction that all who enter advanced mathematics today must meet. This is transfinite induction, and it is based on the axiom of choice, without which one cannot really do much in analysis.

(42.1) Definition I. *A real-valued function f, defined in a set E of a linear space, is said to be convex at the point $z = p \in E$, if for every convex combination $\sum a_i z_i$ of sum p, where each $z_i \in E$, we have*

$$\sum a_i f(z_i) \geq f(p).$$

A point p, at which f is convex according to definition I, will be termed a subbarycentric point for f.

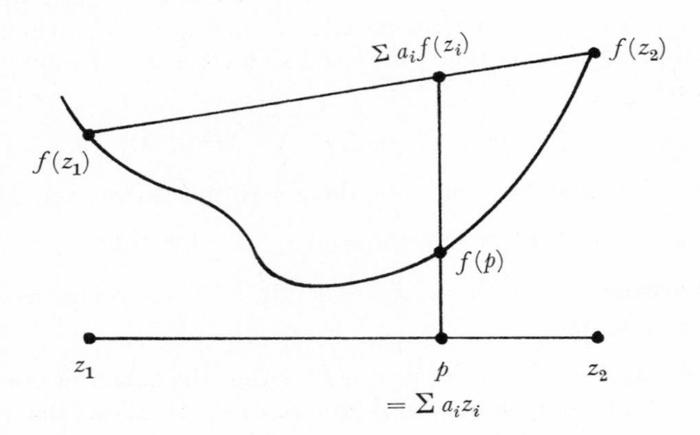

(42.2) Definition II. *A real-valued function f, defined in a set E of a linear space, is said to be convex at the point $z = p \in E$, if there exists a linear function ℓ, defined in a linear subspace that includes the dispersal zone of p in E, such that in this zone we have $\ell \leq f$, with equality at $z = p$.*

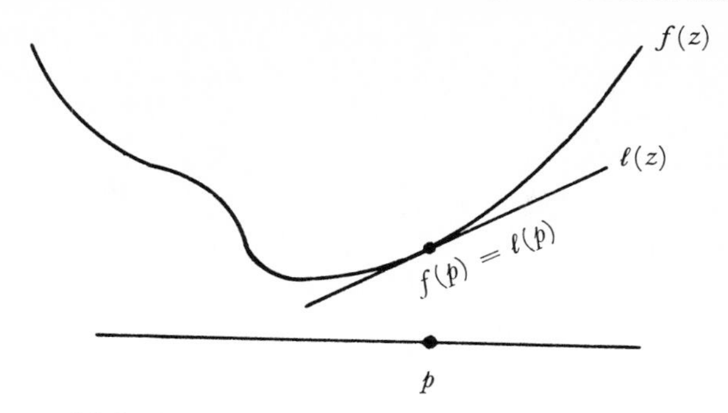

A point p, at which f is convex according to Definition II, will be termed a landing point for f. The corresponding linear function ℓ, which need not be unique, will be termed a landing function for f at this point. (The term supporting linear function, used in the literature, has been discarded).

(42.3) Theorem. *Definitions I and II are equivalent.*

PROOF THAT DEFINITION II IMPLIES DEFINITION I. We have to show that a landing point p is necessarily subbarycentric. Let ℓ be the corresponding landing function, and let $\sum a_i z_i$ be any convex combination of sum p for which each $z_i \in E$. Clearly each $z_i \in E(\bmod p)$, and hence $f(z_i) \geq \ell(z_i)$. Hence

$$\sum a_i f(z_i) \geq \sum a_i \ell(z_i) = \ell(\sum a_i z_i) = \ell(p),$$

and, since $\ell(p) = f(p)$, this shows that p is subbarycentric for f.

The converse implication will be proved later. For the present we adopt definition I.

We shall require some further definitions. Given a real-valued function f, defined in a set E of our vector space, we denote by $\tilde{f}$ and term convex minorant of f the extended real-valued function defined in the convex hull $\tilde{E}$ by writing, for $p \in \tilde{E}$,

$$\tilde{f}(p) = \text{Inf}\left(\sum a_i f(z_i)\right),$$

where the infimum is taken for all convex combinations $\sum a_i z_i$ of sum p, in which each $z_i \in E$.

A set E will be termed convex if $E = \tilde{E}$, and a real-valued function f is termed convex if it is defined in a convex set and $f = \tilde{f}$. We notice further, from the definition of $\tilde{f}$, that f is convex at the point p according to Definition I, if and only if $f(p) = \tilde{f}(p)$.

In general the function $\tilde{f}$ need not be convex: it may take the value $-\infty$, and our definition requires a convex function to be finite. However, we observe that $\tilde{f}$ is convex (Definition I) at any point p at which $\tilde{f}(p) \neq -\infty$. Otherwise there would be a convex combination of points $\tilde{z} \in \tilde{E}$ representing p, for which $\tilde{f}(p)$ would exceed the corresponding center of gravity of the values $\tilde{f}(\tilde{z})$, and therefore we could produce a convex combination of points $z \in E$ representing p, for which, contrary to its definition, the number $\tilde{f}(p)$ would exceed the corresponding center of gravity of the values $f(z)$.

From this remark it follows, in particular, that if $\tilde{f}$ is finite at p, then it is finite in $\tilde{M}$, where $M = E(\bmod p)$, and hence that the restriction of $\tilde{f}$ to the set $\tilde{M}$ is a convex function. This is certainly the case if f is convex at p.

We term cone, with vertex at the origin, a set of points E of our vector space, such that $z \in E$ and $t \geq 0$ together imply $tz \in E$. We term homogeneous a function $f(z)$ defined in a cone E and such that $f(tz) = tf(z)$. (The qualifications "positively" and "of the first order" are to be understood.) In the case of a linear function, this clearly agrees with the definition given in the preceding section, and the cone E then reduces to a vector subspace.

The following remarks are rather obvious:

(42.4) Remarks. (a) *In order that a cone E be convex, it is necessary and sufficient that the relations $z \in E$, $z' \in E$ together imply $z + z' \in E$.* (b) *In order that a homogeneous real-valued function f be convex, it is necessary and sufficient that it be defined on a convex cone E, and that, for every $z \in E$, $z' \in E$, the "subadditivity" relation $f(z + z') \leq f(z) + f(z')$ be satisfied.*

We leave the proof to the reader.

We are now ready to state the theorem from which we shall derive the equivalence of Definitions I and II, as asserted in (42.3).

(42.5) The Hahn-Banach Continuation Principle. *Let f be a convex function defined in a set E of our vector space, and let ℓ be a linear function, defined in a set p of the same space, such that*

$$\ell(z) \leq f(z) \quad \text{for all} \quad z \in E \cap p.$$

Further, let p^* denote the dispersal space of p, generated by E. Then there exists a linear function ℓ^*, defined in p^*, such that $\ell^*(z) = \ell(z)$ for $z \in p$, and that

$$\ell^*(z) \leq f(z) \quad \text{for} \quad z \in E \cap p^*.$$

Proof that (42.5) Implies (42.3). We need only show that the truth of (42.5) implies that Definition II is a consequence of Definition I. Let f_0 be a real-valued function defined in a set E_0 of our vector space, and let $p \in E_0$ be a subbarycentric point for f_0. We shall obtain a linear function ℓ^* defined in the dispersal space p^* of p generated by E_0, such that $\ell^*(z) \leq f_0(z)$ for all z of $E_0 \cap p^*$. We denote by f the restriction of the convex minorant $\tilde{f}_0$ to the convex hull of $E_0 \cap p^*$, which by the dispersal identities is the set $E \cap p^*$, where $E = \tilde{E}_0$. The set $E \cap p^*$ is the dispersal zone of p in E, so that f is a convex function, according to the remark on page 99. Further we have $f(z) \leq f_0(z)$ for $z \in E_0 \cap p^*$. Now the function $\ell(z)$ defined only for $z = p$ by setting it equal to $f(p)$, which is also $f_0(p)$, is a linear function since its set of definition is just one point. According to (42.5), there exists a linear function ℓ^*, defined in p^*, such that $\ell^*(p) = \ell(p)$ and that $\ell^*(z) \leq f(z)$ in $E \cap p^*$. Clearly ℓ^* is the desired linear function, and this completes the proof.

Reduction of (47.5) to a Special Case. We first show that it is no loss of generality to suppose f homogeneous as well as convex, so that f is defined in a convex cone E, and to suppose further that ℓ is homogeneous as well as linear, so that ℓ is defined in a vector subspace p, which contains the origin, and ℓ vanishes at the origin. This is done very simply. We convert the original space into a linear space, by the process of reinterpreting every linear combination $\sum a_i z_i$ as the unitary linear combination obtained by adding the term $a_0 z_0$, where $a_0 = 1 - \sum a_i$, and where z_0 is the old origin. We then enlarge our space by taking a point outside it as a fictitious origin, so that the original space becomes a linear subspace. We then extend the definitions of f and ℓ by homogeneity.

The proof of the homogeneous case of (42.5), to which the general case has thus been reduced, will be based on the following "one step" continuation principle:

(42.6) Lemma of Banach. *Let f be convex and homogeneous, and let E be its cone of definition. Further let ℓ be a homogeneous linear function, defined in a vector subspace p, and* *such that* $\ell(z) \leq f(z)$ *for* $z \in E \cap p$. *Further, let* $z_0 \in E(\text{mod}\, p) - E \cap p$. *Then there exists a homogeneous linear function* $\ell^*(z)$, *defined in* $\langle z_0, p\rangle$, *such that* $\ell^*(z) = \ell(z)$ *for* $z \in p$, *and that* $\ell^*(z) \leq f(z)$ *for* $z \in E \cap \langle z_0, p\rangle$.

PROOF OF (42.6). For $z \in p$ and real t, we shall set $\ell^*(z + tz_0) = \ell(z) + t\alpha$, where α will be chosen presently. This defines ℓ^* in $\langle z_0, p\rangle$, and we have $\ell^*(z) = \ell(z)$ for $z \in p$, so that it only remains to satisfy the condition relating ℓ^* with f. However, if we take account of the special form of ℓ^* and again denote the variable vector of $\langle z_0, p\rangle$ by $z + tz_0$ where $z \in p$, this condition is at once seen to be that, for $z + tz_0 \in E$, we should have

$$\alpha \leq \frac{1}{t}\,[f(z + tz_0) - \ell(z)] \quad \text{if} \quad t > 0,$$

and the opposite inequality if $t < 0$. (For $t = 0$ the condition is already verified by hypothesis.) We now set $z = tz''$ when $t > 0$, and $z = -tz'$ when $t < 0$. By using homogeneity, the inequalities to be verified become

$$\ell(z') - f(z' - z_0) \leq \alpha \leq f(z'' + z_0) - \ell(z''),$$

and they are to hold whenever z', z'' are points of p such that the combinations $z' - z_0$, $z'' + z_0$ lie in the cone E. We denote by u the supremum of the expression on the left, and by v the infimum of that on the right. The inequalities to be verified are then $u \leq \alpha \leq v$, and they can be satisfied, by choice of α, if $v - u \geq 0$. This last will be the case if the stated sets of values of the vectors z', z'' are not empty and if we have, further, for all such values

$$f(z' - z_0) + f(z'' + z_0) \geq \ell(z') + \ell(z'').$$

However, by subadditivity of f and additivity of ℓ [see (42.4)], this inequality is certainly satisfied if $f(z' + z'') \geq \ell(z' + z'')$; this last holds by hypothesis, since the point $z' + z''$ lies in $E \cap p$. (It lies in p because z', z'' do so, and in E because $z' - z_0$, $z'' + z_0$ do.)

It remains to verify that the relevant sets of z', z'' are not empty. As regards z'', the origin $z'' = 0$ is one such point; it lies in p and satisfies $z'' + z_0 \in E$. We still need to find a point $z' \in p$ such that $z' - z_0 \in E$.

By hypothesis, there exist points $z_i \in E$ and positive coefficients c_0, c_i such that the sum $c_0 z_0 + \sum c_i z_i$ is a point of p. By dividing by c_0 we may suppose $c_0 = 1$. Then the point $z' = z_0 + \sum c_i z_i$ lies in p and we have $z' - z_0 = \sum c_i z_i \in E$, since E is a convex cone.

This completes the proof of (42.6).

We can now take stock of the situation. We have yet to prove the homogeneous case of (42.5); instead, we have proved only the one-step continuation lemma (42.6). If our vector space were finite dimensional, we could complete the proof of the homogeneous case of (42.5) by induction. Naturally we do not wish to make any such hypothesis.

As stated at the beginning of this section, our task is thus to find something to replace finite induction, namely "transfinite" induction. This is equivalent to the so-called Zorn lemma, which prospective advanced students meet. For those who are familiar with it or with transfinite induction the rest is an exercise; however, more of this in the next section.

§43. THE CONCEPTUAL HERITAGE OF GEORG CANTOR

We have stressed from the beginning the importance of concepts in contemporary mathematics, and the fact that many of these concepts originated in the calculus of variations. People often ask, "What possible use can concepts have for a practical man?" If this question remains unanswered it may cause a mental barrier, which greatly adds to the difficulty of learning anything new. Therefore we will answer it briefly before passing on to the particular concepts that we need at this stage.

Nearly 150 years ago, engineering students in Paris organized a great protest meeting in which they objected to being made to learn about complex numbers, since these could have no conceivable practical applications. H. Poincaré remarks somewhere (or was it another French mathematician?) that this was about the time of the famous shipwreck of the Méduse, whose survivors suffered unimaginable hardship on a raft, and nearly all died of starvation. Who would have thought that complex numbers would play a part in reducing such sufferings? But they do! Engineers using complex numbers in harmonic analysis devised wireless telegraphy.

Actually, it is abundantly clear that the state of affairs reached at the end of the preceding section needs to be resolved, and that this can only be done conceptually. Moreover, the ability to solve problems conceptually needs to be cultivated, but it is something that cannot be properly tested in any conventional examination, although it is vital in contemporary mathematics. Has anyone ever set an examination in which the candidate is asked to invent a new concept to replace mathematical induction? This is our problem now.

Fortunately for us, in this case we do not have to solve this problem ourselves, for it has already been solved for us. All we have to do is understand the solution found some 75 years ago.

In this one case, the relevant concepts did not arise first in the calculus of variations; in fact, they did not arise out of anything in the previous two thousand years. This is the only known instance where the concepts of one man suddenly gave a whole new direction to mathematics. The man was Georg Cantor. A mathematician, who, at an early age, heard him give a public lecture, once told the author of this book the tremendous impression that Cantor had made on him. Part of the creation of Georg Cantor is of course, set theory, and some of this is now taught in high school and earlier. This is another of the domains of mathematics that many persons once thought could never be of the remotest practical use, and how wrong they were! Elementary sets even find their applications in little collections of murder mysteries. Set theory has well known connections with computer programs, and these affect an untold number of practical projects. However, the part of Cantor's creation that affects us here relates to transfinite numbers and transfinite induction.

Since these notions constitute one of the major mathematical advances of all time, it seems a pity to skimp them. A good place to read about them is Sierpinski's book on cardinal and ordinal numbers, or, if possible, his French monograph of 1928 on transfinite numbers, which is closer to the spirit of Cantor's highly intuitive ideas, and which reads like a novel. Better still, one should read both books and compare them, and also read at least some of Cantor's original papers; it is always best to learn things at first hand. Of course, all this now goes by the name of "naive set theory," and there is a great amount of sophistication to be found in later work, for those who want it. From the point of view of the history of ideas, a good book to read in conjunction with those just cited, is Lusin's French monograph on analytic sets. The reader who elects to read about transfinite numbers in this way will get a great deal of pleasure from doing so, as well as some real insight.

However, for those in a hurry, who desire just the information needed in order to follow the notation and the principal applications, there are many condensed accounts, and this is how most graduate students learn about the subject. (For instance, Chapter XIII of *Real Variables* by Graves.)

In applications, it is usually shorter to employ a procedure equivalent to transfinite induction, but which avoids explicit mention of "transfinite." This procedure was described with many applications by Kuratowski in Volume 3 of the famous journal *Fundamenta Mathematicae*. It had evolved from earlier procedures, some as old as Cantor's theory itself, which had been adopted, in part, as a concession to those unfamiliar with Cantor's concepts. The basic idea was that of a theorem of Hausdorff (Grundzüge der Mengenlehre, Leipzig, 1914). Much later, a corollary that summarizes Kuratowski's procedure was officially recognized by Monsieur Bourbaki (as a souvenir, it is said, of a short trip to Indiana): the "many headed" one decreed that this shortcut to the transfinite be given the status of a (Germanic) "dies irae," and appropriately named Zorn lemma. This is the inescapable lemma that so many graduate students must now meet, while the background, which is so fundamental, is reduced to a minimum.

This compression of mathematics inevitably destroys many of its imaginative and creative aspects. Thus it is that giants are forgotten. Yet this wealth of ideas is still what students need, if they are to grow in stature rather than in sophistry. Nothing of value can be built on shallow foundations.

The story, as well as the work, of Georg Cantor deserves to be remembered. It is indeed a sad one. In his own time, he was declared insane after he had published a pamphlet claiming (as many clergymen now claim) that Christianity is much more beautiful without the virgin birth. Coming after his revolutionary mathematical concepts, this was the last straw. His bitter enemies saw to it that he was kept in one of the terrible institutions of those days for nearly 20 years, until he died.

We shall indicate briefly how the concepts of Cantor complete the proof of (42.5). As stated, the proof will be subject to the axiom of choice. The theory of transfinite numbers makes it possible to give to this axiom the following very strong form:

(43.1) Axiom of Choice. *Any set E can be so ordered that each nonempty subset has a first term.*

A set E which is ordered in accordance with (43.1) is termed well ordered. The statement (43.1), which is generally known as Zermelo's theorem, is the nearest we can get to enumerating the elements of E as we enumerate the positive integers. To enumerate them would make E countable, which is generally not the case.

By adopting this extremely strong form of the axiom of choice, we are, in effect, bypassing transfinite numbers. The fact that we can take as an axiom the possibility of well-ordering an arbitrary set is very remarkable on account of the following principle:

(43.2) Transfinite Induction. *Let $P(x)$ be a property of the element $x \in E$, where E is well ordered, and suppose further:*

(a) *$P(x)$ is true when x is the first term of E.*

(b) *Given $x_0 \in E$, if $P(x)$ is true for every $x < x_0$, then $P(x)$ is true for $x = x_0$.*
Under these assumptions, $P(x)$ is true for every $x \in E$.

(Note. Here and in the sequel, the order relation $<$ is the one according to which E is well ordered.)

To prove (43.2), suppose it false, and let x_0 be the first term of the subset in which $P(x)$ is false. By (a), x_0 is not the first term of E. Further, since it is the first element of the subset, $P(x)$ is true for $x < x_0$; by (b), this implies the truth of $P(x)$ at the term $x = x_0$ of our subset, contrary to the definition of the subset.

We shall not discuss here the philosophical implications of (43.1) and (43.2), nor the sense in which the postulated order $<$ exists. These are important questions affecting the calculus of variations in an abstract setting, since the problem of the calculus of variations is precisely that of determining a first term in a subset. For the present, however, the calculus of variations is still concerned with much more elementary cases. What is clear at this stage is that (43.1) and (43.2) provide a powerful tool for discussing an arbitrary set.

It is convenient to lead up briefly to the inescapable lemma. For this we require the notion of partially ordered set; this is a set in which an order $<$ is given only for certain pairs of elements. The order is transitive, and no element is prior to itself. Subject to (43.1), it is known that every partial order is obtained, by restriction, from an order defined for all pairs, and that it can be so obtained from a whole class of such orders that do not agree for any other pairs. (For references, see Sierpinski's book, p. 188.)

(43.3) Theorem. (*Hausdorff loc cit. p.* 140). *In any partially ordered set, there exists a maximal ordered subset.*

We term an ordered subset maximal if it is not a subset of any other ordered subset. We postpone the proof of (43.3), which will be based on (43.1) and (43.2), and pass on to the following obvious corollary:

(43.4) Zorn Lemma. *Let E be a partially ordered set, such that every ordered subset has an upper bound. Then E has a weak maximal element.*

By a weak maximal element of E, we mean an element $z \in E$ such that the relation $z < x$ does not hold for any $x \in E$. By an upper bound of a subset A of E, we mean an element $z \in E$ such that, for each $y \in A$ for which $y \neq z$, we have $y < z$. To derive (43.4) from (43.3), let A be a maximal ordered subset of E, and let z be an upper bound for A. If z were not a weak maximal element of E, there would be an $x \in E$ such that $z < x$. The element x would clearly satisfy $y < x$ for every $y \in A$, contrary to the definition of A as a maximal ordered subset.

The Zorn lemma is clearly another statement that is of interest in an abstract calculus of variations.

Proof of (42.5). We are now in a position to prove the Hahn-Banach theorem. In fact, as stated, the proof is now a simple exercise in the use of the Zorn lemma. The proof will therefore be subject to (43.3), which we have not yet established, and ultimately subject to the axiom of choice (43.1).

We need treat only the homogeneous case, and we may suppose without loss of generality that p^* is the whole space, so that E coincides with its intersection

$$E \cap p^* = E(\text{mod } p).$$

We consider the set of linear functions λ that are defined in vector subspaces $\Pi \supset p$, and which coincide with ℓ in p, so that, in particular, they all vanish at the origin; and which, further, are subject to the condition

$$\lambda(z) \leq f(z) \quad \text{for} \quad z \in E \cap \Pi.$$

We partially order the set of such functions, by writing $\lambda_1 < \lambda_2$ if $\Pi_1 \subset \Pi_2$, $\Pi_1 \neq \Pi_2$, and if, further, λ_1 coincides with the restriction of λ_2 to Π_1.

Clearly every ordered subset Λ has an upper bound; this is the linear function λ^* defined in the vector subspace $\bigcup \Pi$, where the union is for all $\lambda \in \Lambda$, by setting, $\lambda^*(z) = \lambda(z)$ for any λ such that $z \in \Pi$. Thus by (43.4), the set of λ has a weak maximal element. This clearly contradicts (42.6), unless this element is a linear function defined in the whole vector space. Thus (42.5) is established, subject to (43.3).

Proof of (43.3). We have left this for the last, because it is the only proof of its kind that we shall need.

Let E be the given set and R the partial order. Further, let E be well ordered by $<$, in accordance with (43.1). We write s for any set consisting either of the whole of E or of an element $x \in E$ together with all elements prior to x under $<$; we write $\xi(s)$ for the set that consists of the last term x of s (under $<$), when $s \neq E$.

The set S of such s is then well ordered by the symbol of strict set inclusion, for which we use again $<$. The set S has the last term E. We denote its first term (which consists of the first term of E under $<$) by s_0, and we shall use the letter t to denote, for given $s \in S$, a variable element of S subject to $t < s$.

We now define, for $s \in S$, functions φ, ψ of s such that for each s, $\varphi(s)$ is a maximal ordered subset under R of s, and that

$$\psi(s) = \cup\, \varphi(t) \qquad t < s.$$

(For $s = s_0$, we interpret this to mean that $\psi(s_0)$ is the empty set.) For this purpose, we lay down the following rules:

(a) $\varphi(s_0) = s_0 = \xi(s_0)$

(b) $\varphi(s) = \xi(s) \cup \psi(s)$ if this is a maximal ordered subset of s under R and $s_0 < s$

(c) $\varphi(s) = \psi(s)$ if the condition in (b) is not satisfied, and $s_0 < s$.

It is easy to deduce from (43.2) that each $s \in S$ has the property $P(s)$, that the functions concerned are uniquely defined by the previous rules and that $\varphi(s)$ is a maximal ordered subset of s under R. For this purpose, since $P(s_0)$ is evidently true, we need only verify that, if $P(t)$ is true for all $t < s$, then $P(s)$ is true. Suppose the contrary for a particular $s \neq s_0$.

Then clearly $\psi(s)$ is defined, and, consequently, also $\varphi(s)$, and we must have $\varphi(s) = \psi(s)$. Further $\varphi(s)$ is thus ordered under R, since any two elements of $\varphi(s)$ belong to $\varphi(t)$ for some $t < s$. Since $P(s)$ is false, there is a $t < s$ such that $\xi(t)$ is disjoint from $\varphi(s)$ and $\xi(t) \cup \varphi(s)$ is ordered. Hence if t' is the first such t, we find that on the one hand $\varphi(t') = \psi(t')$, and on the other $\psi(t') \cup \xi(t')$ is a maximal ordered subset of t' under R. This contradicts the rules (b) and (c).

Thus (43.3) is established.

§44. DUALITY OF CONVEX FIGURES

This duality will be important to us in several ways, notably in the definition of Hamiltonians in the large. The z-space is as before, but its origin 0 will affect our definitions. We denote by y an arbitrary real-valued, homogeneous, linear function of z, defined for all z. The space with these y as its points will be termed the dual of our z-space, and its origin is the linear function that vanishes identically. Linear combination of such y is defined in the obvious way. Further, the value taken by the function y at the point z is written as a product yz or zy, indifferently.

From the space of y, with its origin, we define in their turn the homogeneous linear functions u of y, and therefore the dual of y-space, or bidual of z-space, with the u as its points. Among these linear functions u we shall have, in particular, each function of y of the form zy, where z is in our original z-space. In our product notation, these are the functions u of y for which $uy = zy$ for all y, and we say that each such u reduces to a point z. If every u is so expressible, we say that the original z-space is reflexive.

In z-space, we term ray a half-line ℓ issuing from 0 and including the point 0. We term convex figure about 0, or simply convex figure, a convex set E whose intersection with each ray is a finite closed segment. One extremity of this segment is clearly the origin 0; this follows from convexity of the intersection of E with the line containing two opposite rays. The second extremity is termed the frontier point of E on the ray in question, and generally a point z is termed a frontier point of E, if it is the frontier point on the ray from 0 through z. More generally still, if z is any point other than 0, the frontier point on the ray through z has the form λz where $\lambda > 0$, and we set $Q(z) = 1/\lambda$; we complete the definition by writing $Q(0) = 0$. The function Q thus defined is termed function of distance of the convex figure E.

(44.1) Remark. (i) *The function of distance is positive definite, homogeneous and convex.* (ii) *Conversely, any homogeneous, convex, positive definite function $Q(z)$, defined for all z, is the function of distance of a convex figure E, and E is then necessarily the set of z for which $Q(z) \leq 1$.*

PROOF. Let E be a convex figure, and let $Q(z)$ be the function of distance. Clearly E is then the set of z for which $Q(z) \leq 1$, since E has, with each ray, the same intersection as this set. This disposes of the last part of (ii). Clearly, also, $Q(z) > 0$ for $z \neq 0$; in other words, Q is positive definite. Further, to verify that $Q(tz) = tQ(z)$ for $t > 0$, we need only observe that if z is replaced by tz, the frontier point λz remains fixed, so that λ becomes λ/t. Again, if $z = z' + z''$ and

$$Q(z) = 1/\lambda, \qquad Q(z') = 1/\lambda', \qquad Q(z'') = 1/\lambda'',$$

we have

$$\frac{\lambda'\lambda''}{\lambda' + \lambda''}\, z = \left(\frac{\lambda''}{\lambda' + \lambda''}\right) \lambda' z' + \left(\frac{\lambda'}{\lambda' + \lambda''}\right) \lambda'' z''.$$

The point ζ, defined by the left hand side, which lies on the ray through z, is thus a convex combination of the points $\lambda' z'$, $\lambda'' z''$ of E; hence ζ, by convexity, belongs to E and so to the segment from 0 to λz. This requires

$$\lambda \geq \frac{\lambda'\lambda''}{\lambda' + \lambda''}, \qquad \text{i.e.,} \quad \frac{1}{\lambda} \leq \frac{1}{\lambda'} + \frac{1}{\lambda''},$$

which proves subadditivity, and so convexity, of the homogeneous function Q. Thus (i) is established. Finally, to justify the initial assertion of (ii), where Q is now any homogeneous convex positive definite function, we define E as the set of z for which $Q(z) \leq 1$ and we easily verify that E is then a convex figure with Q as its function of distance. This completes the proof of (44.1).

In the sequel, it will sometimes be convenient to picture the points y of the dual space by hyperplanes of the original z-space. Any such hyperplane is defined as the set of z for which some real-valued linear function $\ell(z)$ other than a constant assumes a constant value. We may suppose, by subtracting the constant $\ell(0)$ if necessary, that $\ell(z)$ is homogeneous, and we shall consider only those hyperplanes Π which do not contain 0: we term them polar hyperplanes in z-space. By dividing $\ell(z)$ by a suitable constant, we see that each polar hyperplane Π is associated with exactly one point y of the dual space, such that Π is the set of z for which $yz = 1$. The point y is termed the pole of Π, and conversely Π is termed the polar of y. Similarly, we can introduce polar hyperplanes of y-space, and associate them with points u of the bidual space, which reduces to the original z-space if the latter is reflexive.

Given a convex figure E, we term nonseparating a hyperplane Π defined by an equation $\ell(z) = c$ if the two "open" half-spaces $\ell(z) < c$, $\ell(z) > c$ do not both contain points of E. Clearly, a nonseparating hyperplane Π cannot pass through 0. It is therefore a polar hyperplane, and can be specified by its pole y.

Among the nonseparating hyperplanes Π, we single out those that intersect E: we term them landing hyperplanes. (We object to the current term "supporting" hyperplanes, which conflicts with the other uses of "support".) It is easy to see that a point of E on a landing hyperplane is always a frontier point of E. Conversely, we derive from the Hahn-Banach theorem:

(44.2) Remark. *Through any frontier point of a convex figure E, there must pass at least one landing hyperplane.*

PROOF. Let z_0 be a frontier point and G the line joining it to the origin. In G we define a linear function ℓ_0 by setting $\ell_0(tz_0) = t$ for all real t. On the ray through z_0, this function clearly coincides with the function of distance Q of the figure E, and so does not exceed Q. On the opposite ray, ℓ_0 is negative and Q positive. Thus $\ell_0(z) \leq Q(z)$ in G. By the Hahn-Banach theorem, ℓ_0 has a continuation, which we denote provisionally by the same letter, and which is now defined in the whole z-space, such that $\ell_0(z) \leq Q(z)$ for all z. Since ℓ_0 is still linear, and moreover vanishes at 0, we may identify it with a point y_0 of the dual space. We note that, on the one hand, $y_0 z_0 = 1$, and on the other hand, since $y_0 z \leq Q(z)$, we have $y_0 z \leq 1$ whenever $z \in E$. Therefore the hyperplane Π, given by $y_0 z = 1$, is a landing hyperplane through z_0. This proves our assertion.

By the dual F of a convex figure E we shall mean the set of the poles y of non-separating hyperplanes Π. It clearly consists of those y for which $yz \leq 1$ whenever $z \in E$. (To see this we must bear in mind that the point $z = 0$ lies in E, and that at this point we do not have $yz \geq 1$.)

(44.3) Theorem. (i) *The dual F of a convex figure E of z-space is a convex figure of y-space.* (ii) *If $Q(z)$, $H(y)$ denote, respectively, the functions of distance of E, F, we have*

$$\textbf{(44.4)}\qquad \begin{cases} \text{(a) } \textit{for all } y, & H(y) = \sup\limits_{z \in E} yz; \\ \text{(b) } \textit{for all } z, & Q(z) = \sup\limits_{y \in F} yz; \\ \text{(c) } \textit{for all } y,\ z, & yz \leq H(y)Q(z). \end{cases}$$

(iii) *The supremum, which gives $Q(z)$ in (44.4) (b), is attained for some $y = y_0 \in F$; moreover, if z-space is reflexive, the supremum, which gives $H(y)$ in (44.4)(a), is attained for some $z = z_0 \in E$.*

PROOF. We find it convenient to define H in the first instance, not as stated in (ii), but by the formula (44.4)(a). We can then at once verify its homogeneity and convexity, since we clearly have, on the one hand, $H(ty) = tH(y)$ for $t \geq 0$, and on the other hand,

$$H(y_1 + y_2) \leq \sup_{z \in E} y_1 z + \sup_{z \in E} y_2 z = H(y_1) + H(y_2).$$

This being so, let y_- be any y for which $H(y) \leq 0$. Then $zy_- \leq 0$ for each $z \in E$, and therefore, by homogeneity, for each z of z-space. By passing from z to $-z$, it follows that $zy_- = 0$ for all z, so that y_- can only be the linear function 0, i.e., the origin of the dual space. Thus H is positive definite.

It now follows from (44.4) that H is the function of distance of the set $H(y) \leq 1$, i.e., of the set F, and therefore that F is a convex figure. Further, by our definition (44.4)(a) of H, we have, for $\lambda z \in E$, $(\lambda z)y \leq H(y)$, and we derive (44.4)(c) (where we may suppose $z \neq 0$) by taking $\lambda = 1/Q(z)$.

It remains to establish (44.4)(b) and to show that the supremum is there attained. (The other assertion in (iii) then follows by symmetry.) We may suppose $z \neq 0$, and, by homogeneity, we need only treat the case in which z is subject to $Q(z) = 1$, i.e., in which z is a frontier point z_0. By (44.4)(c), which we proved above, we have $yz_0 \leq 1$ for every $y \in F$, while by (44.2) there exists $y_0 \in F$ such that $y_0 z_0 = 1$. Thus the supremum in question is 1, which is the value of $Q(z_0)$. This completes the proof.

We see, incidentally, that when z-space is reflexive or, in particular, Euclidean, the relation of a convex figure to its dual is reciprocal, and we term such figures (and their functions of distance) polar transforms of one another.

§45. DUALITY OF CONVEX FUNCTIONS

We term finite below an extended real valued function that is not the constant $+\infty$ and never takes the value $-\infty$. We modify our definition of convexity to apply to functions finite below; such a function f will now be termed convex if for each point z_0, the number $f(z_0)$ is the supremum of the values at z_0 of the finite convex functions which nowhere exceed f. Equivalently, $f(z_0)$ is then the supremum of the values at z_0 of the linear functions which nowhere exceed f; for, by Definition II of convexity, each of the finite convex functions in question has at z_0 the same value as a linear function which nowhere exceeds it. From this last remark we derive the following one:

(45.1) Remark. *A function finite below is convex if and only if it is expressible as the supremum of a family of linear functions.*

We pass on to define and discuss duality for convex functions. As we shall see, it is essential to interpret convexity in the more general sense just defined, applicable to functions finite below, as otherwise the symmetry of our relations will be completely disturbed.

We still keep to a fixed origin of z-space, as this fixes also the dual space. However, Q no longer denotes a function of distance, but an arbitrary convex function finite below, defined for all z. The dual of Q, which we also term its Legendre transform, will now be understood to mean the function H, defined in our dual space by the expression

$$H(y) = \operatorname*{Sup}_z \{yz - Q(z)\}.$$

In the case in which Q is a function of distance, this dual is quite distinct from the polar transform considered in the preceding section. Quite generally we have, however, a result analogous to (44.3). To bring out the analogy, we incorporate the definition of dual in our statement under (45.3)(a).

(45.2) Theorem. (i) *The dual of a convex function Q finite below, defined in z-space is a convex function H finite below, defined in y-space.* (ii) *We have*

$$\text{(45.3)} \qquad \begin{cases} \text{(a) } \textit{for all } y, & H(y) = \operatorname*{Sup}_z \{yz - Q(z)\}; \\ \text{(b) } \textit{for all } z, & Q(z) = \operatorname*{Sup}_y \{yz - H(y)\}; \\ \text{(c) } \textit{for all } y, z, & yz \le H(y) + Q(z). \end{cases}$$

(iii) *In the case in which Q is finite valued, the supremum in* (45.3)(b) *is attained for some $y = y_0$ depending on z. Similarly, if z-space is reflexive and H is finite valued, the supremum in* (45.3)(a) *is attained for some $z = z_0$ depending on y.*

Proof. The fact that H is a convex function finite below follows from (45.1), since (45.3)(a) defines H as the supremum of a family of linear functions of y. This proves (i). Moreover, (45.3)(c) is clearly a consequence of the definition (45.3)(a). Thus (ii) reduces to the proof of (45.3)(b). It is enough to show that, given any z_0 and any finite real a less than $Q(z_0)$, there exists a y_0 for which $y_0 z - H(y_0) \geq a$. Now, by (45.1) there is a linear function $\ell_0(z)$ which nowhere exceeds $Q(z)$, such that $\ell_0(z_0) > a$. We may put this linear function in the form $\ell_0(z_0) + y_0(z - z_0)$ where y_0 is in our dual space. Then

$$Q(z) \geq \ell_0(z_0) + y_0(z - z_0) \geq a + y_0(z - z_0).$$

It follows that for all z, $y_0 z - Q(z) \leq y_0 z_0 - a$, and, passing to the supremum in z, we find that $H(y_0) \leq y_0 z_0 - a$, i.e., that $a \leq y_0 z_0 - H(y_0)$, as required. This proves (45.3)(b), or, more precisely, shows that $Q(z_0)$ does not exceed the supremum in question, while the opposite inequality follows from (45.3)(c). Thus (ii) is disposed of. It remains to prove (iii), and by symmetry we need only treat the supremum in (45.3)(b). Q is now finite-valued by hypothesis, so that given any point z_0, Definition II of convexity at z_0 requires the existence of a linear function $\ell_0(z)$ such that $Q(z_0) = \ell_0(z_0)$ and that $Q(z) \geq l_0(z)$ for all z. By the former of these relations, we may set

$$\ell_0(z) = Q(z_0) + y_0(z - z_0)$$

where y_0 is in the dual space. We thus have

$$Q(z) \geq Q(z_0) + y_0(z - z_0); \quad \text{i.e.,} \quad y_0 z - Q(z) \leq y_0 z_0 - Q(z_0).$$

By definition of H, this last implies $H(y_0) = y_0 z_0 - Q(z_0)$; i.e.,

$$Q(z_0) = y_0 z_0 - H(y_0).$$

Further, by (45.3)(c),

$$Q(z_0) \geq y z_0 - H(y) \quad \text{for all } y.$$

Hence the supremum of the right hand side is attained for $y = y_0$ as asserted.

The reader will observe that the definition of H makes sense if we omit the convexity assumption on Q, and that both (45.3)(c) and the statement that H is a convex function finite below remain valid. In that case, however, H turns out to be the dual of a certain convex function finite below, namely the greatest such not to exceed Q. We can find this function by passing to the bidual, as in (45.3)(b).

We conclude this section with a few examples.

(1) Let E, F be dual convex figures, and let Q be the function of distance of E. Then Q is a finite convex function, and a rather smooth one, but we shall see that its Legendre transform is merely finite below; in fact it is the function that vanishes in F and is $+\infty$ elsewhere. (This type of thing partly accounts for the eerie feeling one can get in working with Hamiltonians and duality.) To verify that the Legendre transform vanishes in F, it is enough to observe that for any $y_0 \in F$ the expression $y_0 z - Q(z)$ cannot exceed 0 by (44.4)(c), and that it vanishes for $z = 0$. To verify that it is $+\infty$ for any y_0 outside F we observe similarly that there then exists a point z for which $y_0 z > Q(z)$; by replacing z by tz and making $t \to \infty$ we can thus make the difference $y_0 z - Q(z)$ as large as we please, so that the supremum is $+\infty$.

(2) In place of the function Q of the preceding example, we now consider the function $Q^* = \frac{1}{2}Q^2$. The Legendre transform H^* of Q^* is then $\frac{1}{2}H^2$ where H is now the polar transform of Q. To verify this, we evaluate by Theorem (44.3) the supremum of yz for $Q(z) = t$ and find that its value is $tH(y)$; hence the supremum of $yz - \frac{1}{2}Q^2(z)$ in z is the supremum in t of the expression

$$tH(y) - \tfrac{1}{2}t^2 = \tfrac{1}{2}H^2(y) - \tfrac{1}{2}\{t - H(y)\}^2,$$

which is clearly $\frac{1}{2}H^2(y)$.

(3) More generally, let Φ be a convex function finite below, on the real line, such that $\Phi(0) = 0$, and let Ψ be its dual. We form $Q^* = \Phi(Q)$, $H^* = \Psi(H)$, where Q, H are as before. Then H^* is the Legendre transform of Q^*. The proof is left to the reader. Here (45.3)(c) becomes $yz \leq \Phi(Q(z)) + \Psi(H(y))$. This is weaker than (44.4)(c), since $QH \leq \Phi(Q) + \Psi(H)$.

§46. HAMILTONIANS IN THE LARGE AND REFORMULATED VARIATIONAL THEORY

In this section, the dual z and y spaces will now be Euclidean, and so reflexive, and we identify z with $\dot{x}$. Given a nonparametric Lagrangian $\underline{L}(t, x, \dot{x})$, let $Q(z)$ be the function obtained by fixing t, x and setting $\dot{x} = z$, and let $H(y)$ be the Legendre transform of $Q(z)$; the function H can be regarded as a function of (t, x, y), and written $\underline{H}(t, x, y)$: we term this function $\underline{H}(t, x, y)$ the nonparametric Hamiltonian in the large, corresponding to $\underline{L}(t, x, \dot{x})$. Similarly, given a parametric Lagrangian $\underline{L}(x, \dot{x})$, let $Q(z)$ be the function obtained by fixing x and setting $\dot{x} = z$; we denote by $\underline{H}(x, y)$ the function which, for fixed x is the polar transform of $Q(z)$: we term $\_(x, y)$ the standard parametric Hamiltonian in the large, corresponding to the Lagrangian $\underline{L}(x, \dot{x})$. The words parametric, standard, nonparametric and in the large will at times be omitted. We note that our definitions here assume that $Q(z)$ is a convex function and, in the parametric case, that $Q(z)$ is positive definite. The convexity requirement is clearly satisfied by Taylor's formula with remainder and Definition II of convexity if we suppose that $\underline{L}$ fulfills the Legendre condition for the nonparametric or parametric form.

(46.1) Theorem. *Suppose the Lagrangian $\underline{L}$ continuously twice differentiable. In the nonparametric case, suppose further that the matrix $\underline{L}_{\dot{x}\dot{x}}$ of second derivatives in $\dot{x}$ is positive definite. In the parametric case, suppose that $\underline{L}$ is positive definite and fulfills the parametric Legendre condition of Section 41. Then the local and in the large definitions of Hamiltonian agree near each point (t, x, y) or (x, y) for which y has the form $\underline{L}_{\dot{x}}$. By homogeneity, this is so at every point (x, y) in the parametric case; while in the nonparametric case, they agree and y has the form $\underline{L}_{\dot{x}}$, near any point (t, x, y) at which the Hamiltonian in the large is finite.*

Proof. We may ignore the parametric case: by Section 41 and Example 2 of Section 45, it reduces to the nonparametric one, with $\frac{1}{2}\underline{L}^2$ as its Lagrangian. In the nonparametric case, let $\underline{K}$ be, near (t_0, x_0, y_0), the local Hamiltonian, where y_0 is of the stated form. At all near points (t, x, y), the quantity y still has the stated form $\underline{L}_{\dot{x}}$; in fact $\dot{x}$ is simply $\underline{K}_y$. Hence the linear function of z, given by the expression $zy - \underline{K}(t, x, y)$, is tangent at $z = \dot{x}$ to the convex function of z given by $\underline{L}(t, x, z)$. Since this tangent, by convexity, lies below the graph of $\underline{L}$, we thus have for all z,

$$\underline{L}(t, x, z) \geq zy - \underline{K}; \quad \text{i.e.,} \quad \underline{K} \geq zy - \underline{L}(t, x, z),$$

with equality when $z = \dot{x}$. Therefore $\underline{K}$ coincides with the supremum, which defines our Hamiltonian in the large at (t, x, y). To complete the proof of our statement, it only remains to observe that at any point (t, x, y) at which the Hamiltonian in the large is finite, the maximum of $yz - \underline{L}(t, x, z)$ in z is attained for some $z = \dot{x}$ according to (iii) of Theorem (45.2), and by the elementary theory of maxima and minima we then have $y = \underline{L}_{\dot{x}}$.

An immediate consequence of Theorem (46.1) and of the symmetry of Legendre transforms, or polar transforms, in a reflexive space is that we can now determine the

Lagrangian $\underline{L}$ as soon as we know its dual, the Hamiltonian $\underline{H}$. We can therefore eliminate the Lagrangian from the statement of our problem and regard the Hamiltonian as the primary function, just as it is in the theory of partial differential equations. This assumes $\underline{L}$ finite and convex in $\dot{x}$, and positive definite in the parametric case.

By Theorems (45.2) and (44.3) our problem becomes, in the nonparametric, and in the parametric cases, respectively,

$$\textbf{(46.2)} \qquad \begin{cases} \text{(a)} \displaystyle\int \operatorname*{Max}_{y} \{\dot{x}y - \underline{H}(t, x, y)\}\, dt = \text{Min.} \\[2ex] \text{(b)} \displaystyle\int \operatorname*{Max}_{y} \{\dot{x}y/\underline{H}(x, y)\}\, dt = \text{Min.} \end{cases}$$

In this minimax formulation, we suppose specified which functions $x(t)$, subject to given end conditions, are admissible. We then term suitable a pair of functions $x(t), y(t)$, if $x(t)$ is admissible, and if, for $x = x(t)$, the relevant expression

$$\textbf{(46.3)} \qquad \text{(a)}\ \dot{x}y - \underline{H}(t, x, y), \quad \text{or} \quad \text{(b)}\ \dot{x}y/\underline{H}(x, y)$$

assumes its maximum in y when $y = y(t)$. Our problem is then to seek, for the class of suitable pairs $x(t), y(t)$, the minimum of the integral of the expression (46.3)(a) or (b).

There is an alternative formulation as a conditioned minimum. When $\underline{H}$ is continuously differentiable and the maximum in (46.3)(a) is attained, the elementary theory of maxima and minima shows that $\dot{x} = \underline{H}_y$. Conversely this relation implies that the maximum is attained, since $\underline{H}$ is convex in y, so that the graph of $\underline{H}$ cannot have parallel tangent hyperplanes. Similar remarks apply to (46.3)(b), provided the maximum is there unity; i.e., t is the standard geodesic parameter. Hence we can state our problem as that of the minimum of the integral of (46.3)(a) or (b), subject to the differential equation $\dot{x} = \underline{H}_y$, provided that in (b) we choose for t the standard geodesic parameter.

In this new form, we have a variational problem with a subsidiary relation of the type that we shall meet in optimal control. It is in some respects more delicate than our original problem in terms of its Lagrangian, particularly in regard to necessary conditions.

However, one must never be deterred by superficial difficulties. Necessary conditions have, as the reader realizes by now, heuristic value at most, without an existence theory. With our new formulation we do not even need them to make a guess, since the argument becomes so much closer to Cauchy's method of characteristics. Thus, from the point of view of our sufficiency theory, the new formulation is to be preferred. Incidentally, it allows some economy in smoothness: twice continuous differentiability for $\underline{H}$, instead of three times for $\underline{L}$, and less essential use of the nonsingularity assumption for the matrix $\underline{L}_{\dot{x}\dot{x}}$ or $\underline{H}_{yy}$. We can even cover certain cases in which $\underline{L}$ is not continuously differentiable, for instance when $\underline{L}$ has the form $\varphi(t, x)\psi(\dot{x})$, where φ is twice continuously differentiable, and $\psi(z)$ is the greater of z^2, $2 - z^2$; or, in the parametric case, when $\underline{L}$ has an indicatrix whose shape is that of the figure $\underline{F}$ in Section 24 of Chapter II. We sketch the theory briefly.

We term conjugate slope function a vector function $q(t, x)$ (we consider only the nonparametric case) such that the substitution $y = q$ makes $y\, dx - \underline{H}\, dt$ an exact differential dS, and we write $\underline{\mathscr{I}}(C)$ for the integral (46.2)(a) along a curve C. From the definition of the integrand as a maximum in y, it is clear that

$$\underline{\mathscr{I}}(C) \geq \int_C dS \tag{46.4}$$

and that equality holds only when C satisfies the differential equation $\dot{x} = \underline{\mathrm{H}}_y$ for $y = q$. This remark takes the place of the algorithm of Chapter I, Section 12. The further discussion of exactness and Lagrange brackets now proceeds without introducing $\underline{\mathrm{L}}$; we need only follow the form of the argument in Chapter II, Section 23.

§47. REMARKS ON CLASSICAL INEQUALITIES

The basic inequalities are that of the definition (42.1) of convexity and those of (44.4)(c) and (45.3)(c), which are virtually the definitions of polar and Legendre transforms. These three types are general forms of Minkowski's inequality (all inequalities are really Minkowski's), Schwarz's inequality (of course known much earlier), and Young's inequality (W. H.—not L. C.). The classical inequalities are special cases obtained by verifying that a certain function is convex and by calculating its transforms. Deeper or more elaborate inequalities and applications of convexity will be found in the literature on inequalities, Diophantine approximation, and related topics. There are also inequalities in complex function theory and in the theory of harmonic and subharmonic functions, in the theory of partial differential equations, and so on. We shall limit ourselves to the classical inequalities.

In the following brief discussion we use five simple rules:

(a) Let φ be a continuously twice differentiable real function of a real variable u, subject to $\varphi''(u) > 0$ for all u; then φ is convex.

(b) Suppose that φ, ψ are convex functions; then so are the function $\varphi + \psi$ and Max (φ, ψ).

(c) Let f be a convex function, and let φ be an increasing convex function of the real variable u; then $\varphi(f)$ is convex.

(d) Let f be a convex function; then the set of x for which $f(x) \leq 1$ is a convex set.

(e) Suppose that the real positive definite function f satisfies the following two conditions: $f(tx) = tf(x)$ for $t \geq 0$, and the set of x for which $f(x) \leq 1$ is a convex set with the origin as an interior point; then f is convex.

In the above rules, functions are defined in Euclidean n-space unless otherwise specified. The last rule follows at once from the definition of function of distance; the others are immediate consequences of the notion of convexity.

We note that (a) implies convexity of the exponential function. Hence

$$\exp\left(\sum \alpha_i u_i\right) \leq \sum \alpha_i(\exp u_i) \qquad \left(\alpha_i \geq 0, \sum \alpha_i = 1\right).$$

In this, we set $\exp u_i = a_i$. We obtain

$$\prod a_i^{\alpha_i} \leq \sum \alpha_i a_i \qquad \left(a_i \geq 0, \alpha_i \geq 0, \sum \alpha_i = 1\right). \tag{47.1}$$

This is known as the inequality of arithmetic and geometric means (Theorem 19 of Hardy, Littlewood and Polya, p. 17). The cases of equality can be discussed by the same method.

We pass on to Minkowski's inequality for powers (Theorem 24, p. 30, of the same reference). We set $x = (x_1, \ldots, x_n)$, and we note that the linear function of x, given by the ν-th coordinate x_ν, is of course convex; the same is true of $-x_\nu$, and therefore, by (b) of $|x_\nu|$, whence, by (c), the function $|x_\nu|^p$ is convex for $p \geq 1$. Hence by (b) $\sum_\nu |x_\nu|^p$ is a convex function of x for $p \geq 1$; consequently, by (d), the set of x for which $\sum_\nu |x_\nu|^p \leq 1$ is a convex set, and therefore by (e) the function

$$f(x) = (\sum_\nu |x_\nu|^p)^{1/p},$$

which is homogeneous, is convex, and so subadditive. Hence finally

$$\textbf{(47.2)} \qquad (\sum |x_\nu + y_\nu|^p)^{1/p} \leq (\sum |x_\nu|^p)^{1/p} + (\sum |y_\nu|^p)^{1/p} \qquad (p \geq 1).$$

This is the desired inequality.

For the same function $f(x)$, we now calculate the polar transform $H(y)$. For simplicity we suppose $p > 1$, and we write $q = p/(p-1)$, so that $\dfrac{1}{p} + \dfrac{1}{q} = 1$.

We first observe that the hyperplane tangent to the locus $\sum |x_\nu|^p = 1$ at $x_\nu = a_\nu$ has the form $\sum y_\nu x_\nu = 1$ where $y_\nu = |a_\nu|^{p-1} \operatorname{sgn} a_\nu$ and where sgn (u) means the sign of the real u; i.e., ± 1 or 0. By continuity we need only verify this when all the a_ν are different from 0, and this reduces to the remark that the function $|u|^p = (u^2)^{p/2}$ has the derivative

$$\frac{p}{2}(u^2)^{(p/2)-1} 2u = p\,|u|^{p-1} \operatorname{sgn}(u)$$

for $u \neq 0$. Now since the set $(\sum |x_\nu|^p)^{1/p} \leq 1$ is convex, the landing hyperplanes are tangent at frontier points. Hence the function

$$H(y) = \operatorname*{Sup}_x xy \quad \text{for} \quad f(x) \leq 1, \quad \text{where} \quad f(x) = (\sum |x_\nu|^p)^{1/p},$$

has the value 1 if y has the form $|a_\nu|^{p-1} \operatorname{sgn} a_\nu$ where the a_ν satisfy $\sum |a_\nu|^p = 1$; moreover the supremum in question is then attained for $x_\nu = a_\nu$. In other words, when y has the stated form, we have $H(y) = 1$ provided that $\sum |a_\nu|^p = 1$, i.e., provided $\sum |y_\nu|^q = 1$. Since every y may be so expressed, we find that H is the function of distance of the set of y for which $\sum |y_\nu|^q \leq 1$, so that $H(y) = (\sum |y_\nu|^q)^{1/q}$.

Thus (44.4)(c) becomes in our case

$$\textbf{(47.3)} \qquad xy \leq (\sum |x_\nu|^p)^{1/p}(\sum |y_\nu|^q)^{1/q} \qquad \left(p > 1,\ q > 1,\ \frac{1}{p} + \frac{1}{q} = 1\right).$$

This is known as Holder's inequality (Theorem 13 of Hardy, Littlewood and Polya, p. 24). The cases of equality and the limiting cases $p = 1$, $q = \infty$ and $p = \infty$, $q = 1$ can be treated similarly.

We shall not go into the corresponding special cases of Young's inequality, which are partly covered by Example 3 of Section 45, page 108.

§48. THE DUAL UNIT BALL OF A FUNCTIONAL SPACE

We shall require later some properties of a particular vector-space and of its dual. They are analogues of rather obvious properties of Euclidean space, except that now the relation of a certain convex figure (the unit ball) to its dual need not be reciprocal. The space in question is the first functional space that was studied, and the one most naturally arising in the calculus of variations. It is the space $\mathscr{C}_0(A)$, whose elements are continuous real functions $f(x)$, defined in a fixed bounded closed

Euclidean set A. (If we prefer to free ourselves of all Euclidean hypotheses, A can be a $B \cdot \cdot i$ compact subset of a complete metric space; see below, after Theorem (48.1). In the meantime, our terminology is limited to the Euclidean case.)

Our elements f constitute a vector-space because any linear combination of them with constant coefficients is again an element. In this space, we define as the norm $|f|$ of a vector f, the maximum for $x \in A$ of the absolute value $|f(x)|$. The norm is a function of distance in accordance with Section 44, since for constant real t and for any elements f, f_1, f_2 of $\mathscr{C}_0(A)$ we have

$$|tf| = |t| \cdot |f|, \qquad |f_1 + f_2| \leq |f_1| + |f_2|.$$

The corresponding convex set, given by $|f| \leq 1$, is termed the unit ball U of $\mathscr{C}_0(A)$.

On account of the symmetry relation $|f| = |-f|$, we can metrize $\mathscr{C}_0(A)$ by choosing as the distance of any two elements f_1, f_2 the quantity $|f_2 - f_1|$. In any metric space, a sequence of elements f_n $n = 1, 2, \ldots$, is termed intrinsically convergent if the distance of f_n, f_m tends to 0 as n, m both tend to ∞; it is termed convergent to an element f if the distance of f_n, f tends to 0 as $n \to \infty$; the space is said to be complete if the notions of convergence and of intrinsic convergence coincide. In $\mathscr{C}_0(A)$, intrinsic convergence of the f_n amounts to uniform convergence in A of the $f_n(x)$; as proved in any advanced calculus, there is a continuous limit-function $f(x)$; thus $\mathscr{C}_0(A)$ is a complete metric space with the topology of uniform convergence, and we have relations of the form

$$\text{Lim}\,(a_1 f_1 + a_2 f_2) = (\text{Lim}\,a_1)(\text{Lim}\,f_1) + (\text{Lim}\,a_2)(\text{Lim}\,f_2)$$

when the elements and coefficients describe convergent sequences.

This uniform topology for $\mathscr{C}_0(A)$ corresponds in the calculus of variations to our wide topology, while our former narrow neighborhoods correspond to a second topology, here needed also, which can be applied only to those elements of $\mathscr{C}_0(A)$ that are continuously differentiable. Moreover, since A is not open, continuous differentiability does not concern the elements $f \in \mathscr{C}_0(A)$ directly, but concerns their extensions to open sets. Here, for convenience, we consider only such extensions $\hat{f}(x)$ to open sets which contain the convex hull $\hat{A}$ of A. We write $\mathscr{C}_1(A)$ for the class of functions $f \in \mathscr{C}_0(A)$ that possess such continuously differentiable extensions, and $\mathscr{P}$ for the countable subclass, consisting of polynomials with rational coefficients. A continuous function, defined in A, is the uniform limit of a polynomial (Weierstrass approximation theorem, proved in most advanced calculus books), and so, of one belonging to $\mathscr{P}$. Thus:

(48.1) Theorem. *$\mathscr{P} \subset \mathscr{C}_1(A)$ is dense in $\mathscr{C}_0(A)$.*

In $\mathscr{C}_1(A)$ we define a dashed norm $|f|'$ as the least real $k \geq 0$, such that, for some continuously differentiable extension $\hat{f}$ of f to an open set $\supset \hat{A}$, we have, for all $x \in \hat{A}$, on the one hand $|\hat{f}(x)| \leq k$, and on the other $|D\hat{f}(x)| \leq k$, where $D\hat{f}$ is the gradient of $\hat{f}$. We term dashed unit ball, and denote by U', the set of $f \in \mathscr{C}_1(A)$ for which $|f|' \leq 1$.

In a complete metric space, a set E is termed sequentially compact if, for each sequence of its elements, there is a convergent subsequence. If, in addition, E is closed, in honour of Bourbaki we term it $B \cdot \cdot i$ compact, or bicompact, as it used to be, so that all are happy as in a game of musical chairs.† (When A is merely $B \cdot \cdot i$ compact,

† In one version of this game, ladies sit on gentlemen's laps, but get up and move when the music starts. When the music stops, they frequently manage to sit on the same gentleman's lap as before.

$\mathscr{C}_1(A)$ is replaced by the class of f which satisfy, for some K_f and all pairs x_1, x_2 in A, the condition $|f(x_2) - f(x_1)| \le K_f \cdot |x_2 - x_1|$. The dashed norm is taken to be the greater of $|f|$ and of the least such K_f. The countable dense subset $\mathscr{P}$ can be taken to consist of rational linear combinations of functions of the form $\varphi_{ab}(|x - c|)$, where a, b are rationals subject to $0 < a < b$, while c ranges in a countable dense subset of A, and where $\varphi_{ab}(r)$ is defined for $r \ge 0$ to be linear for $a \le r \le b$ and to take the constant values 1 for $r \le a$, and 0 for $r \ge b$.) In Euclidean space, the sequentially compact sets are known to be the bounded sets (Principle of Bolzano-Weierstrass).

In $\mathscr{C}_0(A)$, one of the earliest results, and, as we shall see in the next Chapter, one of the first to be applied to the calculus of variations, characterized the sequentially compact sets. For this, we term a set of functions $f(x)$ $x \in A$ equicontinuous if, given $\varepsilon > 0$, there exists $\delta > 0$ (where δ does not depend on f), such that for every f in the set and for every pair of points x_1, x_2 of A, whose distance is $<\delta$, we have $|f(x_2) - f(x_1)| < \varepsilon$.

(48.2) Sequential Compactness Theorem. *The set $E \subset \mathscr{C}_0(A)$ is sequentially compact if and only if its members are equicontinuous and uniformly bounded.*

Since the functions $f \in U'$ are uniformly bounded and are equicontinuous (by the mean-value theorem), (48.2) implies:

(48.3) Corollary. *The dashed unit ball U' is sequentially compact.*

PROOF OF (48.2). We first deal with the necessity, and for this purpose we suppose E sequentially compact, and, if possible, that its members are either not equicontinuous or not uniformly bounded. There is then in E a sequence of elements f_n, and in A a corresponding sequence of point-pairs x_{1n}, x_{2n}, or of single points x_n, such that

$$\text{either} \quad |f_n(x_n)| > n + 2, \quad \text{or} \quad |f_n(x_{2n}) - f(x_{1n})| > 3\varepsilon$$

where $\varepsilon > 0$ is fixed, while $|x_{2n} - x_{1n}| < 1/n$. In either case, by passing to a subsequence we may suppose the f_n converge uniformly to a continuous f, and for large n the error in replacing f_n by f is at most ε, or at most 1. Thus, either $|f(x_n)| > n$, or $|f(x_{2n}) - f(x_{1n})| > \varepsilon$, for all large n, which contradicts the continuity of f.

It remains to prove the sufficiency. To this effect, we denote by $\{A_n\}$ an expanding sequence of finite subsets of A, such that each point $x \in A$ is distant $<1/n$ from some point of A_n. We denote further by A_0 the union of the sets A_n. Clearly A_0 is at most countable; we denote its points by $a_1, a_2, \ldots$.

This being so, we suppose E to consist of uniformly bounded, equicontinuous functions, and we denote by $\{f_n\}$ any sequence of elements of E. We have to show that $\{f_n\}$ has a uniformly convergent subsequence. To this effect, we first show that the sequence $\{f_n(x)\}$ has a subsequence which converges at each $x \in A_0$. This is done by the so-called "diagonal method."

Since the numbers $\{f_n(a_1)\}$ are uniformly bounded, there is a subsequence $\{f_{n1}(x)\}$ of $\{f_n(x)\}$ which converges for $x = a_1$. Similarly, from it we can extract a second subsequence $\{f_{n2}(x)\}$, which converges also at $x = a_2$. Generally, from an $(r - 1)$-*st* sequence, we can extract an r-th sequence,

$$f_{1,r}, f_{2,r}, \ldots, f_{n,r}, \ldots$$

of functions of x, which converges at $x = a_r$ as well as at the previous points a_1, $a_2, \ldots, a_{r-1}$. The diagonal sequence

$$\varphi_n = f_{nn} \qquad (n = 1, 2, \ldots)$$

is then, except for its $r - 1$ initial terms, a subsequence of our r-th sequence, and therefore converges at $x = a_r$, for each r. Thus $\{\varphi_n(x)\}$ converges at each point of A_0.

We shall show that the subsequence $\{\varphi_n(x)\}$ of $\{f_n(x)\}$ converges uniformly in A. For this purpose, we choose any $\varepsilon > 0$ and determine the corresponding $\delta > 0$ from the definition of equicontinuity of E. We then determine an integer k so that $\delta > 1/k$, and we denote by B the finite set A_k. To each point $x \in A$ we can then attach a point $b \in B$ so that $|x - b| < \delta$. Further, since $\{\varphi_n(x)\}$ converges in B and the set B is finite, we can determine n_0 so that the relations $n > n_0$, $m > n_0$ imply $|\varphi_n(b) - \varphi_m(b)| < \varepsilon$ for every $b \in B$. However, the error in $\varphi_n(x)$, or $\varphi_m(x)$, resulting from replacing x by the point of B attached to it, is, by equicontinuity, $<\varepsilon$. Thus $n > n_0$, $m > n_0$ imply, for every $x \in A$,

$$|\varphi_n(x) - \varphi_m(x)| < 3\varepsilon,$$

and this shows that the sequence $\{\varphi_n\}$ converges uniformly. Thus (48.2) is proved.

The real-valued linear functions $g(f)$ $f \in \mathscr{C}_0(A)$ constitute the elements g of the dual space. We write gf in place of $g(f)$ for a particular f, and we regard it as the scalar product of the vector f by the dual vector g. (It must not be confused with the operation of multiplying two functions.) We shall restrict ourselves to the class of dual vectors g, for which gf is bounded for $f \in U$. We denote this class by $\mathscr{C}_0^*(A)$ and term it the dutiful dual of $\mathscr{C}_0(A)$. Dual elements not in this class are, in a certain sense, rather wild, and they play no part here.

For an element g of the dutiful dual, we define as norm the quantity $|g| = \text{Sup}\, gf$ for $f \in U$. This is, according to Section 44, the function of distance of the set $|g| \leq 1$, and we term this set the dual unit ball, and denote it by U^*. We also introduce a dashed norm, $|g|' = \text{Sup}\, gf$ for $f \in U'$. Here U' is a smaller set than U, so that we have $|g|' \leq |g|$. In particular the dashed norm is finite in $\mathscr{C}_0^*(A)$, so that, in our dutiful dual, we have the choice of two metrics, derived from the norms $|g|$ and $|g|'$. This is embarrassing, for we shall choose neither.

Indeed, it is usual to define the notion of limit quite differently in $\mathscr{C}_0^*(A)$, and the corresponding notion of convergence is termed weak * convergence:

(48.4) Definition. *For g and g_n $(n = 1, 2, \ldots)$ in $\mathscr{C}_0^*(A)$, we write $g = \text{Lim}\, g_n$ if, for each $f \in \mathscr{C}_0(A)$, we have $gf = \text{Lim}\, g_n f$.*

We shall term positive cone of $\mathscr{C}_0(A)$ the set of continuous non-negative functions, defined in A; and positive cone of $\mathscr{C}_0^*(A)$ the set of $g \in \mathscr{C}_0^*(A)$ for which $gf \geq 0$ whenever f lies in the positive cone of $\mathscr{C}_0(A)$. Further, we shall term a set of elements $g \in \mathscr{C}_0^*(A)$ bounded if the set of their norms $|g|$ is bounded. In our applications in the next Chapters, we shall need to consider only those dual vectors g which lie either in a fixed bounded set or in the positive cone; we shall there make use of the notion of convergence defined in (48.4).

At first sight, this would seem to involve really unpleasant complications. Every student of real variable or point-set topology, is aware of the fact that, whereas convergence resulting from a metric is a simple notion to work with, a definition of the type (48.4) leads to such elaborate procedures as transfinite closure, transfinite repeated limits and the whole Baire classification.

It is therefore quite remarkable that for sequences $\{g_n\}$ that lie either in a bounded set or in the positive cone of our dutiful dual, convergence according to (48.4), i.e., weak * convergence, coincides with the corresponding notion in the dashed metric of $\mathscr{C}_0^*(A)$. This will follow from a metrization lemma for the dual unit ball U^*, proved below. (What is even more remarkable, though we shall not prove it here, is that a corresponding metrization lemma, and analogues or extensions of the other properties of U^*, established below, remain valid for the dual unit balls of the much more general class of normed vector-spaces, which go by the name of Banach spaces.)

(48.5) Metrization Lemma for U^*. *For $n = 1, 2, \ldots$, let $g_n \in U^*$. Then each of the relations* (i) $\operatorname{Lim} g_n = 0$, (ii) $\operatorname{Lim} |g_n|' = 0$, (iii) $\operatorname{Lim} g_n f = 0$ *for each $f \in \mathscr{P}$, is equivalent to the others.*

Proof. Clearly (i) implies (iii). Further, (ii) implies $g_n f \to 0$ for each $f \in U'$, and so (iii), since we can choose $\varphi = \pm f \in U'$ so that $|g_n f| = g_n \varphi \leq |g_n|'$, and since each member of $\mathscr{P}$ is a constant multiple of an $f \in U'$. It will therefore suffice to prove that (iii) implies (i), and that (i) implies (ii).

Suppose (iii) holds. By (48.1), given $f \in \mathscr{C}_0(A)$, we can find, for each $\varepsilon > 0$, an element $f_\varepsilon \in \mathscr{P}$, such that $|f - f_\varepsilon| < \varepsilon$. Hence, writing $f - f_\varepsilon = \pm\psi$, we can choose the sign so that

$$|g_n \cdot (f - f_\varepsilon)| = g_n \psi \leq |g_n| \cdot |\psi| < \varepsilon.$$

Since $g_n f_\varepsilon \to 0$ as $n \to \infty$, by (iii), it follows that $|g_n f| < 2\varepsilon$ for large n, and therefore $g_n f \to 0$. Since this now holds for each $f \in \mathscr{C}_0(A)$, (i) is verified.

Finally, suppose (ii) does not hold. Then for some fixed $\varepsilon > 0$ and an infinity of n there exist $f_n \in U'$ so that $g_n f_n > 2\varepsilon$. By (48.3) we can extract from these f_n a convergent subsequence with a limit $f \in \mathscr{C}_0(A)$, and for this subsequence, we find, when n is large, that

$$g_n \cdot (f_n - f) \leq |g_n| \cdot |f_n - f| < \varepsilon,$$

and therefore that $g_n f > g_n f_n - \varepsilon > \varepsilon$. This shows that $g_n f$ does not tend to 0, so that (i) does not hold when (ii) does not; i.e. (i) implies (ii). This completes the proof.

(48.6) Theorem. *Let E^* be either the positive cone or a bounded set in $\mathscr{C}_0^*(A)$, and let g and g_n $(n = 1, 2, \ldots)$ lie in E^*. Then the relations* $\operatorname{Lim} g_n = g$ *and* $\operatorname{Lim} |g_n - g|' = 0$ *are equivalent.*

It will be seen further on that instead of $g \in E^*$, we need only suppose here $g \in \mathscr{C}_0^*(A)$.

In proving (48.6), we shall use the following:

(48.7) Remark. *For an element g of the positive cone of $\mathscr{C}_0^*(A)$, we have $|g| = gf_1$, where $f_1(x)$ is the constant unity in A.*

In fact, on the one hand, clearly $|g| \geq gf_1$, and on the other hand, $gf_1 - |g|$ is the infimum for $f \in U$ of the expression of $g \cdot (f_1 - f)$, which is ≥ 0 since $f_1 - f$ lies in the positive cone of $\mathscr{C}_0(A)$.

Proof of (48.6). If E^* is the positive cone of $\mathscr{C}_0^*(A)$, we see by (48.7) that each of the two relations $\operatorname{Lim} g_n = g$ and $\operatorname{Lim} |g_n - g|' = 0$ implies the convergence, and so the boundedness, of the sequence of norms $|g_n| = g_n f_1$. We may therefore suppose E^* to be a bounded set of $\mathscr{C}_0^*(A)$. In that case, we can further set $g = 0$ without loss of generality, and, by change of scale, we may suppose $E^* = U^*$, so that (48.6) reduces to (48.5).

(48.8) Theorem. *U^* is $B \cdot\cdot i$ compact in the dashed metric equivalent in it to* (48.4).

PROOF. Let $g_n \in U^*$ for $n = 1, 2, \ldots$. By the diagonal method described in the proof of (48.2), we can extract a subsequence of n for which the numbers $g_n f$ tend to a limit $\ell(f)$ for each f of the countable set $\mathscr{P}$ of (48.1), and therefore in the linear hull F of $\mathscr{P}$. Further, since $|g_n f| \leq |f|$, we see that $\ell(f) \leq |f|$ for $f \in F$. By the Hahn-Banach theorem, there exists $g \in U^*$, i.e., a dual vector for which $gf \leq |f|$, such that for all $f \in F$, $gf = \ell(f)$.

Thus, given any sequence $\{g_n\} \subset U^*$, there exists a subsequence $\{g_m\}$, where m describes a subsequence of the integers n, and an element $g \in U^*$, such that $\text{Lim}\, g_m f = gf$ for every $f \in \mathscr{P}$. But in that case, by the metrization lemma (48.5) for U^*, applied to the functions $\frac{1}{2}(g_m - g)$, the subsequence $\{g_m\}$ has the limit (48.4), and also the limit in the dashed metric given by g. In particular, by taking for $\{g_n\}$ an intrinsically convergent sequence in the dashed metric, we find that, given $\varepsilon > 0$, we have for all large n, if m is suitably chosen in the subsequence,

$$|g_n - g|' \leq |g_n - g_m|' + |g_m - g|' < 2\varepsilon.$$

Thus $\{g_n\}$ converges in the dashed metric, so that U^* is complete. At the same time, we see that U^* is also sequentially compact, and this completes the proof.

From the $B \cdot\cdot i$ compactness of U^*, it follows that we can relax slightly the hypotheses of (48.6), as stated in the comment following that theorem.

§49. THE RIESZ REPRESENTATION

The preceding section applies, in particular, when A is a finite set consisting, say, of the points $1, 2, \ldots, n$ of the real line. In that case $\mathscr{C}_0(A)$ reduces to Euclidean n-space, since the values of a vector $f \in \mathscr{C}_0(A)$ are its n components $f(x)$ $(x = 1, 2, \ldots, n)$. By introducing n unit vectors $f_1, f_2, \ldots, f_n$, each of which has one unit component while the other components vanish, we see that a linear function g is given by the n reals $gf_1, gf_2, \ldots, gf_n$, which we may regard as its components $b_1, b_2, \ldots, b_n$, and that gf is then the sum

$$b_1 f(1) + b_2 f(2) + \cdots + b_n f(n).$$

Our object is to obtain, in this section, a corresponding representation of gf when A is any bounded closed Euclidean set, and $g \in \mathscr{C}_0^*(A)$. Instead of a finite sum, we shall have an integral of the function $f(x)$ with respect to a signed measure μ, which takes the place of the coefficient system $b_1, b_2, \ldots, b_n$. This is the Riesz representation, which we shall prove below.

According to this theorem, there is a dissymmetry between $\mathscr{C}_0(A)$ and its dutiful dual. The elements of the former are continuous functions f; those of the latter are given by signed measures μ. Actually this dissymmetry already appears in the finite-dimensional case considered above, if we take into account the norms of the two spaces. We find that $|f| = |f|'$ is given by the largest of the n numbers $|f(x)|$, while $|g| = |g|'$ is given by the sum of the n numbers $|b_x|$. The topologies derived from these metrics coincide, however, with the usual Euclidean one.

In order to give to the Riesz representation of a dual vector $g \in \mathscr{C}_0^*(A)$ its most elementary form, we shall use, not the notion of a signed measure, but the more elementary notion, which is here equivalent to it, of an additive function of intervals with support in A and of bounded variation. (The passage from this notion to that of a signed measure with the same support is easily adapted from standard results in the theory of the integral, treated by Saks in *Theory of the Integral*, Chapter III.)

In the Euclidean space that constitutes the linear hull of our set A, we denote by Δ_0 a fixed interval containing A in its interior and by Δ a variable interval contained in Δ_0; all intervals will be understood to be closed unless the contrary is stated. We denote by γ a real-valued function of the interval Δ, and we write $\Delta\gamma$ for the value $\gamma(\Delta)$. We term γ a function of intervals. We say that γ has support in A if

$\Delta\gamma = 0$ whenever Δ contains no point of A. We term γ additive if we have

$$\Delta\gamma = \Delta_{1\gamma} + \Delta_{2\gamma},$$

whenever Δ is subdivided into two non-overlapping intervals Δ_1, Δ_2.

An additive function of intervals γ with support in A will be termed of bounded variation if there is a constant K such that for every finite system of non-overlapping intervals $\Delta \subset \Delta_0$, we have $\Sigma\,|\Delta\gamma| \leq K$. The infimum of the set of such constants K is termed the total variation of γ on A, and written

$$\int_A |d_\gamma|. \tag{49.1}$$

By a subdivision σ of an interval Δ, we shall mean its expression as a union of a finite number N of non-overlapping subintervals; we shall denote by $|\sigma|$ the largest of the diameters of the intersections of A with these subintervals; further, we term the subdivision simple if $N = 2$. By the product $\sigma\sigma_1$ of two subdivisions σ, σ_1 of a same interval Δ, we mean the subdivision of Δ into the subintervals expressible as intersections of those occurring in σ with those occurring in σ_1. Similarly, we define the product of any finite number of subdivisions of Δ. A subdivision expressible as a product of simple ones will be termed regular. A subdivision σ will be termed a refinement of a subdivision σ_1 of the same interval if it coincides with $\sigma\sigma_1$. Clearly, every subdivision possesses a regular refinement.

If γ is an additive function of intervals, and σ is a regular subdivision of Δ into subintervals Δ_k $(k = 1, 2, \ldots, N)$, it is easily seen by induction that $\Delta\gamma = \Sigma\Delta_k\gamma$. We shall leave the reader to verify, with the help of the remarks made above, that this can be extended to the following general additivity property: if γ is an additive function of intervals, and a same subset of Δ_0 is expressed in two ways as a finite union of non-overlapping intervals Δ, then the two values of the sum $\Sigma\Delta\gamma$ must agree. (Alternatively, the reader may, if he wishes, simply take this as definition of additivity.)

Given, together with an additive function of intervals γ, with support in A, and of bounded variation, a continuous function $f(x)$ defined in A, we shall define the Stieltjes integral

$$I = \int_A f(x)\, d\gamma. \tag{49.2}$$

To this effect, let σ be a subdivision of Δ_0, and let

$$\Delta_1, \Delta_2, \ldots, \Delta_N$$

be those subintervals, determined by σ, each of which contains at least one point of A, and let

$$\xi_1, \xi_2, \ldots, \xi_N$$

be points of A which lie, respectively, in these N subintervals. We define the Stieltjes integral I as the limit, as $|\sigma| \to 0$, of the sum

$$S = \sum_{k=1}^{N} f(\xi_k)\,\Delta_k\gamma; \tag{49.3}$$

i.e., I is our Stieltjes integral, if, given $\varepsilon > 0$, there exists $\delta > 0$, so that $|\sigma| < \delta$ implies $|I - S| < \varepsilon$, however we choose, subject to $|\sigma| < \delta$, the subdivision σ and the points ξ_k in its subintervals.

(49.4) Theorem of Stieltjes. (i) *The Stieltjes integral* (49.2) *exists.* (ii) *For* $f \in \mathscr{C}_0(A)$, *it constitutes a linear function* gf, *where* $g \in \mathscr{C}_0^*(A)$ *and where* $|g|$ *does not exceed the total variation* (49.1).

PROOF. We shall confine ourselves to (i), since (ii) is even more straightforward. We need only verify that for any two sums S_1, S_2 of the type (49.3) for which, for the corresponding subdivisions σ_1, σ_2, we have $|\sigma_1| + |\sigma_2| < \delta$, we shall have

$$|S_2 - S_1| < \varepsilon K.$$

To this effect, we write $\sigma = \sigma_1\sigma_2$, and denote by Δ_k $(k = 1, 2, \ldots, N)$ the subintervals determined by σ which contain points of A. Every such Δ_k lies in a corresponding pair of subintervals determined by σ_1 and σ_2, respectively, and we denote

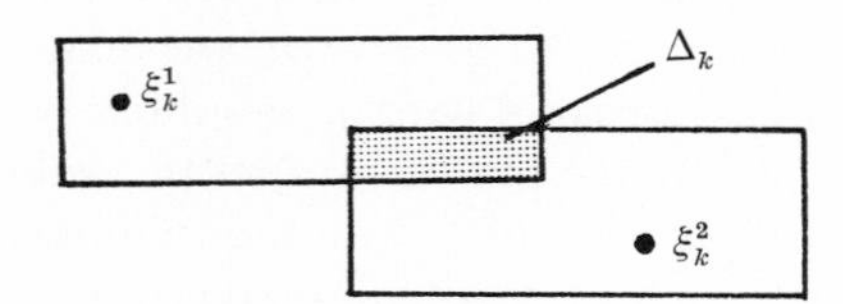

by ξ_k^1, ξ_k^2 the corresponding points ξ, appearing in the expressions of S_1, S_2 similar to (49.3). On account of the general additivity property of γ, and of the fact that $\Delta\gamma = 0$ unless Δ contains at least one point of A, we have

$$S_2 - S_1 = \sum_{k=1}^{N} [f(\xi_k^2) - f(\xi_k^1)]\Delta_k\gamma.$$

Further $|\xi_k^2 - \xi_k^1| \leq |\sigma_1| + |\sigma_2| < \delta$, and we can choose $\delta > 0$ so that this implies that the corresponding difference of f is numerically $<\varepsilon$. Thus $|S_2 - S_1| < \varepsilon K$, where K is any constant not less than (49.1). This completes the proof.

We now come to our main result, which constitutes the converse of (49.4).

(49.5) The Riesz Representation Theorem. *Let* $g \in \mathscr{C}_0^*(A)$. *Then there exists an additive function of intervals* γ, *with support in* A, *such that*

(i) $|g| = \int_A |d\gamma|$,

(ii) $gf = \int_A f(x)\, d\gamma$ *for every* $f \in \mathscr{C}_0(A)$.

PROOF. We begin by embedding $\mathscr{C}_0(A)$ in a larger vector-space Φ. An element $\varphi \in \Phi$ will consist of the system of a finite number of continuous functions φ_k $(k = 1, 2, \ldots, N)$, where each φ_k is defined in the intersection of A with a corresponding interval Δ_k, and the Δ_k are non-overlapping intervals, which, together with a finite number of further intervals, containing no point of A define a subdivision σ of Δ_0. Any such element φ is regarded as unaltered when any Δ_k is replaced by a subdivision of Δ_k, and the single function φ_k is replaced by the system of its restrictions to the intervals into which Δ_k is subdivided. Thus any two elements of Φ can always be regarded as two systems of continuous functions defined on the same system of intersections of A with intervals Δ_k. We can therefore add any two elements of Φ to obtain an element of Φ in the obvious manner. Also, we can multiply an element by a real number. Thus Φ is a vector space. We define in it the norm $|\varphi|$ as the greatest of the norms $|\varphi_k|$ in $\mathscr{C}_0(A \cap \Delta_k)$. Clearly this norm is convex and homogeneous. Clearly also $\mathscr{C}_0(A)$ is a vector subspace of Φ, and the norm $|\varphi|$ agrees with our previous norm $|f|$, when φ reduces to an element $f \in \mathscr{C}_0(A)$.

This being so, let $g \in \mathscr{C}_0^*(A)$, let $|g| = K$, and let $Q(\varphi) = K \cdot |\varphi|$. By the Hahn-Banach theorem, the linear function $\ell(f) = gf$ defined in $\mathscr{C}_0(A)$ and subject to

$\ell(f) \leq Q(f)$ can be extended to a linear function $\ell(\varphi)$ defined in Φ and subject to $\ell(\varphi) \leq Q(\varphi)$, and therefore clearly to $|\ell(\varphi)| \leq Q(\varphi)$. We now denote by Δ the element of Φ that consists of the function unity in $\Delta \cap A$, together with an appropriate further finite system of functions identically zero in intersections of A with other intervals. We define a function of intervals γ by setting $\ell(\Delta) = \Delta\gamma$. Clearly γ is additive and with support in A. Further, if Δ_k are non-overlapping intervals, the element φ obtained from them by linear combination of the corresponding elements of Φ with coefficients ± 1, has norm 1 (or else 0), and we can choose the signs so that $\ell(\varphi) = \sum |\Delta_k\gamma|$. Since $\ell(\varphi) \leq Q(\varphi) = K$, it follows that

$$\text{(49.6)} \qquad \int_A |d\gamma| \leq |g|.$$

Again, if f is any fixed element of $\mathscr{C}_0(A)$, and σ is a subdivision for which $|\sigma|$ is less than a certain positive number δ, the difference between gf and the sum S in (49.3) may be written $\ell(\varphi)$, where φ is now the element of Φ given by

$$\varphi = f - \Sigma_k f(\xi_k)\Delta_k;$$

by choice of δ, we have $|\varphi| < \varepsilon$. Consequently

$$|gf - S| = |\ell(\varphi)| \leq Q(\varphi) < \varepsilon K,$$

which shows that gf is the Stieltjes integral (49.2). This establishes (ii) of our assertion, and (i) is now obtained by combining (49.6) with the opposite inequality, derived from the last part of (49.4).

(49.7) Corollary. *Let* (c) *be the space whose elements* f *are convergent sequences of reals* $\{c_\nu\}$ $\nu = 1, 2, \ldots$ *with the norm* $|f| = \text{Sup}_\nu |c_\nu|$. *Then any element* g *of the dutiful dual* $(c)^*$ *is given by reals* C, C_ν $\nu = 1, 2, \ldots,$ *for which* $|g| = |C| + \Sigma |C_\nu|$ *and*

$$gf = C \lim c_\nu + \Sigma_\nu C_\nu c_\nu$$

for each $f = \{c_\nu\}$ $\nu = 1, 2, \ldots$ *in* (c).

To see this it is sufficient to identify (c) with $\mathscr{C}_0(A)$, by setting $c_\nu = f(1/\nu)$, $\lim c_\nu = f(0)$, and by denoting by A the subset of the real axis formed by the origin and the points $1/\nu$ $\nu = 1, 2, \ldots.$ The reals C, C_ν are then the weights which a measure γ on A associated with the origin and the points $1/\nu$ $\nu = 1, 2, \ldots.$

REMARK. If A is any $B \cdot \cdot i$ compact set, not restricted to be Euclidean, a measure γ on A is defined by Bourbaki to mean an element $g \in \mathscr{C}_0^*(A)$, and $\int f\, d\gamma$ is identified with gf by definition. Theorem (49.5) asserts, for Euclidean sets, that this definition is consistent with the older one.

Chapter V

Existence Theory and its Consequences

§50. INTRODUCTION

We have stressed many times that it does not make sense to talk of necessary conditions without first settling the question of the existence of a solution. Therefore we have avoided necessary conditions and instead have studied sufficient conditions. Thus it is that we came to adopt the method of geodesic coverings and to derive from it an existence theory in the small, and also a more extensive theory in terms of conjugate points. However, this is still not a true theory in the large, which is what one really wants in a practical problem, and it has all been based on a great deal more smoothness than we shall be able to assume in optimal control.

It is therefore time for us to try a different approach, and this means tackling the question of existence. We shall then be in a position to attack not only the necessary conditions, but also further questions such as unicity.

It would seem, therefore, that existential questions, if we find a way of grappling with them, are going to be rather important, whether we like it or not. This may well please the logicians among us, but some of us may have different feelings on the matter. Many persons feel that such intangible considerations ought not to play a dominant part in such a highly practical subject as the calculus of variations, or in optimal control, or, indeed, in mathematics as a whole. In fact, for them, existence does not have the paramount importance attached to it by Descartes, when he proudly proclaimed: "I think, therefore I exist." Is existence something to boast about? A housewife moved to Idaho, because: "In Chicago, one does not live, one just exists." To have to struggle for existence is just a sign of poverty.

This view of existence should not be dismissed lightly. Necessity may force us to grapple with existence, but when all is said and done, existence in mathematics remains neither more nor less than membership of a set which is not empty. It is not nothing (not quite), in fact, it is just a first step, a preliminary formality, something like the acquisition of a passport. Certainly we should not take offense if someone suggests that it ought not to play a dominant part in mathematics. What would we say of foreign travel if it consisted, not of a grand tour of such places as the Louvre, the Sistine Chapel, Windsor Castle, the Taj Mahal, but mainly of the struggle to get a passport!

So now it seems to be the practical man who indulges in speculation—not about existence, but about what mathematics ought to be like. Some may regard this as wishful thinking, but there is more to it than that. Wishful thinking is always a danger, and in the calculus of variations it has been at the root of most errors. It consists in confusing what mathematics ought, perhaps, to be with what mathematics is. The basic fallacy is then that mathematics was created perfect, and that we have no say in the matter. There is no such fallacy in speculating on what mathematics ought to be, and in then trying to modify mathematics accordingly. On the contrary this type of speculation should be rather helpful. In astronomy, it led to abandoning the clumsy notion that the earth is a flat disc supported by sixteen elephants. There is no reason why it should prove less successful in mathematics.

It would be highly satisfactory if we could so order our mathematics that existence would become as self-evident as in the world around us. The question is whether we can so plan mathematics, in particular, the calculus of variations.

Once we state our question of existence in these highly practical terms, to which an engineer would certainly subscribe, the answer becomes amazingly simple. This is the essence of Hilbert's famous statement: "Every problem of the calculus of variations has a solution, provided the word 'solution' is suitably understood."

Of course, this is really only common sense. We have come to conceptual methods from the practical side, and this is where they belong.

Hilbert's papers represent the triumph of such conceptual methods. Others may write unreadable papers of incredible length and complexity, and in some cases achieve remarkable results. This was not Hilbert's way; even his sentences were short, and that is unusual enough in German. The technical perfection of his proofs tended, perhaps, to make his papers appear less like the pioneer papers that they really were and more like the end results of theories that had at last found their ideal expression. Today, after two generations, the developments to which he pointed the way are there for everyone to see.

What one no longer sees is the wonderful Hilbert lucidity and artistry; this has been, we fear, irretrievably lost in the subsequent flood of semisimple hybrid verbiage, which Hilbert would hardly have recognized. Hilbert once even asked: "What is this space you speak of, this Hilbert space?"

No serious student of mathematics should neglect to read at least one of Hilbert's many books, papers and courses of lectures. And since it is often helpful to bring the written word to life by seeing behind it something of the master himself, a student should try to learn something about Hilbert's personality while there are still mathematicians who knew him, the present writer among them, and even some, like Richard Courant, who at one time collaborated with him.

Hilbert's approach to existence theory in the calculus of variations is given in his famous paper "On the Dirichlet Principle." Instead of developing a theory, he illustrates his methods by applying them to particular problems. For this reason, his existence theory has been formulated in various ways, and every writer gives a different version. For instance, the Hilbert approach can be used on a smooth manifold, instead of in Euclidean space. Among the various formulations, one of the most interesting is the general "minimax" version of the existence theorem, due to Marston Morse. We shall not treat it here. However, we shall develop the Hilbert existence theory in several other settings, and we shall draw consequences from it.

The actual Hilbert constructions, which we shall use in the next few sections, necessitate rather restrictive hypotheses, and for several decades these were believed essential. However, Hilbert's line of thought is made clear by the statement we quoted, which contains no such restriction. What this statement means is that existence theorems do not require the machinery of proofs as much as proper definitions. This makes Hilbert the originator of a method widely used throughout analysis today termed the "weak solution method." One of its consequences has been, for instance, the Schwartz theory of distributions. Hilbert's statement inspired also the various theories that we discuss later in this Chapter and in the next, and whose object is to free Hilbert's constructions from restrictive hypotheses. In particular, it inspired the present writer's notion of generalized curve.

That so much should have come from this one simple statement is indeed remarkable. (It is also highly characteristic of Hilbert's work; for instance the notion of a Hausdorff space first appears in one of Hilbert's footnotes, which goes to show how inaccurate our modern terminology has become.) However, the very generality of Hilbert's statement had a curious sequel: when it was reprinted in Hilbert's collected papers, the editors saw fit to correct it by inserting the word regular before the word problem, as if his statement were some work of art in need of a fig leaf. The "correction" is insipid and cowardly.

§51. THE HILBERT CONSTRUCTION AND SOME OF ITS CONSEQUENCES IN THE STANDARD PARAMETRIC CASE

We consider a parametric problem with a positive definite Lagrangian L. We term the problem totally elliptic, if the set of its elliptic points coincides with the whole of x-space. The problem will be said to possess "cheap" extremals if, given $\varepsilon > 0$, there exists a pair of points x_1, x_2, distant $|x_1 - x_2| > 1/\varepsilon$ from one another, and joinable by an extremal C such that $\mathscr{I}(C) < \varepsilon$. A positive definite Lagrangian, or the parametric problem corresponding to it, will be termed positive extradefinite if such (arbitrarily) cheap extremals do not exist; i.e., if for some $\varepsilon > 0$, no pair x_1, x_2 has the stated property.

Cheap extremals have a marked effect, which we shall illustrate in a later section. There is a kindred phenomenon familiar to travelers; the route selected by a passenger between distant cities is strongly affected by the rapid transportation at bargain rates that may be available between certain larger centers.

We denote by ∂C the ordered pair of end-points (x_1, x_2) of a curve C, and by Ω a nonempty bounded closed set of ordered pairs of distinct points (x_1, x_2). We term an admissible parametric curve C a fit curve, if $\partial C \in \Omega$. The problem that will concern us in this section, which we shall term a standard parametric problem, is that of the minimum of $\mathscr{I}(C)$ for fit curves C in the case in which it is totally elliptic and positive extradefinite. If Ω consists of a single ordered pair, we say that the problem is one with fixed ends. We write dC for the diameter of C.

An admissible curve C_0 such that $\mathscr{I}(C_0)$ is the minimum of $\mathscr{I}(C)$ for admissible curves C such that $\partial C = \partial C_0$ is termed minimizing. We term Ω-minimizing a fit curve C_0 such that $\mathscr{I}(C_0)$ is the minimum of $\mathscr{I}(C)$ for all fit curves C. A sequence of fit curves C_ν $(\nu = 1, 2, \ldots)$ is termed Ω-minimizing if $\mathscr{I}(C_\nu)$ tends to the infimum of $\mathscr{I}(C)$ for all fit curves C. A sequence of admissible curves C_ν for which ∂C_ν is a fixed pair (x_1, x_2) is termed minimizing if $\mathscr{I}(C_\nu)$ tends similarly to the infimum of $\mathscr{I}(C)$ for all admissible C such that ∂C is this same pair.

A fit curve C will be termed an Ω-extremal if it is an extremal and satisfies the transversality† conditions. The latter were considered in the nonparametric case in Chapter III, Section 31; they are quite similar in the parametric case which now occupies us, and we shall come to them later in this section.

(51.1) The Basic Hilbert Existence Theorem. *In a standard parametric problem, there exists a solution.*

(51.2) Necessary Conditions Based on the First Variation. *In a standard parametric problem, each solution is an Ω-extremal.*

By a solution, we mean here an Ω-minimizing curve. Later, in accordance with Hilbert's famous dictum, we shall widen our interpretation of solution, but this will not affect the above theorems. We remark that in addition to (51.2) further conditions, not based on the first variation, are necessary. The Weierstrass condition is automatically satisfied on account of ellipticity. However, in the next section we shall come to the parametric form of the Jacobi condition, and this corresponds to matters treated in Chapter III; we shall then be ready for a section dealing with unicity.

The basic concept on which (51.1) and its consequences will be based is that of a minimizing sequence—more particularly, an Ω-minimizing sequence. We term such sequences bounded if the curves C_ν all lie in a fixed cube. We shall require the following:

(51.3) Bounded Ω-Minimizing Sequence Lemma. *If a problem that is elliptic and positive definite in an open set W has an Ω-minimizing sequence situated in a bounded closed subset E of W, then it has a solution furnished by an extremal situated in E.*‡

Proof. Let C_ν $\nu = 1, 2, \ldots$, be the sequence. We choose $\rho > 0$ in accordance with the local existence theorem (29.5) of Chapter II, Section 29, and we write m, M

† The definition of transversality will be given in (51.6).

‡ In applying this lemma in this section, E will be taken to be a cube Q, and W will be the whole of x-space.

for the minimum and maximum of $L(x, \dot{x})$ when $|\dot{x}| = 1$ and $x \in E$. We denote by $|C_\nu|$ the length of C_ν, and by N_ν the smallest integer exceeding $2\rho^{-1}|C_\nu|$.

Since the values of $\mathscr{I}(C_\nu)$ approach a finite limit, the lengths $|C_\nu| \leq m^{-1}\mathscr{I}(C_\nu)$ are uniformly bounded, and therefore so are the integers N_ν. At least one such integer N occurs an infinity of times among the N_ν; we shall restrict ourselves to the corresponding values of ν. We divide C_ν into N arcs, each of length $<\frac{1}{2}\rho$. This is possible, since $N > 2\rho^{-1}|C_\nu|$. We denote the points of division on C_ν by

$$a_0, a_1, a_2, \ldots, a_N.$$

As ν varies, each a_k describes a bounded sequence in E. We extract a subsequence of ν for which each a_k tends to a limiting position. By adding to C_ν, for $k = 1, 2, \ldots, N-1$, pairs of opposite segments from the a_k to their limiting positions, and for $k = 0$ and $k = N$ a single such segment, we can arrange for the points of division a_k to be common to all the C_ν of our subsequence. Since N is fixed and the $2N + 2$ added segments have lengths tending to 0, the increase in $\mathscr{I}(C_\nu)$, which is at most M times the added length, tends to 0. The modified C_ν therefore still constitute an Ω-minimizing sequence. Further, by omitting a finite number of values of ν in our subsequence, we may suppose that the length of the arc of C_ν, between a_{k-1} and a_k, is $<\frac{1}{2}\rho$. We may also clearly suppose $a_{k-1} \neq a_k$ for each k.

C_ν modified
and the modified
points of division a_k

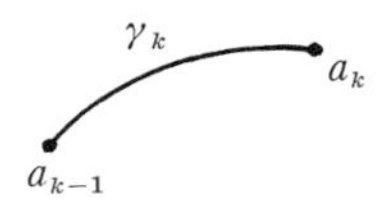

After these changes, we denote by C the curve through the points of division, which is the sum of N extremal arcs γ_k. Here each γ_k is defined, in accordance with theorem (29.5) of Chapter II, Section 29, as the unique minimizing curve for which $\partial\gamma_k$ consists of the pair (a_{k-1}, a_k). From the minimum property of γ_k, we derive by addition in k the relation $\mathscr{I}(C) \leq \mathscr{I}(C_\nu)$. By making $\nu \to \infty$ it follows that C is minimizing.

Clearly this implies further that each subarc of C is a minimizing arc, and in particular that the arc $\gamma_k + \gamma_{k+1}$ is so. Since the end points of this arc are distant $<\rho$, the arc $\gamma_k + \gamma_{k+1}$ is an extremal arc, by (29.5), for each k; hence C is an extremal. This completes the proof.

In order to derive (51.1) from the lemma just proved we shall establish the following result, which is useful in other connections also:

(51.4) Theorem. *In a standard parametric problem, let C_ν $(\nu = 1, 2, \ldots, N)$ be admissible curves for which the numbers $\mathscr{I}(C_\nu)$ are bounded. Then*

(i) *the diameters dC_ν of the C_ν are bounded;*

(ii) *if, further, the C_ν intersect a bounded set Q, independent of ν, the lengths $|C_\nu|$ are bounded.*

REDUCTION OF (51.1) TO (51.4). In view of (51.3), and of the obvious existence of an Ω-minimizing sequence, we need only show that the latter is bounded. This is contained in (51.4)(i).

PROOF OF (51.4). We first observe that (ii) follows from (i). In fact, if (i) holds, we can enlarge Q so that it contains the C_ν. Then $|C_\nu| \leq m^{-1}\mathscr{I}(C_\nu)$, where m is the minimum of $L(x, \dot{x})$ for $|\dot{x}| = 1$, $x \in Q$.

Next we prove that the special case of (i) in which the C_ν are extremals implies the general case. We do so by attaching to each admissible curve C an extremal Γ with the same diameter, such that $\mathscr{I}(\Gamma) \leq \mathscr{I}(C)$. To this effect, let a, b be two points of C, where a is prior to b, such that $|b - a| = dC$. We denote by Ω^* the set of pairs (x_1, x_2) where $x_1 = a$ and x_2 lies on the circumference of center a, which passes through the point b.

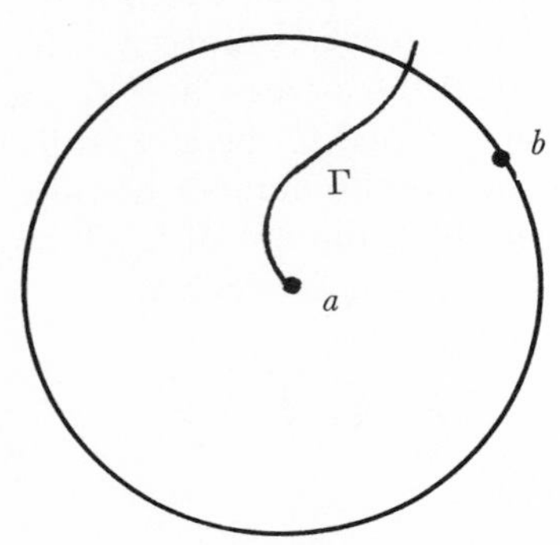

Evidently for the minimum problem with Ω^* in place of Ω, there exists a bounded Ω^*-minimizing sequence, in fact a sequence that does not cross the circumference. Hence by (51.3) there is an extremal Γ, joining a to the circumference, and so of diameter $d\Gamma \geq dC$, such that $\mathscr{I}(\Gamma) \leq \mathscr{I}(C)$. By shortening Γ, if necessary, so that $d\Gamma = dC$ we have the desired extremal.

Finally, to prove the special case of (i), we suppose it false. For any small $\varepsilon > 0$, there would be an extremal $C = C_\nu$ of diameter $dC > 2\varepsilon^{-3}$, for which $\mathscr{I}(C) < \varepsilon^{-1}$. By dividing C into N equal arcs, where $1 \leq N\varepsilon^2 < 2$, we would have, for at least one such arc γ, the relations $d\gamma > \varepsilon^{-1}$, $\mathscr{I}(\gamma) < \varepsilon$. Thus γ would be a cheap extremal, which is excluded if ε is small. This contradiction establishes (51.4) and so (51.1).

PROOF OF PART OF (51.2). Let C be an Ω-minimizing curve. Clearly C is a minimizing curve, and so is any arc of C. We choose ρ as in the proof of (51.3), taking for Q any cube containing C, and we consider any arc γ of C of length $\leq \rho$. Since γ is minimizing, it is an extremal arc by (29.5) of Chapter II, Section 29. Hence C is an extremal also. It remains to show that C satisfies the transversality conditions that we shall now enunciate.

(51.5) Definition of Permissible Variation in Ω. *Let $(x_1, x_2) \in \Omega$. A pair of vectors (X_1, X_2) is termed a permissible variation of (x_1, x_2) in Ω and written $(\delta x_1, \delta x_2)$, if we can define, on an interval of α containing $\alpha = 0$ in its interior, a continuously differentiable pair $(x_1(\alpha), x_2(\alpha))$ with values in Ω such that for $\alpha = 0$, the pair $(x_1(\alpha), x_2(\alpha))$ and its derivative in α coincide, respectively, with (x_1, x_2) and (X_1, X_2).*

(51.6) Transversality Condition. *Let C denote an extremal such that*

$$\partial C = (x_1, x_2) \in \Omega,$$

and let (x_1, y_1), (x_2, y_2) *be the initial and final canonical points of the corresponding canonical extremal. We say that C satisfies the transversality condition if*

$$y_2\,\delta x_2 - y_1\,\delta x_1 = 0$$

for every permissible variation $(\delta x_1, \delta x_2)$ *of* (x_1, x_2) *in* Ω.

We can now resume our interrupted proof.

PROOF OF THE REMAINING PART OF (51.2). With the previous notation, let $x(t)$, $y(t)$ $(0 \leq t \leq 1)$ be a parametric representation of the canonical extremal corresponding to C, and let C_α denote the curve given by the representation

$$x(t, \alpha) = x(t) + \xi(t, \alpha)$$

on the same t-interval, where

$$\xi(t, \alpha) = (1 - t)(x_1(\alpha) - x_1) + t\,(x_2(\alpha) - x_2)\,.$$

Since C is Ω-minimizing, the derivative $\delta\mathscr{I}$ of $\mathscr{I}(C_\alpha)$ in α for $\alpha = 0$ vanishes. Therefore we need only verify that this derivative is $y_2X_2 - y_1X_1$. We find (as in Chapter III, Section 31)

$$\delta\mathscr{I} = \int (L_x X + y\dot{X})\,dt = [Xy]_0^1 + \int (L_x - \dot{y})X\,dt,$$

where X is the derivative in α for $\alpha = 0$ of $x(t, \alpha)$. Since C is an extremal, $\delta\mathscr{I}$ reduces to the difference of Xy at the ends of the t-interval, and this is the desired expression. Thus (51.2) is established.

We shall prove one more result in this section:

(51.7) The Selection Principle for Parametric Extremals. *Let* C_ν $(\nu = 1, 2, \ldots)$ *be extremals of a standard parametric problem, and suppose their initial points situated in a bounded set. Further suppose the sequence of numbers* $\mathscr{I}(C_\nu)$ *bounded. Then there exists a subsequence of* ν *for which the* C_ν *tend to an extremal C, possibly reducing to a single point and the numbers* $\mathscr{I}(C_\nu)$ *tend to* $\mathscr{I}(C)$.

We shall base this on a simplification of the Hilbert construction.

PROOF OF (51.7). By (51.4) the C_ν lie in a bounded set and have uniformly bounded lengths. We denote by Q a cube containing the C_ν. As in the proof of (51.3), we can now define $\rho > 0$, a subsequence of ν, and an integer N, so that N is, for each ν, the smallest integer for which C_ν can be divided into N arcs, each of length $<\frac{1}{2}\rho$. We specialize the subsequence of ν further, so that the points of division on C_ν tend to limiting positions, which we now denote by

$$a_0, a_1, \ldots, a_N.$$

We denote by γ_k the minimizing extremal arc (possibly a single point) such that $\partial\gamma_k = (a_{k-1}, a_k)$, and by C the sum of the arcs γ_k $(k = 1, 2, \ldots, N)$.

Since the points a_{k-1}, a_{k+1} are distant $\leq \rho$, and are limits of corresponding points of C_ν, also distant $\leq \rho$, the minimizing extremal arc which joins them is the limit of the corresponding extremal arc of C_ν of length $\leq \rho$. It must therefore coincide with $\gamma_k + \gamma_{k+1}$, since, for the same reason, γ_k and γ_{k+1} are limits of corresponding arcs of C_ν. Thus each $\gamma_k + \gamma_{k+1}$ is an extremal arc. Similarly $\gamma_k + \gamma_{k'}$ is so if the γ_i reduce to a point for $k < i < k'$. Hence we find that C is an extremal. Further, since each γ_k is limit of the corresponding arc of C_ν, we see that C is limit of C_ν.

Finally, from the minimizing property of γ_k and of the corresponding arc of C_ν, we see that the corresponding integrals of L differ at most by the value of the sum of the integrals of L on a pair of segments, joining corresponding end points. Hence $\mathscr{I}(\gamma_k)$ is the limit of the corresponding integral on the arc of C_ν; by addition $\mathscr{I}(C)$ is the limit of $\mathscr{I}(C_\nu)$ for our subsequence of ν. This completes the proof.

§52. THE PARAMETRIC THEORY OF CONJUGATE POINTS AND THE PARAMETRIC JACOBI CONDITION

In Chapter III, we developed the theory of conjugate points only in the nonparametric case. The passage to the parametric case would be basically an exercise in the procedure of Chapter II, Section 24 (supplemented by the concluding remarks of Section 26), but for the possibility that an extremal may present self-intersections.

We shall try to deal, in an elementary way, with certain curves, which may possess self-intersections, and to define neighborhoods for such curves. We need to do this in order to treat the parametric analogue of the Jacobi theory of conjugate points. We may agree to regard a curve that intersects itself at x_0 as having, at x_0, two

Self-intersecting curve

Neighborhood

or more coincident points, which we distinguish and order by the increasing values of the parameter t along the curve. We need to distinguish, similarly, two or more layers in a neighborhood of such a curve, near the point x_0. We can think of the neighborhood as generated by a small moveable ball, which describes different layers, when the center, which moves along the curves, approaches the various points at which $x = x_0$.

We shall be concerned with the case in which the curve is an extremal of a standard parametric problem, or at any rate a problem in which L is positive definite and in which all relevant points of x-space are elliptic. If Q is a cube containing such an extremal Γ, and we define ρ as previously, it is clear that each arc of Γ of length $\leq \rho$ must be simple, and that two such arcs intersect either not at all, in a single point, or in a single common arc. By dividing Γ into a finite number of such simple arcs γ_k and surrounding each by an ordinary neighborhood W_k, we obtain a system of interlocking ordinary neighborhoods W_k that we shall term a "chained neighborhood of Γ."

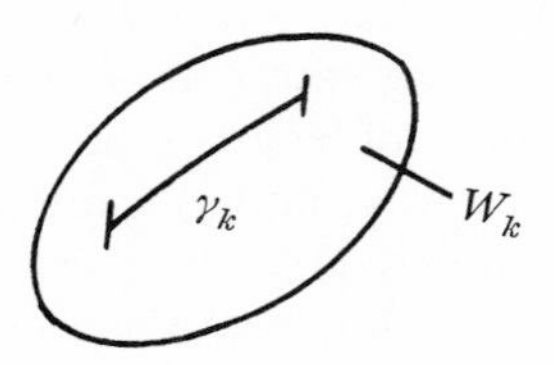

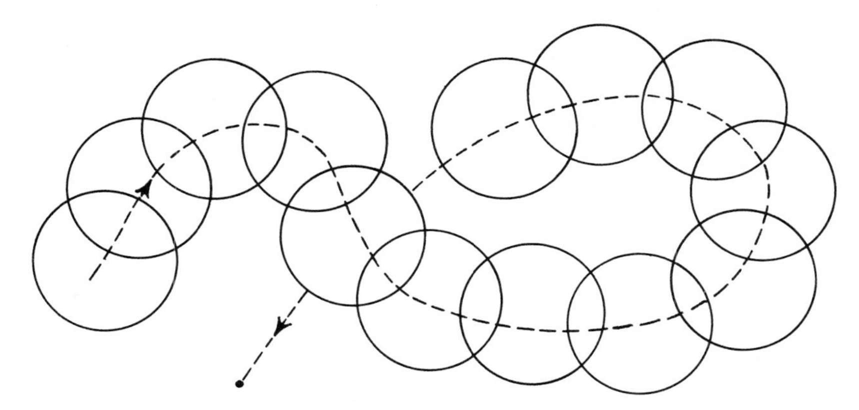

The notion of a chained neighborhood replaces, to some extent, that of a multiple-layered neighborhood, to which we have alluded. The notion is familiar in the theory of analytic functions in connection with analytic continuation; usually the ordinary neighborhoods W_k are then taken to be circular discs. It constitutes the basic tool of the Weierstrass approach, not only to analytic functions, but also, as here, to the parametric version of the theory of conjugate points.

We can regard a chained neighborhood W as the "multiple-layered union" of the interlocking W_k defining it. A point $P \in W$ is then given, not just by its position in x-space, but by a pair of the form (x, W_k) where $x \in W_k$. Two such pairs are identified, if and only if they contain the same x and also have the form $(x, W_{k'})$, $(x, W_{k''})$, where $x \in W_k$ for all integers k subject to $k' \leq k \leq k''$, or to $k'' \leq k \leq k'$.

Similarly a curve C lies in W if and only if it can be decomposed into arcs C_ν ($\nu = 1, 2, \ldots, N$) described in order as ν increases, and there exists an integer-valued function $k(\nu)$ such that

$$k(\nu + 1) - k(\nu) = \pm 1,$$

with the property that $C_\nu \subset W_k$ whenever $k = k(\nu)$. The arcs C_ν need not consist of different sets of points, and some or all of them may reduce to single points.

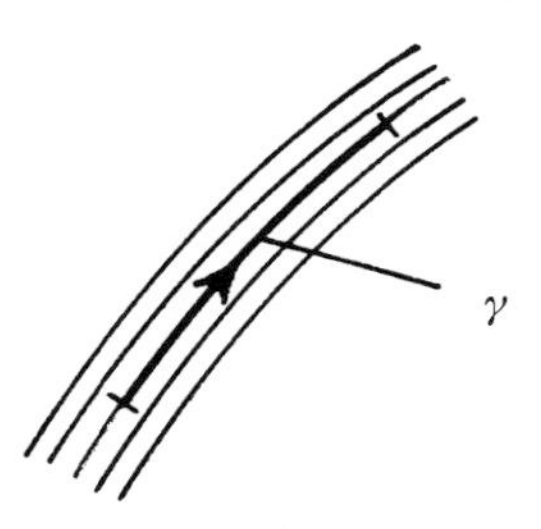

Now let γ be an interior arc of an extremal Γ_0, embedded for $u = 0$ in a family F of parametric extremals Γ_u of the form $x(t, u)$, where t is a geodesic parameter whose range contains, for each u in its interior, the interval Δ on which γ is defined when we set $u = 0$. Here γ may very well have self-intersections.

(52.1) Definition. We say that F covers simply a chained neighborhood of γ if there is a subdivision of Δ into intervals Δ_k, and for each k an open interval

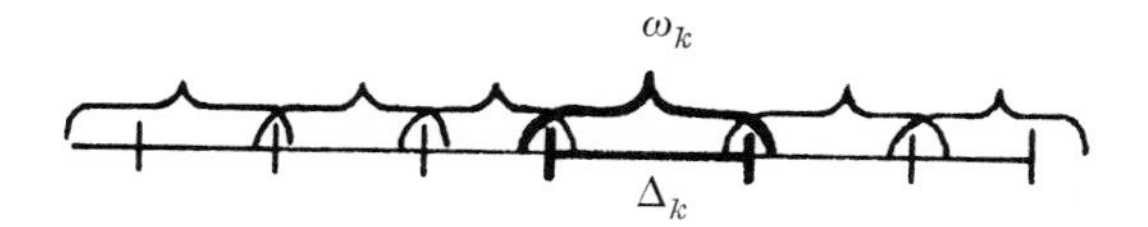

$\omega_k \supset \Delta_k$ such that, if F_k denotes the family defined by the restrictions of $x(t, u)$ to $t \in \omega_k$, and γ_k denotes the arc $t \in \Delta_k$ of γ defined by $x(t, 0)$, then, for each k, γ_k is a simple arc and F_k covers simply an ordinary neighborhood of γ_k.

We shall also need to discuss further the transition from parametric to nonparametric curves, and from parametric to nonparametric problems, so as to be in a position to adapt the theory of Chapter III to the parametric case. This transition is closely connected also with our previous remarks on curves with self-intersections and multiple-layered neighborhoods. Our method of distinguishing coincident points, and coincident portions of neighborhoods, in fact, originally amounted to introducing the parameter t along our curve as an additional coordinate, directed upward, and reducing relevant questions about parametric curves to corresponding questions about nonparametric ones situated in the higher dimensional (t, x)-space.

We attach to each admissible representation $x(t)$ of a parametric curve C the nonparametric curve C^* defined in (t, x)-space by the same function $x(t)$. Since the t-axis is now directed upward, we speak of C^* as a rising curve, situated above C. We term C^* an enhancement of C. (Of course C is the projection of C^*. However, curves in (t, x)-space that are not rising curves may also have such a projection.)

For rising curves, i.e., for nonparametric curves in (t, x)-space, we continue to denote by $\mathscr{I}$ the curvilinear integral of the original Lagrangian $L(x, \dot{x})$. Thus we have

$$\mathscr{I}(C^*) = \mathscr{I}(C),$$

when C^* is an enhancement of C. However, we shall denote by $\mathscr{I}^*(C^*)$ the corresponding curvilinear integral of the nonparametric Lagrangian $L^*(x, \dot{x})$, given by

$$L^* = L^2.$$

This is, except for a factor $\frac{1}{2}$, which we now find it convenient to drop, the nonparametric Lagrangian introduced in Chapter II, Section 24, which satisfies the Legendre condition.

We shall term a rising curve C^* graded if along it, i.e., for the line elements $(x, \dot{x})$ of C^*, we have $L(x, \dot{x}) = \text{const.}$; we term C^* calibrated if the constant is unity. Clearly a calibrated rising curve C^* corresponds to a geodesic representation of its projection C; all calibrated rising curves with a same projection are derived by translations parallel to the t-axis; the corresponding graded C^*, with this projection, are derived by a change of scale on the t-axis.

We recall that, according to the concluding remarks of Section 26, Chapter II, the extremals of L^* are the graded rising curves that project into parametric extremals of L; in other words, they are the graded rising extremals of L.

In this section we shall only need to consider those parametric extremals that issue from a fixed initial point, which we take as origin 0 of x-space. We shall restrict the corresponding parameters t to be initially synchronized at $t = 0$; this means that we limit ourselves also to consider only those extremals of L^* that issue from the origin 0^* of (t, x)-space. We shall denote by Π and Π^* the pencils of such extremals of L and L^*, respectively, with 0 and 0^* as vertices, such that a particular parametric extremal C_0 is embedded in Π, and the corresponding calibrated rising extremal in Π^*. The members of Π will be supposed given by their parametric representations $x(t, u)$ in terms of geodesic parameters t, on some fixed t-interval, and for a small u-domain including the origin of the n-dimensional u-space. (Here, as in Section 36 of Chapter III, u can be taken to be the initial value-difference of the conjugate vector $y(t)$.) The members of Π^* will have (in accordance with the remarks, already referred to, of Chapter II, Section 26) the form

$$x^*(t, u^*) = x((1 + u_0)t, u),$$

where u^* is the point of $(n + 1)$-dimensional space with the same coordinates as u, together with the additional small coordinate u_0.

(52.2) The Transition Lemma. *Let γ be an interior arc of the parametric extremal C_0 embedded in the pencil Π, and let γ^* denote the corresponding arc of the corresponding calibrated rising extremal of the pencil Π^*. Then in order that Π cover simply a chained neighborhood of γ, it is necessary and sufficient that Π^* cover simply an ordinary neighborhood of γ^*.*

PROOF. We may suppose the members of Π situated well inside a fixed cube Q. This fixes our positive number ρ. We write further, once more, m for the infimum of L in the set of $(x, \dot{x})$ for which $x \in Q$, $|\dot{x}| = 1$, and we suppose that the range of u_0 in Π^* includes an interval of the form $|u_0| \leq \delta$, where $\delta^2 < m\rho$, $\delta < 1$, and, further, that 2δ is less than the distance from the origin to the interval Δ of the t-axis, on which γ is defined.

As in the definition (52.1), we divide Δ into a finite number of subintervals Δ_k, and we enclose each of them in an open interval ω_k. We denote by γ_k the arc of γ corresponding to Δ_k, and by Π_k the family derived from Π by restricting t to lie in ω_k. We also define, correspondingly, the arc γ_k^* of γ^*, and the family Π_k^* derived from Π^*, by restricting t to Δ_k in the former case, and by restricting t by the condition $(1 + u_0)t \in \omega_k$ in the latter.

This being so, suppose first that Π covers simply a chained neighborhood of γ, and suppose our Δ_k, ω_k determined accordingly, so that each Π_k covers simply an ordinary neighborhood of the corresponding arc γ_k. It follows that no two members of Π_k^* can intersect, since their projections would be either distinct members of Π_k, which would then have to intersect, or else a same member of Π_k, which would then be self-intersecting; and both these possibilities are excluded by hypothesis. We also see that Π_k^* covers some neighborhood of γ_k^*. In fact, if (t_0, x_0) is any point near enough to γ_k^*, then there is a member of Π_k which passes through x_0 for some value of t near t_0, and we can therefore choose a small u_0 so that the corresponding member of Π_k^* satisfies $x^*(t_0, u^*) = x_0$, i.e., passes through (t_0, x_0). Thus Π_k^* covers simply a neighborhood of γ_k^*. This is now true for each k, and since our curves are nonparametric, it follows that Π^* covers simply a neighborhood of γ^*.

Conversely, suppose that Π^* covers simply a neighborhood of γ^*. Then, however we choose the Δ_k, ω_k as stated above, the family Π_k^* covers simply a neighborhood of γ_k^*, for each k. We make the choice in such a way that each ω_k, is of length $<\delta^2 < m\rho$. This implies that each member of each Π_k has length $<\rho$, and is therefore a simple arc. It implies further that the ratio of any two values of t in a same ω_k lies between the maximum of $(1 + \delta^2/t)$ and the minimum of $(1 + \delta^2/t)^{-1}$, and so between $1 + \delta$ and $1 - \delta$. Thus two such values can always be put in the form t and $(1 + u_0)t$, where $|u_0| < \delta$. Hence if two members of Π_k intersect at a point x, then we can obtain at once two members of Π_k^* which intersect at (t, x). This is impossible by hypothesis. Consequently no two members of Π_k can intersect. Since Π_k evidently covers a neighborhood of γ_k obtained by projection from the neighborhood of γ_k^* and covered by Π_k^*, we see that Π_k covers simply an ordinary neighborhood of γ_k. This is the case for each k, and therefore Π covers a chained neighborhood of γ.

Our lemma is thus established.

We are now ready to define conjugate points.

(52.3) Definition. Let C_0 be a parametric extremal issuing from 0, and let C_0^* denote the corresponding calibrated rising extremal issuing from 0^*. We term a point P of C_0 conjugate to 0, if the corresponding point P^* of C_0^* is conjugate to 0^* for the nonparametric problem with L^* as its Lagrangian. If no such conjugate point P is strictly interior to C_0, we say that C_0 satisfies the Jacobi condition.

(52.4) Necessity of the Jacobi Condition. *Let the extremal C_0 be a minimizing parametric curve. Then C_0 satisfies the Jacobi condition.*

PROOF. We define C_0^* as in (52.3) above. We shall reduce our assertion to the corresponding one for C_0^* with L^* as Lagrangian, and so to Theorem (37.4) of Chapter III, Section 37. Suppose C_0 does not satisfy the condition. By the theorem quoted, there is a nonparametric admissible curve C^* for which $\partial C^* = \partial C_0^*$ and $\mathscr{I}^*(C^*) < \mathscr{I}^*(C_0^*)$; here, moreover, since $L = L^* = 1$ along C_0^*, we have $\mathscr{I}^*(C_0^*) = \mathscr{I}(C_0^*) = \mathscr{I}(C_0) = T$, where T is the value of t at the final extremity. Hence by Schwartz's inequality along C^*

$$\int_{C^*} L\, dt \leq T^{1/2}\left(\int_{C^*} L^*\, dt\right)^{1/2} < T,$$

which shows that the projection C of C^*, which has the same extremities as C_0, satisfies $\mathscr{I}(C) < \mathscr{I}(C_0)$, contrary to the hypothesis that C_0 is minimizing.

(52.5) The Parametric Embedding Theorem and the Thin Triangle Inequality. *Let γ be an arc interior to a parametric extremal C_0, where C_0 issues from 0 and is subject to the Jacobi condition. Then C_0 can be embedded in a narrow pencil Π of the extremals*

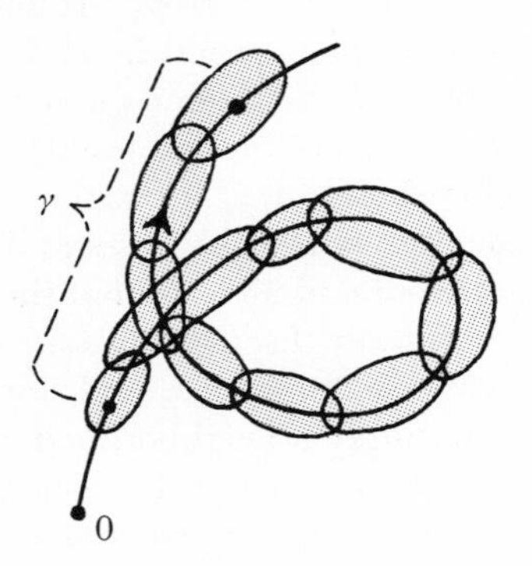

The chained neighborhood of the arc γ of C_0

issuing from 0, such that Π covers simply some chained neighborhood W of γ. Further, if Λ is any admissible curve lying in W, we have

$$\textbf{(52.6)} \qquad \mathscr{I}(\Lambda) \geq \mathscr{I}(C_2) - \mathscr{I}(C_1),$$

where C_1, C_2 are the unique arcs of extremals belonging to Π such that C_1, C_2 join 0, respectively, to the extremities P_1, P_2 of Λ. Equality in (52.6) holds only if Λ is an arc of C_2.

PROOF. The simple covering by Π of some chained neighborhood of γ follows from Theorem (36.2) of Chapter III, Section 26, in view of the transition lemma

(52.2). In the remaining assertions, we may suppose, by addition, that Λ lies in one of the ordinary neighborhoods W_k, by which W is defined. These assertions then follow from the Weierstrass formula (12.6) of Chapter I, Section 16.

§53. THE TONELLI-CARATHEODORY UNICITY THEOREM

Besides giving a meaning to necessary conditions, and in particular to the parametric Jacobi condition, the Hilbert existence theory provides basic new techniques, and these can be applied to other matters besides existence. This is a typical state of affairs in mathematics. It has happened more than once that the insight gained from the study of matters that one might well feel inclined to take for granted, or to dismiss as unimportant, turned out to be extremely helpful in matters whose importance was much more immediate. For instance, there was a great outcry when Camille Jordan published a lengthy proof of the apparently self-evident fact that a simple closed plane curve separates the plane; however the methods that have grown out of his proof and the insight it has helped develop are what led to modern topology, a branch of mathematics with innumerable applications.

It is because we possess now a parametric existence theory that it becomes worthwhile to develop separately the parametric theory of conjugate points. We could go on to adapt similarly, to the parametric form, the Morse theory described in Chapter III. This would give to the Morse theory its proper scope, and the details are carried out in Morse's book. We shall not go into these matters here. However, we shall develop here a related deformation argument of considerable importance. Deformations are really at the root of the Morse theory, and they are there, very rightly, considered in a space of curves, rather than in the original x-space; also, particular importance is then attached to "downward" deformations. Here, however, we shall be concerned with an older version of deformation. We develop it partly for its own sake and partly because it is of a very general nature; it is remarkable that it is not really linked to smoothness assumptions and that it is therefore, in principle, also available for optimal control.

The deformation argument that we shall be concerned with goes back to Weierstrass's theory of analytic continuation. In the calculus of variations, it can be applied very effectively in conjunction with the parametric version of the Jacobi theory of conjugate points, also due to Weierstrass. However, this application was not made by Weierstrass; it first occurred in a letter of Carathéodory to Tonelli, which is discussed in Tonelli's *Fondamenti* (Vol. II, p. 274). All this is well before the Morse theory. It leads to an important unicity theorem.

We do not give to this theorem its most general form. The reader may try for himself to modify the hypotheses and the conclusions. The arguments, as in the preceding sections, are really more important than the actual context to which we apply them. These arguments are not really difficult, or even novel, except perhaps for a new twist here and there. Experienced readers will recognize the pattern long before the proofs end; it is reminiscent not only of analytic continuation, but also of standard parts of advanced calculus, such as the routine proofs of Borel's covering theorem for a segment and for a plane figure. However, routine proofs always seem to find new uses.

In view of the basically elementary nature of the arguments used, this may be a good time for a prospective mathematician to try out his skill at constructing the proofs for himself. A few weeks devoted to this, whether he succeeds to his satisfaction or not, should give him valuable practice, before he goes all out on a thesis problem, which may either make or break him.

We shall term favorable an extremal issuing from 0, which contains no point conjugate to 0. By a favorable problem we shall mean a standard parametric one in which each extremal issuing from 0 is favorable. We shall use deformations of points other than 0, and also of extremals issuing from 0. Both types will, further, be of two kinds: admissible ordinary deformations, and admissible triangular ones. The former are defined in terms of a parameter u whose range U is a segment; the latter

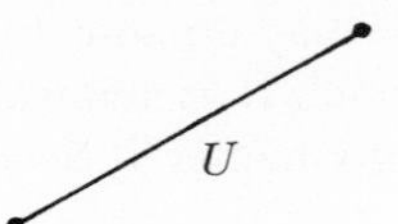

Parameter range for
ordinary deformation

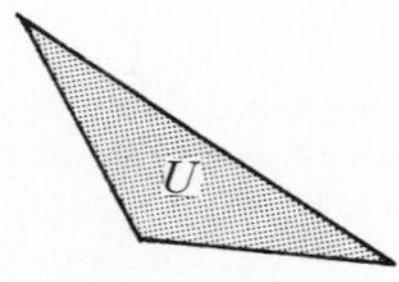

Parameter range for
triangular deformation

in terms of one whose range is a closed triangle. In either case, an admissible deformation of a point $x_0 \neq 0$ is defined to be a continuous, nonvanishing, piecewise continuously differentiable (or Lipschitzian) function

$$\xi(u) \quad u \in U,$$

which is given together with some fixed point $u_0 \in U$, which we term the initial point of U, at which $\xi(u_0) = x_0$ (usually an end or a corner of U). An admissible (ordinary

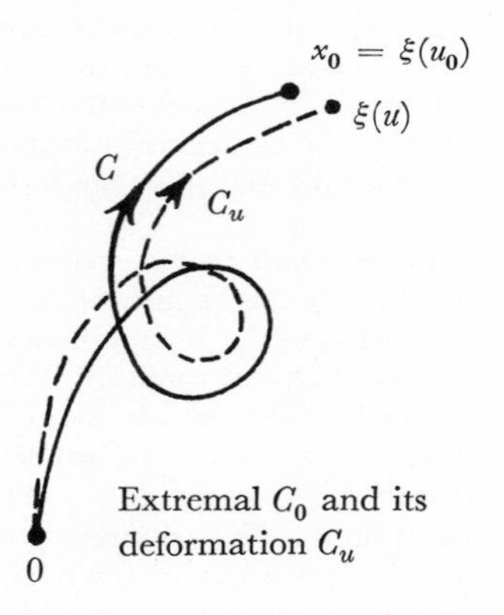

Extremal C_0 and its
deformation C_u

or triangular) deformation of an extremal C, where C joins the origin to a point $x_0 \neq 0$, will be defined by a family

$$C_u \quad u \in U$$

of extremals, where each C_u joins the origin to a corresponding point $\xi(u) \neq 0$, subject to the following conditions:

(i) $\xi(u)$ $u \in U$ is an admissible deformation of x_0.

(ii) The function $T(u) = \mathscr{I}(C_u)$ $u \in U$ is continuous.

(iii) For $u = u_0$, the extremal C_u reduces to C.

(iv) The function $x(t, u)$ $0 \leq t \leq T(u)$, $u \in U$, which provides a geodesic representation of C_u for each constant $u \in U$, is continuous in (t, u).

Given an admissible deformation, thus defined, of an extremal C, we shall term its extremity deformation, the deformation of x_0, defined by the corresponding function $\xi(u)$ $u \in U$. Further, if, for some $u_0^* \in U$, we denote by x_0^*, C^* the point $\xi(u)$ and the extremal C_u for $u = u_0^*$, the deformations of x_0^* and C^*, provided by the same function $\xi(u)$ $u \in U$ and by the same family C_u $u \in U$, will be said to result from the original deformations by transfer to u_0^*. An admissible deformation of C will be termed exclusive if for each $u_0^* \in U$ the deformation of C^* which results from the transfer is the sole admissible deformation of C^* with the same extremity deformation.

A deformation of x_0 or of C will be termed small if the difference $\xi(u) - x_0$, or $x(t, u) - x(t, u_0)$ is small, uniformly in u or in (t, u). We shall need the following preliminary result:

(53.1) Small Deformation Lemma. *Let C be a favorable extremal of a standard problem, and let C join the origin 0 to a point $x_0 \neq 0$. Then, given any admissible small deformation of x_0, there is an exclusive deformation of C, for which it is the extremity deformation.*

PROOF. Let $T_0 = \mathscr{I}(C)$, and let η_0 denote the initial value, at the origin, of the conjugate variable y on C. We denote by Π the pencil of extremals issuing from 0 for which the initial values η of y satisfy, in addition to $H(0, \eta) = 1$, a relation of the form $|\eta - \eta_0| \leq \delta$, for some fixed $\delta > 0$. Along these extremals, we write t for the geodesic parameter which vanishes at the origin. Further, we denote by F the family of the arcs of extremals of Π, for which this parameter is subject to

$$|t - T_0| \leq \delta.$$

For small enough δ, by Theorem (52.5), F covers simply some neighborhood A of x_0. We shrink this value of δ so that the new family lies in A, and we then shrink A so that it is again covered by the family. Then the members of F do not intersect one another, nor themselves. Moreover, this further property of F remains if our new δ is slightly increased.

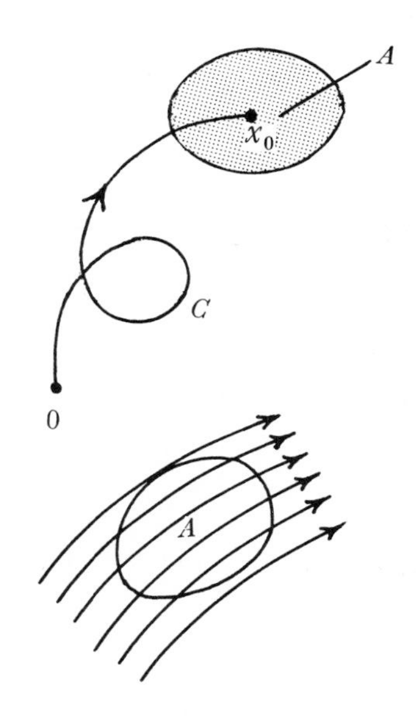

The family F

Having thus fixed δ, and so Π and F, we write B for the set of (t, η) for which

$$|t - T_0| \leq \delta, \qquad |\eta - \eta_0| \leq \delta, \qquad H(0, \eta) = 1;$$

and we write

$$x = \varphi(t, \eta)$$

for the geodesic representation of the members of Π in terms of the initial values η. Thus C is now given by $x = \varphi(t, \eta_0)$ $0 \leq t \leq T_0$. Clearly the set occupied by F may now be expressed as the one-to-one image $\varphi(B)$ of B under the map φ.

Thus the map φ, restricted to B, has an inverse of the form

$$t = \tau(x), \qquad \eta = g(x).$$

This inverse map is of course, like φ itself, continuous. This follows from implicit function theory, or directly, because if a map of a bounded closed set B is continuous and one-to-one, then so is its inverse.

Now let $\xi(u)$ $u \in U$ be any admissible deformation of $x_0 = \xi(u_0)$, such that $\xi(u) \in A$ for all $u \in U$. We denote, for each $u \in U$, by C_u the extremal with the geodesic representation

$$x(t, u) \qquad 0 \leq t \leq T(u),$$

where

$$T(u) = \tau(\xi(u)), \qquad x(t, u) = \varphi(t, g(\xi(u))).$$

Clearly the family C_u $u \in U$ constitutes an admissible deformation of C with the given extremity deformation. We have to show that this deformation is exclusive.

For any fixed $u \in U$, let $\eta_u = g(\xi(u))$. Then η_u is the initial value of y on C_u, so that C_u is the extremal

$$x = \varphi(t, \eta_u) \qquad 0 \leq t \leq T(u).$$

In all this, we could have chosen a slightly larger δ, which we denote by δ^*; the set A can then be kept the same, but B becomes a larger set B^*, and φ is replaced by its one-to-one continuous extension φ^*, defined in B^*. For sufficiently small $\varepsilon > 0$, the set B^* then contains the set B_u of the points (t, η) subject to

$$|t - T(u)| \leq \varepsilon, \qquad |\eta - \eta_u| \leq \varepsilon, \qquad H(0, \eta) = 1.$$

We choose ε so small that $\varphi^*(B_u) \subset A$; this is possible by continuity of φ^* at the point $(T(u), \eta_u)$, whose image is $\xi(u) \in A$. We thus have

$$B_u \subset (\varphi^*)^{-1}(A) = \varphi^{-1}(A) \subset B.$$

The relevant value of ε here depends, of course, on u. With this same ε, we denote by Π_u the family of extremal arcs $\Gamma_{\eta T}$, defined for constant $(T, \eta) \in B_u$ by

$$x = \varphi(t, \eta) \qquad 0 \leq t \leq T.$$

Clearly, for each point $\xi^* \in \varphi(B_u)$, there is one and only one extremal $\Gamma_{\eta T}$ of the family Π_u, which terminates at the point ξ^*. Here the set $\varphi(B_u)$ includes some neighborhood of the extremity $\xi(u)$ of C_u.

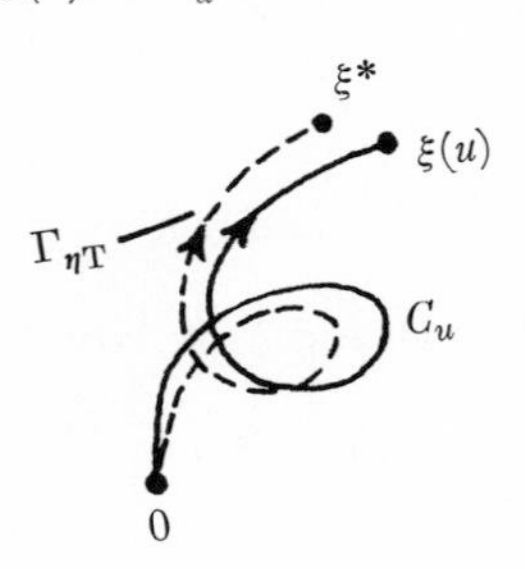

We are now ready to show that our deformation is exclusive. Suppose the contrary. There would then be, for some $u_0^* \in U$, an admissible deformation

$$C_u^* \quad u \in U$$

of an extremal C^*, such that, for $u = u_0^*$, C^* coincides with both C_u and C_u^*, and that, for all $u \in U$, C_u and C_u^* have the same terminal point $\xi(u)$. Further, we would have $C_u \neq C_u^*$ for some $u \in U$. We denote by U^* a segment in U, whose initial point is u_0^*, such that $C_u \neq C_u^*$ for some $u \in U^*$. Further, by choice of axes in u-space, we identify U^* with an interval of reals $u_0^* \leq u \leq u_1^*$.

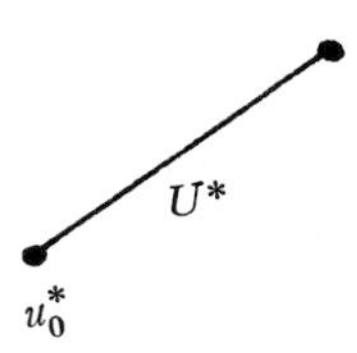

We now denote by ω the supremum of the values of $u^* \in U^*$ such that $C_u = C_u^*$ for $u_0^* \leq u \leq u^*$.

Evidently $C_u = C_u^*$ for $u_0^* \leq u \leq \omega$.

However, for $u > \omega$, it follows from the definition of deformation that, when u is near enough to ω, the curves C_u, C_u^* must lie in the family Π_ω, i.e., in the family Π_u defined above, with ω for u. In this family, we saw that members are uniquely determined by their second extremity, and this is $\xi(u)$ for both C_u, C_u^*. Hence for u slightly greater than ω, we still have $C_u = C_u^*$, contrary to the definition of ω as a supremum.

This completes the proof.

In the case of a favorable problem, we shall establish a more general result:

(53.2) Main Deformation Lemma. *Let C be an extremal of a favorable problem, and let C join the origin to a point $x_0 \neq 0$. Then, given any admissible deformation of x_0, there is an exclusive deformation of C, for which it is the extremity deformation.*

PROOF. Let the given deformation of x_0 be $\xi(u)$ $u \in U$ and let the initial point be u_0, so that $\xi(u_0) = x_0$. We first treat the case in which U is a segment, and we may suppose it situated on the axis of reals. For any two distinct points u, u^* of U, we denote by Λ_{uu^*} the admissible parametric curve in x-space,

$$x = \xi(t) \qquad u \leq t \leq u^*, \qquad \text{if} \quad u < u^*,$$

$$x = \xi(-t) \qquad -u \leq t \leq -u^* \quad \text{if} \quad u > u^*.$$

This being so, let $u_0^* \in U$, $x_0^* = \xi(u_0^*)$, and let C^* be an extremal joining the origin to x_0^*. A subinterval U^* of U, which contains u_0^*, will be termed satisfactory for

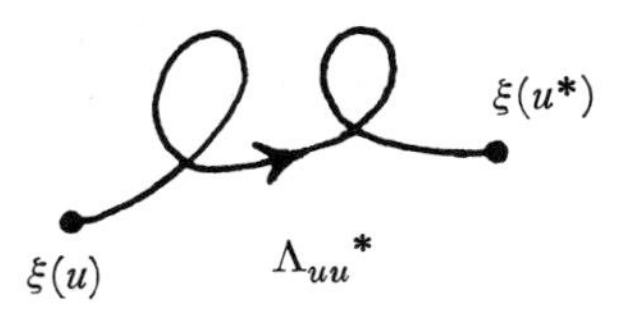

u_0^*, C^* if there is an exclusive deformation C_u^* $u \in U$ of C^* whose extremity deformation is $\xi(u)$ $u \in U^*$, and if, further, the function

$$T^*(u) = \mathscr{I}(C_u^*) \qquad u \in U^*$$

satisfies, for all distinct u, u^* in U^*, the inequality

$$\textbf{(53.3)} \qquad T^*(u^*) - T^*(u) \leq \mathscr{I}(\Lambda_{uu^*}).$$

Clearly, by (53.1) and the thin triangle inequality (52.6), any sufficiently small subinterval U^*, which contains u_0^*, will be satisfactory for u_0^*, C^*.

We wish to show that U is satisfactory for u_0, C. In so doing, we may suppose u_0 to be the first point of U, i.e., that U has the form $u_0 \leq u \leq u_1$. We write Λ for Λ_{uu^*}, when $u = u_0$, $u^* = u_1$.

We denote by ω the supremum of the numbers $u^* \in U$, for which the subinterval $u_0 \leq u \leq u^*$ is satisfactory for u_0, C. Since small intervals of this form are satisfactory, we have $u_0 < \omega$. Clearly every interval of the form $u_0 \leq u \leq \beta$, where $u_0 < \beta < \omega$, is then satisfactory for u_0, C. The corresponding exclusive deformation of C will be written C_u $u_0 \leq u \leq \beta$, and it is evident that C_u does not alter when β is increased, subject to $\beta < \omega$, while u is kept fixed. Thus C_u is defined for all u in $u_0 \leq u < \omega$. Clearly also, every interval of the form $\alpha \leq u \leq \beta$, where $u_0 \leq \alpha < \beta < \omega$, is then satisfactory for each pair u^*, C_{u^*}, where $\alpha \leq u^* \leq \beta$.

Let now Ω be the part in U of a sufficiently small segment to which ω is interior, and denote by

$$u_\nu \quad \nu = 2, 3, \ldots$$

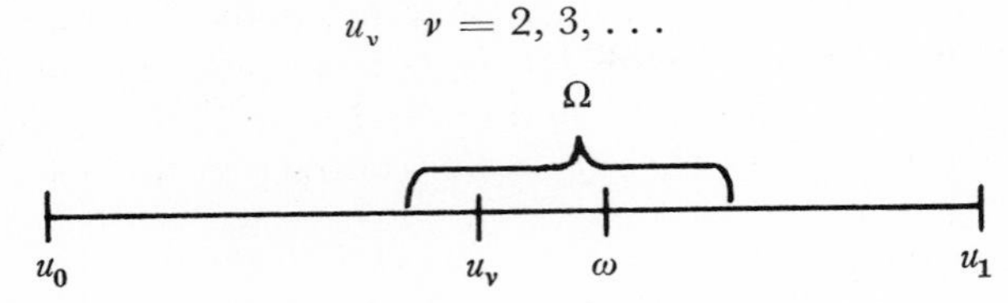

an increasing sequence in U, which tends to ω from below. Since the interval $u_0 \leq u \leq u_\nu$ is satisfactory, the function $T(u) = \mathscr{I}(C_u)$ satisfies for $u_0 \leq u < \omega$ the inequality $T(u_\nu) \leq T(u_0) + \mathscr{I}(\Lambda)$. Hence, by the selection principle for extremals (51.7), there is a subsequence of the u_ν along which the extremals C_u tend to an extremal C^*. Evidently C^* joins the origin to the point $\xi(\omega)$.

By choosing Ω small enough, we ensure that Ω be satisfactory for ω, C^*. We denote by C_u^* $u \in \Omega$ the corresponding exclusive deformation of C^*, and by U^* the union of Ω with the segment consisting of the prior points of U. The segment U^* has the form $u_0 \leq u \leq u^*$, where $\omega \leq u^*$, and this last inequality reduces to equality only if $\omega = u_1$, in which case $U^* = U$.

In order to prove that U is satisfactory for u_0, C_0, it will suffice to show that U^* is so. For in that case we have $u^* \leq \omega$, by definition of ω as a supremum, and therefore $U^* = U$. We shall therefore verify that U^* is satisfactory for u_0, C.

To this effect let N_ν be the set of terms of our subsequence whose values exceed u_ν. For large ν, we have $N_\nu \subset \Omega$, so that then, for $u \in N_\nu$, both C_u and C_u^* are defined, and both terminate at $\xi(u)$. Further, for large ν, both of these extremals will be close to C^*, and by Theorem (52.5) they must then coincide. This coincidence then extends to all $u \in \Omega$ such that $u < \omega$, since the corresponding deformations are exclusive. We can therefore extend the definition of C_u to all $u \in U^*$, simply by writing C_u in place of C_u^*, for $u \in \Omega$. We then see at once that the family C_u $u \in U^*$ defines an exclusive deformation of C. Since the relevant inequality of the type (53.3) extends by addition, it follows that U^* is satisfactory for u_0, C. This establishes (53.2) in the case in which U is a segment.

We pass on to the case in which U is a triangle. We may suppose by subdivision that u_0 is a vertex of U. On any segment S drawn from u_0 to the opposite side of U, we then define an exclusive deformation

$$C_u \quad u \in S$$

of C, by the case already treated;

$$C_u \quad u \in U$$

is thus defined, by varying S, as a family of extremals.

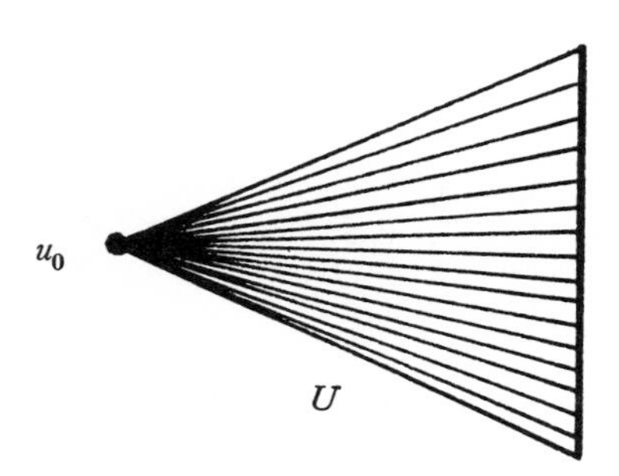

The segment S

For each S, we now construct at u_0 a small angle θ, which is bisected in the neighborhood of u_0 by S, and we denote by Σ the thin triangle consisting of the part of U in the angle θ. Similarly, if S^* is a subsegment of S for which the point nearest u_0 is u_0^*, we denote by U^*, a triangle with a vertex at u_0^*, whose sides at this vertex are

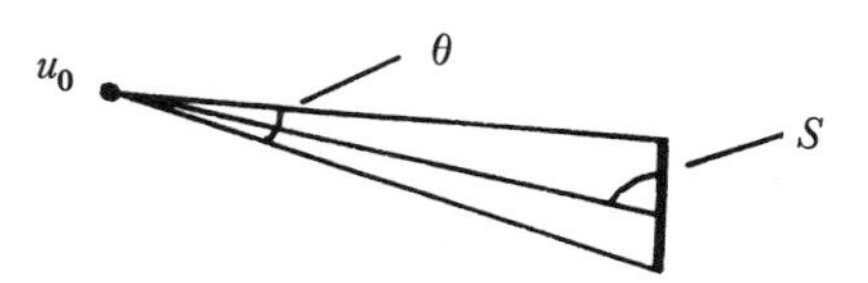

The thin triangle Σ determined by θ

parallel to those of U at u_0, and whose third side passes through the other extremity of S^* and is parallel to the third side of U. We construct at u_0^* a small angle θ^*, which is bisected in the neighborhood of u_0^* by S^*, and we denote by Σ^* the thin triangle consisting of the part of U^* in the angle θ^*.

We shall term the subsegment S^* satisfactory at the point u^*, where $u^* \in S^*$, if there exists a thin triangle Σ^*, determined as above from S^* by an angle θ^* at u_0^*, such that, when u^* is taken as initial point of Σ^*, the family C_u $u \in \Sigma^*$ constitutes an exclusive admissible deformation of the extremal $C^* = C_{u^*}$.

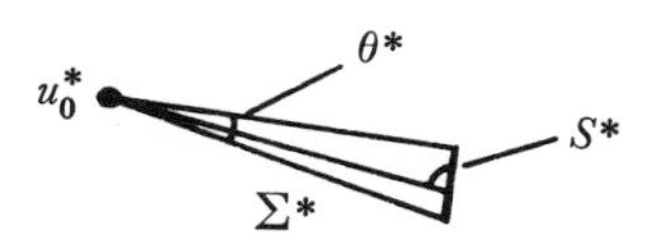

We shall prove that each S is satisfactory at u_0. For this purpose, we shall repeat, in a modified form, the argument used to treat the case of (53.2) in which U was a segment. We keep an S fixed for the present, and we regard it as a segment of reals, with u_0 as its first point, situated in the complex plane. This amounts to making a suitable rotation of axes in the u-plane.

We denote by ω the supremum of the points $\beta \in S$ such that the segment $u_0 \leq u \leq \beta$ is satisfactory at u_0. We write Ω for the intersection with S of a small

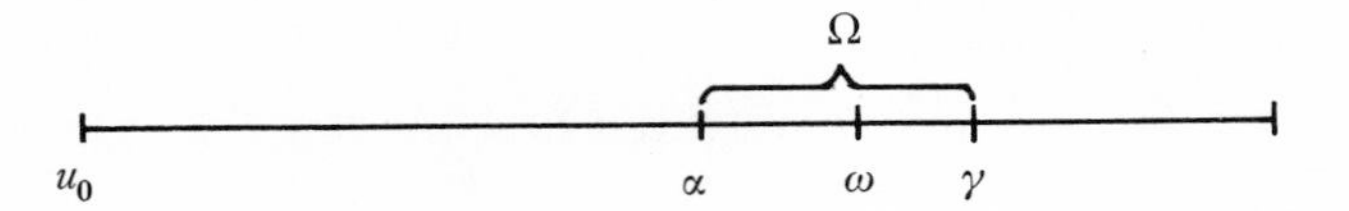

segment of the real axis, which has ω as an interior point. We denote the first and last points of Ω by α and γ, respectively, and we write S_0^* for the segment $u_0 \leq u \leq \gamma$. Everything now hinges on showing that S_0^* is satisfactory at u_0, provided that Ω is small enough.

We now enclose Ω in a small triangle Δ, similar and parallel to U. We do this by taking Ω to be our previous segment S^*, and Δ to be the corresponding U^*. Thus

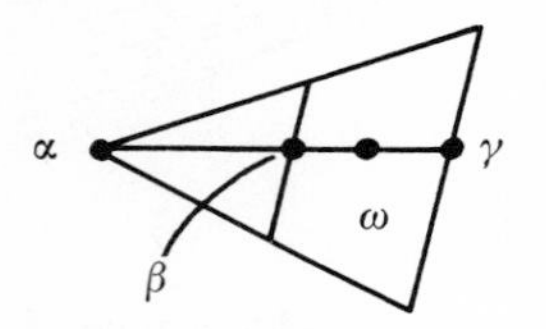

The small triangle Δ

the point α is a vertex of Δ, and the point γ lies on the side ℓ_γ, opposite to α. We choose further any point β for which $\alpha < \beta < \gamma$, and we denote by ℓ_β the segment parallel to ℓ_γ, which joins the two other sides of Δ.

We shall suppose Ω, and therefore Δ, so small that, in accordance with (53.1), there is an exclusive admissible deformation of the extremal $C^* = C_\omega$, which is furnished by a family

$$C_u^* \quad u \in \Delta$$

whose extremity deformation is $\xi(u)$ $u \in \Delta$, and for which the initial point of Δ is taken to be ω.

The points α, γ being thus determined, we choose β as stated above, and we denote by S_1^* the segment $u_0 \leq u \leq \beta$. Since $\beta < \omega$, we can determine an angle θ^* at u_0 for which, if Σ_1^* is the thin triangle it associates with S_1^*, the family

$$C_u \quad u \in \Sigma_1^*$$

constitutes an exclusive admissible deformation of C. The same remains true if we reduce the angle θ^*, and we may therefore suppose it so small that the side of Σ_1^*

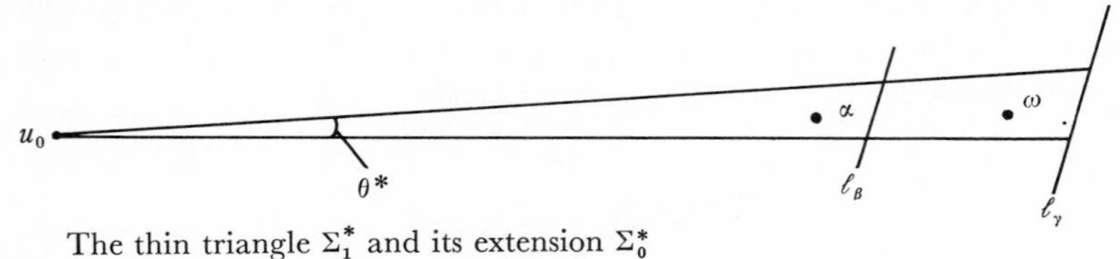

The thin triangle Σ_1^* and its extension Σ_0^*

opposite the vertex u_0 is contained in ℓ_β. With this value of θ^*, we denote by Σ_0^* the thin triangle similarly corresponding to S_0^*.

We now consider any point $\hat{u} \in \Sigma_0^* - \Sigma_1^*$. We write $\hat{S}$ for the segment through $\hat{u}$ which joins the vertex u_0 of U to the opposite side, and u_β for the intersection of $\hat{S}$

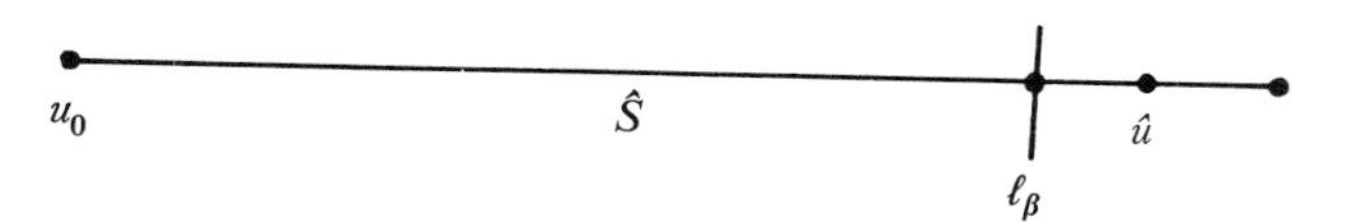

with ℓ_β. We join ω to $\hat{u}$ by a path made up of three segments: the segment $\Gamma \subset S$ from ω to β, the segment $\Gamma_\beta \subset \ell_\beta$ from β to u_β and the segment $\hat{\Gamma} \subset \hat{S}$ from u_β to $\hat{u}$. On each of these segments, the family C_u^* constitutes an exclusive deformation of any of its members, since they lie in Δ. The same is true of the family C_u, since Γ, $\hat{\Gamma}$ lie

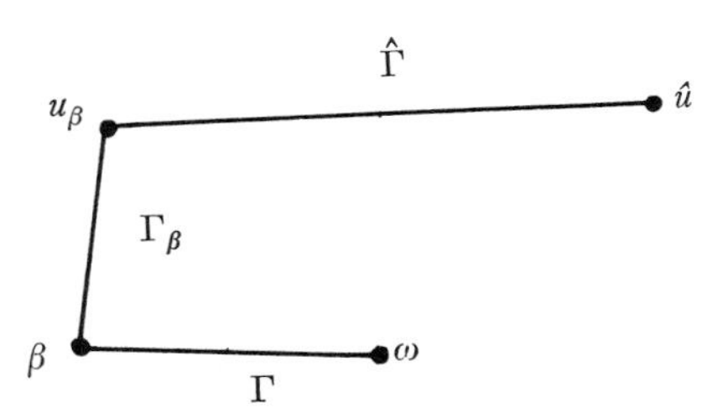

on segments from u_0, and Γ_β in Σ_1^*. Since the two families agree at ω and the extremities of corresponding members are the same, we find, successively, that $C_u = C_u^*$ at β, u_β and at $\hat{u}$.

Thus C_u coincides with C_u^* for all $u \in \Sigma_0^* - \Sigma_1^*$. It follows that the family

$$C_u \quad u \in \Sigma_0^*$$

constitutes an exclusive deformation of C. Thus the segment S_0^* is satisfactory at u_0. By definition of ω, this requires $\gamma = \omega$, and so $S_0^* = S$. Hence S is satisfactory at u_0.

It follows at once that the function $x(t, u)$ which provides the geodesic representation of C_u is continuous in (t, u). Hence the family

$$C_u \quad u \in U$$

constitutes an admissible deformation of C. The latter is evidently exclusive, since the restrictions

$$C_u \quad u \in S$$

are exclusive for each S by the first part of the proof. This establishes (53.3).

(53.4) The Unicity Theorem. *In a favorable problem, there is for each point P of the space one and only one extremal joining the origin to P. This extremal is then simple and constitutes the unique minimizing curve joining the origin to P.*

PROOF. We denote by B the ball $|x| \leq \rho$, and by S the sphere $|x| = \rho$, where ρ is chosen so small that, for each point $P \in B$, there is one and only one extremal in B that joins the origin to the point P, and so that this extremal is then always minimizing. (All this is made possible by Theorem (29.5) of Chapter II, Section 29, with some fixed cube, of center the origin, as the set there denoted by E, and with the whole of space as the set there denoted by W.)

This being so, let P be any point. By Theorems (51.1) and (51.2) there exists a minimizing extremal joining the origin to the point P. We assert that no other extremal joins the origin to P. To prove this, we suppose that two distinct extremals C_1, C_2 join the origin to a same point P, and we shall derive a contradiction.

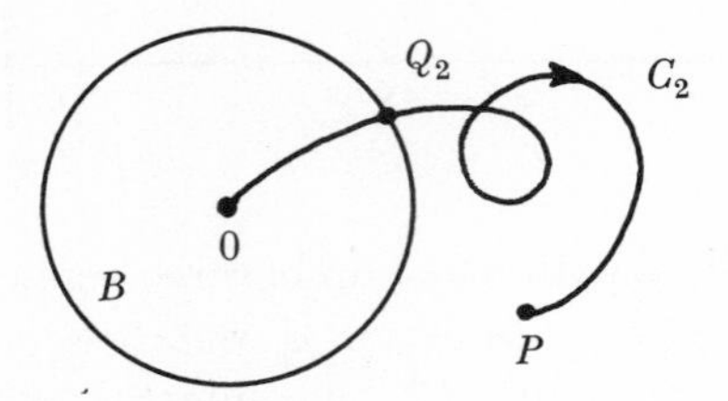

Clearly at least one of them, C_2 say, has points outside B. We denote by Q_2 its first intersection with S, and by Γ_2 the arc of C_2 subsequent to Q_2. If Γ_2 returns into B, we cut C_2 short at the next intersection with S and rename this point P; in that case, we replace C_1 by the unique minimizing extremal from the origin to P, which then lies in B and is distinct from the new C_2. We may therefore suppose, without loss of generality, that Γ_2 contains no interior point of B. In particular, P is not interior to B, so that C_1 must meet S for the first time at some point Q_1. We write Γ_1 for the arc of C_1 subsequent to Q_1, and we may again suppose that Γ_1 contains no interior point of B. We denote by Γ_{12} the curve consisting of Γ_1 followed by Γ_2 reversed, so that Γ_{12} now joins Q_1 to Q_2, via P. We write Γ for the projection of Γ_{12} on S, each point of Γ_{12} being replaced by the point of S on the same half-line from the origin.

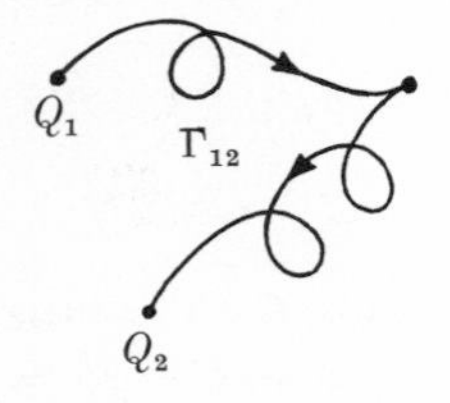

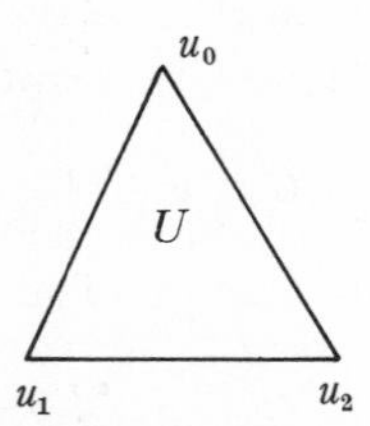

We can now define in various ways, by elementary procedures, a continuous, nonvanishing, piecewise continuously differentiable function

$$\xi(u) \quad u \in U,$$

where U is a triangle with vertices u_0, u_1, u_2, such that when u describes the sides u_1 to u_0, u_2 to u_0 and u_1 to u_2, respectively, $\xi(u)$ describes Γ_1, Γ_2, Γ.

We now denote by γ_1, γ_2 the arcs of C_1, C_2 prior to Γ_1, Γ_2, so that they terminate at Q_1, Q_2. In accordance with our main deformation lemma (53.3), we define an exclusive admissible deformation

$$C_u \quad u \in U$$

of the extremal γ_1, with u_1 as the initial point of U, so that the corresponding extremity deformation is the deformation of Q_1, provided by $\xi(u)$.

On the side from u_1 to u_2, the extremals C_u can at once be identified with the unique extremals in B that join the origin to the points of Γ, since this family is admissible, and the deformation on this side of U is exclusive. It follows that at u_2, the extremal C_u will be γ_2.

On the sides from u_1 or u_2 to u_0, we can similarly identify the extremals C_u as the arcs of C_1 terminating at the various points of Γ_1, or as those of C_2 terminating at the points of Γ_2. At $u = u_0$ the extremal C_u can thus be identified, on the one hand with C_1, and on the other with C_2. It follows that C_1 coincides with C_2, contrary to our assumption.

For each point P there is thus exactly one extremal, which joins the origin to it. Evidently this extremal is then the unique minimizing curve joining these points, and it is therefore simple. This completes the proof.

§54. ABSOLUTE AND HOMOTOPIC MINIMA ON B··i-COMPACT DOMAINS AND MANIFOLDS

In the preceding sections, when applying the Hilbert methods to variational problems in the whole of Euclidean space, we found it necessary to make assumptions, which, in effect, exclude the possibility of solutions that go off to infinity on the way to their destination. It is possible to avoid these restrictions by considering problems in which admissible curves are required to lie in some fixed bounded domain G. Normally such problems belong more properly to optimal control, since they are problems with side-conditions. There is, however, one case, in which the theory is hardly modified at all by the restriction to G, and this case we shall treat here. We term it the geoconvex case.

We can also consider, more generally, problems for curves situated on a given manifold, for instance on the surface of a sphere. Such problems could again be regarded as problems with side-conditions in a Euclidean space in which the manifold is embedded. However, it is often more convenient to treat them intrinsically, in terms of local coordinate systems on the manifold. This is more particularly the case when the manifold is compact and without boundary, as the Hilbert methods then apply without any geoconvexity restriction.

We restrict ourselves, in this section, to the closure $\bar{G}$ of a bounded open domain G of x-space; however, it is understood that x-space can be replaced by any differentiable manifold. Our parametric Lagrangian L will be supposed positive definite, and all points of x-space, or of some open set containing $\bar{G}$, are to be elliptic. We can then determine, in accordance with Theorem (29.5) of Chapter II, Section 29, $\rho > 0$, so that any two points P, Q of $\bar{G}$, distant $<\rho$, can be joined by a unique minimizing curve C_{PQ}, which is also an extremal. We term G geoconvex if there is a positive $\delta < \rho$ such that for every pair of points P, Q of G distant $<\delta$, we have $C_{PQ} \subset G$.

Although geoconvexity may seem, at first sight, to be the kind of generalization of convexity that ought to be basic, it is really an *ad hoc* condition to ensure that curves that approach the frontier of G play no essential part. Its artificiality is most apparent when

$$L(x, \dot{x}) \neq L(x, -\dot{x}),$$

since it requires both C_{PQ} and C_{QP} to lie in G.

We denote by Ω a closed set of ordered pairs P, Q, where $P \in \bar{G}$, $Q \in \bar{G}$. We say of a curve C that its boundary lies in Ω, and we write $\partial C \in \Omega$, if C joins a pair of points P, Q which belong to Ω. We denote by $\mathscr{A}$ the class of admissible parametric curves

C in $\bar{G}$, such that $\partial C \in \Omega$. We term problem of the absolute minimum that of determining a curve $C \in \mathscr{A}$ for which $\mathscr{I}(C)$ attains its minimum for curves in $\mathscr{A}$. We shall also consider a second problem.

For this purpose we shall introduce deformations, not, as in the preceding section, deformations of extremals, but deformations of admissible curves in $\bar{G}$. We shall not require the concept of a triangular deformation, but only the concept that corresponds to what we termed an ordinary deformation. Moreover, the segment that we formerly denoted by U will now be the unit interval $0 \leq u \leq 1$ on the real axis, and the initial point u_0 will be taken to be the first point, namely 0. We term continuous deformation in $\bar{G}$ of an admissible curve C_0 where $C_0 \subset \bar{G}$, a family of admissible curves

$$C_u \quad 0 \leq u \leq 1,$$

each situated in $\bar{G}$, and such that its geodesic representation

$$x(t, u) \qquad 0 \leq t \leq T(u),$$

is given in terms of a continuous function $T(u)$ $0 \leq u \leq 1$, and a continuous function $x(t, u)$ in the corresponding set of (t, u). We term C_0 and C_1, respectively, initial and final curves of the deformation, and we speak of the deformation as being from C_0 to C_1. We term it a homotopy in $\bar{G}$, in the case in which either all the C_u have a same pair of distinct extremities, or all of them are closed curves. We then say that C_1 is homotopic to C_0 in $\bar{G}$. Further, a deformation in $\bar{G}$ will be termed an Ω-homotopy, and we say that C_1 is Ω-homotopic to C_0 in $\bar{G}$, if for each u in $0 \leq u \leq 1$, we have $\partial C_u \in \Omega$.

We shall term Ω locally accessible if for each pair $(P_0, Q_0) \in \Omega$, and each $\varepsilon > 0$ there exists a ball W of the $2n$-dimensional product space, such that for every pair $(P, Q) \in \Omega \cap W$ there exists a continuous curve $(\xi_1(t), \xi_2(t))$ $0 \leq t \leq 1$ in Ω of length $< \varepsilon$ for which the components $\xi_1(t)$, $\xi_2(t)$ describe admissible curves in $\bar{G}$, which join, respectively, P to P_0 and Q to Q_0.

Local accessibility of Ω

This being so, let $\mathscr{A}$ be nonempty and let C_0 be some fixed member of $\mathscr{A}$. We denote by $\mathscr{B}$ the class of curves C that are Ω-homotopic to C_0, where Ω is supposed locally accessible. We term problem of the homotopic minimum that of determining a curve $C \in \mathscr{B}$ for which $\mathscr{I}(C)$ attains its minimum for curves in $\mathscr{B}$. This is our second problem.

As previously, a curve C of the relevant class ($\mathscr{A}$ or $\mathscr{B}$), for which $\mathscr{I}(C)$ attains its minimum, and a sequence of curves of the class along which it tends to its infimum are termed Ω-minimizing. The sequence is termed strictly internal, if there is a closed subset K of G such that all but a finite number of the curves of the sequence lie in K. A curve will be termed strictly internal if it lies wholly in G, internal if it lies in G except, at most, for its end points, and peripheral if it lies wholly on the frontier $\bar{G} - G$ of G. We can now establish the following result:

(54.1) Theorem (Existence of Absolute and Homotopic Minimum in a bounded Domain.) (i) *In either problem, if there is a strictly internal Ω-minimizing sequence, there is at least one solution that is a strictly internal extremal.* (ii) *If G is geoconvex and A is not empty, each of the two problems has at least one solution, and each solution is an internal or peripheral extremal.*

We shall base the proof on the Hilbert construction, supplemented by a few remarks, in particular by the following:

(54.2) Lemma. *Let G be geoconvex. Then any small admissible curve in $\bar{G}$ is homotopic in $\bar{G}$ to a small extremal arc in $\bar{G}$ with the same ends.*

(54.3) Lemma. *Let G be geoconvex, and let γ be a small extremal arc in $\bar{G}$, which contains at least one point of G. Then the interior part of γ lies in G.*

Proof of (54.2). Let γ_0 be the given admissible curve, represented by $x(t)$ $0 \leq t \leq 1$, let P, Q be its extremities and let $R = R(t)$ be its movable point $x(t)$. We denote by γ_u the curve made up of an extremal arc PR or $R = R(u)$, together with

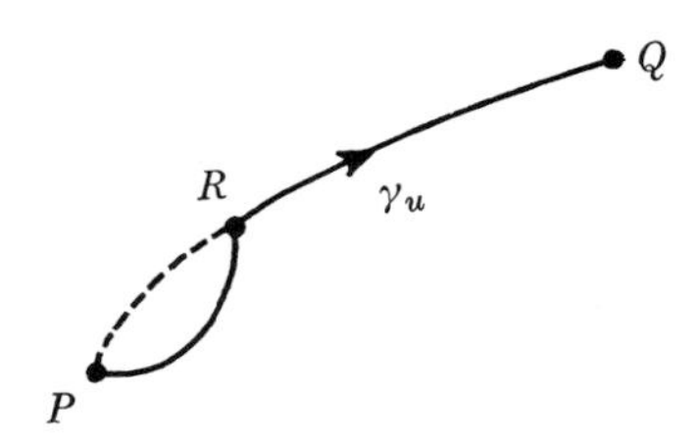

the arc RQ of γ_0. (The extremal arc PR is understood to be the unique one situated in a small ball of center P, and γ_0 is small enough to ensure this unicity.) From the geoconvexity of G, it follows that for sufficiently near points P, R of $\bar{G}$, the extremal PR lies in $\bar{G}$. Thus if γ_0 is small enough, the curve γ_u lies in $\bar{G}$ for each u and provides the required homotopy.

Proof of (54.3). Suppose, if possible, that on γ one of the extremities P, Q, for definiteness the point Q, lies in G, and that the intermediate point R lies on the frontier of G. Since γ is a small extremal through R, we can embed it in a narrow

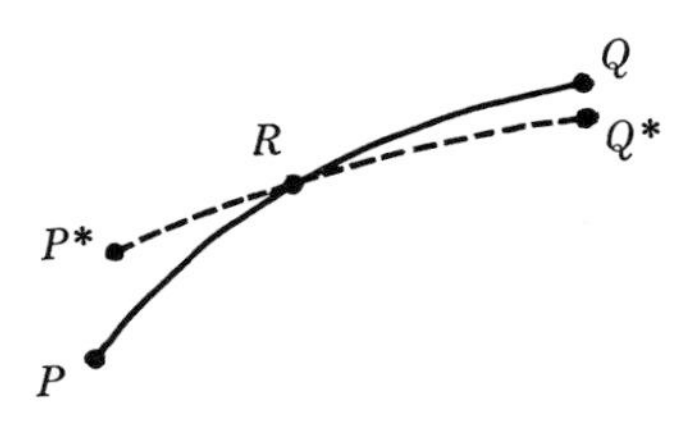

pencil, and there will therefore be an extremal of the pencil through some point P^* of G near P (since $P \in \bar{G}$); this extremal passes through some point Q^* near Q, and Q^* will lie in G since we can arrange, by choice of P^*, that Q^* is as near as we please to the point $Q \in G$. The extremal arc P^*Q^*, which is short with γ and has extremities in G, would thus contain a point R of the frontier of G, contrary to the definition of convexity.

Thus γ cannot possess simultaneously an extremity in G and an interior point on the frontier of G. Hence by shortening γ, we see also that there cannot be two points interior to γ, one of which is in G, and the other on the frontier of G. By combining these facts, we obtain the assertion.

The above lemmas illustrate the convenience of the notion of geoconvexity, which goes back to Carathéodory. This notion seems very useful in problems in which, as in the shortest distance problem, we have $L(x, \dot{x}) = L(x, -\dot{x})$. However, in general, the notion is rather restrictive, and resembles what is known as "over-convexity," instead of just "convexity." The problem of a more satisfactory way of extending convexity for unsymmetrical problems, in which $L(x, \dot{x}) \neq L(x, -\dot{x})$, and of extending (54.1)(ii) correspondingly, deserves attention.

Proof of (54.1). Since the details follow closely those of the proof of (51.3), the Hilbert construction, we shall mainly indicate how they differ from them. We now have to treat two cases, (i) and (ii), in each of two problems, and we shall do so simultaneously. There is a minor difference between the two problems: in treating the homotopic minimum we must verify the existence of certain deformations. There is also a minor difference between (i) and (ii); in case (i) it will be evident that the modifications we make to our curves can be carried out in a slightly enlarged $K \subset G$, whereas in case (ii) we verify that they can be carried out in $\bar{G}$.

In each problem, there exists an Ω-minimizing sequence C_ν $\nu = 1, 2, \ldots$; in (i) this sequence lies in K, while in (ii) it lies merely in $\bar{G}$. We select subsequences of ν, and we modify the relevant C_ν, as in the proof of (51.3); the numbers m, M, ρ are as before, with K or $\bar{G}$ in place of E, except for the substitution of δ for ρ. After dividing the C_ν (of a subsequence) into a fixed number N of small arcs, separated by points of division $a_0, a_1, \ldots, a_N$, we have three modifications to consider.

(a) We arrange for the C_ν (of a subsequence) to join a fixed pair of extremities P, Q, instead of a variable pair P_ν, Q_ν. (This means a_0 and a_N no longer depend on ν.)

In order to achieve this by means of an Ω-deformation, effected in correspondence with the interval $0 \leq u \leq 1$, we add to C_ν, at the stage u of the deformation,

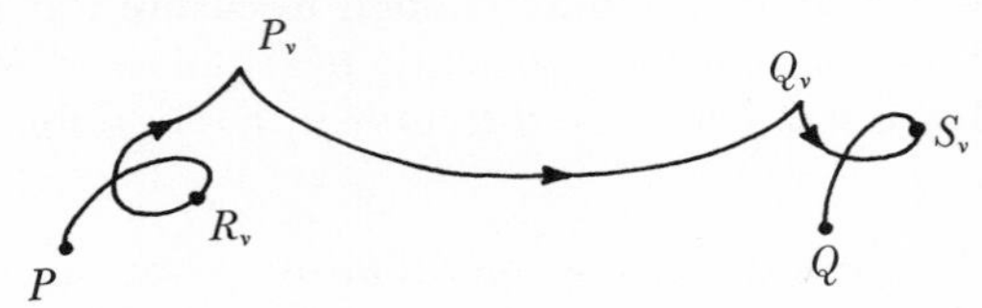

not the entire arcs from P to P_ν and from Q_ν to Q, which provide the desired modification, but only the partial arcs R_ν to P_ν and Q_ν to S_ν, where the pair R_ν, S_ν lies in Ω and depends on u; as u increases, this pair describes, in the product space, a short arc from P_ν, Q_ν to P, Q.

(b) We arrange for the remaining a_k also to be independent of ν.

For any fixed k, let X_ν be the point a_k on C_ν, and let X be the limiting position [for a subsequence selected in the proof of (51.3)]. We join the two points (in either order, it does not matter which) by a short extremal. [In case (ii) this extremal

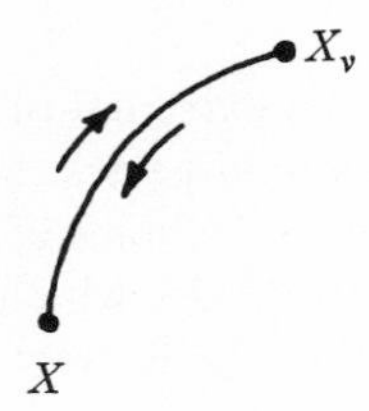

certainly lies in $\bar{G}$.] We denote by λ_k the curve obtained when we describe this short extremal twice, first from X_ν to X, and then back again. We denote by $\lambda_k(u)$, the shorter curve, obtained by describing only a piece of our short extremal, from X_v to some intermediate point Z_v and back again; here Z_v depends on a parameter u, and varies from X_v to X as u increases from 0 to 1. (This shortening of a double run may be illustrated by an unpleasant habit that certain city buses used to have; they turned around before reaching the terminal if they were empty, with the result that prospective passengers might have to wait for more than an hour at the terminal.) The desired modification of C_v is effected by adding the $N - 1$ curves λ_k $k = 1, 2, \ldots, N - 1$. It results from a deformation obtained (for $0 \leq u \leq 1$) by adding, instead, the $\lambda_k(u)$.

(c) We replace the N arcs of C_v from a_{k-1} to a_k, for $k = 1, 2, \ldots, N$, by short extremal arcs γ_k. The resulting curve is then an extremal C.

This modification clearly takes place in $\bar{G}$ in case (ii), by geoconvexity. To effect it by a deformation, we proceed as in Lemma (54.2).

Thus, after these modification we end up, as in (51.3), with a solution C which is an extremal. In case (i), C lies in a slightly enlarged $K \subset G$, while in case (ii) it lies in $\bar{G}$.

Finally, no solution, in case (ii), that contains a point of G can contain also, as an interior point, a point of the frontier of G, since it would then contain a small extremal arc in $\bar{G}$ with this property, contrary to Lemma (54.3).

§55. TOWARD AN AUTOMATIC EXISTENCE THEORY

The object of this section is to illustrate by examples, the kind of difficulty that must be taken into account if an existence theory is to be automatic. Formerly such examples were regarded as counterexamples, i.e., they were thought to prove that no such general existence theory is possible. However, this is not our point of view today. Instead, we attempt rather to extend the notion of solution, in accordance with Hilbert's dictum.

(a) An Analogy. Consider the elementary problem of the minimum of the function of one variable, given by the expression $x^4 - x$. The elementary calculus rules show that the minimum is attained when $4x^3 = 1$, at an irrational value (algebraic) of x. However, we could have formulated this problem at a time when no one had conceived of the notion of irrational number. It would have been, at that time, a problem without solution. The truth is that it makes no sense to state a problem of minimum in a set which is not even closed. Yet in the calculus of variations, problems were formulated when the notion of curve was still very rudimentary.

(b) An Unprofitable Extension. Nowadays, students take in their stride not only irrational numbers, but also very general concepts of functions, maps and so forth. It would seem an anachronism to limit oneself to smooth functions in the calculus of variations. Of course, since derivatives occur, it is natural to require the functions concerned to possess derivatives, at any rate almost everywhere. However, consider, from this supposedly modern point of view, the simplest variational problem of all, the shortest distance problem in the nonparametric form, and, for definiteness, suppose we ask for the minimum of the integral

$$\int_0^1 \sqrt{1 + \dot{x}^2}\, dt$$

for real valued continuous functions $x(t)$, subject to the end-conditions $x(0) = 0$, $x(1) = 1$, where the functions $x(t)$ are subject to the elementary and intuitive condition that the interval $0 \leq t \leq 1$ can be divided into a finite number of segments, on each of which $x(t)$ is either monotone increasing or monotone decreasing. Such functions $x(t)$ possess derivatives almost everywhere, and the class of such continuous functions was at one time the class of functions considered relevant in the theory of Fourier series. In fact, the introduction of this class by Dirichlet was considered an important landmark in that theory, although today such functions seem very tame.

What does the shortest distance problem become when we allow this rather modest extension of the classical admissible functions $x(t)$?

In the class of elementary functions $x(t)$, the solution is furnished by the function $x(t) = t$, and the minimum is $\sqrt{2}$. This is the Euclidean distance of the relevant pair of end points $(0, 0)$ and $(1, 1)$.

However, in the modest enlargement of this class considered by Dirichlet, the solution is quite different. It is provided by a continuous monotone increasing $x(t)$ with derivative almost everywhere 0. The corresponding minimum of our integral is now 1. This has no more relation to the classical version of the shortest distance problem than the problem of the largest Englishman has to that of the largest vertebrate.

(c) THE DISCONTINUOUS NONPARAMETRIC WEAK SOLUTIONS. In a great many nonparametric problems, with non-negative Lagrangians subject to the Legendre condition, it is, nevertheless, necessary to enlarge the classical class of admissible curves by admitting certain curves represented by discontinuous functions. A typical example is furnished by the problem discussed, in part, in the Preamble, of the minimal surface of revolution; this is the problem, in the (t, x)-plane:

$$\int_0^a x\sqrt{1 + \dot{x}^2}\, dt = \text{Min.}, \qquad x(0) = 1, \qquad x(a) = b > 0.$$

Here, if a is large enough, the corresponding parametric version of the problem has a broken solution, made up of a segment of the t-axis, together with two vertical

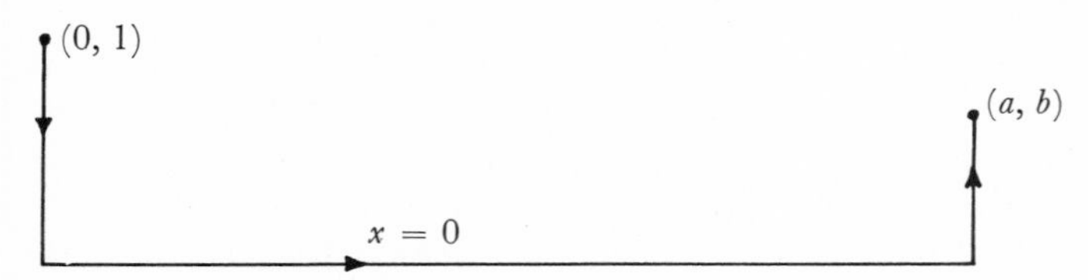

segments. In the nonparametric version, this solution must still be admitted, if the problem is to be properly understood, because the value of $\mathscr{I}(C)$ for this parametric is the limit of $\mathscr{I}(C_\nu)$ for a minimizing nonparametric sequence C_ν $\nu = 1, 2, \ldots$.

In this case, the value of $\mathscr{I}(C)$ is not given by our integral above, when we take $x(t)$ to be the discontinuous function $x(0) = 1$, $x(a) = b$, $x(t) = 0$ otherwise, since our integral is then 0.

(d) WEAK PARAMETRIC SOLUTIONS STRETCHED TO INFINITY. In the parametric form, the preceding example shows the need to admit solutions with corners. It is usual now to admit, more generally, all rectifiable parametric curves, i.e., all parametric curves of finite length. This is the class of parametric curves admitted by Tonelli in his *Fondamenti*. However, in some cases the phenomenon of the existence of cheap extremals, referred to in Section 51, necessitates the admission of curves of infinite length. (In the previous example, the cheap extremal consisting of the t-axis was already responsible for the need to allow solutions with corners.)

Consider the map of the complex ζ- and z-planes given by

$$\zeta = e^z,$$

where $\zeta = \xi_1 + i\xi_2$, $z = x_1 + ix_2$. We study in the z-plane, the shortest distance problem of the ζ-plane. The Lagrangian is

$$L = e^{x_1}\sqrt{\dot{x}_1^2 + \dot{x}_2^2}.$$

The extremals are images of lines $a\xi_1 + b\xi_2 = c$, and they have the form

(55.1) $$e^{x_1 - x_1^0} \cos(x_2 - x_2^0) = 1$$

for $c \neq 0$, or the form $x_2 =$ const. for $c = 0$. The extremals (55.1) are translates of one another and for two points z', z'' such that

$$|x_2' - x_2''| < \pi,$$

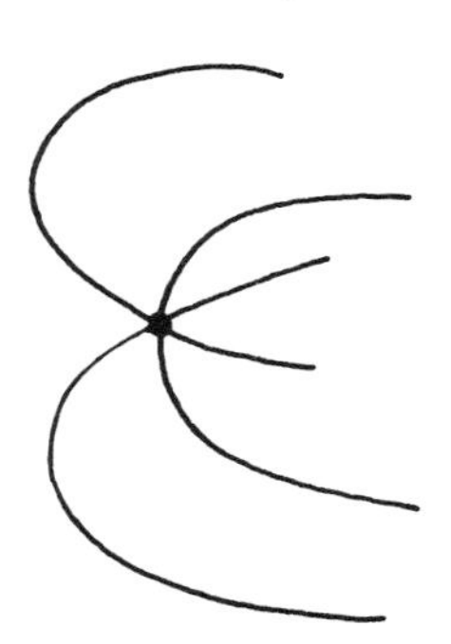

The extremals through a given point

the minimizing curve joining z', z'', is the image of a straight line and is the unique extremal with these extremities. However, in the case

$$|x_2' - x_2''| = \pi,$$

no extremal joins the given points, and the solution is the image of a segment through the origin, so that it consists of two parallels $x_2 =$ const., taken, respectively, from

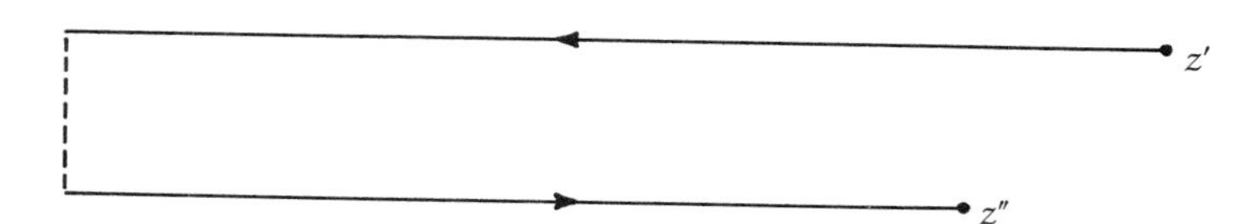

x_1' to $-\infty$, and from $-\infty$ to x_1'' as regards the coordinate x_1. We have to regard them as jointed at infinity, just as their images are at $\zeta = 0$, and this solution can be approximated as close as we wish by a curve whose image avoids the origin. Finally, if

$$|x_2' - x_2''| > \pi,$$

each curve joining our two points has an image, describing an angle $>\pi$ when viewed from the origin, so that the minimum is when this image is a broken line through $\zeta = 0$. This again gives as solution a pair of parallels, as in the case $|x_2' - x_2''| = \pi$. In both these cases, the solution is not what we usually term a curve.

The above example, due to Carathéodory, also serves to illustrate the drastic effects of the presence of cheap extremals. Here, although the Jacobi condition is satisfied on all extremals, and although the problem is everywhere elliptic and positive definite, we see that the extremals through a given point do not cover the plane.

(e) THE SPIRALING OF SOLUTIONS TO THE ORIGIN. We begin with an example known to Euler, which is a simpler form of (c) and (d), in which solutions are now stretched merely to the origin. We consider the map

$$\zeta = \frac{1}{\alpha} z^{\alpha} \qquad (\alpha > 1),$$

and we again take as our problem in the z-plane, the shortest distance problem in the ζ-plane. We obtain as Lagrangian

$$L = |z|^{\alpha-1} \, |\dot{z}|.$$

The extremals are again images of straight lines, and they are given in polar coordinates $z = re^{i\theta}$ by

$$r^{\alpha} \cos \alpha(\theta - \theta_0) = \text{const.},$$

or by $\theta = \text{const.}$ when the image passes through $\zeta = 0$. As in (d), there are two cases to distinguish: when $|\theta' - \theta''| < \pi/\alpha$, the pair of points z', z'' can be joined by just one extremal, and the latter then provides the minimum; while, when $|\theta' - \theta''| \geq \pi/\alpha$, the solution consists of two segments jointed at the origin. The state

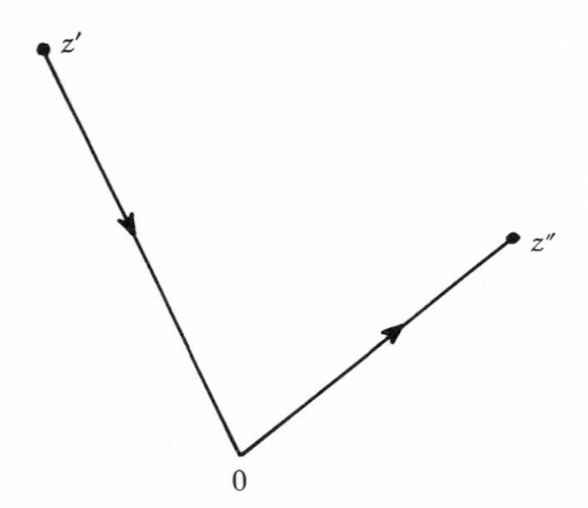

of affairs is here similar to that of (c). The solution may be described as follows: except when the angular distances of z', z'' is less than π/α, we take the best way to the origin, and from there the best way to the destination. (This is almost exactly what a traveler does by train in Britain.)

The previous example can now be given an instructive further twist, due to Hahn, in which the broken line from z' to z'' becomes a pair of spirals, neither of which has a tangent at the origin. Instead of introducing r, θ as polar coordinates of $z = x_1 + ix_2$, we use them as intermediate variables in one or other of the following transformations:

$$\textbf{(55.2)} \qquad \zeta = \frac{1}{\alpha} (re^{i\theta})^{\alpha} \ (\alpha > 1), \qquad z = re^{i(\theta + \log r)};$$

$$\textbf{(55.3)} \qquad \zeta = \frac{1}{\alpha} (re^{i\theta})^{\alpha} \ (\alpha > 1), \qquad z = re^{i(\theta + \frac{1}{2}r^{-2})}.$$

The corresponding Lagrangians are $|z|^{\alpha-2}\sqrt{\varphi}$, $|z|^{\alpha-2}\sqrt{\psi}$, where φ, ψ are, respectively, the innocuous-seeming expressions

$$(x_1\dot{x}_1 + x_2\dot{x}_2)^2 + [(x_1 + x_2)\dot{x}_1 - (x_1 - x_2)\dot{x}_2]^2$$

and

$$(x_1^2 + x_2^2)(\dot{x}_1^2 + \dot{x}_2^2) + (x_1\dot{x}_1 + x_2\dot{x}_2)^2 + 2(x_1^2 + x_2^2)(x_1\dot{x}_2 - x_2\dot{x}_1)(x_1\dot{x}_1 + x_2\dot{x}_2).$$

There is really nothing in the solid respectability of these dull expressions to suggest the intricate artistry of the picture presented by the extremals. It is as if, still only in the interest of cheapness, which is what our minimum problem is about, and with due consideration to the disruptive effect of a sale, the time-honored stability of Harrods or the Army and Navy stores were transformed into the enchanting choreography of Swan Lake.

The extremals whose ζ-images avoid the origin behave normally, but those whose images contain the origin spiral round $z = 0$. They spiral logarithmically in case (55.2), in which the length is finite, and more violently in case (55.3), in which the length is infinite.

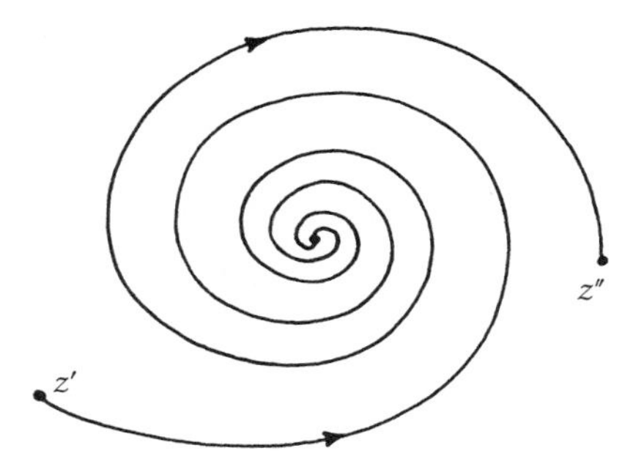

Previously the solution consisted of a broken line; it has now become a spiraling curve made up of a pair of spirals going in and out of the origin. This solution, which has no tangent from either side at the origin, is of finite length in case (55.2), and of infinite length in case (55.3).

This gives some idea, literally, of the lengths to which we must go in a really satisfactory existence theory. However, there will be further complications to come.

§56. FIRST STAGE OF AN ABSTRACT APPROACH: SEMICONTINUITY IN A B··i-COMPACT SET

We shall pass rather rapidly over the approach discussed in this section, since it aims only at finding convenient restrictions, which are satisfied by a number of variational problems, and which render possible a reliable existence theory of an abstract nature. This is the approach selected by Tonelli in his *Fondamenti*. We shall discuss a more general approach in our next Chapter.

The method of Tonelli is related to the classical principle of Weierstrass, according to which a continuous function $f(x)$, defined on a bounded closed set of Euclidean points x, must assume its minimum in that set. Here, instead of a function $f(x)$ defined on a Euclidean set, we have to deal with a function $\mathscr{I}(C)$ defined on a set of things C that we happen to call curves.

Example (a) of the preceding section suggests that it might be helpful if the set of curves were, at any rate, closed in some convenient metric. This set can hardly be so if the curves are restricted to be smooth or piecewise smooth. Also we ought really to insist on a property similar in some way to boundedness of Euclidean sets, and the relevant property, according to Section 48 of the preceding Chapter, appears to be sequential compactness. Thus we should, at this stage, attempt to formulate an existence theory in a B · · i compact class of curves. Such a class, which was studied by Tonelli, is that of curves of uniformly bounded lengths in a cube.

We shall need the following facts about rectifiable curves, i.e., about curves of finite length. First, the length is defined as the supremum of the elementary lengths of inscribed polygons; second, on a curve of finite length we can take the arc length s as parameter, and the function $x(s)$ by which the curve is then represented when s varies from 0 to the length of the curve satisfies the Lipschitz condition

$$|x(s_2) - x(s_1)| \leq |s_2 - s_1|$$

for each pair of values s_2, s_1 in the range of s. Here we find it more convenient to use a parameter t, which has the range $0 \leq t \leq 1$, such that s is a constant multiple of t; the multiple is then the length of the curve. If $x(t)$ is now the representation in terms of this parameter, we have the Lipschitz condition

$$|x(t_2) - x(t_1)| \leq K \cdot |t_2 - t_1|,$$

where K is the length of the curve. It follows at once that rectifiable curves of uniformly bounded lengths are then given on the segment $0 \leq t \leq 1$ by functions $x(t)$ subject to the same inequality for a fixed K, and we can now take K to be the supremum of their lengths. In that case the functions are clearly equicontinuous (see Section 48 of the preceding Chapter), and therefore, if the curves considered lie in a fixed cube, the set of representations $x(t)$ chosen above is, by (48.2) of the section referred to, sequentially compact.

We shall metrize the space of rectifiable curves by identifying each of the curves with the representation defined above. It then becomes a function-space whose members are continuous functions $x(t)$ $0 \leq t \leq 1$. In this space we use, in this section, the topology of uniform convergence. We include among our curves those which reduce to single points. In that case $x(t)$ is a constant and the length is 0.

It is almost obvious that the classical principle of minimum of Weierstrass applies equally well to a continuous function $\mathscr{I}(C)$ defined in a sequentially compact closed set. In fact, the proof is simplified; Weierstrass has to prove that a bounded Euclidean set is sequentially compact, and this part of his proof is not relevant here. Thus, if $\mathscr{I}(C)$ is continuous, it attains its minimum in any closed set of curves C, situated in a fixed cube, and of uniformly bounded lengths.

It looks as if this last statement provides the desired basic existence theorem in the calculus of variations. However, we interrupt our discussion to quote the following little anecdote from Lebesgue's book *In the Margin of the Calculus of Variations*:

"All my papers [on this subject] are connected with a schoolboy's 'joke.' At the Collège de Beauvais, we used to show that, in a triangle, one side is equal to the sum of the other two. Let ABC be a triangle. If A_1, B_1, C_1 are the mid-points of its sides, we have

$$BA + AC = BC_1 + C_1A_1 + A_1B_1 + B_1C.$$

On each of the triangles BC_1A_1, A_1B_1C, proceed as on ABC. We obtain a broken line, formed of eight segments, and equal to $BA + AC$. By continuing in this way, we obtain a sequence of broken lines, which stray less and less from the side BC, and which still have as length the sum

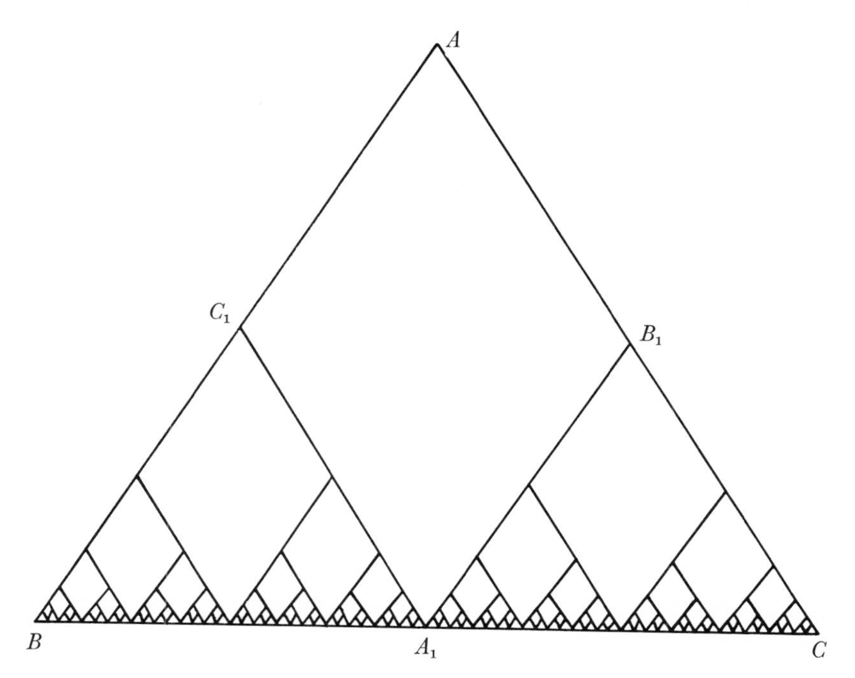

of the two other sides of our original triangle. The pupils at Beauvais concluded from this, that the segment BC, the geometrical limit of our broken lines, had as length the sum of the two other sides $BA + AC$. My schoolfellows saw there no more than a good joke. To me, the argument appeared most disturbing, since I could see no difference between it and proofs relating to the areas and surfaces of cylinders, cones, spheres, and to the length of a circumference."

A lesson to be drawn from this is that the pupil who finds something most difficult to understand may well be far and away the best of the class. Oddly enough, as these lines were being written Bertrand Russell's voice was saying on the wireless that a colleague had told him that, as a student in his class, Wittgenstein "stood out because he was the only one who looked puzzled."

However, what is here more to the point, the anecdote also shows that length is not a continuous function $\mathscr{I}(C)$. In other words, the hypotheses of Weierstrass's principle of minimum are not even fulfilled in the shortest distance problem, the simplest of all variational problems. We cannot then use this principle as a foundation for the calculus of variations. The question now is what can we do instead.

The present writer's father, W. H. Young, used to recall that this very question had been put to him by a young Italian mathematician. His reply was a question: "Can you use semicontinuity?" The young Italian was Leonida Tonelli. Semicontinuity was then still a recent concept, known only to a few. In the hands of Tonelli, it became an important tool in a fundamental new approach to the calculus of variations.

We recall that a function $F(P)$, defined in a set of P in which limits have a meaning, is termed lower semicontinuous at P_0 if it satisfies the following conditions: (i) $F(P)$ is extended real-valued; i.e., its values are reals with the possible addition of $+\infty$ and $-\infty$; (ii) at P_0 the function is defined and we have $F(P_0) \neq -\infty$; (iii) we have $F(P_0) \leq \liminf F(P)$ as $P \to P_0$. If these conditions are satisfied for each P_0 of the set of definition, we term the function $F(P)$ lower semicontinuous.

Of course the Weierstrass principle of minimum remains valid for a lower semicontinuous function $F(P)$ defined on a sequentially compact closed set, i.e., on a B · · i-compact set. For there exists a sequence P_ν for which the infimum is approached; there exists also a subsequence of ν for which the P_ν tend to a limit P_0, and by semicontinuity we have $F(P_0) \leq \lim F(P_\nu) = \operatorname{Inf} F(P)$, which is only possible if the minimum is attained at P_0.

The scope of Tonelli's historic approach to the calculus of variations is seen from the following result:

(56.1) Theorem. *Let $L(x, \dot{x})$ be a parametric Lagrangian, convex in $\dot{x}$. Then $\mathscr{I}(C)$ is lower semicontinuous in any class K of curves of uniformly bounded lengths situated in a cube.*

As an immediate corollary, in view of our new form of the Weierstrass principle of minimum, we have, with the same hypotheses:

(56.2) Theorem. *$\mathscr{I}(C)$ attains its minimum in K, if K is closed.*

Strictly speaking, this theorem already belongs more properly to that part of our subject which deals with minima subject to side-conditions. However, in many problems the data imply, in a rather obvious way, that curves not belonging to some such K can be excluded without loss of generality.

Theorem (56.1) is itself contained in a more general result. Given a rectifiable curve C_0, represented, as previously, in terms of a parameter t $(0 \leq t \leq 1)$ that is a constant multiple of the arc-length s by a function $x_0(t)$, we term the parametric Lagrangian $L(x, \dot{x})$ convex along C_0, if

(i) L is convex in $\dot{x}$ at $\dot{x} = 0$ for each point x of C_0;

(ii) L is convex in $\dot{x}$ at $\dot{x} = \dot{x}_0(t)$ for $x = x_0(t)$, for almost every t in $0 \leq t \leq 1$.

A rectifiable curve C_0, along which $L(x, \dot{x})$ is convex in this sense, will be said to fulfill the Weierstrass condition.

(56.3) Theorem. *In order that $\mathscr{I}(C)$ be lower semicontinuous at C_0 in every class K of curves of uniformly bounded lengths situated in a cube, such that $C_0 \in K$, or, alternatively such that, further, each member of K has the same extremities as C_0, it is necessary and sufficient that C_0 fulfill the Weierstrass condition.*

We remark that if a curve C_0 is minimizing, then $\mathscr{I}(C)$ is lower semicontinuous at C_0 in the class of admissible curves with the same extremities, and therefore also in any subclass. As a corollary of (56.3) we thus have:

(56.4) Necessity of the Weierstrass Condition. *In order that the rectifiable curve C_0 be minimizing, it is necessary that C_0 fulfill the Weierstrass condition.*

The proof of (56.3) will be an easy consequence of the theory of generalized curves, to which we devote our next Chapter.

§§ 57, 58, 59

We are leaving these in blank. The reader can take three deep breaths. They represent the assignments the author sometimes refers to when filling out a leave of absence slip to attend a mathematical meeting. The form for this contains the words: "My classes will be taken care of by" and the author usually writes here: "by additional assignments." We hardly need add that proper breathing spaces are essential in the study of mathematics.

Chapter VI

Generalized Curves and Flows

§60. INTRODUCTION

This Chapter introduces altogether different methods, much more recent ones, originated by the present writer. They will also play a part in optimal control. The Chapter is therefore largely independent of the previous ones, except in regard to auxiliary material related to convexity and functional analysis; it also makes very different demands on the reader as regards familiarity with real analysis. We have therefore chosen to introduce the reader very gently to these new methods and to illustrate fully their place in the general trends that dominate mathematics and all human thought.

The object of the Chapter is to go some way toward providing an automatic existence theory. It would be pointless to set out to do this without adequate tools, and for this purpose the classical concepts of real analysis are insufficient: we need much more generality and flexibility; and we shall continue to need this even more when we penetrate into optimal control. We must therefore redevelop our own concepts as we proceed. We start by revising the notion of curve and, consequently, that of solution of a variational problem or differential equation. These are not arbitrary breaks with tradition; a new building deserves new foundations. Concepts inherited from previous generations are not of divine origin, but man-made. It is for man to change them. This much, at least, we have learned from Galileo.

The concept of generalized curve that we shall develop arises directly out of the calculus of variations. As examples will show, this concept is implicit in various everyday matters familiar to us all. Moreover, since its formulation by the present writer some thirty-five years ago, it has been rediscovered by game theorists in the form of mixed strategies, and still later by dynamic programmers in the form of chattering controls.

The general concept of flow that we shall develop at the same time is related to the solution of differential equations with boundary conditions, and it plays a part in optimal control, as well as in a theory of fluid motion. In Chapter I, Section 12, we spoke of a geodesic flow and of curves of flow in place of the older terms employing the word "field." Here we give to the word flow a more precise meaning, which relates it to fluid motion. It is possible that in this context it may help clear up some of the puzzling phenomena of fluid dynamics, such as turbulence, shock waves and cavitation, which fluid theory attempts to explain as limiting phenomena with small viscosity. (This last is very like the limiting phenomenon that concerned the triangle inequality joke, which we quoted from Lebesgue in the last section of the preceding Chapter.) However, it is in optimal control rather than in fluid theory that we shall need the concept of flow; of course, we use it in this Chapter.

All these concepts are related, to some extent, to Schwartz distributions and, more particularly, to the generalization of distributions furnished by the notion of de Rham currents. We shall not use these related notions here. However, we shall take over from the de Rham theory an important interpretation of the notion of boundary.

§61. INTUITIVE BACKGROUND

We consider several variants of the Beauvais joke concerning the triangle inequality, which we quoted from Lebesgue at the end of the preceding Chapter. These variants can all be stated as variational problems, and the first is a particular case of the so-called Zermelo navigation problem. We prefer here to suppress the analytical details and state it as a practical problem that anyone who likes to go sailing might meet. (We really do mean sailing, not destroying the peace of a stretch

of water with poison gases and the roar of a motor.) The problem is that of sailing against the wind from a point A to a point B, where A, B are midstream points on a river, and B is downstream. This is a problem frequently met by sailing enthusiasts. If we disregard the current for a moment and suppose the river sufficiently wide, every sailor knows that he must tack, i.e., follow a broken line AXB, where AX and

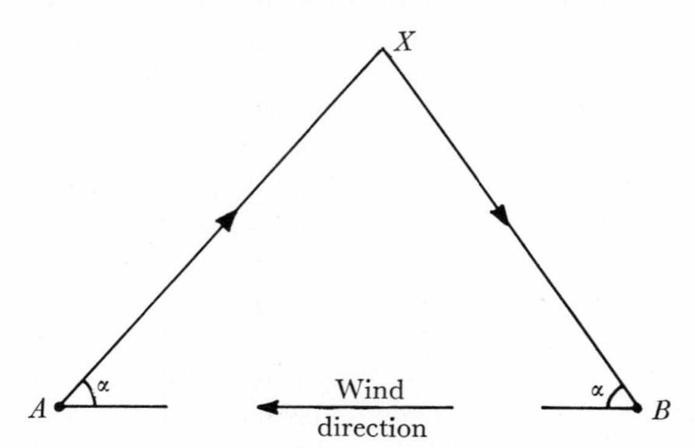

XB make, with AB, at A and at B, a certain same angle α that is the most favorable. In this way, he can actually use the wind to sail against it in two installments, at the most favorable angle α. This takes him from A to B in the least time, if the river is wide enough and there is no current.

Of course, this is not the only solution. Our sailor can just as well tack more than once; i.e., he can follow a broken line with more than one corner, in which each segment still makes the angle α with the direction of AB. For instance, he can follow any of the zigzag paths of four, eight or sixteen segments shown in the figures. The time taken to reach AB along each of these paths, neglecting any delay in changing the direction at a corner, will be the same as along the broken line AXB.

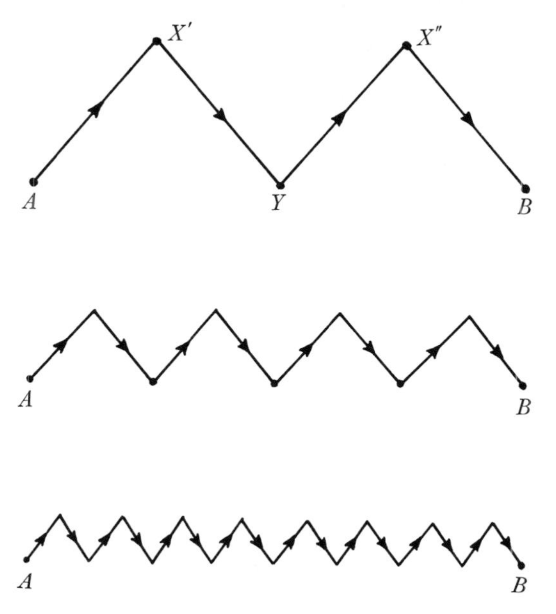

The same applies along a zigzag path consisting of 2^ν equal segments, alternatively parallel to AX and XB. On such a path, by choice of ν, the boat moves away from the segment AB, as little as we please. We can clearly follow such a path even if the river is relatively narrow.

If we now take the current into account, drifting downstream is superimposed on the motion already described. We shall suppose, as occurs in practice, that the current is strongest in midstream. In that case, the best course is obtained by tacking a very large number of times, in order to remain close to AB all the time. Ideally, one should stay on AB itself, by tacking infinitely often. This means that the sails are constantly being shifted from one position to another, as if the boat were directed, at each point, alternately in the directions parallel to AX and to XB.

We thus see that there is an ideal solution, which must be clearly distinguished from the segment AB itself, in which the boat does actually follow the path AB, but is directed, at each point, alternately in the direction of AX and in that of XB.

Our second example is known as Maxwell's problem, which concerns finding the best way up a mountain. We shall think of it partly as a skiing problem, in the days when there were no chair lifts and skiing was an adult sport, not a child's game

Left ski positions

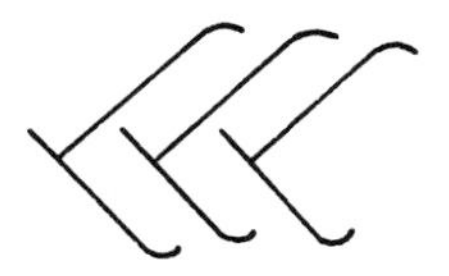

Right ski positions

of sliding down the bannisters and being carried up again. In order to climb up a steep hill it was necessary to place the skis successively in positions at an angle to the direction of ultimate motion. An entirely similar procedure is also used in walking uphill without skis when the slope is rather steep. In that case, the feet are placed at angles corresponding to the direction of ascent, to avoid slipping.

In this second problem, we again suppress the analytical details, and we suppose the problem to differ from the shortest distance problem only on those parts of the terrain where the greatest slope exceeds a certain constant a, which is then the most favorable slope for gaining altitude without slipping back. (This is also a problem that an engineer faces in building a mountain road suitable for cars.) We ask for the best path, under these conditions, from A to a certain summit B.

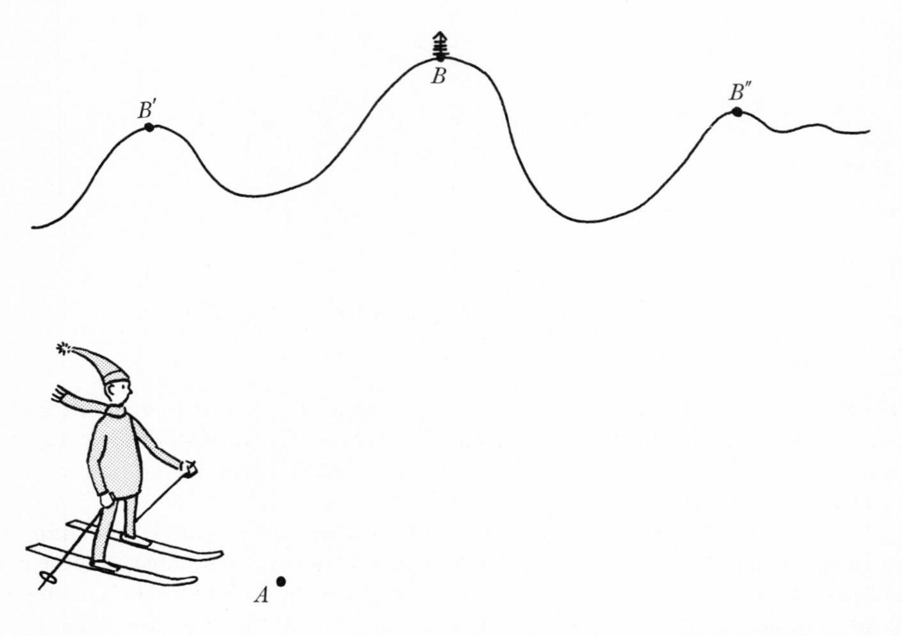

In the case of a convex mountain, it was observed by Maxwell that one can construct a path that winds round the mountain at the favorable slope a until the terrain flattens down sufficiently for the best path to terminate along a geodesic to B. However, in general, when we are faced with a whole range of mountains, such a procedure, if it is possible, may lead up the wrong mountain.

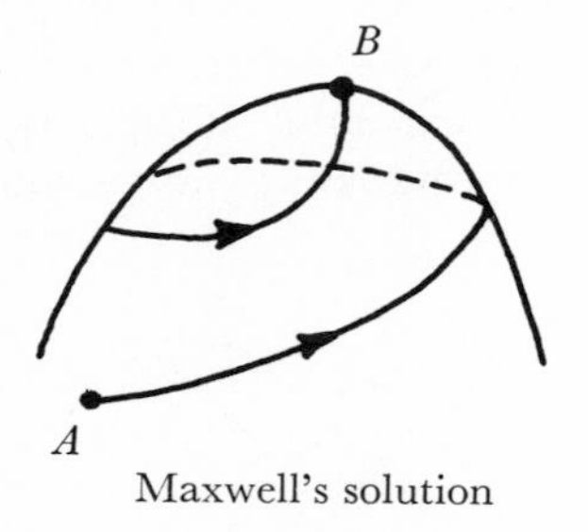

Maxwell's solution

Mountain climbers, skiers and road builders have come up with a more reliable solution, with which we are certain to reach the desired summit B, not some other summit B' or B''. We first draw the geodesic Γ from A to B. The skier simply follows Γ, except that where Γ is too steep he places his skis alternately along two directions of the favorable slope a. He thus describes, in effect, an infinitesimal zigzag on Γ, rather than Γ itself. The road builder, on the other hand, will replace the steep parts of the geodesic by finite zigzags made up of a finite number of smooth portions of slope a,

Part of road builder's solution

with sharp corners; while the mountain climber's solution may consist either of a similar zigzag path or of an infinitesimal zigzag along the geodesic. It is well known to climbers that no gain in time is made by cutting corners on a zigzag mountain path. To avoid slipping, the climber, like the skier, places his feet along the optimal slope a so that he describes the infinitesimal zigzag along the shortcut and takes exactly the same time as along the finite approximating zigzag path.

In the above discussion we have, of course, ignored precipitous slopes, which the mountain climber has other technical ways of tackling, and which the skier and the road builder must avoid.

We pass on to a third example of the same kind, in which, however, we now supply the detailed calculations. We shall express this, for simplicity, in the non-parametric form. We consider the minimum of

$$\int_0^1 (1 + x^2)(1 + [\dot{x}^2 - 1]^2)\, dt$$

for real-valued admissible functions $x(t)$ subject to $x(0) = x(1) = 0$.

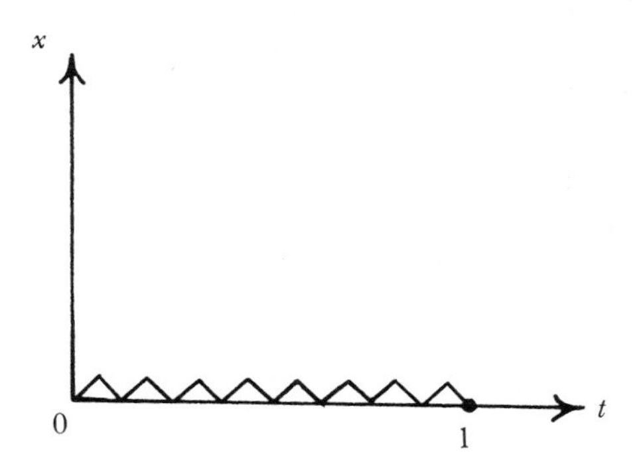

On the broken line of the figure, we have $\dot{x} = 1$ and $\dot{x} = -1$, alternately, on successive parts of a subdivision of the interval $0 \leq t \leq 1$ into an even number of subintervals of equal lengths ε. For the corresponding function $x(t)$, which takes values between 0 and ε, the integrand never exceeds $1 + \varepsilon^2$, and therefore the integral is then at most $1 + \varepsilon^2$.

On the other hand, on any admissible curve defined for $0 \leq t \leq 1$, the integrand is clearly ≥ 1, and only takes the value 1 when we have both $x = 0$ and $\dot{x} = \pm 1$.

It follows that the infimum of our integral is 1, and that it is approached when $x(t)$ is defined by the broken line of the figure, and the length ε of the subdivisions is made to tend to 0.

The solution to this problem of minimum is not given by setting $x = 0$, for then we would have $\dot{x} = 0$ and the integral would be twice too large. In order to obtain a solution, we must enlarge the class of admissible curves, by admitting an infinitesimal zigzag, on which $x = 0$ while $\dot{x}$ is alternatively $+1$ and -1. We can best describe it by assigning to this new "curve," the pair of slopes $+1$ and -1, at each point, each with a weight, or probability, of $\frac{1}{2}$. This is also the description that applies, with slight changes, to the solutions of the two previous examples.

We thus see that in order to arrive at an automatic existence theory, it is necessary to effect a rather radical change in our conception of the notion of admissible curve.

§62. A QUESTION OF SEMANTICS

In the preceding Chapters, the reader was largely left free to retain, for the notion of admissible curve, the interpretation with which he felt most familiar. However, we must commit ourselves to a radical departure from all such traditional interpretations if we are to admit among our curves the strange infinitesimal zigzag intuitively described in the preceding section.

The reader may well ask by what right can we change radically the meaning of the well-established word "curve." This is basically a question, not of mathematics, but of semantics. However, it is a question which profoundly affects mathematics, because of the vital part played by definitions. It is a question that many readers may well find confusing, professional mathematicians included, since, in point of fact, logicians do not agree on the answer.

The question is rather well put in Lewis Carroll's *Through The Looking-Glass*:

"When I use a word," Humpty Dumpty said in a rather scornful tone, "it means just what I choose it to mean—neither more nor less."

"The question is," said Alice, "whether you *can* make words mean so many different things."

"The question is," said Humpty Dumpty, "which is to be master—that's all."

The view put forward by Humpty Dumpty is known as nominalism. It goes back to the sophistry of ancient Greece, and was an important idea in philosophy during the Middle Ages. In mathematics, it came into vogue again in the twentieth century. For instance, G. H. Hardy used to champion it in his lectures on divergent series.

From the point of view of nominalism, we have a perfect right to alter any definition we please. At the opposite extreme, there is the point of view of dogmatism, which Hardy no doubt associated with clergymen and generals, and which may be described by the old doggerel: "When I speak, let no dog bark" and "What I say three times is true." In that case, newcomers like ourselves have no right to change anything at all. However, for those of us who still have an open mind, and who care neither for nominalism nor for dogmatism, the position is less clear.

We shall discuss an intermediate view. It is frequently emphasized that in mathematics the real meaning of a theorem only really appears in the course of the proof. In fact, anyone idiotic enough to merely memorize statements of theorems, ignoring the proofs, is wasting his time. There is much to be said for taking a similar view of definitions; in that case, the real meaning of a term is to be sought in its usage, not in its formal definition. This is no new theory, and it is not limited to mathematics. Plato's *Dialogues* largely consist in seeking in this way the true meaning of certain words. His method may be termed Socratic analysis. A case in point occurs in R. L. Stevenson's Essays. He tells us of the heroine of a novel, who is stated to be a princess; however, as Stevenson says, the moment she speaks we know her to be a fishwife.

On this basis, it is not only a right but a duty to reexamine our definitions in the light of their usage, and to revise them, even quite radically, if they do not fit.

§63. PARAMETRIC CURVES IN THE CALCULUS OF VARIATIONS

Definitions of parametric curves have passed through a substantial period of evolution already, and the ideas which emerged were incorporated into what is now known as a Fréchet curve. There are corresponding definitions of Fréchet surfaces. The definitions are in two stages: the first stage consists in defining a parametric representation of a curve, or surface; the second consists in defining equivalence of two such representations, so as to make clear, when two representations give rise to a same curve, or to a same surface, and when they do not.

A parametric representation of a curve is defined to be a continuous vector-valued function $x(t)$, defined on an interval of reals, usually a finite closed interval $t_1 \leq t \leq t_2$. The parametric representation of a surface is defined similarly, with a variable t that ranges in a two-dimensional figure; however, the latter need not be a plane figure, but can also be a sphere or other elementary two-dimensional surface.

The second stage of the Fréchet definition of curve, or of surface, is more complicated. It is usual to agree that a continuous strictly increasing function $t(\tau)$ $\tau_1 \leq \tau \leq \tau_2$, such that $t(\tau_1) = t_1$, $t(\tau_2) = t_2$, defines by substitution a function $\xi(\tau) = x(t(\tau))$ $\tau_1 \leq \tau \leq \tau_2$ which is regarded as providing another parametric representation of the same curve. In the case of representations of surfaces, the same applies to a continuous homeomorphism $t(\tau)$ of the basic figure, in which t ranges onto a figure in which τ ranges, provided that this is orientation-preserving. However, such parameter changes provide too restricted a notion of equivalence, and the basic idea of Fréchet is to use them, not to define equivalence of two parametric representations of curves, or of surfaces, but to define a distance. Fréchet equivalent representations are then defined by the property of having distance 0.

The definitions of Fréchet have the advantage of also providing a metric. The space of curves is thus a metric space, and we can apply to it many constructions to which we are accustomed in Euclidean space. This makes it possible to treat curves as part of functional analysis. At the time when functional analysis began to be studied, everyone felt that the Fréchet definitions were basically the "right" ones. However, today functional analysis is largely concerned with duality, and this is quite foreign to the Fréchet definitions.

In the calculus of variations, and in analysis generally, the Fréchet definitions do not fit. In the case of curves, the necessary adjustments were made by Tonelli. We need, in the calculus of variations, to define the integral along a curve C of a Lagrangian $L(x, \dot{x})$. This means that we cannot use a representation $x(t)$ unless the integral of $L(x(t), \dot{x}(t))$ exists, and that we cannot regard two representations as equivalent unless they give rise to the same integral. Tonelli, therefore, restricts himself to absolutely continuous representations $x(t)$. The integral of L is then interpreted as a Lebesgue integral of $L(x(t), \dot{x}(t))$, and the equivalence of representations is restricted correspondingly. A more satisfactory way of adapting the Fréchet definitions is to use a different definition of integral of L, due to Weierstrass, which does not necessitate these restrictions, but this is immaterial here.

The point we wish to make is that Fréchet's definitions of curve and surface cannot be used in the calculus of variations as they stand; they have to be modified. They are therefore not sacrosanct. Once we are agreed on this, the only question is how best to effect the necessary modification.

In order to discuss this, we consider two typical examples: the skater's curve, and the surface consisting of a hairy square. The skater's curve, from A to B, consists of the segment $A0$, a figure eight whose two loops join at 0 and the segment $0B$. The hairy square consists of a horizontal square with a number of vertical segments whose lower ends lie on the square.

The skater's curve can be described, from A to B, in two ways: (a) as indicated in the figure, in the order I, II, III, IV, where I is the segment $A0$, II the upper loop of the figure of eight, III the lower loop, and IV the segment $0B$; (b) in the order derived from (a) by interchanging II and III. These two orders correspond to elementary Fréchet curves that we shall denote by C_1 and C_2.

The second example is defined in terms of the thumbtack (or drawing-pin) surface, by the operation of cutting out small circles in the square and replacing them by thumbtacks. It will therefore suffice to describe a single thumbtack surface as a Fréchet surface, by providing a

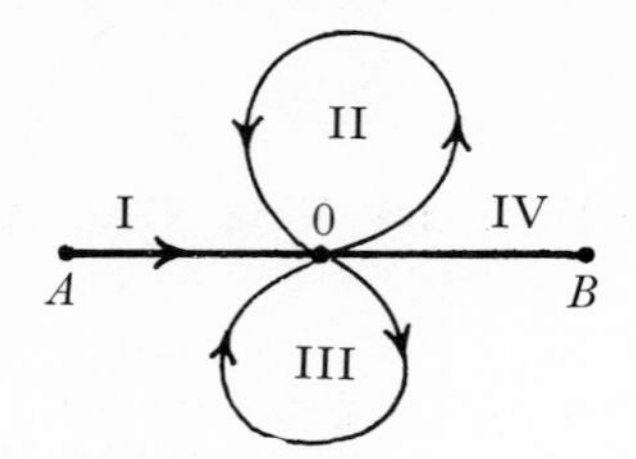

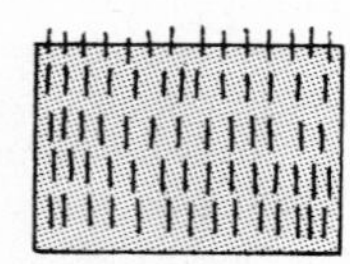

The hairy square
(or grassy patch)

parametric representation on a circular disc $0 \leq r \leq r_2$ in terms of polar coordinates (r, θ) We shall use cylindrical polar coordinates (ρ, φ, z) with a suitable origin 0, in the representation.

The representation has the form

$$\rho = f(r), \qquad \varphi = \theta, \qquad z = g(r),$$

where, for some positive $r_1 < r_2$, the functions $f(r)$, $g(r)$ are given by $f(r) = 0 \;\; 0 \leq r \leq r_1$, and by $g(r) = 0 \;\; r_1 \leq r \leq r_2$, together with $g(r) = 1 - r/r_1 \;\; 0 \leq r \leq r_1$,

$$f(r) = r_2 - r_2 \frac{r_2 - r}{r_2 - r_1} \qquad r_1 \leq r \leq r_2.$$

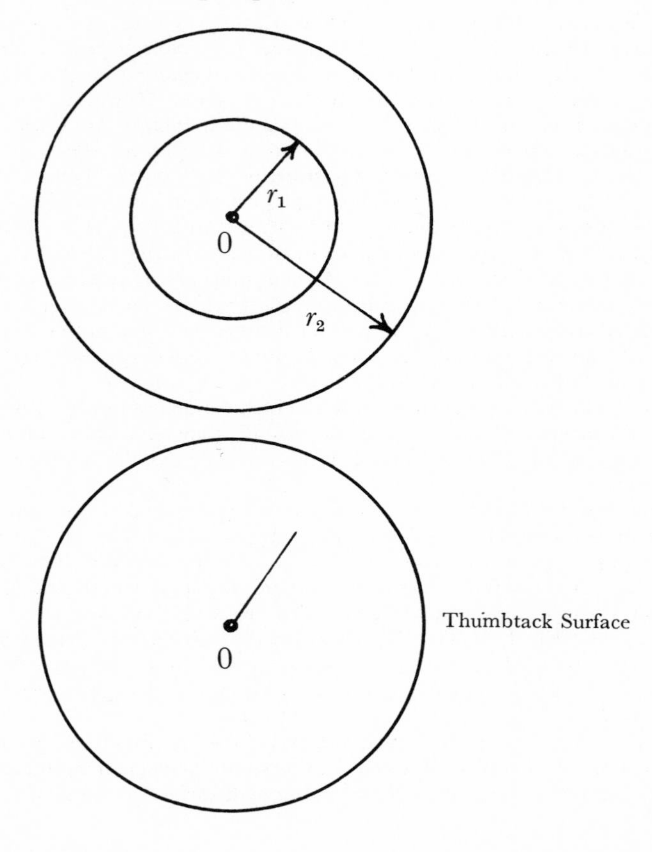

Thumbtack Surface

In the calculus of variations, the "skater's curve" and "hairy square" have caused difficulties quite out of proportion with their simple and intuitive character. According to the Fréchet definitions, there are, as stated above, two quite different skater's curves C_1 and C_2, according to the order in which the two loops of the figure eight are described. Yet in any variational problem we have

$$\mathscr{I}(C_1) = \mathscr{I}(C_2).$$

This means that, if C_1 is a solution of a variational problem, then C_2 is necessarily another solution of the same problem. This is the "identical twin phenomenon": the twins are distinguished by the parting in their hair and by nothing else; and they never appear at the same time, not even in different places. Who will believe that there really are two of them? Is it not rather that a same individual is given two names, according to the parting of his hair? It is, of course, permissible to change a person's name when he changes his parting, but this is hardly a practice that commends itself to us.

Passing to the second example, we denote by S_1 the hairy square, and by S_2 the square without hairs. In two-dimensional variational problems, we consider the minimum, in a class of surfaces S, of the integral over S of some Lagrangian $L(x, J)$, where J is the normal vector defined by the Jacobian matrix at a point of S. (In higher space, J is not a vector but a so-called bi-vector.) If we write $\mathscr{I}(S)$ for the double integral of L over S, it is easy to see that we have, for every such Lagrangian,

$$\mathscr{I}(S_1) = \mathscr{I}(S_2).$$

Thus the distinction between a square and a corresponding hairy square cannot affect variational problems. In this case, since hairs can be added to any surface whatever, this means that in any variational problem with a certain solution S, where S is a two-dimensional Fréchet surface, there are always an infinity of other solutions, which differ from S by a hair, or by a number of hairs. This is as if a person became different with every hair that grows on him. Surely there are limits to the distinctions that need to be made!

We shall here sweep away these artificial distinctions. Two representations of curves will be termed equivalent if and only if they give rise to the same value for the integral of the Lagrangian L, for each L. The class of representations $x(t)$ $t_1 \leq t \leq t_2$ thus equivalent to a given one will be termed a curve C.

In that case, a parametric curve C is determined if and only if for each Lagrangian $L(x, \dot{x})$, we know the corresponding value of the curvilinear integral $\mathscr{I}(C)$. Henceforth, we shall therefore simply identify the notion of parametric curve C, with that of the corresponding operation $\mathscr{I}(C)$ of curvilinear integration along C, since each of C and $\mathscr{I}(C)$ determines the other. This is a shorthand convention, frequently made in mathematics; strictly it is a minor confusion of terms, just as it is not strictly quite correct to denote by the same symbol a point P and the set consisting of a single point P. In analysis, one frequently speaks of the curve $x(t)$, to mean the curve defined by the set of representations equivalent to $x(t)$; if we allow ourselves this slight inexactitude, we can certainly speak, similarly, of the curve $\mathscr{I}(C)$ to mean the curve C for which $\mathscr{I}(C)$ is the operation of curvilinear integration.

§64. ADMISSIBLE CURVES AS ELEMENTS OF A DUAL SPACE

Our discussion will be restricted to curves of finite length, situated in a fixed cube. We shall admit only parametric representations $x(t)$ $t_1 \leq t \leq t_2$ of such curves, for which $x(t)$ is absolutely continuous. A Lagrangian $L(x, \dot{x})$ will now only be considered defined when x lies in the fixed cube, since its values for other x are irrelevant. Further, we shall use the letter f to denote the restriction of L to the set of $(x, \dot{x})$ for which x lies in our fixed cube and $\dot{x}$ lies on the unit sphere $|\dot{x}| = 1$, and we shall write A for this set. The function f, which now determines L by homogeneity, will be termed an integrand. We shall allow it to be an arbitrary continuous function, defined in A and real-valued. Thus f is, in the notation of Chapter IV, Section 48, an arbitrary element of the space $\mathscr{C}_0(A)$.

In a particular variational problem, for rectifiable curves in our fixed cube, we fix the Lagrangian L, or, what amounts to the same, we fix the integrand f. However, we are not concerned with a particular variational problem now, but with the notion of curve, and this notion must apply to all problems. It is therefore f that now must be variable, and C, our curve, that we must keep fixed.

For any fixed admissible curve C, the quantity $\mathscr{I}(C)$, considered for varying Lagrangian L, i.e., for varying $f \in \mathscr{C}_0(A)$, becomes a function $g(f)$. Now the quantity $\mathscr{I}(C)$, regarded as function of the Lagrangian L for fixed C, has rather simple properties. It has the form

$$\int_{t_1}^{t_2} L(x(t), \dot{x}(t))\, dt$$

where $x(t)$ is any absolutely continuous representation of C on a segment $t_1 \leq t \leq t_2$. Evidently, if L has the form $c_1L_1 + c_2L_2$, where c_1, c_2 are constants and L_1, L_2 are Lagrangians, we have

$$\mathscr{I}(C) = c_1\mathscr{I}_1(C) + c_2\mathscr{I}_2(C),$$

where $\mathscr{I}_1$, $\mathscr{I}_2$ are the corresponding integrals of the Lagrangians L_1, L_2. Since, by homogeneity, the integrands f, f_1, f_2 corresponding to L, L_1, L_2 are related by $f = c_1f_1 + c_2f_2$, it follows that $g(f) = c_1g(f_1) + c_2g(f_2)$, i.e., that g is linear. Further, by taking the arc length on C as parameter, we see that when f lies in the unit ball U of $\mathscr{C}_0(A)$ (i.e., when $|f| \leq 1$) the quantity $|\mathscr{I}(C)|$ cannot exceed the length of C. Hence $g(f)$ is bounded for $f \in U$.

This shows that g is an element of the dutiful dual $\mathscr{C}_0^*(A)$. The value $g(f)$ for a particular f can therefore now be written gf, in accordance with Chapter IV, Section 48.

We have agreed to identify C with $\mathscr{I}(C)$, regarded as function of L, i.e., of f. This means that C is now the function $g(f)$, and therefore the element g of $\mathscr{C}_0^*(A)$. Admissible curves have become elements $g \in \mathscr{C}_0^*(A)$, namely those for each of which there is at least one absolutely continuous $x(t)$ $t_1 \leq t \leq t_2$ such that, for each $f \in \mathscr{C}_0(A)$, if L is the Lagrangian corresponding to f, we have

$$gf = \int_{t_1}^{t_2} L(x(t), \dot{x}(t))\, dt. \tag{64.1}$$

The slight inexactitude of identifying in this way a curve C with the corresponding operation $\mathscr{I}(C)$ of curvilinear integration along C, and so with the corresponding element $g \in \mathscr{C}_0^*(A)$, is tolerated in mathematics (if, indeed, we think of it as a lapse from precision at all). We prefer to think that it is not an inexactitude and that we have stumbled onto a much better interpretation of a curve, one which provides a better understanding of what a curve is.

The spirit of modern mathematics is best understood, and best described, in terms of Plato's cave. What we study is no more than a succession of shadows, cast onto the walls of our cave by a great fire outside: shadows as of passers-by along a road behind us.

This allegory is the basis of what Plato calls the dialectic method: we must learn to reconstruct in our minds the simple events outside our cave. This has become the modern scientific method, and it is the basis of modern concepts in mathematics. For us, therefore, an entity is simple, not because we see it, for this merely makes it a shadow in our cave, nor because we can draw it, but because it obeys simple laws. This is also the logical sequel to the theories of Copernicus, which provide simple laws in astronomy, by no longer representing the world as centered around the earth. We must look for concepts which are simple in this sense.

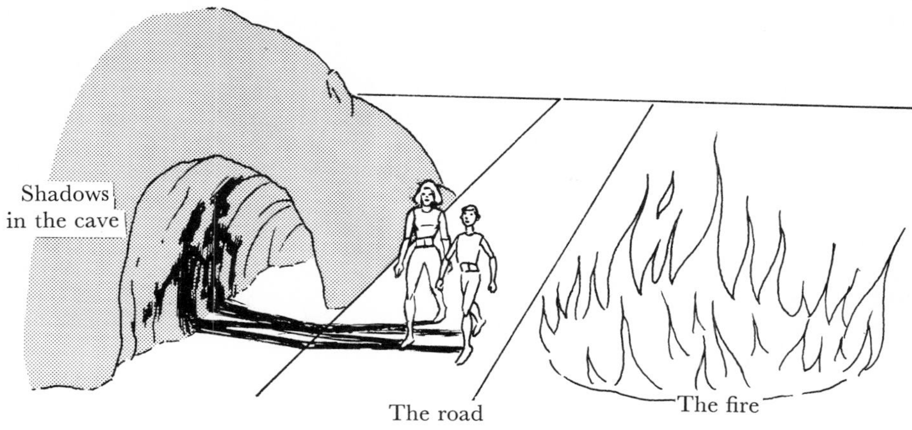

The classical concept of a curve C corresponds very closely to the curves that we see and draw; and such curves can twist and turn and zigzag back and forth; moreover they can have highly complicated self-intersections. This is only the shadow. If we choose to substitute for it the notion of curvilinear integral $\mathscr{I}(C)$, it will become an element g of our dual space $\mathscr{C}_0^*(A)$. This element, of course, we cannot see directly, but only by its shadow C. However, it is g and not C which obeys our criterion of simplicity, for g is a linear function of the new variable $f \in \mathscr{C}_0(A)$.

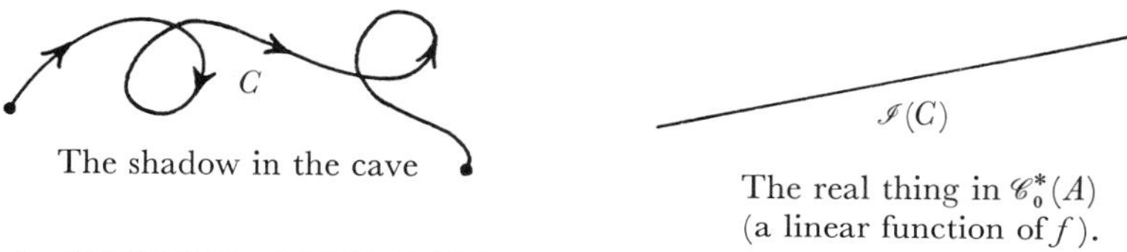

The shadow in the cave

The real thing in $\mathscr{C}_0^*(A)$ (a linear function of f).

§65. A HUMAN ANALOGY

We have remarked more than once on the close connections between the calculus of variations and a number of ideas that have had a profound influence on other parts of mathematics. The preceding section shows that these connections are not all limited to mathematics, and may take us into the much wider context of the great movements which have dominated human thought. We wish to pursue this a little further, and to gain in this way some insight into the nature and role of our dual space and of the curves that we have placed in it.

For this purpose, we shall speak of our curves as if they were not concepts, but beings like ourselves, or, better, as if they were human lives, which do indeed present a certain analogy to curves. We can perhaps imagine that in a variational problem it is perfection for a curve to attain the hoped for minimum, and that a curve twists and turns in its efforts to reach perfection. A reader may well object to this image on grounds that a curve is something that we draw or define by cold symbols, and that it is rather we ourselves who make it twist and turn with such an object. In this respect, we must request a mathematician's right to a little vagueness. Alternatively, we can use the objection itself to strengthen our analogy by appealing to a once popular limerick, which refers to man as "An engine that moves along predestinate grooves—not a bus, but a tram." According to this limerick our own striving is an illusion too. Still, there is no reason why we should not talk of striving, even if something else is really doing it for us, and if so, we should certainly allow ourselves the same freedom when speaking of curves. In any event, it is well within the conventions of language: how else can a cold drawing become a living portrait, or for that matter, an ordered collection of alphabet letters become words and thoughts? If these be fictions, then it is by such fictions that we live.

Thus, all in all, a human life is perhaps rather like a curve, striving as it does for an oft unattainable perfection: "The high that proved too high, the heroic for earth too hard, the passion that left the ground to lose itself in the sky."† The calculus of variations becomes then full of such striving; it is a very human calculus and our curves are very human curves.

† Robert Browning: *Dramatis Personae.* Abt Vogler, Stanza 10.

Indeed, perhaps this is not so farfetched. The illusion is rather that any human activity can be absolutely separated from human beings.

In this light, if we take another look at the rest of mathematics, it may not seem quite as cold and formal and full of arbitrary conventions as the nominalists would have us believe. Abstraction is really very human too; it originates in a kind of senile forgetfulness, as when Littlewood exclaimed to Wisconsin students, "I do wish all these factors $1/(2\pi)$ would be 1, I get so tired of writing them!"—and promptly forgot to do so. This is what abstraction really means: freedom from all that is petty and unimportant.

Therefore, to return to our curves—by all means let us think of our curves not as concepts, but as beings. We can then speak further of the achievements of a curve g as being the values for the various integrands f of the expression gf of (64.1). In the preceding section, we agreed to characterize a curve by its achievements, just as in the Preamble we characterized a function by its effect on others when we were describing Schwartz distributions. This is also how duality and dual functional spaces are appearing in other contexts in analysis.

According to our rule, a curve or any other member $g \in \mathscr{C}_0^*(A)$ is now known only by the values gf for all $f \in \mathscr{C}_0(A)$. No further information is recorded. The inhabitants of $\mathscr{C}_0^*(A)$ carry no birth certificates or identity cards; neither do they receive death certificates. When we desire this type of information, we do not ask for forms to be filled up in triplicate; we simply derive it from what all can see; just as, in *Pygmalion*, the professor can tell from the inflection of a voice where the speaker was born.

This happy state of affairs did not occur in the original space of curves, which obey the Fréchet definitions, or as we shall say, the Fréchet kingdom. There officialdom records not only the birth and death of a curve, but every single intermediate position. However, the curve's achievements remain completely unrecorded. Officially, what matters is only that every two curves be kept at their proper distance in order to prevent indiscretions or upheavals. Also, there must be no children and no pets, in fact, nothing but curves, in the kingdom. It is as exclusive as a country inhabited solely by millionaires, or an army composed only of generals. It is therefore strangely ineffective in carrying out tasks for which curves are not suited, however much they may try. In particular, many variational problems cannot be solved in it. In fact, in spite of being so exclusive, and indeed because of it, the Fréchet kingdom is really very poor in the true sense of the word, much too poor to be a satisfactory setting for the calculus of variations.

On the contrary, we shall find that in this sense $\mathscr{C}_0^*(A)$ is very rich. It contains, besides curves, many other beings. In particular, it contains the infinitesimal zigzags described in the examples of Section 61. To verify this, we need only extend to them the notion of integral, and we can define this notion as the limit of the curvilinear integrals of our Lagrangians on the finite approximating zigzags; for the integral in question then constitutes an element of $\mathscr{C}_0^*(A)$. In this way we shall find that, in $\mathscr{C}_0^*(A)$, each of our variational problems has a solution. In fact, $\mathscr{C}_0^*(A)$ contains everything that a curve tries to be and fails: this must be heaven for a curve.

We shall continue our analysis of $\mathscr{C}_0^*(A)$ now that our reader feels, perhaps, more at home there.

§66. GENERALIZED CURVES AND FLOWS, AND THEIR BOUNDARIES

We term linear form, or simply form, a Lagrangian L, or the corresponding integrand f, if there is a continuous vector-valued function $a(x)$ such that

$$\textbf{(66.1)} \qquad L(x, \dot{x}) = \dot{x}a(x),$$

where the right hand side is understood as a scalar product of two n-dimensional vectors. In particular, the above form will be termed exact, and written $\partial\varphi$, if there exists a continuously differentiable scalar function $\varphi(x)$ such that

$$\textbf{(66.2)} \qquad a(x) = \operatorname{grad} \varphi(x).$$

We recall further, from the definition (48.4) of Chapter IV, Section 48, that in $\mathscr{C}_0^*(A)$ a sequence g_ν $\nu = 1, 2, \ldots$ converges to an element g, if, for each $f \in \mathscr{C}_0(A)$, the values $g_\nu f$ converge to gf. This notion of convergence is particularly well suited to the calculus of variations, since we are there concerned, at any given time, with only one problem, and so with only one integrand f. It automatically implies that if C_ν is a sequence of curves with limit C in the new sense, then $\mathscr{I}(C_\nu)$ tends to $\mathscr{I}(C)$. This disposes, at one stroke, of the need for special restrictions such as occur in the Tonelli approach, which requires semicontinuity of $\mathscr{I}(C)$. With our new notion of convergence, which we shall term fine convergence when we wish to distinguish it from our previous traditional convergence of curves, $\mathscr{I}(C)$ becomes a continuous function of C.

At the same time, fine convergence clears up the paradox which troubled Lebesgue at Beauvais: in the sense of fine convergence, the broken line no longer tends to the third side of the triangle, but tends instead to an element of $\mathscr{C}_0^*(A)$ not expressible as an admissible curve. This fine limit is what we termed an infinitesimal zigzag. Our variational problem needs then to be reformulated, so that not only curves, but their fine limits, become admissible.

An element of $\mathscr{C}_0^*(A)$ will be termed a generalized curve, if it is expressible as a fine limit of a sequence of curves. Further, we shall term generalized flow any element of the positive cone of $\mathscr{C}_0^*(A)$, i.e., any $g \in \mathscr{C}_0^*(A)$ such that, for all $f \in \mathscr{C}_0(A)$, the relation $f \geq 0$ implies $gf \geq 0$. Clearly every generalized curve is a special case of a generalized flow.

For any generalized flow g, and in particular for any generalized curve, we note, as in Chapter IV, Section 48, that the norm $|g|$ is the value of gf when f is the constant unity. Since the corresponding Lagrangian is $L(x, \dot{x}) = |\dot{x}|$, we speak of this norm as the length of g, just as in the case of a rectifiable curve.

We shall term boundary ∂g of an element $g \in \mathscr{C}_0^*(A)$ the restriction $g\partial\varphi$ of the function $g(f) = gf$ to those integrands $f \in \mathscr{C}_0(A)$ which are exact forms $\partial\varphi$.

In the case of a curve g, we shall write provisionally $\hat{\partial} g$ for the following quantity, which we may term the elementary boundary of g: we set $\hat{\partial} g = 0$ if g is closed, while $\hat{\partial} g$ is to denote the ordered pair x_1, x_2 of the end points of g, if g is not closed. We shall verify that for a curve g, $\hat{\partial} g$ and ∂g determine one another.

To this effect, we first remark that if g is a curve and $\varphi(x)$ a continuously differentiable function,

$$g\partial\varphi = \varphi(x_2) - \varphi(x_1), \tag{66.3}$$

where x_1, x_2 is the ordered pair of end points of g. By taking for $\varphi(x)$, in turn, the various components of x, we see that ∂g determines the difference $x_2 - x_1$, and that the latter vanishes when $\partial g = 0$. It follows that the relations $\partial g = 0$ and $\hat{\partial} g = 0$ are equivalent, and moreover it is clear from (66.3) that $\hat{\partial} g$ determines ∂g. It remains to show that in the case $\partial g \neq 0$, the pair x_1, x_2 is determined by ∂g. It will be sufficient to obtain in terms of ∂g an expression for the sum

$$\varphi(x_1) + \varphi(x_2).$$

The desired expression will turn out to be

$$\frac{2(g\,\partial\Phi)(g\,\partial\psi) - (g\,\partial\varphi)(g\,\partial\Psi)}{(g\,\partial\psi)^2}, \tag{66.4}$$

where ψ is any continuously differentiable function such that $g\,\partial\psi \neq 0$, and where Φ, Ψ are its products by φ, ψ. To show that (66.4) has the stated value, it is sufficient to evaluate it as function of x_1, x_2, by using (66.3) and the corresponding formulae with φ replaced by ψ, Φ, Ψ.

The same argument can be applied to a sequence g_ν $\nu = 1, 2, \ldots$ of curves which tends to a generalized curve g. We find then that if $\partial g = 0$, the difference of the end points of g_ν must tend to 0, by (65.3) applied to g_ν; we also find if $\partial g \neq 0$, then, by choosing ψ so that $g\ \partial\psi \neq 0$, and therefore so that $g_\nu\ \partial\psi \neq 0$ for all large ν, that the end-points of g_ν tend to definite limits x_1, x_2. By adding small pairs of directed segments to g_ν, it follows that every generalized curve g is the limit of a sequence of curves g_ν $\nu = 1, 2, \ldots,$ such that $\partial g = \partial g_\nu$ for all ν. Thus the boundaries of generalized curves are the same as those of traditional admissible curves. We shall speak of a closed generalized curve g if $\partial g = 0$, while, if $\partial g \neq 0$, we define the end points x_1, x_2 of g in terms of ∂g exactly as for traditional curves.

We recall from Chapter IV, Section 48, Theorem 48.6, that in the positive cone of $\mathscr{C}_0^*(A)$, fine convergence agrees with convergence in the dashed metric. This has the important consequence that the set of generalized curves is closed; it is the closure of the set of traditional rectifiable curves. For if g is a fine limit of generalized curves, and we choose any $\varepsilon > 0$, then, in the dashed metric, g is distant $<\varepsilon$ from a generalized curve, and so $< 2\varepsilon$ from a traditional curve; hence g is the fine limit of a traditional curve.

We see how smoothly we can operate in our dual space with the notion of fine convergence, although it is no more than convergence for each f of a sequence of our functions $g(f)$, and every student of advanced calculus learns about the pitfalls of such nonuniform convergence. This suggests perhaps that such pitfalls need not be permanent in mathematics if we can plan things better. To distinguish so sharply between closely related things is not necessarily in the spirit of mathematics in the long run. Mathematics was not invented for lawyers or botanists.

We pass on to consider the structure and the boundary of a generalized flow, i.e., of an arbitrary element of the positive cone of $\mathscr{C}_0^*(A)$. The simplest such element is not a generalized curve, nor even an ordinary curve, but a line element; we mean by this an element $g \in \mathscr{C}_0^*(A)$ such that there exists a pair $(x, \dot{x}) \in A$ for which we have, for every $f \in \mathscr{C}_0(A)$, $gf = f(x, \dot{x})$. It is easy to see that if such a pair exists, it is uniquely determined by g; in fact, we obtain each coordinate of x, or $\dot{x}$, by specializing f suitably. It will be remarked that formerly it was the pair $(x, \dot{x})$ that we termed line element, whereas now it is the corresponding g; the change is slight, since each determines the other, and in fact, we may sometimes allow ourselves the slight inaccuracy of identifying the two.

Line elements are not only the simplest elements of $\mathscr{C}_0^*(A)$, they are also the most fundamental. Indeed, the Riesz representation may be regarded as expressing in terms of them any element $g \in \mathscr{C}_0^*(A)$ whatever. According to it, if we write temporarily α for $(x, \dot{x})$ and g_α for the corresponding line element of $\mathscr{C}_0^*(A)$, to any $g \in \mathscr{C}_0^*(A)$ we can associate a signed measure μ in A, such that

$$\textbf{(66.5)} \qquad |g| = \int_A |d\mu|, \quad \text{and} \quad gf = \int_A g_\alpha f\, d\mu$$

for every $f \in \mathscr{C}_0(A)$. It will be convenient to rewrite the second relation simply as

$$\textbf{(66.6)} \qquad g = \int_A g_\alpha\, d\mu.$$

We can express this by saying that any $g \in \mathscr{C}_0^*(A)$ is a signed mixture of line elements g_α. Moreover, here, the elements g of the positive cone of $\mathscr{C}_0^*(A)$ are simply those elements of $\mathscr{C}_0^*(A)$ for which the corresponding μ are ≥ 0: they are the positive mixtures of our line elements.

This last remark follows from a simplification of the proof of Theorem (49.5) of Chapter IV, Section 49. Or, alternatively, it can be deduced from (i) and (ii) of that theorem, i.e., from (66.5) above, as follows: when g is in the positive cone, we have $|g| = g \cdot 1$, and this may now be written

$$\int_A |d\mu| = \int_A d\mu.$$

By combining this with the inequalities

$$\int_A f\,|d\mu| \geq \int_A f\,d\mu, \qquad \int_A (1-f)\,|d\mu| \geq \int_A (1-f)\,d\mu$$

which are always valid when $0 \leq f \leq 1$, it follows that, for $0 \leq f \leq 1$, and hence by linearity for all $f \in \mathscr{C}_0(A)$, we have

$$\int_A f\,|d\mu| = \int_A f\,d\mu = gf,$$

so that, in the representation of g, the measure μ can be replaced by its total variation, i.e., by a non-negative measure.

Next to the line elements, we shall consider as simplest in $\mathscr{C}_0^*(A)$ first the weighted line elements, derived from them by multiplication by non-negative constants, and second the generalized line elements, defined as positive mixtures of the form (66.6) of line elements g_α which all correspond to pairs $(x, \dot{x})$ with a same first member x. We shall speak of such line elements as passing through the point x, or concentrated at the point x, and their mixture as a generalized line element through x, or concentrated at x. Alternatively, a generalized line element will sometimes be referred to as a turbulent line element, or in full, as a weighted line element with turbulence, when we wish to evoke an analogy with fluid motion, that we sketch below.

Weighted line elements, like the line elements from which they are derived, will be attached to pairs $(x, \dot{x})$. However the constant factor will now be the magnitude $|\dot{x}|$. This means that the weighted line element is now identically 0 if $\dot{x} = 0$, and that otherwise it is the multiple $|\dot{x}|$ of the line element $(x, \dot{x}/|\dot{x}|)$.

To a generalized line element, given by (66.6) and concentrated at the point x, we shall attach further a weighted line element, termed its resultant, defined as follows. Let θ_α denote the direction $\dot{x}$ attached to g_α, and let

$$\bar{\mu} = \int 1\,d\mu, \qquad \bar{\theta} = \int \theta_\alpha\,d\mu.$$

Then the resultant is defined as the product of $\bar{\mu}$ by the weighted line element corresponding to the pair $(x, \bar{\theta})$. In other words, it is given by $(x, \bar{\dot{x}})$, where $\bar{\dot{x}} = \bar{\mu}\bar{\theta}$.

It will often be convenient to think of a pair $(x, \dot{x})$ as representing a minute portion of a fluid situated, at a given time, at the point x, and moving with a momentum $\dot{x}$. We can then imagine a generalized line element at the point x to arise in one of two equivalent ways. In the one case, we may suppose our fluid to consist of many streams of a rarefied gas, which move through one another in different directions θ_α near the point x; the generalized line element (66.6) then represents, at this point, the superposition of momenta of distinct minute fluid portions, and so describes there the motion of the mixture of the various streams.

The second and more common way in which our generalized line element can arise, is mathematically less simple. We now think of our fluid as water flowing under a bridge, from which we observe that at the point x the momentum of a small portion is the vector $\bar{\dot{x}}$ given by

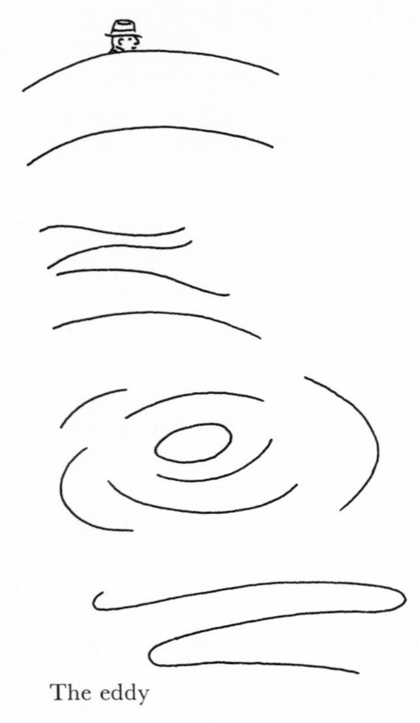

The eddy

our resultant; and that, around the point x, the relative motion of the water near x is one for which the fluid particles describe small closed curves. On these curves, the directions are those of the vectors $\theta_\alpha - \bar{\theta}$, and these occur in proportions determined by their magnitudes and by the measure μ. A full discussion requires a theorem that we shall not prove, and we therefore limit ourselves to the special case, in which μ is a discrete measure which associates a finite number of weights μ_α with the directions corresponding to certain values of α only. In this case the closed curves are similar to the closed polygon of the vectors $\mu_\alpha(\theta_\alpha - \bar{\theta})$. The general case actually reduces by superposition to the case of $\leq n + 1$ weights, because a measure μ on the unit sphere of n-space such that $\int \theta \, d\mu(\theta) = 0$ is the superposition of a set of discrete measures with the same property, each of which affects at most $n + 1$ values of θ.

The relative motion along these small closed curves, which we must really think of as infinitely small, but described many times over, we speak of as turbulence. Of course, we do not actually observe this limiting situation in water; and indeed, in water, the relative motion will not be along polygonal paths. However, even the extreme case where the closed polygon degenerates into that of two equal and opposite vectors can very well be visualized in certain viscous fluids, in which case the turbulence consists of a back and forth vibration at the point x.

We shall pursue the fluid analogy further, now in relation to arbitrary generalized flows.

For simplicity, we shall consider a fluid motion at a given time, or in steady motion. According to Euler, the motion is then specified if we know for each point x the corresponding velocity $\dot{x}$ and the fluid density. However, to avoid *a priori* assumptions, we shall not speak of a density, but of a measure μ, which, of course, is to be ≥ 0. We shall consider here only the case in which μ is finite and its support is bounded. The preceding discussion then makes clear that the Eulerian conception of fluid motion needs to be generalized to allow for the phenomena described above.

The Eulerian specification is equivalent to providing a measure μ on a set of pairs $(x, \dot{x})$ such that, in the support of μ, there is just one $\dot{x}$ to each x. To allow for a set of rarefied gases passing through one another, the obvious extension is that of providing any measure μ on a set of pairs $(x, \dot{x})$. Here μ is as before ≥ 0 and finite and its support will be supposed bounded. If we strengthen this by stipulating that $|\dot{x}| = 1$, we see that, by the Riesz representation, our generalized Eulerian fluid motion is specified by exactly the same things as a generalized flow. Here, the restriction $|\dot{x}| = 1$ is of secondary importance for, on the one hand, in fluid motion velocities occur multiplied by masses, which can be arbitrary, so that the momenta are unaffected by the restriction; on the other hand, the restriction $|\dot{x}| = 1$ was made here for the convenience of parametric problems, and will not occur in optimal control.

An alternative generalization of Eulerian fluid motion can be similarly derived from our second way of illustrating a generalized line element, and it turns out to be, in fact, equivalent to the above. It consists in a measure μ in x-space, together with the specification, at each point x, of a generalized line element through that point. We thus have now, at each relevant x, not only a mean velocity $\bar{\dot{x}}$, but also what we have termed turbulence. It is intuitive that there is an equivalent way of specifying an arbitrary generalized flow g in our sense; this could be done by changing (66.6) so that α is now the variable point x, and g_α a corresponding generalized line element through this point. However, to deduce this from the Riesz representation requires a form of Fubini's theorem rarely found in analysis books, and we shall not do so.

We have thus given the reader a reasonable picture, or at least reasonable first impressions, of the beings present in the positive cone of $\mathscr{C}_0^*(A)$, alongside of our curves and generalized curves.

Of the elements of $\mathscr{C}_0^*(A)$ not in the positive cone, we shall mainly remark that they have the same boundaries as generalized flows. Any such element, by the Riesz representation, has the form $g = g_1 - g_2$, where g_1, g_2 lie in the positive cone. We define $\hat{g} = g_1 + \hat{g}_2$, where $\hat{g}_2$ is the element of the positive cone for which, for each $f \in \mathscr{C}_0(A)$,

$$\hat{g}_2 f = g_2 \hat{f} \quad \text{where} \quad \hat{f}(x, \dot{x}) = f(x, -\dot{x}).$$

Clearly $\partial \hat{g}_2 = -\partial g_2$, so that $\partial g = \partial \hat{g}$ where $\hat{g}$ lies in the positive cone of $\mathscr{C}_0^*(A)$.

This means that the elements of the positive cone cannot be distinguished by their boundaries from those not in this cone. Clearly, however, many of them can be so distinguished from curves.

§67. PARAMETRIC REPRESENTATION OF GENERALIZED CURVES

In $\mathscr{C}_0^*(A)$, or in its positive cone, only the elements identified with our curves or generalized curves will appear as solutions of our variational problems. Nevertheless, there are advantages in knowing one's neighbors, large or small. In this section, we show that generalized line elements play, in regard to generalized curves, a part analogous to that of line elements in regard to curves. Thus a generalized curve differs from a traditional curve only by the turbulence attached to its line elements.

(67.1) Representation Theorem. *The element $g \in \mathscr{C}_0^*(A)$ is a generalized curve if and only if there exists a Lipschitzian vector-valued function $x(t)$ $0 \leq t \leq 1$, and for almost each t a generalized line-element g_t with the resultant $(x(t), \dot{x}(t))$, such that $|g_t|$ is uniformly bounded and that*

(67.2)
$$g = \int_0^1 g_t \, dt.$$

We recall that $x(t)$ is termed Lipschitzian, if there exist a constant K, such that, for all relevant pairs t_1, t_2,

$$|x(t_2) - x(t_1)| \leq K \cdot |t_2 - t_1|.$$

Further we interpret (67.2) to mean that, for each $f \in \mathscr{C}_0(A)$,

(67.3)
$$gf = \int_0^1 g_t f \, dt;$$

and the right hand side may be considered to generalize the traditional expression for a curvilinear integral of the Lagrangian L corresponding to f. In fact, if g_t reduces to the weighted line element corresponding to the resultant, we see that $g_t f$ reduces to $L(x(t), \dot{x}(t))$.

We shall prove separately the necessity and the sufficiency parts of our assertion. We shall start with the former, which will turn out to be largely an exercise in the use of equicontinuity and of the diagonal method.

Proof of Necessity. By hypothesis g is the fine limit of curves g_ν $\nu = 1, 2, \ldots$ The length $K_\nu = |g_\nu|$ of g_ν tends to the length $|g|$ by fine convergence, and therefore remains below some fixed constant K. We shall choose for g_ν a parametric representation $x_\nu(t)$ $0 \leq t \leq 1$ such that $K_\nu t$ is the arc length. The functions $x_\nu(t)$ then satisfy uniformly in ν the Lipschitz condition

$$|x_\nu(t_2) - x_\nu(t_1)| \leq K \cdot |t_2 - t_1|,$$

for every pair of values t_1, t_2 of t. Moreover we have almost everywhere

$$|\dot{x}_\nu(t)| = K_\nu \leq K.$$

Since the $x_\nu(t)$ are thus equicontinuous, and their values lie in a fixed cube, there is a subsequence which converges uniformly to some function $x(t)$ $0 \leq t \leq 1$. We shall limit ourselves to this subsequence.

For any subinterval Δ of $0 \leq t \leq 1$, we now denote by Δg_ν the arc of g_ν defined for $t \in \Delta$ by $x_\nu(t)$. The length $|\Delta g_\nu|$ is then $K_\nu\,|\Delta|$, where $|\Delta|$ denotes the length of Δ. Thus

$$\textbf{(67.4)} \qquad |\Delta g_\nu| \leq K\,|\Delta|, \quad \text{i.e.} \quad |\Delta g_\nu f| \leq K\,|f| \cdot |\Delta|$$

for each $f \in \mathscr{C}_0(A)$. To a sequence Δg_ν for any fixed Δ, we can therefore apply (in a ball of $\mathscr{C}_0^*(A)$ of radius K in place of the unit ball) Theorems (48.6) and (48.8) of Chapter IV, Section 48, and extract a finely convergent subsequence. We shall show, however, that we can perform this extraction once for all, to obtain a subsequence of ν along which Δg_ν converges finely for each Δ, simultaneously.

We first arrange for such a simultaneous extraction for each Δ of a countable succession $\Delta_1, \Delta_2, \ldots$. To this effect, we proceed by induction: we can extract from the given sequence of ν a subsequence along which Δg_ν converges finely when $\Delta = \Delta_1$; for each k we can extract from the k-th subsequence a $(k+1)$-st for which Δg_ν converges finely when $\Delta = \Delta_k$. The diagonal subsequence then has the desired property for each $\Delta = \Delta_k$, $k = 1, 2, \ldots$. Henceforth we limit ourselves to this diagonal sequence, taking for the Δ_k intervals, with initial points at 0, for which, as k varies, the final points describe the rationals of $0 < t < 1$. We shall show that the subsequence of ν thus arrived at has the desired property for every Δ. It will be enough, by subtraction, to consider intervals Δ with initial point 0; we denote any such interval by Δ_t, where t is the final point of Δ_t.

We now write, for each $f \in \mathscr{C}_0(A)$ and for $0 \leq t \leq 1$,

$$\varphi_\nu(t, f) = (\Delta_t g_\nu) f.$$

The difference of φ_ν at two values of t for a same f is of the form $\Delta g_\nu f$, where Δ is the t-interval with these values as extremities. It follows from (67.4) that, for fixed f, the functions φ_ν are equicontinuous in t. Since they converge to a limit at rational points t as $\nu \to \infty$, it follows, as in the proof of Theorem (48.2), of Chapter IV, Section 48, that they converge uniformly in $0 \leq t \leq 1$ to a limit $\varphi(t, f)$. Thus $\Delta_t g_\nu f \to \varphi(t, f)$ for each t and f, and therefore Δg_ν converges finely for each Δ, as asserted above.

Proceeding with our proof, we next show that there is a subset T of $0 \le t \le 1$ of measure 1 at each point of which the function $\varphi(t, f)$ just constructed has, for each f, a derivative $\dot\varphi(t, f)$ with respect to t. We shall prove this by similar stages, first for a single f, then for a countable set of f, and finally for all f. (All without tears!)

To this effect, we write Δg for the fine limit of Δg_ν, so that $\varphi(t, f) = (\Delta_t g)f$, and $(\Delta g)f$ is now the difference $\Delta\varphi$ of φ at the two ends of the interval Δ. By taking the limit in ν in (67.4), we have

$$\textbf{(67.5)} \qquad |\Delta g| \le K\,|\Delta|, \qquad |(\Delta g)f| \le K\,|f| \cdot |\Delta|.$$

From this last relation, it follows that $\varphi(t, f)$ for fixed f is a Lipschitzian function of t and so has a derivative $\dot\varphi(t, f)$ except in a set E_f of t of Lebesgue measure 0. Hence if f_k $k = 1, 2, \ldots$ is a countable family of functions in $\mathscr{C}_0(A)$, and T denotes the complement of the union of the sets E_f $f = f_k$, we see that T has Lebesgue measure 1 and that for each point $t_0 \in T$ the derivative $\dot\varphi(t_0, f_k)$ exists for each f_k of the family. We shall now choose for our countable family, the class $\mathscr{P}$ of Theorem (48.1) in Chapter IV, Section 48. In that case, we shall see that at any point t_0 of the corresponding set T the derivative $\dot\varphi(t_0, f)$ exists for every $f \in \mathscr{C}_0(A)$. This is equivalent to showing that for intervals Δ with one end at t_0, which are situated in $0 \le t \le 1$, and whose lengths tend to 0, the limit of

$$\textbf{(67.6)} \qquad \frac{\Delta g}{|\Delta|} \cdot f = \frac{\Delta g}{|\Delta|} f_k + \frac{\Delta g}{|\Delta|} (f - f_k)$$

exists, or, equivalently, that the difference of the upper and lower limits is less than any preassigned positive number. This difference is however unaltered if we replace f by $f - f_k$, since the first term on the right of (67.6) has the limit $\dot\varphi(t_0, f_k)$. By (67.5) this difference is thus at most $2K \cdot |f - f_k|$ which is arbitrarily small by choice of k, since $\mathscr{P}$ is dense in $\mathscr{C}_0(A)$. Thus $\dot\varphi(t_0, f)$ must exist, as asserted above.

We can now proceed once more with our proof. For each $t = t_0 \in T$, the limit of the expression (67.6) thus exists for every f, i.e., the fine limit of the elements $\Delta g/|\Delta|$ exists. We shall denote this fine limit by g_t. We then clearly have, for each f

$$\int_0^1 g_t f\,dt = \int_0^1 \dot\varphi(t, f)\,dt = \varphi(1, f) - \varphi(0, f)$$
$$= \varphi(1, f) = gf,$$

so that (67.3), and therefore (67.2), hold. (Still without tears!)

It remains to discuss the nature of the element $g_t \in \mathscr{C}_0^*(A)$, and for simplicity we set $g_t = 0$ when t does not lie in T. We denote by t_0 again any fixed point of T, and by A_0 and $A\rho$ the parts of A for which, respectively, x is equal to $x(t_0)$, or distant from it by $\le\rho$, where ρ is sufficiently small and positive. We shall write $|f|_0$ and $|f|\rho$ for the supremum of $|f(x, t)|$ in A_0 and in A, respectively. Evidently, for any sufficiently small Δ which contains t_0, the arc $x_\nu(t)$ $t \in \Delta$ will lie in a ball of radius ρ and center $x(t_0)$, for all large ν, so that in (67.4) and (67.5), we can, for such a Δ, replace $|f|$ by $|f|\rho$. Hence, for $t = t_0$, $g_t f$, as the limit of the left hand side of (67.6) as $|\Delta| \to 0$, will be, in absolute value, $\le K\,|f|\rho$ for every ρ, and therefore

$$\textbf{(67.7)} \qquad |g_t f| \le K\,|f|_0 \quad \text{for} \quad t = t_0.$$

It follows at once that if $f_0(x, \dot x)$ denotes the function $f_0(\dot x) = f(x(t_0), \dot x)$, then for $t = t_0$ we have $g_t(f - f_0) = 0$, and therefore $g_t f = g_t f_0$. Thus g_t is completely determined by the values $g_t f_0$ for functions $f_0(\dot x)$, independent of x, defined on the unit sphere $|\dot{x}| = 1$. These values constitute an element of a dual space $\mathscr{C}_0^*(B)$ where B is this unit sphere. Evidently, g_t lies in the positive cone, and therefore there exists a measure $\mu \geq 0$ such that $g_t f_0 = \int_B f_0(\dot{x})\, d\mu$, and $\int d\mu \leq K$ by (67.7). Thus, for any $t = t_0 \in T$, we see that g_t is a generalized line element concentrated at $x(t_0)$, and $|g_t| \leq K$. To verify that its resultant is $x(t_0)$, $\dot{x}(t_0)$ we take for $f(x, \dot{x})$ any component of $\dot{x}$, and we verify that the quantity $g_t f = \dot{\varphi}(t_0, f)$ is this component of $\dot{x}(t_0)$. However, $\varphi_\nu(t, f)$ is here the corresponding component of $x_\nu(t) - x_\nu(0)$, so that its limit $\varphi(t, f)$ is the same component of $x(t) - x(0)$, and therefore $\dot{\varphi}(t_0, f)$ is the desired component of $\dot{x}(t_0)$. This establishes the necessity.

A proof of this kind, which involves relatively few ideas and uses them more than once, should eventually be relegated to a computer. Unfortunately, at present computers are not quite up to this kind of routine work, so we must have the patience to go through it. In this case the result is of much greater interest than the proof, and constitutes the main part of our theorem. It shows how little a generalized curve really differs from a traditional one. The difference lies in what we have termed turbulence. We can think of it as a kind of local throbbing, invisible to the eye but capable of being felt or heard. The human eye tends to superpose what it perceives, as when a mixture of yellow and blue becomes green. The ear, and still more the touch, tend rather to distinguish simultaneous sensations, so that, for instance, a group of notes becomes a chord, and not the single note which is their mean value. Of course the eye can perceive something that approximates to turbulence, or to a mixture of colors—alternate yellow and blue strips are not green.

Proof of Sufficiency. By hypothesis g now has the form stated; we shall show it to be a fine limit of curves by showing that there exists a curve at an arbitrarily small dashed distance. To this effect we produce, at successive small dashed distances elements g_1, g_2, g_3, the last of which will be a curve—in fact, a polygon.

To derive g_1, we replace $x(t)$ by $(1 - \varepsilon)x(t)$ and at the same time we replace the measure μ, which defines g_t, by $(1 - \varepsilon)\mu$, for almost every t. It is evident that as $\varepsilon \to 0$, $g_1 f \to gf$ for each f. Thus g_1 tends to g, so that we can choose it at an arbitrarily small dashed distance. The object of introducing g_1 is to ensure, on the one hand, that our constructions stay in the same basic cube of x-space, and on the other hand, that the constant K which is the supremum in t of $|g_t|$ is not increased. Both these are therefore reduced in the ratio $1 - \varepsilon$ in this preliminary approximation to g. In other respects g_1 has exactly the same form as g, and we shall now write simply $x(t)$ and μ in place of their products by $(1 - \varepsilon)$.

In deriving g_2 we shall have $x(t)$ unaltered; however, we shall alter μ for almost every t by replacing it with a discrete measure, which attaches weights $\mu_\alpha(t)$ to a fixed finite set of unit vectors θ_α. We shall do this so that $\int \theta\, d\mu$ is unaffected and remains $\dot{x}(t)$, while $\int d\mu$ is altered arbitrarily little; in fact, for each $f(\theta)$, $\int f\, d\mu$ is altered arbitrarily little when f is continuous. The construction of the weights $\mu_\alpha(t)$, which is quite elementary, is given below. The construction clearly leads to an element g_2, which can be made to tend finely to g_1, and which can therefore be chosen at an arbitrarily small dashed distance from it. The element g_2 then has the same form as g except that the measures μ that define its genearlized line elements are subject to the restriction described above. In addition we shall arrange, for convenience, that the weights $\mu_\alpha(t)$ are all strictly positive.

The alteration in any of our measures μ is as follows. We choose $\delta > 0$, and we decompose the unit sphere of the directions θ of n-space into a large enough finite number N of small compartments, i.e., into disjoint sets Θ_α of small diameter, where $\alpha = 1, 2, \ldots, N$. In each compartment we choose a representative direction θ_α and we arrange that δ exceed all the values of $|\theta - \theta_\alpha|$ for $\theta \in \Theta_\alpha$, $\alpha = 1, 2, \ldots, N$. We set, further, $m = N + 2n$, and we define $2n$ additional directions θ_α, $\alpha = N + 1$,

$N + 2, \ldots, m$, as the directions which are parallel or antiparallel to the n coordinate axes. We now define the weights μ_α first for $\alpha = 1, 2, \ldots, N$, by setting

$$\mu_\alpha = \delta/m + \int_{\Theta_\alpha} d\mu, \qquad (\alpha = 1, 2, \ldots, N).$$

In order to define the remaining weights μ_α, we set

$$\xi = \int \theta \, d\mu - \sum_{\alpha=1}^{N} \theta_\alpha \mu_\alpha = \sum_{\alpha=1}^{N} \int_{\Theta_\alpha} (\theta - \theta_\alpha) \, d\mu - \frac{\delta}{m} \sum_{\alpha=1}^{N} \theta_\alpha.$$

The vector ξ has magnitude $|\xi| \leq \delta(\bar{\mu} + 1)$ where $\bar{\mu}$ stands as previously for $\int d\mu$. We now define the remaining μ_α as follows:

$$\mu_\alpha = \delta/m + \text{Max}\,(\xi\theta_\alpha, 0) \qquad (\alpha = N + 1, \ldots, m).$$

Here $\xi\theta_\alpha$ is a scalar product, and Max (a, b) denotes the greater of any two numbers a, b. These definitions imply

$$\sum_{\alpha=N+1}^{m} \theta_\alpha \mu_\alpha = \sum_{\alpha=N+1}^{m} \theta_\alpha \,\text{Max}\,(\xi\theta_\alpha, 0) = \xi.$$

Thus, when we extend the sum to all $\alpha = 1, 2, \ldots, m$, we have

(67.8)(i) $$\sum_\alpha \theta_\alpha \mu_\alpha = \xi + \left(\int \theta \, d\mu - \xi \right) = \int \theta \, d\mu,$$

and this is, by hypothesis, $\dot{x}(t)$ almost everywhere. On the other hand, if R denotes the set of at most n values of $\alpha > N$ for which $\xi\theta_\alpha > 0$, we have

(67.8)(ii) $$\sum \mu_\alpha - \bar{\mu} = \delta + \sum_{\alpha \in R} \xi\theta_\alpha \leq \delta + \delta\sqrt{n};$$

moreover, for any continuous function $f(\theta)$ defined for $|\theta| \leq 1$, whose maximum modulus is M, and for which ε_δ denotes the oscillation, i.e., the supremum of $|f(\theta) - f(\theta^*)|$, for $|\theta - \theta^*| \leq \delta$, we find that

$$\left| \sum_\alpha f(\theta_\alpha)\mu_\alpha - \int f(\theta) \, d\mu \right| = \left| \sum_{\alpha=1}^{N} \int_{\Theta_\alpha} \{f(\theta_\alpha) - f(\theta)\} \, d\mu + \Lambda \right|$$

where

$$|\Lambda| = \left| \frac{\delta}{m} \sum_\alpha f(\theta_\alpha) + \sum_{\alpha \in R} f(\theta_\alpha)\xi\theta_\alpha \right| \leq M(\delta + \delta\sqrt{n}).$$

Thus

(67.8)(iii) $$\left| \sum_\alpha f(\theta_\alpha)\mu_\alpha - \int f(\theta) \, d\mu \right| \leq \varepsilon_\delta + M(\delta + \delta\sqrt{n}),$$

so that $\int f(\theta) \, d\mu$ is altered as little as we please (uniformly in t) by the passage to our discrete measure with the weights μ_α. The construction of g_2 is now complete except for one thing: we need to know that these weights, as functions of t, are measurable.

This is an annoying detail, since nonmeasurable functions are met rather less frequently than the abominable snowman. However, a professional in any field never takes an unnecessary chance, whether he be a soldier, an astronaut, a racing driver, an acrobat or a mountain guide. Similarly, in mathematics no conceivable possibility, however remote, is excluded until we prove that it cannot occur. The small additional trouble should not be shirked here; no one should deny himself, for so little, a professional's full confidence in his own powers, which so often makes all the difference between a first rate and a second rate mind.

By hypothesis, the quantity $g_t f = \int f \, d\mu$ is integrable, and therefore measurable in t, for each $f \in \mathscr{C}_0(A)$. In particular $\int f(\theta) \, d\mu$ is measurable in t for each continuous f which depends on θ only. However, if f_ν, $\nu = 1, 2, \ldots$ are functions of θ for each of which $\int f_\nu \, d\mu$ is measurable in t, and if the f_ν converge boundedly to a limit f, then, by term by term integration, we see that $\int f \, d\mu$ is the limit of a measurable function of t, and is therefore measurable in t. It follows that $\int f \, d\mu$ is measurable in t when f is any Borel measurable function of θ. In particular, by taking for it the function which is 1 for $\theta \in \Theta_\alpha$ and 0 otherwise, we see that

$$\int_{\Theta_\alpha} d\mu \qquad (\alpha = 1, 2, \ldots, N)$$

is a measurable function of t, provided that we stipulate, as we shall, that each Θ_α is sufficiently elementary, and therefore certainly a Borel set.

Clearly the first N weights μ_α are then measurable functions of t; this implies that the corresponding vector ξ is so likewise; the same is then true of the projections $\xi\theta_\alpha$ $\alpha > N$, and so of the quantities Max $(\xi\theta_\alpha, 0)$, and so finally of the remaining weights μ_α.

For convenience, we now write

$$\lambda_\alpha(t) = \int_0^t \mu_\alpha(\tau) \, d\tau.$$

We shall see that our element $g_2 \in \mathscr{C}_0^*(A)$ can now be defined entirely in terms of the $\lambda_\alpha(t)$ and of its initial point $x(0)$. In fact, by (67.8)(i), $\dot{x}(t)$ has almost everywhere the value $\sum \theta_\alpha \mu_\alpha$, so that

$$x(t) - x(0) = \sum_\alpha \theta_\alpha \lambda_\alpha(t);$$

and we can solve for $x(t)$, and substitute for it accordingly, when we define g_2 by setting, for each $f \in \mathscr{C}_0(A)$,

$$g_2 f = \int_0^1 \sum_\alpha \mu_\alpha(t) f(x(t), \theta_\alpha) \, dt = \sum_\alpha \int_0^1 f(x(t), \theta_\alpha) \, d\lambda_\alpha(t).$$

We remark that, of course, in view of (67.8)(i), (ii), (iii), the element $g_2 \in \mathscr{C}_0^*(A)$ satisfies the various conditions originally laid down for it; in particular, by choice of δ, the element g_2 is at an arbitrarily small dashed distance from g_1, since, as $\delta \to 0$, it is clear that $g_2 f \to g_1 f$ for each $f \in \mathscr{C}_0(A)$.

We shall now approximate to the functions $\lambda_\alpha(t)$ uniformly by certain piecewise-linear, monotone increasing functions $s_\alpha(t)$ $0 \leq t \leq 1$. For this purpose we divide the interval $0 \leq t \leq 1$ first into a large number ν of equal intervals Δ, and then each Δ into m further intervals Δ_α $\alpha = 1, 2, \ldots, m$, in general unequal. We do this in such a way that the ratio of the length $|\Delta_\alpha|$ of Δ_α to the length $|\Delta| = 1/\nu$ of Δ is

$$\frac{\Delta\lambda_\alpha}{\Delta\lambda},$$

where $\Delta\lambda_\alpha$ denotes the increase of $\lambda_\alpha(t)$ in the interval Δ, and $\Delta\lambda$ the corresponding increase of the function

$$\lambda(t) = \sum_\alpha \lambda_\alpha(t).$$

Since the functions $\lambda_\alpha(t)$ are strictly increasing, each Δ_α is thus a nonvanishing interval in Δ.

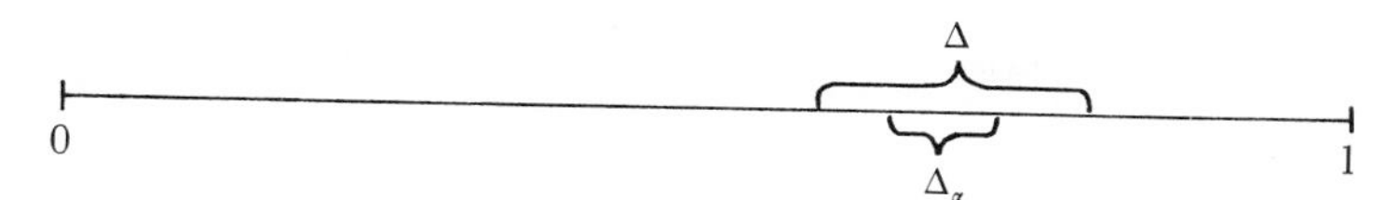

We now define $s_\alpha(t)$ as follows: $s_\alpha(t)$ agrees with $\lambda_\alpha(t)$ at the two ends of each Δ; $s_\alpha(t)$ is continuous; $s_\alpha(t)$ is linear in Δ_α; $s_\alpha(t)$ is constant in each of the two parts of Δ, to the left or right of Δ_α. Thus in each Δ, the function $s_\alpha(t)$ is a piecewise linear function whose slope vanishes. An exception is Δ_α, where the slope has the value

$$\frac{\Delta\lambda_\alpha}{|\Delta_\alpha|} = \frac{\Delta\lambda}{|\Delta|},$$

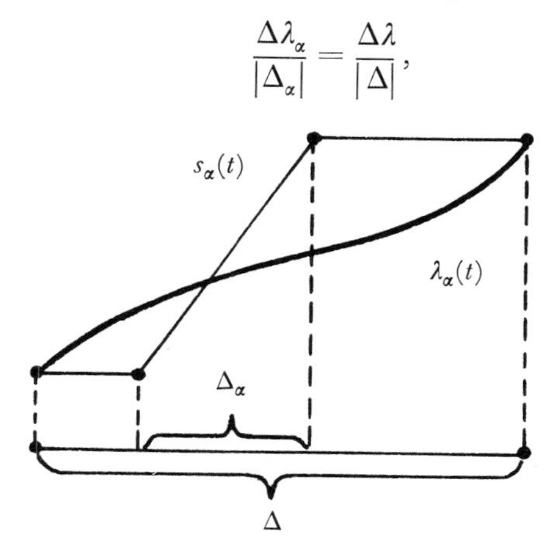

The functions λ_α, s_α in Δ

which cannot exceed our constant K, since λ is an indefinite integral of $\sum \mu_\alpha$, which sum is $\leq K$ by (67.8)(ii), since we arranged that $\bar{\mu} \leq (1 - \varepsilon)K$, and δ is small enough. Thus $\dot{s}_\alpha(t) \leq K$ in each corresponding Δ_α, and $\dot{s}_\alpha(t)$ vanishes otherwise. Further, the difference $|s_\alpha(t) - \lambda_\alpha(t)|$, which vanishes at the ends of each Δ, cannot exceed $\Delta\lambda_\alpha$, which is at most $K\,|\Delta_\alpha|$. This tends to 0 uniformly in t as $\nu \to \infty$; in fact the sum in α of these differences is at most K/ν.

In terms of the $s_\alpha(t)$ we now define a vector-valued $\hat{x}(t)$ exactly as we expressed $x(t)$ in terms of the $\lambda_\alpha(t)$, i.e., we set, for $0 \leq t \leq 1$,

$$\hat{x}(t) = x(0) + \sum_\alpha \theta_\alpha s_\alpha(t).$$

Evidently $\hat{x}(t)$ $0 \leq t \leq 1$ provides the parametric representation of a polygon, and the side corresponding to any Δ_α has the direction θ_α. We shall denote this polygon by g_3. This means that g_3 is defined by identifying, for each $f \in \mathscr{C}_0(A)$, the expression $g_3 f$ with the corresponding curvilinear integral; the latter can be evaluated by summing in α the contribution of the sides of direction θ_α. We thus find that

$$g_3 f = \sum_\alpha \int_0^1 f(\hat{x}(t), \theta_\alpha)\, ds_\alpha(t).$$

We note also that the values of $\hat{x}(t)$ approximate uniformly to those of $x(t)$, and so lie in our basic cube, and, further, that the length $\sum s_\alpha(1)$ of our polygon is at most K. It only remains to verify that g_3 is at an arbitrarily small dashed distance from g_1, i.e., that, as $\nu \to \infty$, each $g_3 f$ tends to $g_2 f$. Since g_2 is now fixed, m is fixed, and we need only show that

$$\int_0^1 f(\hat{x}(t), \theta_\alpha)\, ds(t) \to \int_0^1 f(x(t), \theta_\alpha)\, d\lambda_\alpha(t),$$

or what amounts to the same, since clearly

$$\left| \int_0^1 \{f(\hat{x}(t), \theta_\alpha) - f(x(t), \theta_\alpha)\}\, ds_\alpha(t) \right|,$$

which is less than K times the maximum of the brace under the integral sign, certainly tends to 0, that

$$\int_0^1 f(x(t), \theta_\alpha)\, ds_\alpha(t) \to \int f(x(t), \theta_\alpha)\, d\lambda_\alpha(t)$$

as $\nu \to \infty$. It will clearly be enough, therefore, to show that, for every continuous function $f(t)$ $0 \le t \le 1$, we have

$$\int_0^1 f(t)\, ds_\alpha(t) \to \int_0^1 f(t)\, d\lambda_\alpha(t).$$

This last is basically a special case of a Riemann-Lebesgue lemma in the theory of Fourier series, or it can be regarded as a special case of a theorem for Stieltjes integrals. To prove it, we may observe that it is certainly true when $f(t)$ is replaced by a step function $\varphi(t)$. Hence the upper limit, as $\nu \to \infty$, of the expression

$$\left| \int_0^1 f(t)\, ds_\alpha(t) - \int_0^1 f(t)\, d\lambda_\alpha(t) \right|$$

is unaffected if $f(t)$ is replaced by $f(t) - \varphi(t)$. By choosing φ so that $|f(t) - \varphi(t)|$ remains less than a preassigned positive constant η, we find that our upper limit is at most $2K\eta$, which is arbitrarily small, and therefore that this upper limit vanishes.

This completes the proof.

§68. EXISTENCE OF A MINIMUM

The admission of our generalized curves and their characterization as turbulent analogues of traditional curves provide a satisfactory basis for the Euler-Lagrange approach to the calculus of variations, at any rate in problems in which it is clear *a priori* that we can restrict our curves to lie in a fixed cube and to possess uniformly bounded lengths. In fact, as we shall see, we have then an automatic existence theory.

The problems we have been treating are of the following type: given a set B_0 of boundaries of curves and a certain integrand $f_0 \in \mathscr{C}_0(A)$, we wish to determine the infimum of the quantity gf_0 for admissible curves g such that $\partial g \in B_0$. We assume here that only curves g situated in a fixed cube, and of uniformly bounded lengths, need be considered. We denote the desired infimum by I_0.

The generalized version of this problem is as follows: let B_1 denote the closure of B_0; we seek the infimum I_1 of the quantity gf_0 for generalized curves g in the same cube, and of uniformly bounded lengths, such that $\partial g \in B_1$. However, we see at once that $I_1 = I_0$, i.e., that the two versions are equivalent. For on the one hand, $I_1 \le I_0$, since I_1 is an infimum in a larger set; and on the other hand, with the dashed distance, traditional curves with $\partial g \in B_0$ are clearly dense in the relevant set of generalized curves, and the quantity gf_0 is continuous in g in this topology. We are thus fully justified in substituting the generalized version of the problem for the original one.

Clearly, in this generalized formulation, I_1 is always an attained minimum. In fact, since $I_0 = I_1$, there is a minimizing sequence g_ν $\nu = 1, 2, \ldots$ such that $\partial g_\nu \in B$ and $g_\nu f_0 \to I_1$. By the hypothesis, the curves g_ν lie in the fixed cube and have uniformly bounded lengths $|g_\nu|$, so that they are elements of a multiple of the conjugate unit ball, which is $B \cdot \cdot i$ compact. Therefore there is a subsequence whose limit is a generalized curve g. Clearly $gf_0 = \lim_\nu g_\nu f_0 = I_1$, and $\partial g \in B_1$. Thus, in its generalized formulation, our problem of minimum always has a solution.

However, we see at once that the same is true of a much wider class of problems. There is no need to restrict ourselves here to the minimum of a quantity of the special form gf_0; any continuous real function $\Phi_0(g)$ could be used instead, where Φ_0 is continuous in the dashed topology. Nor is it necessary to admit all curves and generalized curves which satisfy the boundary conditions. For instance, we can restrict ourselves to those g for which gf_1 has a given value a, where f_1 is a given integrand. This is an isoperimetric type of problem. Similarly we shall see that an existence theory continues to hold when we come to deal with problems of optimal control.

Generalized solutions are also important from the practical point of view, particularly when the problem is already known to possess a traditional solution. This is the case, for instance, in Maxwell's problem of the quickest way up a mountain, which we discussed earlier. If the mountain is convex, there is always one solution consisting of a traditional curve that spirals round the mountain until it reaches the gentler slope near the top. However, there is a quite different generalized solution, which we have already described, and which can be approximated by a zigzag mountain path.

Generally, any generalized solution g is, of course, the limit of an approximate solution g_ν $\nu = 1, 2, \ldots,$ and for practical purposes this approximate solution is all that we really want. Such an approximate solution here tends, not to a "visible" solution of the original problem, but to what we may regard as a "hidden" solution, which only has a meaning in the generalized problem.

The same phenomenon occurs in various contexts, for instance in fluid mechanics, where a hidden solution is frequently exhibited as the limit of a viscous one, as the viscosity tends to 0. In fact, the whole background of the theory of generalized curves has its roots in highly practical considerations.

§69. THE NATURE OF THE GENERALIZED SOLUTIONS

It now makes sense to speak of necessary conditions, and since our generalized curves are characterized by a local turbulence, together with a parametric representation $x(t)$ $0 \leq t \leq 1$, the necessary conditions will be of two kinds: those which concern the local turbulence, and those which concern the nature of the curve C, defined by $x(t)$ $0 \leq t \leq 1$. We fix again an integrand $f_0 \in \mathscr{C}_0(A)$.

Exceptionally, here, in order to compare our conditions with classical ones of the calculus of variations, we allow C to be a Fréchet curve, which therefore need not be unique. We term C a trajectory described by our generalized curve. We shall understand by the turbulence problem along C that of the minimum of gf_0 in the class of generalized curves g, each of which describes the given trajectory C.

A generalized curve g of the stated class will be said to satisfy the Weierstrass condition along C if, for some Lipschitzian parametric representation $x(t)$ $0 \leq t \leq 1$ of C, and for some subset T consisting of almost all t of that interval, we can express g as an integral

$$g = \int_0^1 g_t \, dt$$

where, for $t \in T$, g_t denotes a generalized line element, with $|g_t|$ uniformly bounded and with $\big(x(t), \dot{x}(t)\big)$ as its resultant, and where further the relations

$$\text{(i) } \hat{g}f_0 \geq 0, \qquad \text{(ii) } \hat{g}f_0 \geq g_t f_0,$$

are satisfied, respectively, for $0 \leq t \leq 1$, and for $t \in T$, the former for every generalized line element $\hat{g}$ with the resultant $(x(t), 0)$, the latter for every generalized line element with the resultant $\big(x(t), \dot{x}(t)\big)$.

The above definition is not affected if we restrict $\hat{g}$ in both cases, to be of the form

$$\hat{g} = \int \hat{g}_\alpha \, d\mu = \sum_\alpha \mu_\alpha \hat{g}_\alpha,$$

where μ is a measure obtained by attaching weights μ_α to a finite set of labels α, and where the $\hat{g}_\alpha$ are line elements $\big(x(t), \theta_\alpha\big)$ at the point $x(t)$, whose directions θ_α we select, on the unit sphere of directions, either arbitrarily, or from some dense countable subset. In either case, the change merely requires approximating to our generalized line elements $\hat{g}$, by those of the more special form described, which have the same resultant; this can be done exactly as in the sufficiency part of the proof of Theorem (67.1).

It follows that (i) above expresses for each $x \in C$ the convexity in $\dot{x}$, at $\dot{x} = 0$, of the Lagrangian $L(x, \dot{x})$ defined by f_0. Similarly (ii) above expresses for each $x = x(t)$ $t \in T$ its convexity at $\dot{x}(t)$, but only in the special case in which g_t reduces, for these t, to the weighted line element $\big(x(t), \dot{x}(t)\big)$ that is its resultant, i.e., only in the special case where g is a curve. In this special case, it also follows from a change of variable lemma, (69.1) below, that (i) ensures that (ii) can be made to hold for any Lipschitzian representation $x(t)$ of C on $0 \leq t \leq 1$, if it holds for one of them. When g is a curve, we thus have here the same Weierstrass condition along C, as we stated just prior to Theorem (56.3) in Section 56, where we made a particular choice of the parameter t as a constant multiple of the arc length.

In the general case, we note that (i) concerns only C and f_0, not g_0; however, it must still be regarded as an integral part of the definition, for we shall see that it still affects (ii), much as in the special case where g is a curve, by making possible certain simple parameter changes, in accordance with the following lemma:

(69.1) Change of variable lemma. *Let $s(t)$ $0 \leq t \leq 1$ be Lipschitzian, nondecreasing and subject to $s(0) = 0$, $s(1) = 1$, and let T_0 be the set of t for which its derivative vanishes. Then there exists a Borel set T, which consists of almost all t of $0 \leq t \leq 1$ not in T_0, and which is such that*

(a) *$s(t)$ maps T one-to-one onto a set S consisting of almost all points of $0 \leq s \leq 1$.*

(b) *In T and S, respectively, at corresponding points, the derivatives ds/dt and dt/ds of $s(t)$ and of the inverse function $t(s)$ exist and do not vanish, and their product is unity.*

(c) *If $\varphi(t)$ $0 \leq t \leq 1$ is Borel measurable, bounded and vanishes in T_0, and if $\psi(s)$ $0 \leq s \leq 1$ is the measurable function equal in S to $\varphi\big(t(s)\big) \dfrac{dt}{ds}$, then*

$$\int_0^1 \varphi(t) \, dt = \int_0^1 \psi(s) \, ds.$$

PROOF. For any set E in the unit interval, we write $s(E)$ for the set of values of $s(t)$ $t \in E$, and $s^{-1}(E)$ for the set of values of t for which $s(t) \in E$. We observe that, for any interval I of values of t, and by addition, for any open set O of these values, the measure $|s(I)|$, or $|s(O)|$, of the image-set is the integral on I, or on O, of (ds/dt). Hence, for any open set E of values of s, we find, by taking for O the open set $s^{-1}(E)$, that

$$|E| = \int_{S^{-1}(E)} \left(\frac{ds}{dt}\right) dt.$$

This formula is true also when E is the unit interval, and by subtraction we find that it holds when E is any closed set of values of s. Hence by successive passage to the limit, it holds for any Borel set E of values of s. Moreover, since the right hand side is unaltered if we restrict the range of integration to the set T_1 in which $ds/dt > 0$, we may rewrite the formula

$$|E| = \int_{T_1 \cap S^{-1}(E)} \left(\frac{ds}{dt}\right) dt.$$

In particular, we see that E has measure 0 if and only if $T_1 \cap s^{-1}(E)$ has measure 0, or, what amounts to the same thing, since ds/dt exists almost everywhere, if and only if $s^{-1}(E) - T_0$ has measure 0.

We now denote further by $t(s)$ $0 \leq s \leq 1$ an inverse function of $s(t)$, so that $t(s)$ is strictly increasing and is uniquely determined except at its discontinuities, which are at most countable, and which correspond to the intervals of constancy of $s(t)$. Clearly, therefore, $t(s)$ is uniquely defined in $s(T_1)$, so that the map defined by $s(t)$ $t \in T_1$ is one-to-one. We note also, by the formula found above, for the measure of a set of s, that the complement of $s(T_1)$ has measure 0. Since $t(s)$ has a derivative almost everywhere, we can therefore determine in $s(T_1)$ a Borel subset S whose complement in the unit interval has measure 0, so that $t(s)$ has a derivative dt/ds in S. We shrink S if necessary, so that its image under $t(s)$ is a Borel set (this, in fact, is automatic, but we can certainly effect it here without altering the measures, since sets of measure 0 remain so under the map $s(t)$ in T_1). Thus S is the one-to-one image under $s(t)$ of a Borel set T, and both derivatives dt/ds, ds/dt exist at corresponding points, so that their product must be unity. In this way we obtain (a) and (b) of our assertion. Finally (c) is now verified first in the case in which $\psi(s)$ reduces to the characteristic function of a set E, the relevant formula being then equivalent to the one obtained previously for $|E|$; the general case then follows by finite linear combination and passage to the limit, in a manner which will be familiar to readers of Saks' Theory of the integral.

(69.2) Corollary. *Let C be a rectifiable Fréchet curve not reducing to a point, and let g denote a generalized curve given, as in Theorem (67.1), by generalized line elements g_t, in terms of a Lipschitzian parametric representation $x(t)$ $0 \leq t \leq 1$ of C. Further suppose that $g_t = 0$ whenever $\dot{x}(t) = 0$. Then we can arrange for the parameter t to be a constant multiple of the arc length along C.*

PROOF. For any integrand $f \in \mathscr{C}_0(A)$, we write

$$\varphi(t) = g_t f \qquad (0 \leq t \leq 1),$$

so that $\varphi(t)$ vanishes almost everywhere in the set in which $s(t)$ has a vanishing derivative. By applying (69.1)(c) to an equivalent function, we find that

$$gf = \int_0^1 g_t f\, dt = \int_0^1 \left(\frac{dt}{ds}\right) g_{t(s)} f\, ds,$$

and the generalized line element

$$\left(\frac{dt}{ds}\right) g_{t(s)} \qquad 0 \leq s \leq 1$$

thus has the desired properties when we write it g_s.

We are now ready to discuss our turbulence problem. We prove two results, which clearly imply Theorem (56.3).

(69.3) Theorem. *In order that a generalized curve g provide a solution of the turbulence problem along a trajectory C described by g, it is necessary and sufficient that it satisfy along C the Weierstrass condition.*

(69.4) Theorem. *In order that a generalized curve g provide a solution of the turbulence problem along a trajectory C described by g, it is necessary and sufficient that gf_0 be the infimum of the numbers c such that c is the limit of $\mathscr{I}(C_\nu)$ for some sequence C_ν $\nu = 1, 2, \ldots$ of curves of uniformly bounded lengths, which tends, in the Fréchet sense, to C.*

Theorems (69.3) and (69.4) bring out very clearly that the Weierstrass condition is fundamentally both necessary and sufficient. This is what one would like all conditions to be.

Proof of (69.3). We first verify the necessity of the two parts (i) and (ii) of the Weierstrass condition. If (i) were not satisfied at some $x_0 \in C$, we could proceed as follows to diminish gf_0. First we could introduce a piecewise-linear map (in three pieces) of the t-interval on itself, so that after the parameter change, $x(t)$ would take the constant value x_0 in some t-interval $t_1 \leq t \leq t_2$; the expression of g in the form $\int g_t \, dt$ would, of course, be adjusted to this substitution. We could then further define a generalized line element $\hat{g}$ with the resultant $(x_0, 0)$, such that $\hat{g}f_0 < 0$; and, by adding $\hat{g}$ to g_t throughout the subinterval $t_1 \leq t \leq t_2$, we could diminish gf_0 by the addition of $(t_2 - t_1)\hat{g}f_0$ without altering the associated parametric representation $x(t)$ further.

We shall also find it possible to diminish similarly gf_0 in the case in which, in some set E of positive measure, the condition (ii) is not satisfied, for an appropriate $\hat{g}$ depending on $t \in E$. In that case, we need $\hat{g}$ to depend measurably on t and to have bounded norm, uniformly for $t \in E$.

In order to arrange this, in some set E of positive measure, we note that, as stated earlier, (ii) remains unsatisfied if we restrict $\hat{g}$ to be of a special form there described. Similarly, we can restrict it to have the form $\hat{g}_1 + \hat{g}_2$ of the sum of two generalized line elements, the first of which, $\hat{g}_1$, is obtained by attaching rational weights μ_α to a finite number $N - n$ of directions θ_α, selected from some fixed countable dense set, while the second, $\hat{g}_2$, attaches real weights μ_α to n orthogonal further directions θ_α, selected from those parallel or antiparallel to the n axes. Thus $\hat{g}_2$ is determined by $\hat{g}_1$ and by the resultant of $\hat{g}$, while $\hat{g}_1$ describes at most a countable set. We can then decompose E into countably many parts, one of which at least is of positive measure and will continue to be denoted by E such that in each part, (ii) is unsatisfied for a $\hat{g}$ of norm less than some fixed integer, and of the above form $\hat{g}_1 + \hat{g}_2$, with $\hat{g}_1$ now fixed. This $\hat{g}$ then satisfies in the new set E the desired further conditions.

This being so, we replace g_t by this $\hat{g}$ in E. The alteration clearly diminishes gf_0.

Conversely, we verify that, if (i) and (ii) hold, gf_0 cannot be diminished. By taking $\hat{g}$ to be g_t in (i) and 0 in (ii), we see $g_t f_0$ vanishes for almost every t at which $\dot{x}(t) = 0$. We may therefore replace g_t by 0 whenever $\dot{x}(t) = 0$ without altering gf_0. And since the case in which C reduces to a point is trivial, we may therefore suppose, by (69.2), that $t = s$, a constant multiple of the arc length along C. This being so, let $\tilde{g}$ be any other generalized curve that describes the same trajectory C. We represent $\tilde{g}$ as the integral $\int \tilde{g}_t \, dt$ associated with a certain Lipschitzian parametric representation $x(t)$ of C. Here, $\tilde{g}_t f_0 \geq 0$ by (i) wherever $\dot{x}(t) = 0$. We therefore do not increase $\tilde{g} f_0$ by replacing $\tilde{g}_t$ by 0 wherever $\dot{x}(t) = 0$. In order to prove that $\tilde{g} f_0 \geq g f_0$, we may therefore suppose that $\tilde{g}_t = 0$ wherever $\dot{x}(t) = 0$. Hence, as before, we may suppose that $t = s$. This being so, we evidently now have $\tilde{g}_t f_0 \geq g_t f_0$ for almost all t by (ii), and therefore $\tilde{g} f_0 \geq g f_0$. This completes the proof.

Proof of (69.4). It is enough to show that the class of numbers C is identical with that of the values of $\tilde{g} f_0$ for generalized curves $\tilde{g}$ that describe C. Evidently every such value is a number c of the class. We must therefore verify the converse, namely that every number c has the form $\tilde{g} f_0$. To this effect, let $\tilde{g}$ be a fine limit of a subsequence of the C_ν that define c; such a fine limit exists since the lengths are bounded, and by definition of fine limit $\tilde{g} f_0$ coincides with the limit c of $\mathscr{I}(C_\nu)$. Further, according to the proof of the necessity of (67.1), there exist parametric representations $x_\nu(t)$ $0 \leq t \leq 1$ of the C_ν which tend uniformly along the subsequence to the parametric representation $x(t)$ $0 \leq t \leq 1$ of a trajectory described by $\tilde{g}$. Evidently this trajectory can only be C, and this completes the proof.

From (69.3) and (69.4) we derive the following result:

(69.5) Corollary. *Let $\hat{L}(x, \dot{x})$ denote the infimum of $\tilde{g} f_0$ for generalized line elements $\hat{g}$ with the resultant $(x, \dot{x})$ and suppose $\hat{L}(x, 0) = 0$, or equivalently $\hat{L}(x, 0) \neq -\infty$, for all x. Then the minimum of $g f_0$ for generalized curves g which describe a given trajectory C, and also the infimum of the set of numbers c of (69.4) has the value*

(69.6) $$\int_C \hat{L}(x, \dot{x}) \, dt.$$

The generalized problem of minimum is thus reduced to a traditional one, first formulated by Tonelli, with the Lagrangian $\hat{L}$. Of course, in many problems in practice, $\hat{L}$ does not exhibit the desirable classical smoothness.

We can now go on to apply the classical Euler Lagrange algorithm that leads to the extremals, either to the problem of minimum of (69.6), or directly to the generalized curvilinear integrals of $g f_0$. In fact, it is really at this point that we are at last in a position to start on the classical calculus of variations, as conceived by Euler and Lagrange.

This is indeed what we propose. However, we shall do so in the more general setting of optimal control, to which we devote our second volume.

Appendix I

SOME FURTHER BASIC NOTIONS OF CONVEXITY AND INTEGRATION

§70. INTRODUCTION

The material of this Appendix belongs more properly at the end of Chapter IV. It is material that we shall use in part of Appendix II. However, its object is also to provide additional background to help the reader in the important task of tackling today's literature on many matters related to those treated in this book. In particular, it will help him to undertake further reading on convexity and on functional analysis. This is a virtual necessity if he wishes to go on to research problems in our subject.

The topics we cover here are not treated in their full generality. They include separation theorems for certain convex cones, vector integration of continuous functions, and the characterization of a closed convex hull by centers of measures.

§71. SEPARATION THEOREM FOR A CONVEX CONE IN $\mathscr{C}_0(A)$

For the next few sections, A denotes, as at the end of Chapter IV, any bounded closed Euclidean set, and we shall be concerned with the functional spaces $\mathscr{C}_0(A)$, $\mathscr{C}_0^*(A)$. These could be replaced by certain more general spaces, without affecting our arguments. For instance, the straightforward separation theorem of this section can be restated and established in the same way for any vector space in which we are given (as a seminorm) a non-negative homogeneous convex function $|f|$ of the element f, subject to the evenness condition $|-f| = |f|$.

By the distance

$$Q(f_0, E)$$

of an element $f_0 \in \mathscr{C}_0(A)$ from a set $E \subset \mathscr{C}_0(A)$, we mean the quantity

$$\operatorname*{Inf}_{f \in E} |f - f_0|.$$

(71.1) Lemma. (i) *If E is a cone, $Q(f, E)$ is homogeneous in f.* (ii) *If E is convex, $Q(f, E)$ is convex in f.*

(71.2) Separation Theorem in $\mathscr{C}_0(A)$. *Let E be a convex cone in $\mathscr{C}_0(A)$ and let f_0 be an element of $\mathscr{C}_0(A)$ at a positive distance $Q(f_0, E) = d$ from E. Then there exists a linear function gf $f \in \mathscr{C}_0(A)$, where $g \in \mathscr{C}_0^*(A)$, such that*

$$|g| = 1/d, \qquad gf_0 = 1, \qquad gf \leq 0 \quad \text{for all} \quad f \in E.$$

Proof of (71.1). Here (i) is obvious, so that we need prove only (ii). Let $f_0 = tf_0' + (1-t)f_0''$ where $0 < t < 1$ and where f_0', f_0'' lie in $\mathscr{C}_0(A)$. Given $\varepsilon > 0$, we determine in E two elements f', f'' for which the distances $|f' - f_0'|$, $|f'' - f_0''|$ differ by $<\varepsilon$ from their infima $Q(f_0', E)$, $Q(f_0'', E)$, respectively. If f denotes the element $tf' + (1-t)f''$ of E, it follows that

$$Q(f_0, E) \leq |f - f_0| \leq t\,|f' - f_0'| + (1-t)\,|f'' - f_0''|.$$

Finally, by making $\varepsilon \to 0$, we obtain the relation which expresses the desired convexity, namely

$$Q(f_0, E) \leq tQ(f_0', E) + (1-t)Q(f_0'', E).$$

Proof of (71.2). We set, for brevity, $q(f) = Q(f, E)/d$. Clearly, since the origin is in E, we have $Q(f, E) \leq |f|$, and so $q(f) \leq |f|/d$. Moreover, by (71.1), $q(f)$ is a convex homogeneous function of f. According to (42.2) of Chapter IV, Section 42, where we gave an equivalent definition of convexity, there is at f_0 a linear function $\ell(f)$ termed landing function, and possibly not homogeneous, such that $\ell(f_0) = q(f_0)$ and that $\ell(f) \leq q(f)$ for all f. Clearly $\ell(0) \leq q(0) = 0$. Further, if $0 < t < 1$, linearity of $\ell(f)$ implies

$$(1-t)\ell(0) + t\ell(f_0/t) = \ell(f_0) = q(f_0) = tq(f_0/t).$$

Here the extreme right is $\geq t\ell(f_0/t)$, and by comparing with the extreme left, we see that $\ell(0) \geq 0$, and so, that $\ell(0) = 0$. Thus $\ell(f)$ is homogeneous. Hence we may write $\ell(f) = gf$ where $g \in \mathscr{C}_0^*(A)$.

Evidently $|g| \leq 1/d$ and $gf_0 = 1$. Moreover, for $f \in E$ we have $gf \leq q(f) = 0$. It only remains to verify that $|g| \geq 1/d$. To this effect, given $\varepsilon > 0$, we can determine $f \in E$ so that $Q(f_0, E)$ differs by $<\varepsilon$ from $|f - f_0|$. Moreover

$$|g| \cdot |f_0 - f| \geq gf_0 - gf = 1.$$

By making $\varepsilon \to 0$, we obtain $|g|\, Q(f_0, E) \geq 1$, i.e., $|g|\, d \geq 1$, and this completes the proof.

§72. THE LEMMA OF THE INSUFFICIENT RADIUS

In order to tackle the corresponding dual separation theorem, we need an important lemma of Banach. We give this lemma here only in $\mathscr{C}_0^*(A)$, as its general form is based on transfinite closure, which we shall not require. However, we urge the reader to look up the general case in Banach's book (pp. 119–121), where it occurs in the course of the proof of a separation theorem for a linear subspace. Banach's book is still the "bible" of functional analysis, and the ideal way of learning is still in the really great books and papers. Such works are timeless. One learns much less from so-called up-to-date books. Great books are never up-to-date in that sense, for they are full of creative ideas from which their author does not seek to squeeze the utmost himself.

We shall be concerned, in this section, with a set $\Gamma \subset \mathscr{C}_0^*(A)$, an element $g_0 \in \mathscr{C}_0^*(A)$ not belonging to Γ, and a positive number R. We term the latter an insufficient radius from g_0, if

$$R < |g - g_0| \quad \text{for every} \quad g \in \Gamma.$$

Given g_0, Γ and an insufficient radius R, we term significant a set $E \subset \mathscr{C}_0(A)$, if, for each $g \in \Gamma$, there exists at least one corresponding $f \in E$, such that

$$R\,|f| < |(g - g_0)f|.$$

(72.1) Lemma of the Insufficient Radius. *Let g_0, Γ and an insufficient radius R be given, and suppose that Γ is bounded and w^*-closed. Then there exists a finite significant set E.*

The above lemma is related to the notion of decidability in the foundations of mathematics and in the theory of computing machines. An equivalent statement is the following, also due to Banach:

(72.2) Sequential Version of the Lemma. *Let g_0, Γ and an insufficient radius R be given, and suppose that Γ is w^*-closed. Then, in the unit ball U of $\mathscr{C}_0(A)$, there exists a sequence f_ν $\nu = 1, 2, \ldots$, such that $f_\nu \to 0$ and that no element $g \in \Gamma$ can satisfy for all ν the inequalities $|(g - g_0)f_\nu| \le R$.*

Proof of the Equivalence of (72.1) and (72.2). Suppose (72.2) holds, and let g_0, Γ, R be as in (72.1). Since Γ is bounded, there exists a finite number M such that $|g - g_0| \le M$ for all $g \in \Gamma$. We choose the f_ν as in (72.2), and since they tend to 0 we can determine ν_0 so that $|f_\nu| \le R/M$ for $\nu > \nu_0$. Clearly every $g \in \Gamma$ then satisfies the inequalities

$$|(g - g_0)f_\nu| \le R$$

for $\nu > \nu_0$. Therefore by (72.2) no $g \in \Gamma$ can satisfy them for $\nu \le \nu_0$, and still less can it satisfy the stronger inequalities

$$|(g - g_0)f_\nu| \le R\,|f_\nu| \qquad \nu \le \nu_0.$$

This means that the set E of the f_ν $\nu \le \nu_0$ is a significant set, so that (72.1) must then hold.

Conversely, suppose (72.1) holds and let g_0, Γ, R be as in (72.2). We choose an increasing sequence of reals R_k $k = 1, 2, \ldots$, which tends to ∞ and has R as its first term R_1, and we denote by Γ_k the subset of Γ for which

$$R_k < |g - g_0| \le R_{k+1}.$$

By (72.1) there is then a significant finite set E_k for g_0, Γ_k, R_k. By multiplying the members of E_k by suitable constants, we may suppose $|f| = R/R_k$ for $f \in E_k$. In that case, no $g \in \Gamma_k$ can satisfy, for all $f \in E_k$, the inequalities

$$|(g - g_0)f| \le R.$$

Since $\Gamma = \cup\Gamma_k$, no $g \in \Gamma$ can satisfy them for all $f \in \cup E_k$. The assertion of (72.2) follows at once by ordering the set $\cup E_k$ as a single sequence, in the obvious way. The equivalence of (72.1) and (72.2) is thus established.

Proof of (72.1). If (72.1) were false, we could determine for each positive integer k a member g_k of Γ, such that

$$|(g_k - g_0)f| \le R \cdot |f|$$

for each f of the set E_k consisting of the first k members of the dense countable subset

$\mathscr{P}$ of $\mathscr{C}_0(A)$, which we introduced in Section 48 of Chapter IV, and which we here suppose suitably ordered as a sequence. Since Γ is bounded, we could find a subsequence of the g_k which tends (w^*) to a limit g, and the latter evidently then satisfies the inequality

$$|(g - g_0)f| \leq R\,|f|$$

for every $f \in \mathscr{P}$, and consequently for every $f \in \mathscr{C}_0(A)$. This last implies $|g - g_0| \leq R$ contrary to hypothesis, since g, as a w^*-limit of the g_k, belongs to Γ.

§73. THE DUAL SEPARATION THEOREM

This second separation theorem for a convex cone is deeper than the one of Section 71. It applies in the dual of a Banach space. We state it here for $\mathscr{C}_0^*(A)$, and this is what we shall use subsequently. However, the more general version is proved in the same way, except that it uses then the stronger form of the lemma of the insufficient radius, which is given in Banach's book. The pair of separation theorems should be classed, with fix-point theorems, as tools that no analyst should be without.

(73.1). Separation Theorem for a Convex Cone in $\mathscr{C}_0^*(A)$. *Let Γ be a w^*-closed convex cone in $\mathscr{C}_0^*(A)$, let g_0 be an element of $\mathscr{C}_0^*(A)$ not belonging to Γ, and let R be a positive number such that*

$$R < |g - g_0| \quad \textit{for every} \quad g \in \Gamma.$$

Then there exists an element $f \in \mathscr{C}_0(A)$ such that

$$|f| \leq 1/R, \qquad g_0 f = 1, \qquad gf \leq 0 \quad \textit{for all} \quad g \in \Gamma.$$

Proof. Since R is an insufficient radius, we can define a sequence of elements $f_\nu \in U$ $\nu = 1, 2, \ldots$ subject to the conditions stated in (72.2). We shall now construct the desired element $f \in \mathscr{C}_0(A)$ to have the form

$$f = \sum C_\nu f_\nu,$$

and for this purpose it will be enough to make the C_ν satisfy the following conditions: they are to be real constants such that

$$\textbf{(73.2)} \qquad \sum |C_\nu| \leq 1/R, \qquad \sum C_\nu g_0 f_\nu = 1, \qquad \sum C_\nu g f_\nu = 0$$

for every $g \in \Gamma$. In fact, since $f_\nu \in U$, the first of these relations implies the convergence in $\mathscr{C}_0(A)$ of the series by which we define f, and moreover the relation $|f| \leq 1/R$, while the other two relations (73.2) then become $g_0 f = 1$ and $gf = 0$ for $g \in \Gamma$. It therefore only remains to show that there exist constants C_ν $\nu = 1, 2, \ldots$ subject to (73.2).

To this effect, we remark that since $f_\nu \to 0$, we have $gf_\nu \to 0$ for each $g \in \mathscr{C}_0^*(A)$, and hence that we can embed the sequences $\{gf_\nu\}$ in the space (c) of convergent sequences. We denote by E the set in (c) thus formed of the sequences $\{gf_\nu\}$ for which $g \in \Gamma$, and by e_0 the element of (c) consisting of the sequence $\{g_0 f_\nu\}$. Clearly E is, like Γ, a convex cone.

The space (c) in which E and e_0 are now situated is, however, no longer a dual space, but a Banach space. In fact, as we observed at the end of Section 49 of Chapter IV, it is of the type $\mathscr{C}_0(A)$ for a certain different A. Moreover, according to (72.2), no element $e \in E$ can satisfy the inequality $|e - e_0| \leq R$, since $|e - e_0|$ is the supremum in ν of $|(g - g_0)f_\nu|$. It therefore follows, in the notation of (71.2), that $Q(e_0, E) \geq R$, so that our first separation theorem applies. We thus infer, from the expression found for a dual element in (49.7) of Chapter IV, Section 49, the existence of constants $C, C_1, C_2, \ldots$, such that

$$|C| + \sum |C_\nu| \leq 1/R,$$

$$C \lim g_0 f_\nu + \sum C_\nu g_0 f_\nu = 1,$$

$$C \lim g f_\nu + \sum C_\nu g f_\nu = 0 \quad \text{for} \quad g \in \Gamma.$$

Here the first relation implies the first one in (73.2), while the other two reduce to the corresponding ones of (73.2), since $\lim g f_\nu = 0$ for every $g \in \mathscr{C}_0^*(A)$. This completes the proof.

§74. A LOCALIZATION LEMMA FOR A $B \cdot\cdot i$-COMPACT SET

The remaining sections of this Appendix lead up to a characterization of the closed convex hull of a $B \cdot\cdot i$-compact set in a Banach space, and for this purpose we shall need some vector integration. We denote by B, for the present, any $B \cdot\cdot i$-compact set in a metric space.

We recall that on such a set Borel's covering theorem is valid. We shall need a very particular case which is that, given $\varepsilon > 0$, the set B can be covered by a finite number of open balls of radius ε. We verify this very readily, by observing that there exists in B a finite subset E such that every point of B is distant $< \varepsilon$ from E.

(If there were no such subset, we could easily construct a sequence of points of B, each at a distance $\geq \varepsilon$ from the previous ones, and so from all the others, contrary to compactness. In fact, starting with any point P_1, we could choose any point P_2 at a distance $\geq \varepsilon$ from P_1, then any point P_3 at a distance $\geq \varepsilon$ from both P_1 and P_2, and so on.)

From this special case of Borel's covering theorem, we deduce the following "localization lemma":

(74.1) Lemma. *Let B denote a $B \cdot\cdot i$-compact subset of a metric space, and let $\varepsilon > 0$. Then there exist a finite number of continuous functions h_i, defined on B and subject to $0 \leq h_i \leq 1$ and $\sum h_i = 1$, such that each h_i vanishes outside some corresponding ball of radius ε.*

Proof. Let $\varphi(r)$ be a continuous monotone decreasing function defined for $r \geq 0$, such that

$$\varphi(r) = 1 \qquad 0 \leq r \leq \varepsilon/2,$$

$$\varphi(r) = 0 \qquad r \geq \varepsilon.$$

Further, let

$$B_1, B_2, \ldots, B_N$$

denote the intersections with B of balls of radius $\varepsilon/2$, which constitute a covering of B, and let $S_i(r)$ denote the intersection with B of the sphere of radius r, concentric with the ball determining B_i. We denote by φ_i the function defined on B, which takes the constant value $\varphi(r)$ on $S_i(r)$, for each $r \geq 0$. We set further

$$h_1 = \varphi_1, \qquad h_2 = (1 - h_1) \cdot \varphi_2,$$

and generally, for $i = 2, 3, \ldots, N$, we define

$$h_i = (1 - \psi_i) \cdot \varphi_i \quad \text{where} \quad \psi_i = \sum_k h_k \qquad (k < i).$$

From these relations we infer that

$$\psi_{i+1} = \psi_i + h_i = \psi_i + (1 - \psi_i) \cdot \varphi_i,$$

and therefore that

$$1 - \psi_{i+1} = (1 - \psi_i) \cdot (1 - \varphi_i).$$

We thus find that the values of the functions h_i, ψ_i, like those of the φ_i, must lie in the unit interval, and, moreover, that in B_i, where $\varphi_i = 1$, we have

$$\psi_{i+1} = \psi_{i+2} = \ldots = 1.$$

Since the B_i cover B, this implies that throughout B, $\sum h_i = 1$. Finally, we observe that, as multiples of the φ_i, the h_i vanish at distances $\geq \varepsilon$ from the centers of the balls determining the B_i, and hence that all the assertions of (74.1) are satisfied.

§75. RIESZ MEASURES

We shall need, in the sequel, only a rather superficial acquaintance with the notion of measure, since we shall integrate only functions that are continuous. We therefore adopt here the Bourbaki convention explained at the end of Chapter IV, Section 49, whereby, in agreement with the Riesz representation, a measure on B is simply an element of $\mathscr{C}_0^*(B)$.

We shall limit ourselves to the case of a non-negative measure, which is thus an element of the dual positive cone. We refer to such a measure as a Riesz measure. It can here quite well be continued as a Borel measure by means of the method of monotone sequences of W. H. Young, but we shall not use this fact.

For a Riesz measure μ, we have automatically the linearity of the operation

$$\int_B \varphi(x)\, d\mu$$

on the functions $\varphi \in \mathscr{C}_0(B)$. Moreover the relation $\varphi \leq \psi$ implies

$$\int_B \varphi(x)\, d\mu \leq \int_B \psi(x)\, d\mu.$$

Further, a sequence of Riesz measures μ_ν $\nu = 1, 2, \ldots$ converges to a Riesz measure μ, if it does so in the weak * topology of $\mathscr{C}_0^*(B)$, i.e., if for each $\varphi \in \mathscr{C}_0(B)$ we have

$$\lim_\nu \int_B \varphi(x)\, d\mu_\nu = \int_B \varphi(x)\, d\mu.$$

We remarked in Chapter IV, Sections 48 and 49, that the results, there proved, apply with minor modifications when the bounded closed Euclidean set A, which occurs there, is replaced by a $B \cdot\cdot i$-compact set B. In this way, or by appealing to the still more general corresponding result in the dual of any Banach space, we see that, from any bounded sequence of Riesz measures, we can extract a convergent subsequence.

In this connection we observe that in place of the functions $\varphi_{ab}(|x - c|)$, whose rational linear combinations were to be used to form the dense subset $\mathscr{P}$ of $\mathscr{C}_0(B)$, it is more convenient to take the countable set of the systems of functions $h_i(x)$ introduced in the preceding section, where we now choose $\varepsilon = 1/\nu$, $\nu = 1, 2, \ldots$. We can then verify that $\mathscr{P}$ is dense by a simplification of the arguments of the next section.

§76. EUCLIDEAN APPROXIMATION TO A BANACH VECTOR FUNCTION

We denote by $\mathscr{F}$ a Banach space, and its elements f will be termed vectors. We shall denote the norm of an element f by $|f|$, and sometimes by $Q(f)$, when a more distinctive notation seems called for. A continuous function $f(x)$ $x \in B$, whose values lie in $\mathscr{F}$, must now be clearly distinguished from an element $f \in \mathscr{F}$, and we shall therefore write it $f(\cdot)$. For consistency of notation, we write similarly $\varphi(\cdot)$ for a real continuous function $\varphi(x)$ $x \in B$. The functions $f(\cdot)$ will be termed Banach vector functions, or simply vector functions. They constitute the elements of a further Banach space $\mathscr{F}(\cdot)$, in which we define the norm

$$|f(\cdot)| = \operatorname*{Sup}_{x \in B} |f(x)|.$$

We term Euclidean vector function a finite linear combinations of vectors $f_i \in \mathscr{F}$ with continuous real functions $\varphi_i(\cdot)$ as coefficients. We can write this combination

$$\sum f_i \varphi_i(\cdot), \quad \text{or} \quad \sum f_i \varphi_i(x) \qquad x \in B.$$

We term it Euclidean because it involves only a finite number of vectors of $\mathscr{F}$.

(76.1) The Approximation Lemma. *Let $f(\cdot)$ be a Banach vector function and let $\delta > 0$. Then there exists a Euclidean vector function $\hat{f}(\cdot)$ such that*

$$|f(\cdot) - \hat{f}(\cdot)| < \delta.$$

PROOF. We choose $\varepsilon > 0$ so that the oscillation of the vector function $f(\cdot)$ in a distance ε is $<\delta$, and we determine accordingly the functions $h_i(\cdot)$ of the localization lemma (74.1). We denote by f_i the value of $f(x)$ at the center of the ball determining the set B_i, which occurs in the proof of that lemma, and we choose

$$\hat{f}(\cdot) = \sum f_i h_i(\cdot).$$

Then, for $x \in B$, we have

$$f(x) - \hat{f}(x) = \sum [f(x) - f_i] \cdot h_i(x),$$

so that, for any such x, the norm of the left hand side is less than the quantity

$$\delta \cdot \sum h_i(x) = \delta,$$

and therefore its maximum in x is $<\delta$, as asserted.

§77. AN ELEMENTARY NORM ESTIMATE

We shall need the following simple inequality:

(77.1) Lemma. *Let μ be a Riesz measure on B, and let $M(x)$ and M denote, respectively, the norm in $\mathscr{F}$ for constant x and the norm in $\mathscr{F}(\cdot)$, of the Euclidean vector function $\sum f_i \varphi_i(\cdot)$. Then*

$$\left| \sum f_i \int_B \varphi_i(x)\, d\mu \right| \leq \int_B M(x)\, d\mu \leq M \int_B 1\, d\mu.$$

PROOF. We write b_i and b for the quantities

$$\int_B \varphi_i(x)\, d\mu \quad \text{and} \quad Q(\sum f_i b_i).$$

We may suppose that $b \neq 0$. The vector $u_0 = \sum f_i b_i / b$ then satisfies $Q(u_0) = 1$. Hence, in the dual of $\mathscr{F}$, there is an element y_0 such that $y_0 u_0 = 1$ and $y_0 f \le Q(f)$ for all $f \in \mathscr{F}$. We set $\lambda_i = y_0 f_i$. Then

$$\sum \lambda_i \varphi_i(x) = y_0 \sum f_i \varphi_i(x) \le Q(\sum f_i \varphi_i(x)) = M(x),$$

while $\sum \lambda_i b_i = y_0 \sum f_i b_i = y_0(u_0 b) = b$. Thus

$$b = \int_B \sum \lambda_i \varphi_i(x)\, d\mu \le \int_B M(x)\, d\mu \le M \int_B 1\, d\mu,$$

as asserted.

§78. VECTOR INTEGRATION

We define this in two stages. The integral in μ of a Euclidean vector function

$$f(\cdot) = \sum f_i \varphi_i(\cdot)$$

can now, as a result of the case $M = 0$ of (77.1), be defined consistently as the expression

$$\sum f_i \int_B \varphi_i(x)\, d\mu,$$

since, for a Euclidean vector function given in two different ways, our estimate for the norm of the difference of the two expressions for the integral vanishes. Thus our integral is defined by the above process in the dense subset of $\mathscr{F}(\cdot)$, which consists of Euclidean vector functions.

The estimate (77.1) can now be interpreted to mean that the integral in μ, regarded as a function of $f(\cdot)$, defined in this subset, is uniformly continuous in the norm-metric of $\mathscr{F}(\cdot)$.

From this uniform continuity we can infer that the operation has a unique extension to the whole of $\mathscr{F}(\cdot)$, which retains the property of uniform continuity. In fact, if I_ν is the integral in μ of a Euclidean function $f_\nu(\cdot)$ tending to $f(\cdot)$, the lemma shows that the norms in $\mathscr{F}$ of the differences $I_\nu - I_{\nu'}$ are small with those in $\mathscr{F}(\cdot)$ of $f_\nu(\cdot) - f_{\nu'}(\cdot)$. Thus $\lim I_\nu$ exists as a vector in $\mathscr{F}$. Similarly we see that this limit does not alter when we approximate $f(\cdot)$ by another sequence of Euclidean vector functions. The value of this limit may now be defined to be

$$\int_B f(x)\, d\mu.$$

By passage to the limit, we can now infer that this integral is a linear operation in $\mathscr{F}(\cdot)$ and that it satisfies the norm inequalities

$$Q\left[\int_B f(x)\, d\mu\right] \le \int_B Q[f(x)]\, d\mu \le |f(\cdot)| \int_B 1\, d\mu.$$

In particular, it is the desired uniformly continuous extension; it is clearly the only one.

We also note the following result:

(78.1) Theorem. *Let μ_ν $\nu = 1, 2, \ldots$ be Riesz measures tending to a Riesz measure μ, i.e., such that, for every $\varphi(\cdot) \in \mathscr{C}_0(B)$, we have*

$$\int_B \varphi(x)\, d\mu = \lim_\nu \int_B \varphi(x)\, d\mu_\nu.$$

Then we have also, for every $f(\cdot) \in \mathscr{F}(\cdot)$,

$$\int_B f(x)\, d\mu = \lim_\nu \int_B f(x)\, d\mu_\nu.$$

In fact, this last formula is evident in the case of a Euclidean vector function. Hence, by subtracting an appropriate choice of this Euclidean one from an arbitrary Banach vector function, we find easily that, for the latter, as $\nu \to \infty$, the upper and lower limits of the integral in μ_ν differ by as little as we please from the integral in μ. Thus the limit again exists and is the integral in μ, as asserted.

Vector integration can be used to formulate a rather general variational problem, for which the author originally provided an automatic existence theory some thirty years ago, in terms of generalized curves. In the next section, we shall use it for a very different purpose.

§79. CLOSURE OF A CONVEX HULL

We consider the special case in which $B \subset \mathscr{F}$, and we choose for $f(\cdot)$ the identity function, given by $f(x) = x$ $x \in B$. Given on B a unit Riesz measure μ, i.e., one for which

$$\int_B 1\, d\mu = 1,$$

we term center of the measure μ the point of $\mathscr{F}$ given by the vector

$$\int_B x\, d\mu.$$

Deliberately, we eschew here the term center of gravity, which we reserve for corresponding finite combinations. Besides, gravity is out of place when there are no weights.

(79.1) Theorem. *The closure of the convex hull of a $B \cdot\cdot i$-compact subset B of a Banach space $\mathscr{F}$ consists of the centers of unit Riesz measures on B.*

Proof. We observe that the set of these centers is closed. For if x_0 is the limit in $\mathscr{F}$ of centers x_ν of unit Riesz measures μ_ν $\nu = 1, 2, \ldots$, we can select a subsequence, as remarked in Section 75, for which μ_ν converges to a unit Riesz measure μ, and by (78.1) the center of the measure μ is then the limit x_0 of x_ν. Thus the set of centers of Riesz unit measures on B, which evidently includes the convex hull of B, must include the closure of this convex hull.

It remains to show that each such center lies in this closure. To this effect, we approximate the identity function $f(x) = x$ in B, by the Euclidean vector function $\sum f_i h_i(\cdot)$, where the f_i are now points of B and the $h_i(\cdot)$ are our localizing functions. If we attach to the points f_i the weights

$$b_i = \int_B h_i(x)\, d\mu,$$

the finite sum $\sum f_i b_i$ tends, by what we have seen, to the center of the measure μ. This finite sum is in the convex hull of B, since we clearly have $b_i \geq 0$, $\sum b_i = 1$, and this completes the proof.

The theorem just proved is still a rather elementary version of much sharper results, in which the unit measures concerned are restricted to a subset of B, consisting of extreme points. These improvements, which have been studied mainly by Choquet, are important in potential theory. For the theory of Choquet, extreme points, see also a paper of Bishop and deLeeuw.

Appendix II

THE VARIATIONAL SIGNIFICANCE AND STRUCTURE OF GENERALIZED FLOWS

§80. INTRODUCTION

The enlargement of the class of admissible curves, which results from the introduction of generalized curves, is only the first step to a further enlargement, by which we admit also all generalized flows, which satisfy the prescribed boundary conditions. It is only in this still wider setting that modern duality methods attain their full scope.

We shall verify, of course, that the minimum in a problem is not lowered by this further enlargement. This may come as a surprise, since the elements of $\mathscr{C}_0^*(A)$, now admitted, include beings very different from curves, and some of them are very strange beings indeed. It is actually much easier to prove than to explain. The proof is connected with the basic algorithm of Huygens, on which much of the theory developed in this book has been constructed.

However, after giving the proof we must still give the real reason lying behind it, which will occupy most of this Appendix. Incidentally, it also requires the results established in Appendix I. This real reason lies in the fact that many generalized flows are actually excluded by the nature of the prescribed boundary conditions. To establish this fact, we need a theorem that characterizes those generalized flows that possess a certain type of boundary. We term this theorem the Lagrange representation theorem (for the generalized flows in question). This is because the need for this type of representation goes back to Lagrange's work on fluid mechanics.

The notion of generalized flow we have used is closest to the Eulerian description of fluid motion. The classical theory of fluids imposes, however, an additional condition, which is termed the equation of continuity. This is what corresponds here to a restriction on the boundary. Subject to the equation of continuity and to classical smoothness assumptions, it is shown in books on fluid mechanics that the motion has an alternative description, due to Lagrange. (The Lagrange description is used in those problems whose solution is illustrated by the beautiful diagrams of streamlines that fluid dynamicists get to know so well.) Lagrange's description consists of decomposing the motion of fluids into that of a family of streamlines. It is this decomposition, or, if we prefer, the putting together of the streamlines to make up the fluid motion, that also constitutes the essence of our representation theorem. To make this quite precise, we need to know in what proportions the fluid distributes itself among the various streamlines, or, as we say, we must express it as a mixture of streamlines in these proportions.

§81. POLYGONAL FLOWS

It is convenient to begin by illustrating the notion of mixture and the type of theorem we shall aim at in a very simple special case. Moreover, we shall need the discussion of this special case before embarking on the announced further enlargement of the class of admissible curves in the calculus of variations.

The notion of mixture will be defined for certain sets of measures, or, equivalently, for certain subsets of the positive cone of $\mathscr{C}_0^*(B)$, for a suitable B. In particular, it will be defined for certain sets of curves and generalized curves. In this section we shall limit ourselves to mixtures of finite sets. Given a finite set of measures μ_1, $\mu_2, \ldots, \mu_N$, we term mixture of this set any measure of the form $\sum c_i \mu_i$, where the c_i are non-negative constants. The measures concerned will here be on the set A of Chapter VI, i.e., on the Cartesian product of a cube of x-space with the unit sphere of $\dot{x}$.

In particular, a segment in this cube is such a measure. Here a segment is understood to be oriented. It consists of a curve that possesses a parametric representation $x(t)$ $0 \leq t \leq 1$, where $x(t)$ is linear in t and does not reduce to a constant. In accordance with Chapter VI, this curve, which is now a segment, is defined to be the corresponding element of the positive cone of $\mathscr{C}_0^*(A)$. In other words it is a Riesz measure. We can therefore define a mixture of a finite number of segments s_i, and write it as the finite sum $\sum a_i s_i$ where the a_i are non-negative constants. Of course we may ignore any term with coefficient $a_i = 0$. Such a mixture of segments we term a polygonal flow. It can be pictured in our minds as a fluid motion in a finite number of very narrow tubes along the segments; the fluid velocity is unity, and a_i is the linear density in s_i. Of course the tubes need not be material tubes, and they need not lead into one another. For instance they can all fan out from a point, as when water issues from a garden hose and divides into a finite number of streams without our having to supply a large number of narrow tubes issuing from the orifice. In this case, the streams are curved, but we can equally conceive of their being straight.

The polygonal flow will be termed a polygon if the coefficients $a_i \geq 0$ are integers. The simplest case is that of a digon: it consists of the sum $s_1 + s_2$ of a pair of equal and opposite segments. The reader may have some difficulty in picturing this as a fluid motion; it corresponds better to the flow of traffic on the two sides of a straight highway. However, from a great distance, the flow of traffic is not very different from that of fluid particles. Alternatively, by subdivision, we can express our digon as a sum of a very large number of quite small digons, and in the limit we represent it in terms of a degenerate form of local turbulence. This can very well be realized in nature, though we do not normally speak of it as fluid motion, but rather as a longitudinal vibration along a segment, such as occurs along an elastic filament, or, conceivably, in the flow of an alternating electric current along a wire.

Besides digons, we shall consider the special cases of polygons that are the simple polygonal arc and the simple closed polygon. These notions we need not elaborate.

We observe, however, that a simple closed polygon is closed in the elementary sense of geometry, whereas here the term closed, applied to an arbitrary generalized flow g, means that the boundary ∂g vanishes. It is easy to see that a simple closed polygon is closed in this sense also, so our terminology remains consistent.

In picturing a polygonal flow as a fluid motion, we have taken for granted a fiction, to which fluid dynamicists are well accustomed, whereby fluid can be created at one point, a source, move along a curve or a segment, and be annihilated at the second extremity, a sink. On the other hand, there is less need to strain one's imagination in picturing a fluid motion corresponding to a simple closed polygon, since the fictitious sources and sinks at the corners destroy one another, and we can omit them altogether.

We have thus two kinds of polygonal flows, which our intuition distinguishes very clearly: those that involve the fiction of sources and sinks, and those that do not. The following theorem makes this distinction both simpler and sharper.

(81.1) Theorem. *A polygonal flow p is closed if and only if it is expressible as a mixture $\sum c_i p_i$, with positive coefficients c_i, of digons and simple closed polygons p_i.*

Proof. The condition is clearly sufficient; we have to prove it necessary. We express as a mixture of a finite set S of segments s, with coefficients $a_s > 0$, a given closed polygonal flow $p = \sum s a_s$. We denote by E the finite set of points which are vertices of p, so that E consists of the initial points P_s and final points Q_s of the segments $s \in S$. We may suppose by a preliminary subdivision, if necessary, that two segments of S that are not equal and opposite have no interior points in common.

Since the integral on each $s \in S$ of an exact integrand $\dot{x}$ grad $\varphi(x)$ is the difference $\varphi(Q_s) - \varphi(P_s)$ at the two ends of s, the vanishing of ∂p is expressed by the validity for every continuously differentiable real function φ of the relation

$$\sum a_s \varphi(P_s) = \sum a_s \varphi(Q_s).$$

By choosing φ to vanish in E except at a single vertex, we see that each such vertex is an initial point of at least one $s \in S$ (and also a final point of another).

Thus for any vertex $x_1 \in E$, there is a segment $s_1 \in S$ with the initial point x_1; further, if x_2 denotes the final point of s_1, there is at least one segment $s_2 \in S$ with the initial point x_2; generally, from the ν-th vertex $x_\nu \in E$ thus obtained, we can draw at least one segment $s_\nu \in S$ to a $(\nu + 1)$-st vertex $x_{\nu+1} \in E$.

Since E is a finite set, the sequence of the x_ν contains repetitions. By discarding initial terms we may suppose that x_1 is the first to be repeated, and that it recurs for the first time as x_{N+1}. In that case, the expression $q = \sum s_j\, j \leq N$ is clearly either a digon or a simple closed polygon, and we can set

$$p = r + \lambda q,$$

where λ is the smallest of the coefficients a_s for $s = s_1, s_2, \ldots, s_N$, and where r is a closed polygonal flow, consisting of a mixture of segments taken from a proper subset S_1 of S.

Since S_1 has fewer members than S, our assertion now follows by induction with respect to the number of segments of S.

Theorem (81.1) illustrates the drastic structural restrictions implicit in a boundary condition. The theorem has, of course, a k-dimensional extension in n-space, and basically this is a restatement of matters well known to students of topology.

§82. THE BASIS OF MODERN DUALITY IN THE CALCULUS OF VARIATIONS

Modern duality refers here to the use of our dual space $\mathscr{C}_0^*(A)$, as distinct from Hamiltonian duality, which has a classical origin. The preceding theorem, which was really one of elementary topology, can be slightly modified to become a key result for the application of this duality. We apply it in $(n + 1)$ dimensions to a closed polygonal flow $p + q$, where p is in n dimensions and has the same boundary ∂s_0 as a segment s_0, and where q has the reverse boundary $-\partial s_0$ and consists of a pair of segments joined at an additional vertex outside n space. By removing q again, we get an expression for p, and so the following:

(82.1) Theorem. *Let p be a polygonal flow with the same boundary $\partial p = \partial s_0$ as a segment s_0. Then $p = p' + p''$, where $\partial p'' = 0$, and where p' is a mixture $\sum c_i p_i$ of a finite number of simple polygonal arcs p_i for which $\partial p_i = \partial s_0$.*

Evidently in (82.1) we must have $\sum c_i = 1$, or as we shall say, $\sum c_i p_i$ is a unit mixture. For we have

$$\partial s_0 = \partial p' = \sum c_i \, \partial p_i = \sum c_i \, \partial s_0.$$

(82.2) Corollary. *Let Q be the class of simple closed polygons, P that of polygonal flows p such that $\partial p = \partial s_0$, where s_0 is a given segment, and P' the subclass of P consisting of simple polygonal arcs. Further let $f_0 \in \mathscr{C}_0(A)$ satisfy $qf_0 \geq 0$ for all $q \in Q$. Then* Inf *pf_0 is the same for $p \in P'$ as for $p \in P$.*

Proof. We first observe that the inequality $qf_0 \geq 0$, valid by hypothesis for a simple closed polygon q, remains valid by passage to the limit, when q is a digon, since the latter is a limiting form (in $\mathscr{C}_0^*(A)$) of a simple closed triangular polygon. By (81.1), the inequality then also holds when q is any closed polygonal flow. Hence, if we write $m = \operatorname{Inf} pf_0$ for $p \in P'$, we derive from (82.1), for any $p \in P$, the inequality

$$pf_0 \geq \sum c_i m,$$

where the c_i are as in (82.1), and so satisfy $\sum c_i = 1$ by the remark made after (82.1). Thus $pf_0 \geq m$, so that the infimum for $p \in P$ is $\geq m$. Evidently this infimum cannot be $> m$, since $P \supset P'$, and this establishes our assertion.

§83. THE VARIATIONAL CONVEXITY PRINCIPLE IN ITS ELEMENTARY FORM

We term simplicial boundary the boundary $\beta = \partial p$ of a polygonal flow p. We see at once that if β is simplicial so is $-\beta$, since we can reverse all the segments of which p is a mixture. Also, any mixture of a finite number of simplicial boundaries is a simplicial boundary, since it bounds the corresponding mixture of polygonal flows, which is itself a polygonal flow. It follows that any linear combination of simplicial boundaries is a simplicial boundary. In other words, simplicial boundaries β constitute a vector space.

We shall denote this space provisionally by Ω_0, and we define in it the norm $|\beta|$ as the infimum of the length $|p|$ of polygonal flows p such that $\beta = \partial p$. Thus Ω_0 is a normed vector space; however, it is not complete. We shall discuss its completion later.

We denote again by f_0 an integrand such that $qf_0 \geq 0$ for every simple closed polygon q. We shall write $m(\beta)$ for the infimum of pf_0 for polygonal flows p such that $\beta = \partial p$. The following result constitutes a principle of fundamental importance:

(83.1) Convexity Principle. *$m(\beta)$ is a convex homogeneous function of β in Ω_0. Moreover $m(\beta) \leq |\beta| \cdot |f_0|$.*

PROOF. We saw in the proof of (82.2) that $qf_0 \geq 0$ for every closed polygonal flow q. Hence $m(0) \geq 0$, and therefore, evidently, $m(0) = 0$, since there exist arbitrarily short closed polygonal flows. Further we see at once that $m(c\beta) = cm(\beta)$ for $c > 0$ and that $m(\beta + \beta') \leq m(\beta) + m(\beta')$. By taking $\beta' = -\beta$, it follows that $m(\beta)$ cannot be $-\infty$. Further the relation $m(c\beta) = cm(\beta)$ clearly holds for $c = 0$. Thus $m(\beta)$ is homogeneous and convex. Finally, the inequality in the assertion follows by taking the infimum on both sides in the relation $pf_0 \leq |p| \cdot |f_0|$. This completes the proof.

(83.2) Corollary. *With the same hypotheses, let $\beta_0 \in \Omega_0$. Then there exists a linear homogeneous real function $\ell(\beta)$, defined for $\beta \in \Omega_0$, such that $\ell(\beta_0) = m(\beta_0)$, and that*

(83.3) $$\ell(\beta) \leq m(\beta) \quad \textit{for all} \quad \beta \in \Omega_0.$$

This follows at once from (83.1) together with either the alternative definition of convexity or the Hahn-Banach theorem.

§84. A FIRST EXTENSION

In this section, we show that the infimum $m(\beta)$ of pf_0 for polygonal flows p with the boundary $\beta \in \Omega_0$ remains unaltered if we admit all generalized flows g with this boundary; in other words, we show that $m(\beta)$ is the infimum of gf_0 for generalized flows with the boundary β. In so doing, we may suppose, as before, that $qf_0 \geq 0$ for every simple closed polygon q, since otherwise we find easily that $m(0) = -\infty$, and hence that $m(\beta) = -\infty$ for every $\beta \in \Omega_0$, in which case our assertion is self-evident. Further it will suffice to prove, in the notation of (82.2), the relation

(84.1) $$gf_0 \geq \ell(\beta)$$

for every generalized flow g such that $\partial g = \beta$; this is because when $\partial g = \beta_0$ it follows that $gf_0 \geq \ell(\beta_0) = m(\beta_0)$, and therefore that $m(\beta_0)$ does not exceed the infimum of gf_0 for generalized flows g subject to $\partial g = \beta_0$; in that case it must equal this infimum, since the polygonal flows are a subclass; our assertion must then hold since β_0 is arbitrary in Ω_0.

Thus everything depends on our establishing (84.1). In effect, our proof of that inequality will be based on a variant of the classical algorithm of Huygens, which has already helped us so much in this book. The general form of this algorithm is substantially (83.3) above, and does not exhibit the desirable smoothness, which is required for its convenient application. We therefore combine it with a familiar smoothing process, which consists in forming mean values over small cubes.

The smoothing process necessitates shrinking slightly the original cube of x-space, in which admissible curves and so forth were to be situated. This means that in part of our argument, our generalized flows will belong to a dual space $\mathscr{C}_0^*(A_-)$, where A_- is the Cartesian product of our slightly shrunk cube with the unit sphere of $\dot{x}$. However, the final result is not affected.

Let $S(x)$ denote the value taken by $\ell(\beta)$ when β is the boundary of the segment joining a fixed point (the origin) to the point x. We write, for x in the shrunk cube, $\bar{S}(x)$ and $\bar{f}_0(x, \theta)$ for the expressions

$$\int S(x + \varepsilon\xi)\, d\xi \quad \text{and} \quad \int f_0(x + \varepsilon\xi, \theta)\, d\xi,$$

where integration is over the unit cube and where ε is a small positive number. We observe that if $\beta = \partial s$, where s is the segment from x' to x'',

$$S(x'') - S(x') = \ell(\beta) \leq sf_0.$$

From this it follows, first (by combining it with the corresponding inequality for the opposite segment, and by observing that the extreme right is $\leq |s| \cdot |f_0|$) that S is Lipschitzian, and therefore that $\bar{S}$ is certainly continuously differentiable. Further it follows, by forming mean values, that

$$\bar{S}(x'') - \bar{S}(x') \leq s\bar{f}_0.$$

Here the left hand side may be written $s\bar{\psi}$, where $\bar{\psi}(x, \theta)$ is the exact integrand θ grad $\bar{S}(x)$. Hence $s\bar{\psi} \leq s\bar{f}_0$, and, by dividing by the length of s and making this length $\to 0$, while the initial point and the direction of s are kept fixed, we find that

$$\bar{\psi}(x, \theta) \leq \bar{f}_0(x, \theta)$$

for all $(x, \theta) \in A_-$. It follows that for any generalized flow $g \in \mathscr{C}_0^*(A_-)$,

$$g\bar{\psi} \leq g\bar{f}_0.$$

In this last inequality, suppose $\partial g = \partial p = \beta$ say, where p is a polygonal flow. Since $\bar{\psi}$ is exact, we can identify $g\bar{\psi}$ with $p\bar{\psi}$, which is a mixture of $s\bar{\psi}$ for a suitable finite set of segments s. It can thus be expressed as a mixture of corresponding differences of $\bar{S}$, which tend to those of S as $\varepsilon \to 0$. Thus $g\bar{\psi} \to \ell(\beta)$. Clearly also, $g\bar{f}_0 \to gf_0$ as $\varepsilon \to 0$, so that the desired inequality (84.1) follows, subject to the additional assumption that $g \in \mathscr{C}_0^*(A_-)$. This assumption can now, however, be removed at once by a passage to the limit, in which we express g as the limit of a similar generalized flow, derived from it by a change of scale.

§85. THE ENLARGEMENT PRINCIPLE AND THE FIRST CLOSURE THEOREM FOR GENERALIZED FLOWS

Let f_0 denote again an integrand in $\mathscr{C}_0(A)$ such that $qf_0 \geq 0$ for every simple closed polygon q situated in A, and let β_0 be the boundary of a segment in A. The quantity $m(\beta_0)$ is then the infimum of pf_0 for simple polygonal arcs p with the boundary β_0, on account of (82.2). It is also, by the preceding section, the infimum of gf_0 for all generalized flows g with this boundary. In particular, it is the infimum of gf_0 for any class of generalized flows g with the boundary β_0 that includes at least the simple polygonal arcs with this boundary. For instance, it is the infimum of gf_0 for rectifiable curves g with the boundary β_0, and it is also the corresponding infimum for generalized curves with this boundary. Of course these curves and generalized curves are supposed to lie in A, i.e., to belong to $\mathscr{C}_0^*(A)$. However, we make here no restriction of uniform boundedness of the lengths of the curves concerned. Thus if f_0 is subject to the condition just stated, the infimum of its integral along rectifiable curves in A with given end points is unaltered if we admit also generalized curves, and even generalized flows, with the same boundary. We term this the enlargement principle.

The identity of the infimum for polygonal and for generalized flows, with a same simplicial boundary β, can also be expressed as a closure theorem, which shows that such a boundary condition imposes a fundamental restriction on a generalized flow.

(85.1) Theorem. *In order that a generalized flow g_0 possess a simplicial boundary β_0, it is necessary and sufficient that g_0 be the limit of a polygonal flow with the same boundary.*

PROOF. The condition is clearly sufficient, since the notion of limit is in the w^* sense. We have to prove it necessary. Let Γ_0 be the set of polygonal flows p such that ∂p is a non-negative real multiple $k\beta_0$ of the given boundary for some k, and let Γ_1 denote the w^* closure of Γ_0. Clearly Γ_0 and Γ_1 are convex cones.

To prove our assertion, it will suffice to show that $g_0 \in \Gamma_1$. For if $\beta_0 = 0$, this is the assertion, while if $\beta_0 \neq 0$ the relation $g_0 \in \Gamma_1$ means the existence of $p' \in \Gamma_0$ such that $p' \to g_0$; here $\partial p'$, which has the form $k\beta_0$, is the restriction to exact integrands of the functional p', and as such tends to $\partial g_0 = \beta_0$. The previous statement implies that $k \to 1$, so we can now express g_0 as the limit of the polygonal flow $p = p'/k$, which has the boundary β_0.

It remains to prove that $g_0 \in \Gamma_1$. Suppose the contrary. Since convergence in norm implies w^* convergence, there would exist a positive number R such that

$$|g - g_0| > R \quad \text{for all} \quad g \in \Gamma_1.$$

We can thus apply the separation theorem (73.1) in $\mathscr{C}_0^*(A)$, which we proved in Appendix I, Section 73. If we write f_0 for the integrand $-f$ where f is as in that theorem, we find that there would exist $f_0 \in \mathscr{C}_0(A)$ such that $gf_0 \geq 0$ for all g in Γ_1, while $g_0 f_0 = -1$ and $|f_0| \leq 1/R$. In particular we would have, on the one hand, $qf_0 \geq 0$ for every simple closed polygon q, since 0 is a non-negative multiple of β_0, and on the other hand, similarly, $m(\beta_0) \geq 0$. By the previous section these imply $g_0 f_0 \geq 0$ contrary to $g_0 f_0 = -1$. This completes the proof.

§86. THE EXTENSION TO CONSISTENT FLOWS AND BOUNDARIES

So far we have used only the dashed metric, equivalent to w^* convergence for our purposes, in the study of generalized flows and of their boundaries. However, we defined a norm for boundaries $\beta \in \Omega_0$, and we shall now extend its definition.

Let β bound some generalized flow, and let G_β denote the class of generalized flows with the boundary β. We write

$$|\beta| = \operatorname*{Inf}_{g \in G_\beta} |g|.$$

By taking for f_0, in Section 84, the integrand unity, we see that in the case of a simplicial boundary β the infimum is unaltered if we replace G_β by the subclass consisting of its polygonal flows. Thus our notation agrees with that used formerly in Ω_0.

We now define, for any $g \in \mathscr{C}_0^*(A)$, the norm

$$\|g\|$$

as the greater of the two numbers $|g|'$ and $|\partial g|$. We term it the consistent norm to indicate that the corresponding notion of limit is indeed consistent, both with the w^* limit for generalized flows (equivalent to the dashed notion) and with the limit in norm for their boundaries. We shall term consistent, in their turn, the corresponding metric, the topology and the notions of limit and closure.

Finally, generalized flows belonging to the consistent closure of the class of polygonal flows will be termed consistent flows, and the boundary of such a consistent flow will be termed a consistent boundary. We shall denote by Ω the space of consistent boundaries.

The highly restrictive character of a boundary condition is shown again by the following:

(86.1) Theorem. *The class of consistent flows is identical with that of the generalized flows g such that $\partial g \in \Omega$.*

This is really an extended closure theorem, and we can state it in a form similar to (85.1):

In order that $\partial g_0 \in \Omega$ hold for the generalized flow g_0, it is necessary and sufficient that g_0 be the limit of a polygonal flow p such that $|\partial g_0 - \partial p| \to 0$.

Proof. We need only prove this necessary. Suppose then that $\partial g_0 \in \Omega$. By hypothesis, there exists g_1 so that $\partial g_0 = \partial g_1$ and that g_1 is the w^* limit of a polygonal flow p_1, for which $\partial p_1 - \partial g_1$ bounds some g of small norm. Since

$$\partial(g_0 + g) = \partial(g_1 + g) = \partial p_1,$$

which is simplicial, therefore by Theorem (85.1) $g_0 + g$ is itself the limit of a polygonal flow p with $\partial p = \partial p_1$. We choose this p so that $g_0 + g - p$ has dashed norm $< |g|$, and we find easily that $\|g_0 - p\| < 2\,|g|$, which is arbitrarily small.

We can go on to extend the results of Sections 83 to 85, and in particular the convexity principle.

(86.2) The Extended Variational Convexity Principle. *Let $f_0 \in \mathscr{C}_0(A)$ and, for $\beta \in \Omega$, let G_β denote the class of generalized flows g such that $\partial g = \beta$. Further, let $m(\beta) = \operatorname{Inf} gf_0$ for $g \in G_\beta$. Then for $\beta \in \Omega_0$, $m(\beta)$ coincides with the infimum of pf_0 for polygonal flows $p \in G_\beta$. Moreover $m(0) = 0$ if and only if $qf_0 \geq 0$ for every simple closed polygon q. In that case $m(\beta)$ is convex and homogeneous for $\beta \in \Omega$; otherwise $m(\beta)$ is the constant $-\infty$.*

Proof. The case in which $\beta \in \Omega_0$ has already been disposed of in Section 84 applies in particular when $\beta = 0$. The remaining assertions are proved exactly as in the original form of the principle (83.1).

The ease with which we have established (86.1) and (86.2) may induce some readers to suppose that there is nothing much to be gained by introducing these extensions, just as American ice cream is not given more substance by blowing in more air. It is true that the new form of the convexity principle does not help very much with classical problems, in which $m(\beta)$ is wanted only when β consists of the boundary of a segment. Its purpose is, however, to render possible the study of much more general problems, for instance the measure in the set of initial directions at the origin of minimizing arcs that end on the unit circumference with a given measure distribution of terminal points.

The view is sometimes expressed, and by quite eminent mathematicians, that the value and interest to be attached to a piece of mathematics is directly related to the amount of really hard work that goes into it. This is undoubtedly very true, but it must be borne in mind that this hard work is best done behind the scenes, and that much of it goes into putting the material in a form which is easily grasped. If a reader attaches value only to what he finds hard to follow, he is liable to reach a very distorted picture of mathematics today. Similarly, a pioneer in motoring may have judged of the power of a car by the amount of noise and dust that it raised, but this is hardly apt in our time. In mathematics, those whose criterion of the value of a result is based on weighing the pages in which it is proved, or on measuring the time needed to grasp the proof with a stop-watch, have experienced a number of shocks in modern times, as simple proofs were found for what had previously required long and involved arguments. The truth is that mathematics is really like a work of art: it requires infinite pains, but the final result shows nothing of them, nothing to distract the viewer from the deep understanding and insight that it brings to him.

The convexity principles (83.1) and (86.2) are quite basic, and the difference between them is relevant only in problems in which more general boundaries occur than in the classical theory. Their importance is due to the dual definition of convexity. They lead at once to the existence, as in (83.2), of a certain linear function $\ell(\beta)$ with, by now, very familiar properties. In this way, the existence of a minimum can be expressed by a necessary and sufficient condition in terms of $\ell(\beta)$, which may be considered the modern form of the variational algorithm of Huygens:

(86.3) Theorem. *Let $f_0 \in \mathscr{C}_0(A)$ and let g_0 denote a generalized flow subject to $\partial g_0 = \beta_0 \in \Omega$; further let $m(\beta)$ $\beta \in \Omega$ be defined as in* (86.2). *Then, in order that*

$$g_0 f_0 = m(\beta_0),$$

it is necessary and sufficient that there exist a homogeneous linear function $\ell(\beta)$ $\beta \in \Omega$ such that $\ell(\beta_0) = g_0 f_0$ and that $\ell(\beta) \leq g f_0$ for all generalized flows g with boundary $\partial g = \beta \in \Omega$.

Here the sufficiency is obvious, while the necessity follows from (86.2), since we clearly have $m(\beta_0) \neq -\infty$, so that $q f_0 \geq 0$ for every closed polygon q.

§87. PRELIMINARY INFORMATION ON MIXTURES AND ON THE LAGRANGE REPRESENTATION

The study of the implications of Theorem (86.3) demands that of the structure of a consistent flow, and this is what the Lagrange representation is about. We shall need to extend the notion of mixture.

Let μ be a Riesz unit measure on a $B \cdot\cdot i$-compact set B whose elements are Riesz measures on a $B \cdot\cdot i$-compact set A, which will here be our usual Cartesian product of an x cube with the $\dot{x}$ unit sphere. We term unit Riesz mixture of B the center of the measure μ. Since B consists of generalized flows, we can write the mixture

$$\int_B g_b \, d\mu,$$

where g_b is the identity function of the element $b \in B$.

More generally, we term mixture of a set B of our generalized flows, any generalized flow expressible in the form of a finite or countable sum

$$g = \sum c_\nu g_\nu,$$

where the c_ν are real and non-negative, and where each g_ν is a unit Riesz mixture of a $B \cdot\cdot i$-compact subset B_ν of B. This means, of course, that we have, for each $f \in \mathscr{C}_0(A)$,

$$gf = \sum c_\nu g_\nu f,$$

so that in particular, by taking for f the constant unity,

$$|g| = \sum c_\nu |g_\nu| < \infty.$$

If g is a mixture of B, the elements of B are termed the constituents. On account of the analogy with the Lagrange specification of a fluid motion in terms of stream-lines, to which we referred in Section 80, the expression of g as a mixture of a particular set of constituents will be spoken of, in the few cases that we shall study here, as a Lagrange representation. To stress this analogy, we shall temporarily refer to a generalized curve as a stream. Further, if we denote, as in Theorem (67.1) of Chapter VI, Section 67, by g_t $0 \leq t \leq 1$ the system of generalized line elements which defines a generalized curve

$$\int_0^1 g_t \, dt,$$

and if E denotes a closed subset of positive measure of the interval $0 \leq t \leq 1$, we may speak of the generalized flow

$$\int_B g_t \, dt$$

as an intermittent stream, or jet. Streams or jets of unit length will be termed unit streams or jets.

We shall mainly consider mixtures in which the set B of the constituents consists of one of the following systems: (a) consistent flows; (b) unit streams or jets, or else streams or jets of lesser length; (c) closed streams.

We first consider case (c), i.e., the question of the Lagrange representation of a generalized flow g, when the constituents are closed generalized curves. Of course such a representation cannot exist unless g is itself, at any rate, closed. However, we shall see that even then it need not exist. This is shown by a simple example, due to E. Bishop. We give this example here as it will help us realize the kind of difficulty to be overcome. However, we shall slightly modify the details, so as to avoid using a high-powered ergodicity theorem.

We consider the classical representation of a torus in 3-space by a vector valued function $x(u, v)$ of period unity in each of the real variables u, v. The function $x(u, v)$ is elementary, and we shall not need its expression; it is of course differentiable as often as we please, and it provides a one-to-one map of the half-open unit square onto the torus. We denote by λ an irrational number which will be kept fixed. At each point (u, v), we mark the direction parallel to the line $v = \lambda u$, and we denote,

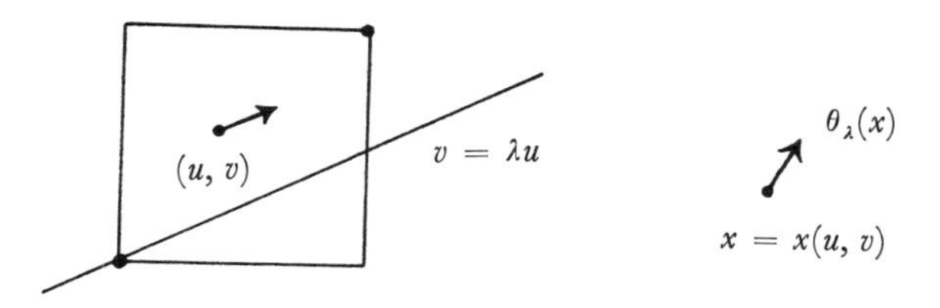

at the corresponding point $x = x(u, v)$ of the torus, by $\theta_\lambda(x)$ the unit vector whose direction corresponds to the one marked at (u, v).

This being so, we define a generalized flow g as follows: to each integrand $f \in \mathscr{C}_0(A)$, we associate the corresponding Lagrangian $L(x, \dot{x})$, and we define gf to be the value of the integral over the (u, v) unit square

$$\iint L[x(u, v), x_u + \lambda x_v]\, du\, dv. \tag{87.1}$$

Clearly this can be written as the integral on the torus, with respect to an appropriate measure in x, of the function $f(x, \theta_\lambda(x))$. It follows that in expressing g as a mixture of streams, we need only consider ordinary parametric curves subject to the differential equation $dx/ds = \theta_\lambda(x)$, where s is the arc length. These curves are images of the lines $v = \lambda u + \text{const.}$, and because of the irrationality of λ none of them can be closed. Thus g is not a mixture of closed streams.

On the other hand, we shall see that g itself is closed, i.e., that $\partial g = 0$. To this effect we make use of periodicity to express (87.1) as the ratio I_ν/ν, where I_ν is the corresponding integral on a parallelogram bounded by the lines $u = 0$, $u = \nu + 1$,

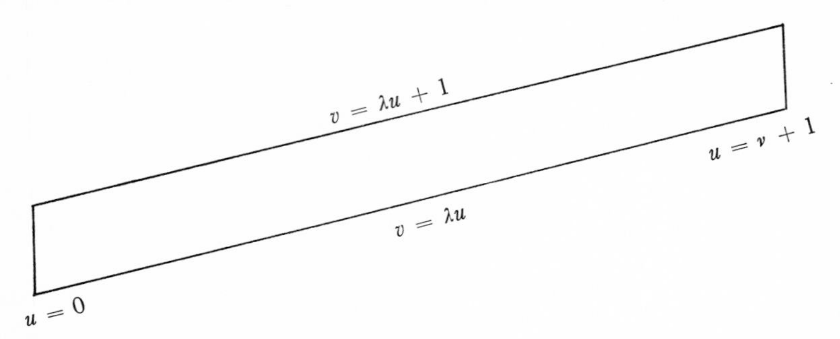

$v = \lambda u$, $v = \lambda u + 1$. If $L(x, \dot{x})$ corresponds to an exact integrand f, i.e., has the form

$$L(x, \dot{x}) = \dot{x} \operatorname{grad} \varphi(x),$$

and if we set $\Phi(u, v) = \varphi[x(u, v)]$, we see that the integral along a parallel to $v = \lambda u$ of the function under the integral sign in (87.1) is a difference of Φ at the ends, which are congruent to two points of the unit square, and therefore that it is bounded for large ν. Hence, for our exact integrand, I_ν is bounded in ν, so that I_ν/ν tends to 0. It follows that $gf = 0$ for exact f and therefore that $\partial g = 0$.

§88. FURTHER COMMENTS ON MEASURES, MIXTURES AND CONSISTENT FLOWS

We shall need a few routine facts, which we base on notions and arguments that go right back to the earliest work of the creators of the modern theory of measure and integration. In particular, we shall need to approximate in a certain way to a Riesz measure. We begin with an elementary lemma, which occurs in the early work of W. H. Young in a slightly sharper form, according to which the points of nonuniform convergence are, in certain cases, "visible" as discontinuities of the limit function. The lemma of W. H. Young was stated for functions on a segment, but the arguments do not require this.

(88.1) The Visibility Lemma. *Let f_ν $\nu = 1, 2, \ldots$ be continuous non-negative functions defined on a $B \cdot \cdot$ i-compact set B, let the series $\Sigma\, f_\nu(x)$ converge for each $x \in B$, and let its sum be a continuous function. Then the series converges uniformly in B.*

Proof. This is an exercise in Borel's covering theorem. By hypothesis, the function $r_m(x)$ $x \in B$, defined as the corresponding sum for $\nu > m$ is continuous. Given $\varepsilon > 0$, we determine for each x_0 an m_0 so that $r_{m_0}(x_0) < \varepsilon$, and a neighborhood Δ in which, for this m_0,

$r_{m_0}(x) < 2\varepsilon$. A finite number of the Δ cover B; we denote by M the largest of the corresponding numbers m_0. Since $r_m(x)$ decreases as m increases, we find that $r_m(x) < 2\varepsilon$ for all $m \geq M$ and all x. Hence the convergence of the series is uniform as asserted.

We pass on to the notion of restriction of a Riesz measure. Let B' denote a closed subset of a $B \cdot \cdot\, i$-compact set B, and let $B'' = B - B'$. Further let μ denote a Riesz measure on B. We shall define two Riesz measures μ', μ'' which we term the restrictions of μ to B', B'', respectively, and which satisfy $\mu' + \mu'' = \mu$. Instead of the integrals on B of a continuous f with respect to μ', μ'', we shall write

$$\int_{B'} f(x)\, d\mu, \qquad \int_{B''} f(x)\, d\mu.$$

We shall define the former of these integrals first in the case in which $f(x) \geq 0$ for $x \in B'$. Its value is then to be

$$\operatorname*{Inf}_{\varphi} \int_B \varphi(x)\, d\mu$$

where the infimum is taken in the class of functions $\varphi(x)$ $x \in B$, which are continuous and non-negative and which coincide with $f(x)$ in the subset B'. In the case of an arbitrary continuous function f on B, we define

$$\int_{B'} f(x)\, d\mu = \int_{B'} f_1(x)\, d\mu - \int_{B'} f_2(x)\, d\mu$$

where $f_1(x) = \text{Max}\,(f(x), 0), f_2(x) = \text{Max}\,(-f(x), 0)$. Further, we define the second of our integrals by setting

$$\int_{B''} f(x)\, d\mu = \int_B f(x)\, d\mu - \int_{B'} f(x)\, d\mu.$$

With these definitions, it is quite evident that

$$\int_{B'} cf(x)\, d\mu = c \int_{B'} f(x)\, d\mu.$$

Before proving the corresponding additivity relation, we establish the following:

(88.2) Lemma. *Let $f(x) \geq 0$ for $x \in B'$ and let $f_\nu(x)$ $x \in B$ $\nu = 1, 2, \ldots$ be a monotone descending sequence of continuous functions which coincide with $f(x)$ for $x \in B'$ and which have the limit 0 for each $x \in B''$. Then*

$$\int_{B'} f(x)\, d\mu = \operatorname*{Lim}_{\nu} \int_B f_\nu(x)\, d\mu.$$

PROOF. Let $\varphi(x)$ $x \in B$ denote any continuous function that coincides with $f(x)$ for $x \in B'$ and which is ≥ 0 for $x \in B''$, and let $\varphi_\nu(x)$ denote, for each x, the greater of the two numbers $\varphi(x)$ and $f_\nu(x)$. Then the sequence of functions φ_ν is monotone descending and its limit is the continuous function φ. Since the φ_ν are continuous also, we can apply the visibility lemma (88.1) to the differences $\varphi_\nu - \varphi_{\nu+1}$. We thus find that φ_ν tends uniformly to the function φ. Consequently

$$\text{Lim} \int_B f_\nu(x)\, d\mu \leq \text{Lim} \int_B \varphi_\nu(x)\, d\mu = \int_B \varphi(x)\, d\mu,$$

and by taking the infimum we find that

$$\text{Lim} \int_B f_\nu(x)\, d\mu \leq \int_{B'} f(x)\, d\mu.$$

This completes the proof, since the opposite inequality is obvious.

From (88.2) we derive at once the addition theorem:

$$\int_{B'} \{f_1(x) + f_2(x)\}\, d\mu = \int_{B'} f_1(x)\, d\mu + \int_{B'} f_2(x)\, d\mu$$

in the case in which f_1, f_2 are non-negative, and therefore also a corresponding formula for the integrals of a finite number of continuous non-negative functions. This formula clearly extends to a finite number of functions, each of which is continuous and of constant sign, by the simple procedure of transferring certain terms to the other side. Hence we derive at once the addition theorem in the case in which f_1, f_2 are continuous functions, no longer restricted in sign. Thus, finally,

$$\int_{B'} f(x)\, d\mu$$

defines a Riesz measure μ' on B. If we now set $\mu'' = \mu - \mu'$ and observe that, for a non-negative continuous f,

$$\int_{B''} f(x)\, d\mu$$

is non-negative, like the corresponding integral on B', we see that μ'' is again a Riesz measure on B. Further, it easily follows that

$$\left| \int_{B'} f(x)\, d\mu \right| \le |f|_{B'} \int_{B'} 1\, d\mu,$$

where $|f|_{B'}$ denotes the supremum for $x \in B'$ of $f(x)$. This is simply because when we add or subtract this number to or from $f(x)$, we obtain a function of constant sign. Similarly we obtain a corresponding inequality with B'' in place of B'.

(88.3) Lemma. *Let B' describe an expanding sequence of closed subsets of B such that B is their union, and suppose as before that B is $B \cdot\cdot$ i-compact and that μ is a Riesz measure on B. Then*

$$\int_{B-B'} 1\, d\mu \to 0.$$

PROOF. It evidently follows from our definitions above that

$$\int_{B-B'} 1\, d\mu = \operatorname*{Sup}_{\psi} \int_B \psi(x)\, d\mu,$$

where the supremum is for the class of continuous functions $\psi(x)$ $x \in B$ such that $\psi(x) = 0$ for $x \in B'$ and $\psi(x) \le 1$ for $x \in B - B'$. We denote by B_ν the sequence of the sets $B - B'$, and by ψ_ν a corresponding sequence of the relevant functions ψ, so chosen that for a given $\varepsilon > 0$,

$$\int_B \psi_\nu(x)\, d\mu \tag{88.4}$$

differs from the corresponding supremum by $<2^{-\nu}\varepsilon$. We denote by $\chi_\nu(x)$ the value $\psi_\nu(x)$ if $\nu = 1$, and the lesser of the values $\chi_{\nu-1}(x)$, $\psi_\nu(x)$ if $\nu > 1$. Evidently

$$\int_{B_\nu} 1\, d\mu - \int_B \chi_\nu(x)\, d\mu = \int_{B_\nu} \{1 - \chi_\nu(x)\}\, d\mu \le \int_{B_\nu} (\{1 - \psi_\nu(x)\} + \{1 - \chi_{\nu-1}(x)\})\, d\mu$$
$$< \varepsilon(2^{-\nu} + 2^{-(\nu-1)} + \cdots + \tfrac{1}{2}) < \varepsilon.$$

Further, the functions $\chi_\nu(x)$ form a monotone descending sequence, whose limit is evidently 0 since they vanish outside the B_ν, which shrink to the empty set. Arguing as in the preceding lemma, we deduce from the visibility lemma (88.1) that the expression (88.4) tends to 0. Hence the quantity

$$\operatorname*{Lim}_{\nu} \int_{B_\nu} 1\, d\mu$$

is $\le \varepsilon$, and so vanishes as asserted.

A Riesz measure μ on B has support in the closed subset $B_0 \subset B$, if $\int f(x)\, d\mu = 0$ for every $f \in \mathscr{C}_0(B)$ such that $f(x)$ vanishes throughout B_0. This implies that if f_1, f_2 are continuous in B and satisfy the relation $f_1(x) \le f_2(x)$ throughout B_0, then

$$\int_B f_1(x)\, d\mu \le \int_B f_2(x)\, d\mu.$$

To see this we may suppose by subtraction that $f_1 = 0$; if we then set $f(x) = \text{Max}\{f_2(x), 0\} - f_2(x)$, we find that $\int f(x)\, d\mu = 0$, so that the integral of f_2 coincides with that of the non-negative function $\text{Max}\{f_2(x), 0\}$.

We note that here the restriction μ' of any Riesz measure μ on B to the closed subset $B' \subset B$ has support in B'. By an easy induction, we derive:

(88.5) Localization Lemma. *Let B' be the union of a finite number of closed subsets B_ν of the $B \cdot\cdot i$-compact set B. Then the restriction to B' of a Riesz measure on B can be expressed as a sum of Riesz measures μ_ν, where the support of μ_ν is in B_ν.*

So far, in this section we have treated only integrals of scalar functions. We can now also integrate any vector function $f(x)$ with respect to the restriction μ', so that the symbols

$$\int_{B'} f(x)\, d\mu, \qquad \int_{B-B'} f(x)\, d\mu$$

extend to vector functions. We recall that these vector functions are understood to be continuous. Here we need only the case in which both B and the values of our vectors f lie in $\mathscr{C}_0^*(A)$ with the dashed norm. We shall use the letter b instead of x to denote an element of B, and the letter g instead of f to denote a vector, i.e., an element of $\mathscr{C}_0^*(A)$. Thus a vector function now has the form $g(b)$ $b \in B$. However, we shall be interested mainly in mixtures, as where $g(b)$ is the identity map $g_b = b$, or, more generally, in the case where $g(b)$ differs from the identity map only by a Euclidean vector function. Further, all vectors concerned will lie in sets of bounded (undashed) norm, so that the dashed topology is still that of w *.

In addition to the dashed norm, the quantities $|g|$, $|\partial g|$ will play a part, and we must relate them to the dashed, or w *, topology, and to the notion of vector integral.

(88.6) Lemma. *In the w^* topology of $\mathscr{C}_0^*(A)$, the quantities $|g|$, $|\partial g|$ are lower semicontinuous. They are also convex and homogeneous.*

PROOF. We need only prove the first statement. We first deal with $|g|$. In the positive cone, this can be written $g \cdot 1$ and is continuous; however, in $\mathscr{C}_0^*(A)$ we can still show that it is lower semicontinuous, although not in general continuous. To this effect, let g be the w^* limit of g_ν. Given $\varepsilon > 0$, we choose $f_0 \in \mathscr{C}_0(A)$ subject to $|f_0| \leq 1$, $|g| \leq gf_0 + \varepsilon$. Then

$$|g| - \varepsilon \leq gf_0 = \operatorname*{Lim}_{\nu} g_\nu f_0 \leq \operatorname*{Lim\,inf}_{\nu} |g_\nu|,$$

whence $|g| \leq \text{Lim inf}\, |g_\nu|$. Thus $|g|$ is lower semicontinuous.

We now tackle $|\partial g|$. We choose $\hat{g}_\nu$ to satisfy

$$\partial \hat{g}_\nu = \partial g_\nu, \qquad |\hat{g}_\nu| \leq |g_\nu|, \qquad |\hat{g}_\nu| \leq |\partial g_\nu| + \varepsilon.$$

We can then determine a subsequence of ν along which, first, the inferior limit of $|\partial g_\nu|$ becomes a limit, and, second, $\hat{g}_\nu$ has a w^* limit $\hat{g}$. For any exact f, we have, in this subsequence,

$$\hat{g}f = \text{Lim}\, \hat{g}_\nu f = \text{Lim}\, g_\nu f = gf,$$

so that $\partial \hat{g} = \partial g$. Moreover, for the same subsequence,

$$|\partial g| \leq |\hat{g}| \leq \text{Lim inf}\, |\hat{g}_\nu| \leq \varepsilon + \text{Lim}\, |\partial g_\nu|,$$

so that finally $|\partial g| \leq \text{Lim inf}\, |\partial g_\nu|$, which establishes the lower semicontinuity of $|\partial g|$ and so completes the proof.

We shall also need some standard inequalities. These, again, are not immediate because our definition of vector integral uses the dashed norm. We denote by $g(b)$ $b \in B$ a w^* continuous function on the w^* $B \cdot\cdot i$-compact set $B \subset \mathscr{C}_0^*(A)$, whose values lie in $\mathscr{C}_0^*(A)$, and by μ a Riesz measure on B. We write M and $\hat{M}$ for the suprema of $|g(b)|$ and $|\partial g(b)|$ subject to $b \in B$, and we set

$$g = \int_B g(b)\, d\mu, \qquad c = \int_B 1\, d\mu.$$

(88.7) Lemma. *With the above hypotheses and notation, we have* (i) $|g| \leq Mc$, *and* (ii) $|\partial g| \leq \hat{M}c$.

PROOF. The integral for g is the w^* limit of a finite sum g_ν of the form $\sum c_i g(b_i)$ where c_i is the integral of a localizing function $h_i(b) \geq 0$, and $\sum h_i(b) = 1$. Then $\sum c_i = c$ and $c_i \geq 0$. By convexity and homogeneity, the relevant inequalities hold for g_ν, and so, by semicontinuity, for g.

The preceding proof illustrates the importance of the semicontinuity lemma (88.6). Another consequence of that lemma is that the consistent norm $\|g\|$ also is lower semicontinuous in the w^* topology.

This last has the important consequence that, if E is a finite set of generalized flows, and we choose any $\varepsilon > 0$, then the set E_ε of the generalized flows whose consistent distance from E is $\leq \varepsilon$ is w^* closed.

Thus, if E is a finite set of polygonal flows, then for any $\varepsilon' > 0$, the set $E_{\varepsilon'}$ of generalized flows whose consistent distance from E is $\leq \varepsilon'$ is w^* closed. If we fix ε', we can now define an expanding sequence of finite sets E of polygonal flows such that every consistent flow belongs to the union of the corresponding $E_{\varepsilon'}$. Let Q_N be the class of polygonal flows $q = \sum s a_s$ that are mixtures of $\leq N$ segments s of total length $\sum |s| \leq N$ and have coefficients $a_s \geq 0$ of sum $\leq N$. Let P_N be the subclass of Q_N obtained by restricting the coefficients to a sufficiently dense finite subset of the real interval from 0 to N, and, moreover, the ends of the segments s to a sufficiently dense finite subset of our basic cube in x-space. As the ν-th of our sets E we shall take the union of the ν first sets P_N $N = 1, 2, \ldots, \nu$.

By choice of P_N, each $q \in Q_N$ has, from some $p \in P_N$, a consistent distance $\|p - q\| < \varepsilon'/2$. By Theorem (86.1), every consistent flow g satisfies, for some polygonal flow q, the relation $\|g - q\| < \varepsilon'/2$. Since $q \in Q_N$ for some N, we see that $\|g - p\| < \varepsilon'$ for some $p \in P_N$, so that g lies in the corresponding set $E_{\varepsilon'}$.

With the help of this remark, we shall show that the class of consistent flows is closed under mixture. This is the following:

(88.8) Theorem. *Let g be a mixture of consistent flows. Then g is itself a consistent flow.*

It was with this theorem in mind that we developed the previous measure theory notions in this section. They make it possible to avoid some unpleasant routine verifications of measurability.

PROOF. If the mixture consists of a finite sum

$$\sum c_\nu g_\nu,$$

we see at once that, given $\varepsilon > 0$, there exists a polygonal flow p such that $\|g - p\| < \varepsilon$; it is sufficient to take for p a corresponding mixture, with the same coefficients, of polygonal flows p_ν such that the norms $\|g_\nu - p_\nu\|$ are sufficiently small. Again, if the mixture consists of an infinite sum of the above form, then the norm of the sum from N to ∞ is the sum, for these ν, of the terms $c_\nu g_\nu \cdot 1$, and is $<\varepsilon/2$ for a large N. Since the consistent norm is no greater, we see at once, by applying the case of a finite sum with $\varepsilon/2$, that there is again a polygonal flow p such that $\|g - p\| < \varepsilon$.

If the mixture is an integral

$$\int_B g_b \, d\mu,$$

where g_b is the identity function in B, i.e., $g_b = b$ for $b \in B$, and where B is a $B \cdot \cdot i$-compact set of consistent flows in the dashed (or w^*) topology, and μ is a unit Riesz measure on B, then we write

$$\int_B g_b \, d\mu = \int_{B'} g_b \, d\mu + \int_{B''} g_b \, d\mu,$$

where $B'' = B - B'$ and where B' is the intersection of B with a set of the form $E_{\varepsilon'}$, for $\varepsilon' = \varepsilon/3$. Here $E_{\varepsilon'}$ is constructed, as in the remark preceding the statement of Theorem (88.7), in terms of one of the finite sets E of polygonal flows, there defined.

Since B is bounded in norm, there is a constant M so that $|g_b| \leq M$, and so

$$\left(\int_{B''} g_b \, d\mu\right) \cdot f \leq M \int_{B''} 1 \, d\mu$$

for each $f \in \mathscr{C}_0(A)$ such that $|f| \leq 1$. By lemma (88.3) we can thus arrange for the norm of

$$\int_{B''} g_b \, d\mu$$

to be as small as we please, and, *a fortiori*, arrange for its consistent norm to be $<\varepsilon'$.

In B' each element is at a consistent distance $\leq \varepsilon'$ from the finite set E. Thus B' is a union of a finite number of sets B_ν, which are its intersections with closed balls in the consistent metric, of radii ε'. The balls are w^* closed by (88.6), and their centers are polygonal flows $p_\nu \in E$. By (88.5) there exist corresponding Riesz measures μ_ν, with supports in the B_ν, such that their sum is the restriction μ' of μ to B'. We write c_ν for $\int 1 \, d\mu_\nu$. Clearly

$$\int_B (g_b - p_\nu) \, d\mu_\nu = \int_B g_b \, d\mu_\nu - c_\nu p_\nu.$$

By lemma (88.7) for the quantity $|\partial g|$, and by the corresponding trivial inequality for the dashed norm, we see that the consistent norm of the above difference is at most $2c_\nu\varepsilon'$. Hence, by addition

$$\left\| \int_{B'} g_b \, d\mu - \sum c_\nu p_\nu \right\| \leq 2\varepsilon',$$

and finally

$$\left\| \int_{B} g_b \, d\mu - \sum c_\nu p_\nu \right\| < 3\varepsilon' = \varepsilon,$$

which shows that our mixture is at an arbitrarily small consistent distance from a polygonal flow, and is therefore consistent, as asserted.

§89. THE LAGRANGE REPRESENTATION OF A CONSISTENT FLOW

As already explained, in order to bring out the fluid analogy, we refer to a generalized curve as a stream. In particular, a generalized curve of length 1 will be referred to as a unit stream. We shall also need the notion of an intermittent stream, or jet. We mean by this a generalized flow derived from a generalized curve by subtracting a countable set of its arcs.

An equally important analogy is that between consistent flows and the geodesic flows of Chapter I, which themselves resemble classical fluid flows. If our consistent flow is in some sense a smooth enough mixture of curves, the latter correspond to the flow curves of a geodesic covering. This correspondence holds also in much more general cases, when we extend the notion of geodesic covering, as we shall in optimal control.

We shall prove here the following main results:

(89.1) Theorem. (i) *Every closed generalized flow is a mixture of unit streams.* (ii) *Every generalized flow with a simplicial boundary is a mixture of bounded streams.* (iii) *Every generalized flow with a consistent boundary is a mixture of bounded intermittent streams.*

In view of our previous results, part (iii) of the above statement amounts to the identity of the following three classes of generalized flows:

(a) Those that are consistent
(b) Those with consistent boundaries
(c) Those that are mixtures of bounded jets

Proof of (89.1)(i). By multiplying by a constant, we need only prove the assertion for a closed generalized unit flow g. The latter is, by Theorems (85.1) and

(81.1), the fine limit of a closed polygonal flow of the form

$$q = \sum_{i=1}^{N} c_i p_i$$

where the p_i are closed polygons, and the coefficients c_i are positive reals. We can make the c_i rational without affecting the limit, and we express them as fractions with a same large denominator ν, which depends on q. We choose ν large compared with N, i.e., such that $N/\nu \to 0$ as $q \to g$.

The numerators of the c_i will now be absorbed into the p_i by replacing each p_i by this integral multiple, which is itself a closed polygon. Further, we add to each p_i a digon, thus connecting it to the next. The total length added is at most a constant multiple of N/ν, so that g is still the fine limit of q after these modifications. In this case the sum $\sum p_i$ becomes a single closed polygon p. By adding one or more additional digons, without affecting the limit, we can suppose that the length $|p|$ is an integer λ.

Thus g is the limit of p/ν, i.e., for each $f \in \mathscr{C}_0(A)$, we have $gf = \lim pf/\nu$. By taking $f = 1$, $g \cdot 1 = |g| = 1$, we find that $\lambda/\nu \to 1$. Consequently $g = \lim p/\lambda$, so that we can now identify λ with ν; i.e., we can suppose $|p| = \nu$. This means that g is the fine limit of a polygonal flow q of the form p/ν, where $|p| = \nu$ is an integer. We subdivide the closed polygon p into ν arcs γ_k where $|\gamma_k| = 1$. Then q is a convex combination of arcs γ_k of unit length.

This being so, we denote by B the set of generalized curves of length unity. This set is w^* closed and contains the arcs γ_k. Thus q lies in the convex hull of B. Consequently g lies in the w^* closure, or fine closure, of B. However w^* limits are equivalent to those of the dashed metric of $\mathscr{C}_0^*(A)$, and B as a closed subset of the unit ball is $B \cdot \cdot i$-compact in that metric. By Theorem (79.1) of Appendix I, it follows that g is a center of measure of B, i.e., a unit Riesz mixture of B. This completes the proof.

It will be observed that the set B in the above proof includes generalized curves that reduce to generalized line elements; i.e., each of them may be concentrated at a single point. It is easily seen that in this case the resultant of the line element vanishes.

Before proving the remaining parts of Theorem (89.1), we shall develop machinery by means of which these parts can be derived from (i) above. We shall term σ-polygonal flow a generalized flow expressible as a countable mixture of segments.

(89.2) Lemma. *Let $\beta \in \Omega$. Then there exists a σ-polygonal flow p such that $\beta = \partial p$.*

Proof. By hypothesis $\beta = \partial g$ for some consistent limit g of a polygonal flow. Hence, given a convergent series $\sum \varepsilon_\nu$ of positive terms, there is a polygonal flow q_ν, such that $\|g - q_\nu\| < \varepsilon_\nu$. We set $p_1 = q_1$ and for $\nu > 1$ we determine a polygonal flow p_ν so that

$$\partial p_\nu = \partial q_\nu - \partial q_{\nu-1}, \qquad |p_\nu| < 2\,\|q_\nu - q_{\nu-1}\|.$$

Evidently $|p_\nu| < 4\varepsilon_\nu$, so that the series $\sum p_\nu = p$ converges (in all norms) and constitutes the required σ-polygonal flow such that $\beta = \partial p$.

Next we shall require a lemma on the mixture of restrictions of measures. This is really a special form of Fubini's theorem.

(89.3) Localization Lemma for Mixtures. *Let γ be a unit Riesz mixture*

$$\int \gamma_\alpha \, d\mu$$

of Riesz measures γ_α on a $B\cdots$ i-compact set B, and let γ', γ'_α denote the restrictions of γ, γ_α to a closed subset $B' \subset B$. Then γ' is a unit Riesz mixture of the restrictions γ'_α.

If we regard μ as a measure on the set of labels α, rather than on the set of measures γ_α, this is a matter of establishing the formula

$$\textbf{(89.4)} \qquad \gamma' = \int \gamma'_\alpha \, d\mu.$$

Unfortunately, even good texts in real analysis fail to give Fubini's theorem in a form general enough to include this very simple result.

PROOF OF (89.3). By (88.2), the restrictions can be expressed in terms of a monotone descending sequence of continuous functions f_ν associated to any non-negative $f \in \mathscr{C}_0(B)$, so that

$$\gamma' f = \lim \gamma f_\nu, \qquad \gamma'_\alpha f = \lim \gamma_\alpha f_\nu.$$

Clearly, however,

$$\gamma f_\nu = \int \gamma_\alpha f_\nu \, d\mu,$$

whence, the sequences being monotone descending, we obtain

$$\lim \gamma f_\nu = \int \lim \gamma_\alpha f_\nu \, d\mu,$$

and therefore $\gamma' f = \int \gamma'_\alpha f \, d\mu$. This last formula extends to any $f \in \mathscr{C}_0(B)$ when we express the latter as a difference of two non-negative functions, and this ensures the validity of (89.4). Our lemma is thus established.

We can now return to our main theorem.

PROOF OF (89.1)(ii) AND (iii). The parts will be dealt with similarly, and we begin with (iii). We embed our x-space in a Euclidean $\hat{x}$-space, by adding a dimension, and we embed correspondingly A in an analogous set $\hat{A}$ with two added dimensions. We regard the old space and set as the restrictions of the new ones, so that they are derived by making the additional coordinates vanish. A segment of $\hat{x}$-space that has, at most, one point in x-space will be termed extraneous, and so will a polygon, polygonal flow or σ-polygonal flow that is expressible as a mixture of extraneous segments. Clearly, by replacing segments of x-space by broken lines, any σ-polygonal flow can be replaced by an extraneous one with the same boundary. Similar remarks apply to a polygon and to a polygonal flow.

This being so, let g be any generalized flow for which $\partial g \in \Omega$. Any such generalized flow is a Riesz measure on A, and may be regarded as a Riesz measure on $\hat{A}$ with support in A. Further, by (89.2) and the remark made above, there is an extraneous σ-polygonal flow p such that $\partial p = -\partial g$. Thus $g + p$ is, in our new space, a closed, generalized flow, and g is its restriction to A. By (i) and (89.3), $g + p$ is a mixture of unit streams, and g is the mixture of their restrictions to A.

Now each of these unit streams has a representation of the type (67.1), and the restriction to A is simply obtained by restricting the parameter t to the closed set for which the relevant moving point $\hat{x}(t)$ lies in x-space. This restriction is thus an intermittent stream, so that (iii) is established.

To prove (ii) we proceed similarly, but we combine the argument with induction. We suppose known that when g is a generalized flow whose boundary coincides with that of a mixture of $\leq N - 1$ segments, we can express g as a mixture of streams of lengths ≤ 1. This is true by (i) for $N = 1$. From this inductive hypothesis, we have to derive a corresponding statement with $N - 1$ replaced by N. We shall do this by adding to g a polygonal flow p consisting of a positive real multiple of an extraneous broken line L. We denote by $\hat{L}$ the subset of $\hat{A}$, for which $\hat{x}$ and the direction at $\hat{x}$ are along L. We choose p so that $g + p$ has the same boundary as a mixture of $\leq N - 1$ segments. Then

$$g + p = \int \hat{g}_\alpha \, d\mu$$

where each $\hat{g}_\alpha$ is a stream of length ≤ 1. Further, by (89.3), since $g + p$ has support in $A \cup \hat{L}$, we can arrange that each $\hat{g}_\alpha$ has support in this set. Moreover, since g is the restriction of $g + p$ to A, it is the mixture of the restrictions of the $\hat{g}_\alpha$ to A. By making use again of the representation of our stream $\hat{g}_\alpha$ in Theorem (61.1), the restriction is found to result from removing at most two arcs of L. Thus (ii) is established.

Lectures on the Calculus of Variations and Optimal Control Theory

---

Volume II

OPTIMAL CONTROL THEORY

Preamble

THE NATURE OF CONTROL PROBLEMS

§1. INTRODUCTION

We now make a fresh start. Volume I is best forgotten for the time being while we look around. In taking up a new topic, one should not be above using quite primitive methods at first. In the same way, one who visits a new country need not arrive with an army of bulldozers, and a student who embarks on a thesis must be prepared to try out a number of conjectures and to test them with the most elementary of computations. This is not yet the time to look for applications of the Hahn-Banach theorem, and we must expect a certain amount of discomfort.

Thus it is that engineers and others had been studying optimal control for quite a few years before they realized that it is part of the calculus of variations. However, they brought to its study one very important change of outlook: unhampered by tradition, they no longer laid down artificial assumptions of smoothness.

The problems of optimal control are, in fact, more general than those we studied in Volume I. Of course, the methods which we made available in the later Chapters and Appendices of Volume I apply to much more general problems than those we discussed there. For instance, the existence theory based on generalized curves was developed by the author for a problem of the form

$$\Phi\left(\int f(x, \dot{x})\, dt\right) = \min$$

where f is a function with values in a Banach space, and Φ is a real-valued function in that space. The variables x, $\dot{x}$ are as in the problems of Volume I. In the literature, one finds also problems in which the integral to be minimized is replaced by those of the following types:

$$\iint f\big(t, u, x(t), \dot{x}(t), x(u), \dot{x}(u)\big)\, dt\, du,$$

$$\int f\big(t, x(t), \dot{x}(t), x^*(t)\big)\, dt;$$

the problems they lead to are known as those of Fubini-Tonelli and Cesari-Sanchez.

Optimal control problems arise in a different manner, which involves a more fundamental change. They are problems with side-conditions. Such problems are as old as the calculus of variations itself. They originate with the legend of the foundation of Carthage.

We all know the story of Dido, who was granted as much land as she could surround with the hide of an ox. Never underestimate the power of a woman! After very carefully cutting the hide into an extremely long, thin string, she determined the largest stretch of ground that she could surround with it. In so doing, she solved a so-called isoperimetric problem; its solution was, of course, a circular disc. So much for the myth that women can't do mathematics!

An isoperimetric problem is one in which we seek the minimum of one variational integral (or in Dido's case, the maximum), in the class of curves for which another such integral (the length in her case) has a prescribed value. Alternatively, we can stipulate that the value of the second integral is not to exceed the prescribed value, and this is usually the form in which (as in Dido's case) the problem occurs in practice.

Isoperimetric problems are treated in detail in Tonelli's *Fondamenti*, and were carefully studied by Euler, who formulated what is known as Euler's isoperimetrical rule.

Problems of minima with side-conditions, or constraints, include also a classical problem of Lagrange. This concerns the minimum of

$$\int L(t, x, \dot{x})\, dt$$

in a class of admissible curves $x(t)$ which satisfy a differential equation

$$\Phi(t, x, \dot{x}) = 0. \tag{1.1}$$

More generally, we may have several differential equations as constraints, or, what comes to the same, Φ can be vector-valued. We can also throw in an isoperimetric constraint whereby

$$\int \Psi(t, x, \dot{x})\, dt \tag{1.2}$$

has a prescribed value. This general problem was considered by Lagrange. In practice, just as in the isoperimetric case, one has to consider also the case where some of the above equality-constraints are replaced by inequalities.

§2. THE MULTIPLIER RULE

For his problem Lagrange introduced a method of multipliers, by which he thought to have reduced it to a problem without constraints. The Lagrange multipliers are the analogues of those he had introduced in the corresponding ordinary problem of constrained maxima and minima in the differential calculus.

Lagrange simply observed, first, that for curves which satisfy the constraints, the problem of minimum with the Lagrangian L is equivalent to the one with any Lagrangian of the form

$$L + \lambda\Phi + \kappa(\Psi - \dot{\psi}) \tag{2.1}$$

where κ is a constant, and λ, ψ are functions of t, and where ψ has prescribed end-values and 0 as initial value. The values of κ, λ, ψ will be appropriate vectors when

Φ, Ψ are vector-valued, and in that case the relevant products are scalar products of vectors. The new Lagrangian, given by (2.1), can be regarded as a function

$$\tilde{L}(t, x, \dot{x};\ \kappa, \lambda, \dot{\psi}) \tag{2.2}$$

and we can consider the more general problem of minimum for the corresponding variational integral in the space enlarged by the new variables, and with the additional constraint

$$\dot{\kappa} = 0. \tag{2.3}$$

In this new problem, however, if we ignore the constraints, Lagrange observes that the Euler equations are

$$\begin{cases} \dfrac{d}{dt}(\tilde{L}_{\dot{x}}) = \tilde{L}_{x} \\ \dfrac{d}{dt}(\tilde{L}_{\dot{\kappa}}) = \tilde{L}_{\kappa} \\ \dfrac{d}{dt}(\tilde{L}_{\dot{\lambda}}) = \tilde{L}_{\lambda} \\ \dfrac{d}{dt}(\tilde{L}_{\dot{\psi}}) = \tilde{L}_{\psi} \end{cases} \tag{2.4}$$

and that the last three clearly reduce to

$$\dot{\psi} = \Psi,$$

together with (1.1) and (2.3). According to him, the whole problem with the original constraints is thus reduced to that of the minimum, without constraints of the new variational integral, for the appropriate end-value of ψ, since the Euler equations for this problem include the constraint equations.

It goes against the grain to find fault with an argument at once so beautiful and so simple. However, this is no excuse for its reappearance, every so often, in so-called accounts and introductions that claim to present the calculus of variations to engineers or other supposedly uncritical persons. In fact, as stated, the conclusion is wrong, and even Lagrange's rather simple-minded contemporaries had doubts about it. Nevertheless, it can be put right by a rather slight modification, which Lagrange's argument could not possibly account for.

A superficial analysis shows that the argument contains a number of fallacies and confusions. In the first place, it runs counter to Perron's paradox, and it makes no proper distinction between necessary and sufficient. In the second place, there is a basic and quite unjustified assumption either that the new quantities introduced are smooth, or that this does not matter.

If we go into any sort of detail, the argument looks even worse. Thus, if we start from a curve $x(t)$ that provides a minimum subject to the constraints, the argument does not ensure that it can be regarded as the projection in (t, x)-space of a curve in the enlarged space of $(t, x, \kappa, \lambda, \psi)$, which provides a minimum for the new problem. What it asserts is the converse: if this new minimum is attained by a curve in the enlarged space, then the projection provides a minimum in the original problem with the constraints, and certain equations are satisfied. However, this projection may be a different curve from $x(t)$, and its existence depends on the additional hypothesis that the new problem without constraints does have a solution. This last does not follow from any known theorem, and indeed, since the initial and final values of λ are not prescribed, we have here the phenomenon to which we drew attention in the Preamble of Volume I, by which a curve that starts from a line, instead of from a definite point of that line, should be allowed to oscillate infinitely near the line, and to have no initial point. This means that any existence

theorem for the new problem without constraints would have to bring in generalized solutions, stretching to infinity, as in Chapter V, Section 55(d), of Volume I. No such automatic existence theorem has been established.

Nowadays, mathematicians still come up with simple and beautiful theorems. However, many of them never get published.

§3. OPTIMAL CONTROL AND THE LAGRANGE PROBLEM

If we exclude isoperimetric constraints, the Lagrange problem concerns a minimum in the class of curves which satisfy the differential equation

$$\Phi(t, x, \dot{x}) = 0. \tag{3.1}$$

Here Φ is a vector of a certain dimension m, or, in particular, a scalar if $m = 1$. The equation (3.1) thus represents a certain locus, or variety, in the space of $(t, x, \dot{x})$. We shall consider it for constant (t, x) as a variety in $\dot{x}$, and we denote the latter by $\mathscr{M}$.

Today, no one defines a variety $\mathscr{M}$ by an equation such as (3.1). One objection to this type of definition is that the structure and the dimension of $\mathscr{M}$ are not derivable from Φ in any simple manner. Thus, one would like to say that the dimension of $\mathscr{M}$ is $n - m$. However, the equation (3.1) is equivalent to $|\Phi| = 0$, in which case m is replaced by unity. The sensible thing is to define $\mathscr{M}$, at least locally, by solving (3.1) in terms of certain of the components of the vector $\dot{x}$. A more symmetrical procedure is, however, just as satisfactory, if not more so, and it is universally employed today. It consists in representing $\mathscr{M}$ parametrically in terms of a parameter u. Here u is in general a vector, and varies in a certain set U. The variety $\mathscr{M}$ is then given by

$$\dot{x} = \varphi(t, x, u). \tag{3.2}$$

Thus the modern form of the Lagrange problem is the search for the minimum of the variational integral for curves $x(t)$ and parameters $u(t)$ which satisfy (3.2). In the Lagrangian $L(t, x, \dot{x})$ it is convenient to substitute for $\dot{x}$ in terms of (t, x, u) from (3.2). We shall allow ourselves to write the resulting function simply $L(t, x, u)$, discarding our original notation.

The new form of Lagrange's problem is thus that of the minimum of

$$\int L(t, x, u)\, dt$$

for curves $x(t)$ and parameters $u(t)$ subject to (3.2). This is the basic problem of control theory.

The parameter u, or its components considered as scalar parameters, are termed control parameters, or simply controls. The engineer thinks of them as controls on appropriate dials, while the mathematician regards them as parameters. Of course, the variety $\mathscr{M}$ can be represented in terms of a new parameter v by setting $u = u(v)$ where the map $u(v)$ is one-to-one. This corresponds to providing a new set of dials v, which are used to control the original dials u, as in regulating a television set without getting up from one's arm chair.

We see that there is no real difference between the Lagrange problem and optimal control; the latter is simply a more up-to-date formulation. Apparent minor differences are sometimes pointed out, but they are really quite insignificant. For instance, it is noted that the control u is restricted to a set U, and that this set is normally defined, not by an equation, but by inequalities; however the zeros of the function Φ can very well occupy whole domains. Again $L(t, x, u)$ may seem more general than we get by substitution for $\dot{x}$ in a corresponding Lagrangian in $(t, x, \dot{x})$, but it is also a special case when the whole problem is viewed in space of (t, x, u) instead of (t, x). Finally, there are possible differences in the smoothness required of our various functions in the two problems; however, these are only temporary, since we have by now learned that in variational problems the original setting must be modified in accordance with the needs of an existence theory.

At any rate, it is clear that in studying optimal control we can benefit from the experience others have gained the hard way in studying the Lagrange problem.

§4. THE SAD FACTS OF LIFE

We have already seen something of the morass of "plausible" reasoning into which we might have been drawn. Therefore, we had best take stock of the kind of difficulties that have to be reckoned with, before we attempt to tackle them. We shall illustrate these difficulties.

a. Rigidity. We take, in three dimensions, the x_2-axis vertical, and the axes of t, x_1 horizontal. We consider, through a point P, the curves $x_1(t)$, $x_2(t)$ with piecewise continuous tangent, which satisfy

$$\dot{x}_2 = \sqrt{1 + \dot{x}_1^2}. \tag{4.1}$$

For fixed P, any such curve is clearly determined as soon as we know its projection in the (t, x_1)-plane. Moreover, the difference of its x_2-coordinates at the two extremities coincides with the length of the projection. Hence, if we choose the projection to be a segment, we obtain a curve subject to (4.1), for which the second extremity Q cannot be joined to P by any other curve, subject to (4.1).

The above example, which we take from Carathéodory, illustrates a very disturbing state of affairs, which we term rigidity. The classical Euler-Lagrange algorithm, which we discussed in Volume I, in the Preamble and elsewhere, and the very name of the calculus of variations, depend on our being able to "vary" our curves; this we cannot do here while P, Q are fixed.

b. ANOMALY. Let $x(t)$ $t_1 \leq t \leq t_2$ satisfy (3.1), and let P, Q denote the extremities $(t_1, x(t_1))$, $(t_2, x(t_2))$. A pair of vectors δP, δQ is termed a permissible variation of the extremities P, Q if it consists of the derivatives for $\alpha = 0$ of a point-pair $P(\alpha)$, $Q(\alpha)$ that are extremities of curves $x(t, \alpha)$ $t_1(\alpha) \leq t \leq t_2(\alpha)$, where α is a real parameter whose range includes $\alpha = 0$ in its interior, and where these curves satisfy the following two conditions: (i) they are solutions of (3.1), and (ii) they reduce smoothly to $x(t)$ $t_1 \leq t \leq t_2$ for $\alpha = 0$. The solution $x(t)$ $t_1 \leq t \leq t_2$ is then termed abnormal (or anomalous) if there do not exist $2n$ linearly independent permissible variations δP, δQ of its extremities. Historically, the possibility of such an anomaly proved extremely inconvenient in attempts to justify the multiplier rule. It is easy to see that the example discussed in (a) has this unpleasant peculiarity.

c. LACK OF DESIRABLE CLOSURE PROPERTIES. The same example will now be made into a control problem. We consider, for $-1 \leq u \leq 1$, the differential equations

(4.2)
$$\dot{x}_1 = u, \qquad \dot{x}_2 = \sqrt{1 + u^2}.$$

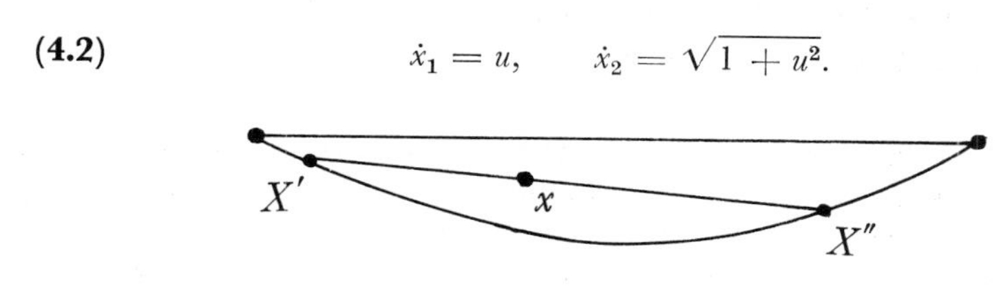

$\mathscr{H}$ and its convex hull

In the $(\dot{x}_1, \dot{x}_2)$-plane, these equations define an arc of hyperbola $\mathscr{H}$. We shall term

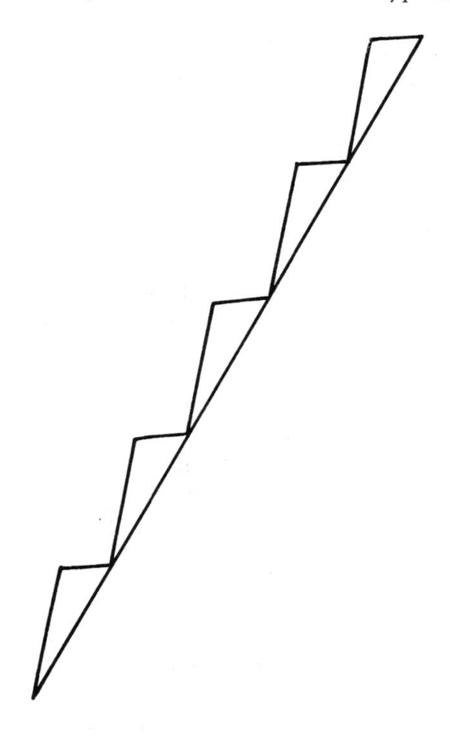

trajectory a curve $x(t)$, now nonparametric, in space of $(t, x) = (t, x_1, x_2)$, which is (say) continuous and piecewise continuously differentiable, and for which the derivative $\dot{x} = (\dot{x}_1, \dot{x}_2)$ lies in $\mathscr{H}$ for each relevant t.

For such trajectories, an optimal control problem would concern the minimum of some integral subject to suitable initial and final conditions on the $x(t)$. We shall see, however, that the set of curves in which such a minimum is sought is by no means closed; according to Volume I, Chapter V, Section 55(a), this problem does not really make sense. To this effect, consider in (t, x)-space a curve $x_0(t)$, which reduces to a segment and is given by a linear function, such that the derivative $\dot{x}_0$ lies, not in $\mathscr{H}$, but at some other position X in the convex hull of $\mathscr{H}$. Thus $\dot{x}_0$ has the form $\alpha X' + (1 - \alpha)X''$, where $0 < \alpha < 1$, and where X', X'' lie on $\mathscr{H}$. We can now approximate uniformly to $x_0(t)$ by a piecewise linear function, represented by a zigzag in the figure, for which the slope is alternately X' and X'', in portions of our t-interval, whose lengths are in the ratio $\alpha:(1 - \alpha)$.

§5. A FIRST REVISION OF THE EULER EQUATION AND OF THE MULTIPLIER RULE

More than a hundred years of efforts went into attempts to salvage Lagrange's faulty argument. Its main object was to establish for a minimizing curve the equations (2.4), and in this regard the second of these merely fixes $\dot{\psi}$, while the last two reduce to (2.1) and (2.3); we can ignore them if κ is to be constant and the given curve is to satisfy (1.1). In that case, we can remove the term in $\dot{\psi}$ and write simply

$$\tilde{L}(t, x, \dot{x}, \kappa, \lambda) = L + \lambda\Phi + \kappa\Psi, \tag{5.1}$$

and the main assertion is that $x(t)$ satisfies, for some constant (vector) κ and some (vector-valued) function $\lambda(t)$, the Euler equation

$$\frac{d}{dt}(\tilde{L}_{\dot{x}}) - \tilde{L}_x = 0. \tag{5.2}$$

Unfortunately this assertion is false.

We can see this very simply by considering the example (a) of the preceding section. There, only one curve satisfying (1.1) joints the two given points; this curve certainly provides a minimum, since it is the only curve in the relevant class. Therefore to assert that it must satisfy, for an arbitrary L, equations such as (5.2) is clearly absurd.

The fact that in a set with only one member the minimum is automatically assumed for this member reminds one of a regrettable episode in the career of an efficiency expert. On being consulted by a big business firm, he collected material on the efficiency of the employees in the various departments, and made a list in which, for each department, he named the least efficient employee. In a few cases this was difficult to decide, and the name on his list was finally determined by tossing a coin. He then submitted his list to the head of the firm, and, on his advice, all those on the list were fired. It so happened that in one department there was an employee so capable and so hard working that he managed to do, extremely well, all the work of the department himself, with the aid of the usual mechanical devices. He, of course, was fired automatically, as a result of the efficiency expert's visit, and the whole firm collapsed when he had left.

In the example, which shattered Lagrange's assertion, we had

$$\Phi = \dot{x}_2 - \sqrt{1 + \dot{x}_1^2}, \qquad \Phi_{x_1} = \Phi_{x_2} = 0, \qquad \Phi_{\dot{x}_2} = 1$$

and

$$\Phi_{\dot{x}_1} = \frac{-\dot{x}_1}{\sqrt{1 + \dot{x}_1^2}}$$

Thus our curve, with a segment as its projection in the (t, x_1) plane, does satisfy a Euler equation, namely the one, not for L, but for Φ, the equation

$$\frac{d}{dt}(\Phi_{\dot{x}}) = \Phi_x.$$

On the basis of such examples, it was suggested that the Euler equation (5.2) be modified by setting, in place of (5.1),

(5.3) $$\tilde{L}(t, x, \dot{x}, \kappa_0, \kappa, \lambda) = \kappa_0 L + \lambda\Phi + \kappa\Psi,$$

where κ_0 is a further real constant, and where, in (5.2), we now add the stipulation that $\kappa_0, \kappa, \lambda$ do not vanish simultaneously. We shall term this the revised form of the Euler equation (5.2), and of the Lagrange multiplier rule.

In the case of optimal control, we are concerned with pairs $x(t), u(t)$ which satisfy (3.2) and the inclusion $u \in U$. The function $\tilde{L}$ of (5.3) is then

$$\kappa_0 L(t, x, u) + \lambda(x - \varphi(t, x, u)),$$

and the Euler equation in x becomes

(5.4) $$\dot{\lambda} = \kappa_0 L_x - \lambda\varphi_x.$$

The corresponding equation in u is not usually relevant, and must actually be changed to an inequality unless u happens to be an interior point of U. Of this we shall hear more in due course. As regards (5.4), we shall meet this differential equation again, and it is as well to know where it comes from, since writers on optimal control are apt to introduce it without explanation.

However, to return to the suggested modified form of $\tilde{L}$ given in (5.3) above, it may seem something of an anticlimax that so much fuss and a hundred years of research should in the end perhaps amount to no more than this little insertion of a constant κ_0, and all because of the disturbing effect of a rather rare phenomenon of rigidity, or anomaly. If the reader feels this, he is quite right, for in fact, although proofs of the necessity of the revised form of the Euler equation were finally obtained, all this was wasted effort, and had to be done over again in a different way, in order to obtain a stronger result.

And then, when all is said and done, it falls apart once more, like a house of cards; there is no substance in it as long as we have no existence theory. All this time we have been occupied with an error that was no more than a red herring, when without an existence theory, according to Perron's paradox, it is quite senseless to speak of necessary conditions.

What is here so serious is not the rare phenomenon of rigidity or anomaly, but the almost universal one of lack of desirable closure properties. Indeed, if we re-examine example (c) of Section 4, we find that this unfortunate state of affairs is not tied to any special example, but results simply from the nonlinearity of the constraining equations (4.2).

If and when we overcome this basic difficulty, it will be time enough to go into the proofs of so-called necessary conditions. For the present, even if we go through their proofs, we cannot use them except to motivate guesses, and for such guesses the proofs are superfluous.

§6. THE WEIERSTRASS CONDITION, TRANSVERSALITY, HAMILTONIANS AND A STRONG REVISED EULER RECIPE

Ignoring isoperimetric constraints, we have now

(6.1) $$\tilde{L}(t, x, \dot{x}, \kappa_0, \lambda) = \kappa_0 L + \lambda\Phi,$$

where we shall stipulate further that the constant κ_0 be non-negative, and that when it vanishes, the vector λ does not. The expression $\tilde{L}$ may at times be written $\tilde{L}(\dot{x})$, if we wish to vary only $\dot{x}$. Thus, for fixed t, x, κ_0, λ, we write

$$\tilde{\mathscr{E}}(\bar{\dot{x}}, \dot{x}) = \tilde{L}(\bar{\dot{x}}) - \tilde{L}(\dot{x}) - (\bar{\dot{x}} - \dot{x})\tilde{L}_{\dot{x}};$$

this is now the Weierstrass excess function $\tilde{\mathscr{E}}$, or in full:

$$\tilde{\mathscr{E}}(t, x, \bar{\dot{x}}, \dot{x}, \kappa_0, \lambda),$$

and in it $\bar{\dot{x}}$, $\dot{x}$ will always be understood to be subject to the relations

$$\Phi(t, x, \dot{x}) = \Phi(t, x, \dot{x}) = 0.$$

A line element $(t, x, \dot{x})$ complete with multipliers κ_0, λ and subject to the constraint will be termed strong if $\tilde{\mathscr{E}}(\bar{\dot{x}}, \dot{x}) \geq 0$ for all $\bar{\dot{x}}$ subject also to the constraint. This is the Weierstrass condition.

We shall understand by an extremal, a solution of the Euler equation

$$\frac{d}{dt}\tilde{L}_{\dot{x}} = \tilde{L}_x,$$

and of the constraining differential equation (3.1) It will be understood that an extremal is thus associated with a definite corresponding multiplier pair $\kappa_0, \lambda(t)$, the former of which κ_0 is constant. We term it strong if its line elements $(t, x(t), \dot{x}(t))$ complete with this multiplier pair are strong.

Finally, if P, Q are the extremities, and η_P, η_Q denote the values at P, Q of the "momentum" vector η with $n + 1$ components, given by the scalar $\tilde{L} - \dot{x}\tilde{L}_{\dot{x}}$ and the vector $\tilde{L}_{\dot{x}}$, again for the corresponding multiplier pair, we say that the extremal satisfies the transversality condition, for a problem in which there are end-conditions, if for all permissible variations $\delta P, \delta Q$ of P, Q, we have (by analogy with Section 9 of the Preamble to Volume I)

$$\eta_P\,\delta P - \eta_Q\,\delta Q = 0.$$

This being so, we now formulate the following analogue of the Euler recipe used in the Preamble to Volume I: In a problem of minimum subject to the constraint (3.1), look for the solutions among the strong extremals which satisfy the transversality condition.†

† A slightly stronger transversality condition will be given in the form of Pontrjagin's maximum principle established at the end of Chapter III.

We shall term this the strong revised Euler recipe. The fact that we now lay down rather more conditions in it is helpful in narrowing down the suspected solutions, though, of course, the real work starts after that.

For the reasons explained in the preceding section, and very abundantly in Volume I, the recipe requires no proof. When we use it, we must verify that the extremals it leads us to do have the property of minimum; no proof of any so-called necessity can allow us to dispense with this all-important verification. This is only permissible if, as in Volume I, and in spite of the seemingly insuperable difficulties listed in Section 4, we succeed in developing a suitable sufficiency theory in a later Chapter.

For fixed (t, x), let E be the set of pairs z_0, z subject to

$$\textbf{(6.2)} \qquad \Phi(t, x, z) = 0, \qquad L(t, x, z) = z_0,$$

and let E_0 be the subset for which the matrix of the partial derivatives in z of the vector-valued function Φ has maximal rank. Further, we suppose that our problem of minimum with constraints is nonparametric. We term true Hamiltonian of the problem the quantity

$$\textbf{(6.3)} \qquad \mathscr{H}(t, x, y, y_0) = \operatorname*{Sup}_{(z_0, z) \in E} y_0 z_0 + yz,$$

where y is an n-dimensional vector, and y_0 a scalar subject to $y_0 \leq 0$. If we set $y_0 = -1$ and omit the constraint $\Phi = 0$ from (6.2), we find that $\mathscr{H}$ reduces to the nonparametric Hamiltonian (in the large), defined in the spirit of Young's inequality, in Volume I, Chapter IV, Section 46. Instead of this true Hamiltonian, various local Hamiltonians occur in the past literature on the Lagrange problem. However, they are, as we shall see, somewhat misleading, and we discuss them in the next section.

In what follows, if $(t, x, \dot{x})$ is a line element, we shall write, for short, $l_0 = L(t, x, \dot{x})$. The line element will be termed nonsingular if $(l_0, \dot{x}) \in E_0$. Its completion by multipliers κ_0, λ will mean the completed line element with these multipliers.

The quartet (t, x, y, y_0) of arguments of $\mathscr{H}$ will be called a strong canonical point through the nonsingular line element $(t, x, \dot{x})$ if the maximum in (6.3) is attained for the pair $(l_0, \dot{x}) \in E_0$; for fixed (t, x) we then term (y, y_0) a conjugate slope to $\dot{x}$. This means that in (z_0, z)-space, the set E has, at the point $(l_0, \dot{x})$ of its subset E_0, a landing hyperplane, given by $y_0 z_0 + yz = \mathscr{H}$. The latter is then, of course, also a tangent hyperplane at this point; it thus belongs to the linear family of such hyperplanes, and these are tangent at $(l_0, \dot{x})$ to the various hypersurfaces of (z_0, z)-space of the form:

$$\kappa_0 L + \lambda \Phi = \kappa_0 z_0.$$

This is how the Lagrange multipliers really arise, and not by any hocus-pocus. We can now choose the multipliers so as to identify coefficients, taking account of sign requirements for y_0, κ_0. We find

$$\textbf{(6.4)} \qquad y_0 = -\kappa_0, \qquad y = \tilde{L}_{\dot{x}}(t, x, \dot{x}, \kappa_0, \lambda).$$

From this we derive:

(6.5) Canonical Form of the Weierstrass Condition. *In order that* (t, x, y, y_0) *be a strong canonical point through the nonsingular line element* $(t, x, \dot{x})$, *it is necessary and sufficient that some strong completion* $(t, x, \dot{x}, \kappa_0, \lambda)$ *satisfy* (6.4).

To see this, it is sufficient to observe that, if (6.4) holds, and we set $\mathscr{H} = y_0 l_0 + y\dot{x}$, we have the identity

$$\tilde{\mathscr{E}}(z, \dot{x}) = \mathscr{H} - y_0 z_0 - yz.$$

In practice, this means that the Weierstrass condition can be verified in terms of our Hamiltonian. The same is true of the transversality condition, since the momentum vector corresponding to $\tilde{L}$ is y, $\mathscr{H}$ when (6.4) holds. A canonical form for the Euler equation and a restatement of everything in terms of optimal control are still missing. It is desirable to go into these formal matters before tackling any concrete problem, in case they should help to reduce our work.

§7. THE CLASSICAL CONSTRAINED HAMILTONIANS

As in the unconstrained case, only local definitions occur in the literature. In the parametric case, they should be compared with a parametric true Hamiltonian, and it is convenient to define the latter for a positive definite $L(x, \dot{x})$ and for a constraint $\Phi(x, \dot{x}) = 0$; here L, Φ are positively homogeneous in $\dot{x}$. In this case, we need no auxiliary scalar y_0, and we define

$$\mathscr{H}(x, y) = \operatorname*{Sup}_{z} yz,$$

where the supremum is for vectors z subject to the relations $L(x, z) = 1$, $\Phi(x, z) = 0$.

We shall begin with a simple example, which is the parametric counterpart of (4.1) and (4.2) in Section 4. We set $x = (x_0, x_1, x_2)$, and we consider the minimum of the length integral $\int |\dot{x}|\, dt$ subject to the constraint

(7.1) $$\dot{x}_2^2 = \dot{x}_0^2 + \dot{x}_1^2.$$

The indicatrix, i.e., the set of $\dot{x}$ for which $L = 1$, $\Phi = 0$, is here a pair of circles, in which the unit sphere of $\dot{x}$ meets the cone (7.1). Its convex hull is the solid piece of cylinder between the two circles. The figuratrix, i.e., the frontier of the dual convex figure, consists of two symmetric portions of right circular cones, stuck

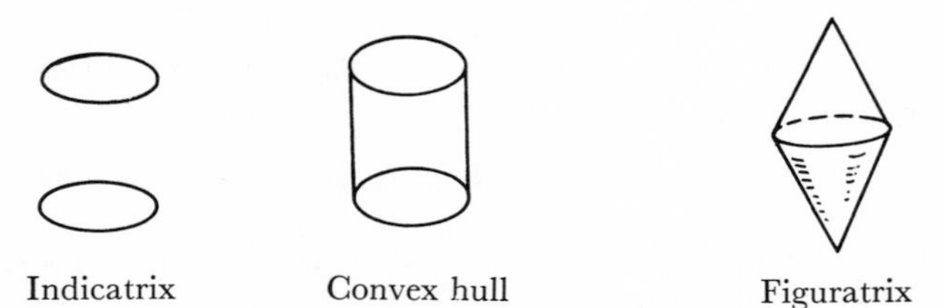

together. The two vertices correspond to the two bounding circular discs of the cylindrical figure, and the circle of intersection of the two portions of cones corresponds to the cylindrical boundary. All other points of the figuratrix correspond to the two circular rims. This is the standard way in which dual convex figures correspond to one another when there are edges, plane faces and so on.

Our parametric Hamiltonian $\mathscr{H}$ agrees with the one obtained in Volume I, Chapter IV, in Sections 44 and 46 if L is replaced by $+\infty$ for forbidden values of $\dot{x}$.

It is thus the function of distance of the dual convex figure. Since it equals unity on the figuratrix, and is first order homogeneous, we deduce, by a simple calculation, that

$$\mathscr{H}(y) = \frac{1}{\sqrt{2}}\{\sqrt{y_0^2 + y_1^2} + |y_2|\}.$$

This is the same as we would have found for the unconstrained problem, in which L has as indicatrix the frontier of the convex hull of our pair of circles. The Hamiltonian is smooth except for values of y which lie on the y_2-axis, or in the (y_0, y_1)-plane. A local definition would exclude such y, which are just the values which are important in constructing the figuratrix, as the convex hull of the two vertices and of the circular edge. For this reason, local definitions are apt to give a false impression of smoothness which is really quite irrelevant.

In order to introduce these classical local definitions, we must go back to the classical geometrical interpretation of duality. We shall revert to the nonparametric case, which is what really concerns us here. We shall ignore isoperimetric constraints, set $\kappa_0 = 1, y_0 = -1$ when relevant, and suppress the variables (t, x). We term Φ-locus the set of z for which $\Phi(z) = 0$. We have then to make the classical Legendre transformation on the restriction of the function $L(z)$ to the Φ-locus.

To this effect, we must determine the linear functions tangent to this restriction, i.e., the hyperplanes tangent to its graph. This is a singular case of duality, and dimension is by no means preserved. The graph in question perhaps has "few points," but it still has many tangent hyperplanes according to the classical point of view: for instance, for a locus consisting of a single point, all hyperplanes through it are considered tangent. Thus it is that, as in the discussion of the preceding section, leading up to (6.4), we regard as tangent hyperplanes at a particular point $z = \dot{x}$ of our graph all the hyperplanes through it which contain every tangent line at that point. These hyperplanes are those tangent to graphs of functions of the form $L(z) + \lambda\Phi(z)$. (Strictly, we should write here $\kappa_0 L$, rather than L, but we agreed to set $\kappa_0 = 1$; this amounts to allowing, as geometers do, λ to have "infinities.")

To get our Hamiltonian, we must now reinterpret these hyperplanes, or rather the linear functions whose graphs they are, as points of the dual space. We obtain a dual locus consisting of these points, and we have to express it locally as the graph of $\mathscr{H}$. The singular nature of the transformation does not affect the dimension of the dual locus. However, it still leaves a trace: the dual locus is a ruled hypersurface; it has on it line segments, and indeed linear varieties of the same dimension as the vector Φ. This is because hyperplanes through a same $(n - k)$-dimensional tangent subspace transform into points on a same k-dimensional linear variety.

So far this is only a local version of what we did in the preceding section, in the large. It leads locally to the equations we obtained in (6.4), and no further. The big question is still how to express the Euler equation in this Hamiltonian setting, and how to recover the values of the Lagrange multiplier λ, which, after all, can be interpreted in physical problems as a reaction-force. This last is the clue to the answer, and the classical analysts and geometers came up with the following solution: instead of the given constraint $\Phi = 0$, we consider the family $\Phi = c$ for constant values of c; together with the relevant quantities and equations for $c = 0$, we can then consider also their derivatives in c. The idea is the classical form of what we have called the conceptual method: where we look for a solution in terms of new concepts, classical analysts would look for one in terms of additional variables.

We pass on to the analytical details. We limit ourselves to a $(t, x, \dot{x}, \lambda)$-neighborhood of a line element $(t_0, x_0, \dot{x}_0)$ accompanied or completed by a value λ_0 of the multiplier. We consider in it the family of Lagrangians

$$\hat{L}(t, x, \dot{x}, \lambda) = L(t, x, \dot{x}) + \lambda\Phi(t, x, \dot{x}),$$

and we assume that the bordered matrix

$$\text{(7.2)} \qquad \begin{pmatrix} \hat{L}_{\dot{x}\dot{x}} & , & \Phi_{\dot{x}} \\ \Phi_{\dot{x}} & , & 0 \end{pmatrix}$$

is nonsingular. Of course, we assume, as is implied in the assumption just made, that the dimension of the vector Φ is $<n$. However, its main object is to exclude cases in which, because of some undue linearity (say), certain equations do not have unique solutions locally.

To our family of Lagrangians $\hat{L}$, which depend on the parameter λ, we shall associate a corresponding family of Hamiltonians $\hat{\mathscr{H}}$, depending on the parameter c. For this purpose, we introduce variables y, c by setting

$$\text{(7.3)} \qquad y = \hat{L}_{\dot{x}}(\dot{x}, \lambda), \qquad c = \Phi(\dot{x}).$$

We shall allow ourselves to write y_0 for the value of y, given by the former of these relations, when the completed line element is the given one $(t_0, x_0, \dot{x}_0, \lambda_0)$. We do this temporarily, while the symbol is free. The initial value of c is, of course, 0. Near $(t_0, x_0, y_0, 0)$ we have then local solutions of (7.3), of the form

$$\dot{x} = \xi(t, x, y, c), \qquad \lambda = \eta(t, x, y, c),$$

since the matrix (7.2) is nonsingular. We define

$$\text{(7.4)} \qquad \hat{\mathscr{H}}(t, x, y, c) = y\xi + c\eta - \hat{L}(t, x, \xi, \eta).$$

The second equation (7.3) may now be written $c = \partial\hat{L}/\partial\lambda$, so that all this is similar to the theory of local Hamiltonians of Volume I, Chapter II, Section 22. It is just a matter of renaming variables. The calculations made there show that, subject to (7.3),

$$\text{(7.5)} \qquad \hat{\mathscr{H}}_t + \hat{L}_t = \hat{\mathscr{H}}_x + \hat{L}_x = 0, \qquad \hat{\mathscr{H}}_y = \dot{x}, \qquad \hat{\mathscr{H}}_c = \lambda.$$

The definition (7.4) is the most convenient for $\hat{\mathscr{H}}$. It could, however, be written more shortly $y\xi - L(t, x, \xi)$, since the terms in η cancel. From the family $\hat{\mathscr{H}}$, we now derive $\mathscr{H}$ by setting $c = 0$, and we shall allow ourselves to write $\mathscr{H}_c$ for $\hat{\mathscr{H}}_c$ when $c = 0$. Since $\mathscr{H}_c$ is thus the value of λ from (7.5), we can now substitute it for the function η, while ξ is, of course, $\mathscr{H}_y$. What these calculations do not indicate is that the graph of $\mathscr{H}$ contains linear subvarieties in the variables y; however, we may note that the matrix $\mathscr{H}_{yy}$ is singular, and of rank complementary to the dimension of Φ. To see this, we remark that since ξ is $\mathscr{H}_y$, we have

$$\Phi(t, x, \mathscr{H}_y) = 0,$$

and by partial differentiation in y it follows that

$$\Phi_{\dot{x}}\mathscr{H}_{yy} = 0 \quad \text{when} \quad \dot{x} = \mathscr{H}_y.$$

Here the rank of $\Phi_{\dot{x}}$ is the dimension of Φ, since (7.2) is nonsingular; the rank of $\mathscr{H}_{yy}$ is thus at most the complementary dimension. It cannot be less than this, because, as at the end of Section 22 in Volume I of Chapter II, the identity matrix is the product of (7.2) and a certain bordered matrix containing $\mathscr{H}_{yy}$.

All this easily extends to the case in which κ_0, κ are present. The family of Lagrangians is then

$$\tilde{L}(t, x, \dot{x}, \kappa_0, \kappa, \lambda) = \kappa_0 L + \lambda\Phi + \kappa\Psi.$$

In the corresponding family of Hamiltonians

$$\tilde{\mathscr{H}}(t, x, y, c, -\kappa, -\kappa_0),$$

to be associated with it, we retain, for simplicity of notation, the parameters κ, κ_0, instead of changing their signs and calling them by different letters.

We replace $\hat{L}$ by $\tilde{L}$ in the matrix (7.2) and in the equations (7.3). The solutions of (7.3) then give $\dot{x}$, λ as functions of $(t, x, y, c, -\kappa, -\kappa_0)$ which we again denote by ξ, η. We now add additional variables ψ, ψ_0 subject to

$$\textbf{(7.6)} \qquad \dot{\psi} = \Psi(t, x, \dot{x}), \qquad \dot{\psi}_0 = \tilde{L}(t, x, \dot{x}),$$

and by substituting for $\dot{x}$ the function ξ, these give $\dot{\psi}$, $\dot{\psi}_0$ as functions ω, ω_0 of $(t, x, y, c, -\kappa, -\kappa_0)$. We then define, as functions of these variables,

$$\tilde{\mathscr{H}} = y\xi + (-\kappa)\omega + (-\kappa_0)\omega_0.$$

As before, we write $\mathscr{H}$, $\mathscr{H}_c$ for $\tilde{\mathscr{H}}$, $\tilde{\mathscr{H}}_c$ when $c = 0$. We could, of course, have proceeded exactly as before by adding parameters e, e_0 in (7.6) and only equating these to 0 at the end. However, this would have no purpose since the conjugate variables corresponding to the additional multipliers κ, κ_0 have already been identified with the latter, except for change of sign. These variables are conjugate to those introduced by (7.6), and since the latter do not appear explicitly in $\mathscr{H}$, the Euler equations give $\dot{\kappa} = \dot{\kappa}_0 = 0$, so that, on any extremal, κ, κ_0 are constant. This means that on any extremal we can rename $\kappa_0 L + \kappa\Psi$ as our Lagrangian in place of L, so that $\mathscr{H}$ is as in our earlier discussion.

Exactly as in Volume I, Chapter IV, Section 46, we can now further identify our local Hamiltonian with that of Section 6, apart from isoperimetric constraints. Thus, subject to the nonsingularity of (7.2), we seem to have the desirable state of affairs alluded to at the end of the preceding section. Actually, this additional proviso restricts us to the neighborhood of "nice" canonical points, and, as we might guess from the example with the constraint (7.1), this spoils things in the large. Therefore we shall go into the whole question afresh in the context of optimal control; in any case, all our remarks so far, in this Preamble, are introductory, intended to do no more than lead into optimal control.

We have based these remarks on the classical Lagrange problem, since it is met also in connection with mechanics and related topics. However, they apply, with only a slight change, to the so-called problem of Bolza, which is a little more general, since it concerns the minimum, in the class of curves C, which satisfy given constraints of the type (1.1), (1.2) and appropriate boundary conditions, not of the integral $\mathscr{I}(C)$ of our Lagrangian L on C, but of a sum $\mathscr{I}(C) + \mathscr{J}(\partial C)$, where $\mathscr{J}$ is a continuous function of the boundary of C. Actually, the problem of Bolza is still of a very special type compared with those considered in the Introduction, and they can be taken, again, for the same class of curves.

§8. CONTROLS AND THE MAXIMUM PRINCIPLE

As stated in Section 3, optimal control is the modern form of the Lagrange problem. The constraints are now written

$$\dot{x} = \varphi(t, x, u) \tag{8.1}$$

and u is here restricted to a domain U, which is taken to be bounded and closed in some Euclidean space, or, more generally, $B \cdot \cdot i$-compact (compact in the sense of Bourbaki). In the simplest cases, U is a segment or a circumference of a circle, or else the Cartesian product of a finite member of segments and/or, circumferences. In practice the segments or circumferences are dials on a control board. However, more complicated cases occur in the control of space flights, where one control station hands over control to another on the other side of the globe. In such a case, the controls are similar to local coordinates on a differentiable manifold.

For the present, we shall restrict ourselves to curves $x(t)$ and controls $u(t)$ such that $u(t)$ is piecewise continuous, and $x(t)$ is continuous and piecewise continuously differentiable. Later we shall relax these hypotheses, and the reader may, if he wishes, adopt from the start this more general interpretation. The curve $x(t)$ is termed a trajectory, and $u(t)$ a corresponding control, if (8.1) is satisfied wherever the derivative $\dot{x}(t)$ and the control $u(t)$ are continuous. The function φ will be supposed continuously differentiable at present.

We are concerned with the minimum of an integral of the form

$$\int L(t, x, u)\, dt$$

for trajectories $x(t)$ and corresponding controls $u(t)$ such that the extremities of $x(t)$ satisfy prescribed conditions. The Lagrangian $L(t, x, u)$ is here supposed continuously differentiable at present. We speak of L as a Lagrangian, although formerly a Lagrangian had the form $L(t, x, \dot{x})$. The difference is of secondary importance, and from $L(t, x, u)$ we could define

$$\hat{L}(t, x, \dot{x}) = \operatorname*{Inf}_{u} L(t, x, u) \tag{8.2}$$

where the infimum is taken for values of u, which satisfy, for fixed $(t, x, \dot{x})$, the constraint (8.1).

Generally speaking, as already remarked, there are no important differences between the Lagrange problem and our present one. However, both the introduction

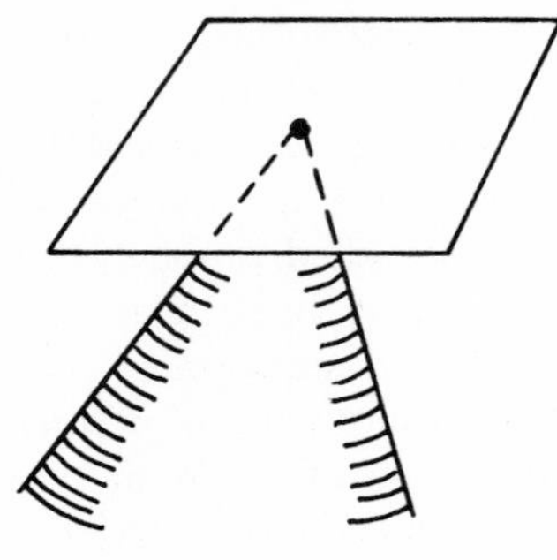

Landing hyperplane at vertex of a cone

of (8.2), and the fact that the domain of u is bounded and closed, which means, in practice, that it is defined by inequalities, have the effect of making the data less smooth than was customary, so that where formerly a landing hyperplane of a certain graph contained at least one tangent line, this need no longer be so. For instance, a landing hyperplane at a vertex of a cone need not be tangent at all. Thus multipliers, which arise from tangency considerations, can no longer fully describe the geometrical state of affairs, and the Weierstrass condition must be reformulated in terms of convexity or Hamiltonians; incidentally, the singular nature of Hamiltonians will be somewhat enhanced.

None of this need trouble us much at this stage, since we are only looking for a convenient substitute for our revised Euler recipe; we must just try to take it into account in a rather natural way. Clearly, we should start by introducing Hamiltonians, and in so doing we find that several possibilities suggest themselves.

a. THE CONTROLLED HAMILTONIAN $\tilde{\mathscr{H}}(t, x, y, y_0, u)$. Treat (t, x, u) as a point and introduce the further canonical variables y, v, conjugate to x, u, as well as multipliers and the constants $\kappa_0 = -y_0 \geq 0$. We can then write

$$\tilde{L}(t, x, u, \lambda, \kappa_0) = \kappa_0 L + \lambda(\dot{x} - \varphi),$$

$$y = \tilde{L}_{\dot{x}} = \lambda, \qquad v = \tilde{L}_{\dot{u}} = 0,$$

$$\tilde{\mathscr{H}}(t, x, y, y_0, u) = y_0 L + y\varphi.$$

The Hamiltonian $\tilde{\mathscr{H}}$, which we call controlled since it contains the argument u, is simply our former local Hamiltonian for the new variables. However, since $\dot{x}$ only appears linearly and $\dot{u}$ not at all, the implicit equations can be solved by inspection, globally. The identities $\tilde{L}_x = -\tilde{\mathscr{H}}_x$, $\tilde{L}_u = -\tilde{\mathscr{H}}_u$ and $\tilde{L}_t = -\tilde{\mathscr{H}}_t$ are moreover evident.

Since v is the constant 0, there is no sense in the relation $\dot{u} = \tilde{\mathscr{H}}_v$ unless we use some special device, as with $\mathscr{H}_c$ in the preceding section. The remaining Euler equations are:

(8.3) $\quad$ (i) $\dot{x} = \tilde{\mathscr{H}}_y$, $\quad$ (ii) $\dot{y} = -\tilde{\mathscr{H}}_x$, $\quad$ (iii) $0 = \tilde{\mathscr{H}}_u$.

The third of these should be struck out, because in most problems u turns out to lie on the frontier of its domain U. The first, of course, is just (8.1). We have thus gained one equation, namely (ii), which may be written

(8.4)
$$\dot{y} = -y_0 L_x - y\varphi_x.$$

b. AN ALTERNATIVE HAMILTONIAN. Since nothing is being proved, we argue as plausibly as we like. However, it does perhaps seem more reasonable to think of the control variable u as playing the part of a time derivative. We therefore set $u = \dot{\zeta}$, and we stipulate that $\zeta(t)$ is to be, like $x(t)$, continuous. If we now consider our problem in (t, x, ζ)-space, a strange thing happens! We do not obtain an improvement of the naive approach of (a), but merely weaker results. $\tilde{L}$ is as before, but in it u is now $\dot{\zeta}$, and the conjugate of the extra variable ζ is $\eta = L_u^*$; the method therefore necessitates first of all the added assumption that this last equation can be solved for u, and this means that it is only a local method, at best. The Hamiltonian receives the extra term ηu, which would have been 0 according to (8.3) (iii); this last equation, which can now be written $\eta = 0$ in view of the value found for η above, is replaced by the weaker one $\dot{\eta} = 0$. Otherwise, the Euler equations are as before.

c. THE TRUE HAMILTONIAN. In defining the analogue of (6.3), simply replace L by the expression $\hat{L}$ given by (8.2). This is clearly equivalent to setting

$$\mathscr{H}(t, x, y, y_0) = \operatorname*{Sup}_{u,z} \{yz + y_0 L(t, x, u)\} \tag{8.5}$$

where the supremum is taken for all pairs u, z subject to

$$u \in U, \qquad z = \varphi(t, x, u),$$

and where, as previously, y_0, which is $-\kappa_0$, is ≤ 0. (This last is the reason why our final expression is a supremum.) We observe at once that $\mathscr{H}$ is related very simply to the controlled Hamiltonian $\tilde{\mathscr{H}}$, by the formula

$$\mathscr{H} = \operatorname*{Max}_{u \in U} \tilde{\mathscr{H}}(t, x, y, y_0, u), \tag{8.6}$$

and the maximum is attained for some $u = u_0 \in U$, since U is bounded and closed (or $B \cdot \cdot i$-compact). This means that if E denotes the subset of (z, z_0)-space, given parametrically in terms of u, for fixed (t, x), by

$$z_0 = L(t, x, u), \qquad z = \varphi(t, x, u),$$

we have in E

$$y_0 z_0 + yz \leq \mathscr{H}(t, x, y, y_0),$$

with equality at the point of E for which $u = u_0$; so that the equation $y_0 z_0 + yz = \mathscr{H}$ is that of a landing hyperplane to E at this point. This is precisely what we shall take as our new Weierstrass condition; it limits us to the values of u for which the maximum is attained in (8.6). At the same time, since y, $-\mathscr{H}$ define the momentum, the transversality condition will be taken to be

$$[y\, \delta x - \mathscr{H}\, \delta t]_1^2 = 0,$$

where 1, 2 refer to the end points, and $(\delta x, \delta t)$ is a virtual displacement of either end.

Thus the true Hamiltonian once again provides us with forms of the Weierstrass and transversality conditions. On the other hand, it is, perhaps, somewhat lacking in smoothness, more so than in the Lagrange problem, and at first glance at least, we can hardly expect it to provide the Euler equation as well.

We are thus back in the dilemma we met in the Lagrange problem. Disregarding (b) as of no interest, we have two Hamiltonians: which should we choose?

Actually the solution stares us in the face. Here, as in many other instances, first thoughts turn out to be best, in spite of the oversimplification on which they rest. Thus it is that we do not choose the more sophisticated "true" Hamiltonian, but our original, naive controlled one. However, we replace at the same time (8.3)(iii) by the stipulation that the value of the control variable u be such that the maximum is attained in (8.6).† This is the famous "maximum principle" of Pontrjagin and his fellow workers. With this added stipulation, the very simple controlled Hamiltonian acquires all the advantages of the true Hamiltonian.

The proof of the necessity of the maximum principle, given in the book of Pontrjagin, Boltyanskii, Gamkrelidze and Mischchenko, henceforth referred to simply as *Optimal Processes*, represents, in a sense, the culmination of the efforts of mathematicians, for considerably more than a century, to rectify the Lagrange multiplier rule. Moreover, the principle itself is of fundamental importance; it is the foundation of the whole of optimal control. On the other hand, as already pointed out, in the absence of any existence theory, it is open to the same general criticism as the Euler-Lagrange algorithm, in the Preamble to Volume I, an algorithm nonetheless fundamental in modern analysis and in the Schwartz theory of distributions.

---

† Thus we maximise, by choice of u, a kind of "instantaneous performance," given by $\tilde{\mathscr{H}}$.

Incidentally, here existence runs counter to the fundamental difficulty to which we drew attention under (c) in Section 4, above. Thus any claim that it is physically obvious is refuted by Lebesgue's comments in Section 56 of Chapter V of Volume I. In our view, a proof of necessity, without existence, is illusory and leaves us, in the end, with no more than a recipe to be tested; at best, it provides motivation, and this we have provided too. Therefore, exactly as in Volume I, we postpone any discussion of necessity until we have reformulated the whole setting of optimal control so as to reestablish existence.

§9. THE MAXIMUM PRINCIPLE AND ITS SPECIAL CASES AS DEFINITIONS

In Volume I, the Euler equation was used mainly to define the notion of extremal, not as a necessary condition. Here the maximum principle will be given a similar use, but we shall not trouble to coin a special name.

Given a problem of optimal control, as described in the preceding section, a trajectory $x(t)$ and a corresponding control $u(t)$, $(t_1 \leq t \leq t_2)$ will be termed subject to the maximum principle if there exists a constant $y_0 \leq 0$ and a continuous, piecewise continuously differentiable, vector-valued function $y(t)$, subject to the following conditions:

(9.1)

(i) For any t, $y(t), y_0$ are not both 0.

(ii) At $(t, x(t), y(t), y_0)$, the function of u

$$\tilde{\mathscr{H}}(t, x, y, y_0, u) = y_0 L + y\varphi$$

assumes, for $u = u(t)$, its maximum $\mathscr{H}$.

(iii) For the arguments $t, x(t), y(t), y_0, u(t)$, we have the canonical Euler equations

$$\dot{x} = \tilde{\mathscr{H}}_y, \qquad \dot{y} = -\tilde{\mathscr{H}}_x.$$

(iv) The end points satisfy the transversality condition†

$$[y\,\delta x - \mathscr{H}\,\delta t]_1^2 = 0.$$

In the preceding definition, all is clear except the precise meaning of the transversality condition. This we shall elaborate in a few special cases, which is all that will concern us for the present. A completely general interpretation of transversality is desirable when the pair of end points is allowed to describe a closed set of $(2n + 2)$-dimensional space, but this Preamble is not the place for it.

(1) First suppose that the ends are fixed. Then the transversality condition falls away.

(2) Next suppose that the x-coordinates of the ends are fixed, but not the time coordinate. Then the condition becomes

$$[\mathscr{H}\,\delta t]_1^2 = 0;$$

in particular, if the time coordinate is fixed at one end, P, and unrestricted at the other, Q, then $\mathscr{H}$ vanishes at Q.

(3) At one end, P, the space and time coordinates are fixed, while at the other, Q, the time t is unrestricted and the space variable x is restricted to a hypersurface, which possesses at Q a continuous tangent hyperplane Π. Then at Q, $\mathscr{H}$ vanishes and y is orthogonal to Π. (Similarly, if x is restricted to the intersection of a finite number

† A slightly stronger transversality condition will be given in the form of Pontrjagin's maximum principle established at the end of Chapter III.

of such hypersurfaces, then y is orthogonal to the intersection of the corresponding tangent hyperplanes.)

(4) The ends P, Q lie on a smooth variety given parametrically in $(2n+2)$-dimensional space in the form

$$(t_1, x_1, t_2, x_2) = R(v),$$

where R is vector-valued and continuously differentiable, and v is a scalar, or vector, parameter, such that (P, Q) corresponds to an interior point of its range. In that case, if η denotes the $(2n+2)$-dimensional vector given by the values of $\mathscr{H}$, $-y$ at the first end, and those of $-\mathscr{H}, y$ at the other, we interpret the condition to mean that, for each partial derivative R_i of R in a component of v, we have

$$\eta R_i = 0.$$

In making use of transversality, the following remarks are useful. In cases (2) and (3), instead of verifying that $\mathscr{H}$ vanishes at Q, we can check its value at any other time by remarking that $\mathscr{H}$ is subject to the differential equation

$$\textbf{(9.2)} \qquad \dot{\mathscr{H}} = \tilde{\mathscr{H}}_t\big(t, x(t), y(t), y_0, u(t)\big).$$

Since $u(t)$ is piecewise continuously differentiable, we need derive (9.2) only on any arc for which it is continuously differentiable. We can then differentiate totally, by the elementary calculus rules, noting, however, that by the maximum property (ii), $\tilde{\mathscr{H}}_u$ vanishes, and that by the canonical Euler equations (iii), the terms $\dot{x}\tilde{\mathscr{H}}_x + \dot{y}\tilde{\mathscr{H}}_y$ cancel one another. This leaves us with (9.2). For instance, if the time does not appear explicitly, or as we say, if the problem is autonomous, $\mathscr{H}$ will then vanish at Q, if and only if it vanishes at each other point of the trajectory. Again, in case (iii), if $x(t)$ stays on one side of the hypersurface near Q, and does not happen to be tangent to it, we can determine the direction of y at Q. We know it to be along the normal, either inward or outward, and we have, further, at Q,

$$\textbf{(9.3)} \qquad y\dot{x} = \mathscr{H} - y_0 L = -y_0 L$$

which has the sign of L.

We shall consider specially problems in which φ does not contain t explicitly and L is the constant unity. We speak of such a problem as time-optimal. We shall further suppose that the end conditions are those of (3) above: the initial position and initial time are given, the final position is on the given hypersurface or else at a given point, termed (in either case) the target, and the final time is (of course) unrestricted.

In such a problem, by (9.2), $\mathscr{H}$ is the constant 0, since it vanishes at the second extremity. The condition (9.1)(i), that $y(t), y_0$ be not both 0, is then equivalent to the single condition $y(t) \neq 0$, since $\mathscr{H} = 0$ and $y(t) = 0$ together imply $y_0 = 0$. In this case, we shall follow the practice of "optimal processes" in subtracting from our controlled and true Hamiltonians the constant y_0. We write

$$\tilde{H} = \tilde{\mathscr{H}} - y_0, \qquad H = \mathscr{H} - y_0.$$

In such a time-optimal problem, a trajectory $x(t)$, together with a corresponding control $u(t)$ $(t_1 \leq t \leq t_2)$, is subject to the maximum principle if there exists a non-vanishing, continuous, piecewise continuously differentiable, vector-valued function

$y(t)$ subject to the following conditions:

(9.4)

(i) At $(t, x(t), y(t))$ the function

$$\tilde{H}(t, x, y, u) = y\varphi$$

assumes, for $u = u(t)$, its maximum H.

(ii) For the arguments $t, x(t), y(t), u(t)$, we have the canonical Euler equations

$$\dot{x} = \tilde{H}_y, \qquad \dot{y} = -\tilde{H}_x.$$

(iii) H is a constant ≥ 0.

(iv) At the final extremity $t = t_2$, in the case where the target is a hypersurface, y is normal to the hypersurface, and so directed that $y\dot{x} \geq 0$.

With these definitions, we can now state simply the recipe that we shall use for producing trajectories and corresponding controls that we suspect of providing the desired minimum: they are those which obey the maximum principle.

As in the Preamble to Volume I, we need hardly repeat that such a suspicion does not constitute any sort of proof. In applying our method to individual problems, the work is thus divided into two parts: (a) finding our suspects according to the maximum principle, and (b) proving that they do in fact provide the desired minimum. Just as in Volume I, the actual proof will be the main thing. However, since we have still no theory for it, we must expect it to depend on a few miracles.

§10. SOLUTIONS OF TWO ELEMENTARY TIME-OPTIMAL PROBLEMS

We shall consider two controlled acceleration problems, on a line, which we take as x-axis, for a particle whose initial position and velocity are given. We denote by u a control variable subject to $-1 \leq u \leq 1$.

A. The Simplest Controlled Stop Problem. We ask for the least time in which to bring the particle to rest at the origin, if the acceleration $\ddot{x}$ is our control variable u.

B. Controlled Slowing of an Oscillator. The position of the particle is now governed by the equation $\ddot{x} + x = u$. We speak of the particle as an oscillator, and of the quantity $\frac{1}{2}\dot{x}^2 + \frac{1}{2}x^2$ as its energy. We ask for the least time in which to reduce the energy to a given level, or, in particular to 0—in which case the particle is at rest at the origin.

Both problems are time-optimal ones of the type described in the preceding section if we set $\dot{x} = X$ and treat them in the (x, X)-plane. Similarly, the conjugate vector will be written (y, Y). We shall refer to (x, X) as a phase point and to (x, X, y, Y) as a canonical phase point. Also, instead of fixing the initial value of t, we shall fix the final value, and take it as origin of the time axis.

As an exercise, the reader might try the problem, similar to (A), in which the acceleration $\ddot{x}$ is $u - g$, where g is a constant subject to $0 < g < 1$.

As background to our discussion, we recommend the reader to refer, on the one hand, to *Optimal Processes*, and on the other to Bellman's *Dynamic Programming*. We have many times stressed the importance of studying the original accounts, and not only later simplified versions.

The examples themselves occur earlier, of course, but they are only illustrations. In *Optimal Processes* there is also a critical review of the basic idea of Bellman. However, this basic idea, which occurs already in Carathéodory, and is used extensively in the book by Hardy, Littlewood and Polya, is perfectly sound, since necessary conditions do not really mean anything in themselves. What is required is only that the conditions obtained be proved sufficient. In *Optimal Processes* this is done 100 pages later, and only in the case in which the target reduces to a point. In order to apply these later theorems, we need the fact that problems (A) and (B) are linear. Here we shall give complete solutions directly, on the model of the Carathéodory and Hardy-Littlewood-Polya approach, which is also that of Bellman (incidentally, it is the method used in the Preamble to Volume I).

The trajectories and controls that obey the maximum principle will, for the moment, be referred to as suspected optimal ones. In their determination, the reader will find the account in *Optimal Processes*, and the careful illustrations there, most helpful. Our account is, of course, longer, since we prove that the suspected optimal trajectories and controls are the actual solutions.

THE SUSPECTS IN PROBLEM A. The function φ is here the time derivative (X, u) of (x, X). Hence

$$\tilde{H} = yX + uY, \qquad H = yX + |Y|.$$

From the Euler equations

$$\dot{y} = -\tilde{H}_x = 0, \qquad \dot{Y} = -\tilde{H}_X = -y,$$

we find that

$$y = \text{const.}, \qquad Y = -yt + \text{const.},$$

and the suspected optimal control is

$$u = \text{sign}\,(Y) = \text{sign}\,(-yt + \text{const.}) = \pm 1;$$

yt can change sign only once. Further, since H is a non-negative constant we have $iX + |Y| = \text{const.} \geq 0$.

The suspected optimal trajectories, according to the maximum principle, are thus made up of arcs on which u is the constant $+1$ or -1, and since u can pass only once from one of these values to the other, any such a trajectory can consist of at most two such arcs. To find these arcs, we integrate, for $u = \pm 1$, the constraint equations $\dot{x} = X$, $\dot{X} = u$. We obtain parabolic arcs

$$x = \tfrac{1}{2}u\tau^2 + \text{const.}, \qquad X = u\tau,$$

where $u = \pm 1$ and $\tau = t + \text{const.}$; they constitute two systems

$$\tfrac{1}{2}X^2 - ux = \text{const.} \qquad (u = \pm 1).$$

In one of them $(u = +1)$, X increases with t, and we speak of an upward parabola; in the other $(u = -1)$ X decreases, and we speak of a downward one.

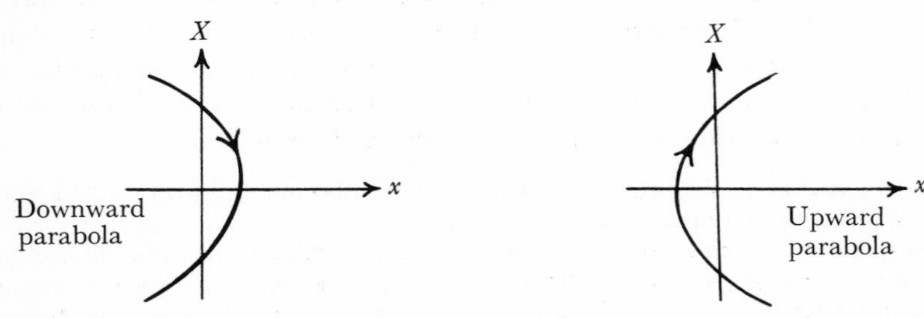

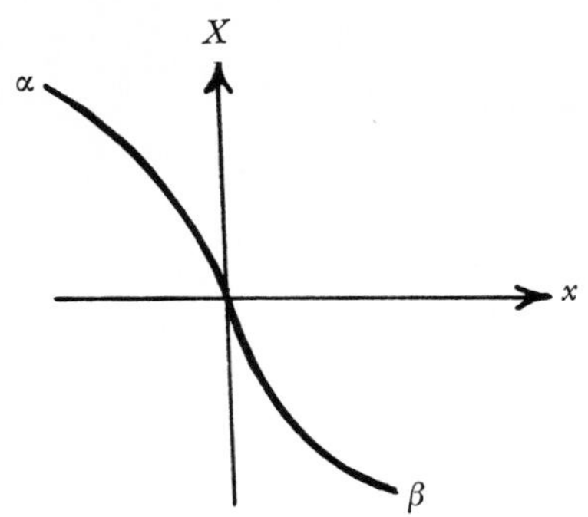

Two of our parabolic arcs constitute smooth suspected optimal trajectories. They are the ones which terminate at the origin (for $t = 0$). They are given by

$$\begin{aligned} x &= \tfrac{1}{2}ut^2 \\ X &= ut \end{aligned} \qquad (t \leq 0),$$

where $u = \pm 1$. We denote them by α and β; they are described as shown in the figure.

Clearly, an initial phase point $P = (p, \dot{p})$, above $\alpha + \beta$, can be joined to $\alpha + \beta$ by just one downward parabola, and the arc so joining it ends at a phase point $Q = (q, \dot{q})$ of β. Similarly, an initial phase point below $\alpha + \beta$ can be joined to $\alpha + \beta$ by just one upward parabola, and the arc so joining it ends at a phase point of α.

It follows that for each position of P, there is just one suspected optimal trajectory, with the initial phase point P, that terminates at the origin. For P on α or β, it is the appropriate subarc of α or β. For P above $\alpha + \beta$, it consists of the downward parabolic arc PQ, together with the arc QO of β. For P below $\alpha + \beta$, it is similarly an upward parabolic arc, together with an arc of α.

Proof of Optimality in Problem A. This is the most important part, since everything so far has only been a more or less well-motivated guess. We denote by $-T(p, \dot{p})$ the initial time at P on our suspected optimal trajectory; since the final time at the origin is $t = 0$, we see that T is the suspected least time from P to the origin. We shall calculate T explicitly. We may suppose P above $\alpha + \beta$.

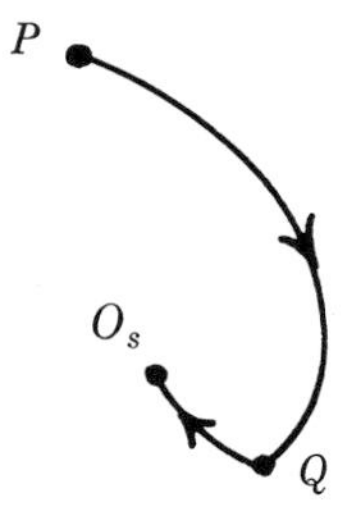

On the arc PQ we have

$$u = -1, \qquad X = -t + \text{const.}$$

while on QO,

$$u = +1, \qquad X = t.$$

Hence,

$$\dot{p} - \dot{q} = t_Q - t_P, \qquad \dot{q} = t_Q$$

so that

$$T(p, \dot{p}) = -t_P = \dot{p} - 2\dot{q}.$$

Also,

$$q = \tfrac{1}{2}\dot{q}^2, \qquad p + \tfrac{1}{2}\dot{p}^2 = q + \tfrac{1}{2}\dot{q}^2,$$

so that

$$\dot{q}^2 = p + \tfrac{1}{2}\dot{p}^2,$$

and here $\dot{q}$ is the negative square root, since Q is in the fourth quadrant. Consequently, for P above $\alpha + \beta$,

$$T(p, \dot{p}) = \dot{p} + \sqrt{2\dot{p}^2 + 4p}.$$

By changing the directions of both axes, we obtain, for P below $\alpha + \beta$,

$$T(p, \dot{p}) = -\dot{p} + \sqrt{2\dot{p}^2 - 4p}.$$

Both formulae lead to $T = \dot{p}$ on α and to $T = -\dot{p}$ on β.

We now write (x, X) in place of $(p, \dot{p})$, so that T becomes a function $T(x, X)$ of our original variables, and we write

$$g(x, X, u) = 1 + XT_x + uT_X,$$

except on $\alpha + \beta$ where we set $g = 0$. Then, for $-1 \leq u \leq 1$, we find that, above $\alpha + \beta$,

$$g = (1 + u)\left(1 + \frac{2X}{\sqrt{2X^2 + 4x}}\right) \geq 0, \dagger$$

and that, below $\alpha + \beta$,

$$g = (1 - u)\left(1 - \frac{2X}{\sqrt{2X^2 - 4x}}\right) \geq 0.$$

Consequently, for $-1 \leq u \leq 1$, we have $g \geq 0$ for all x, X. This is the crucial fact that we shall use in our proof. Of course, it is not at all an obvious consequence of the maximum principle.

We remark further that no admissible trajectory can describe any part of α or β in reverse. For if we write the equation of α or of β in the form $X^2 = 2u_0x$, we find by differentiating along such a trajectory that $X\dot{X} = u_0\dot{x}$, which, by the constraint equations, may be written $Xu = u_0X$, so that $u = u_0$. This is the same control as for the arc of α or β, which leads to the origin. Therefore, it cannot reverse the direction.

On any arc above, below or on $\alpha + \beta$, which belongs to an admissible trajectory $x(t)$, $X(t)$ subject to the constraint equations, we thus have

$$g = \frac{d}{dt}\{t + T(x, X)\}.$$

It follows by decomposing an arbitrary admissible trajectory into its parts above, below, and on, $\alpha + \beta$, that, for such trajectory,

$$0 \leq \int g\, dt = [t + T].$$

In particular, for a trajectory from P to O, we find that $t_P + T \geq 0$. This completes the proof.

With very little trouble, we could show that the solution is unique.

† For instance, above β in the fourth quadrant, $4x \geqslant 2X^2$ and so $|2X| \leqslant \sqrt{2X^2 + 4x}$.

THE SUSPECTS IN PROBLEM B. The function φ, which equals the time derivative of (x, X), is now given by $(X, u - x)$. We have thus

$$\tilde{H} = yX + Y(u - x), \qquad H = yX - Yx + |Y|.$$

The Euler equations give

$$\dot{y} = -\tilde{H}_x = Y, \qquad \dot{Y} = -\tilde{H}_X = -y;$$

hence $Y = A \sin (t - t_0)$ where $A > 0$ and t_0 are constants. The control u for which $\tilde{H}$ is maximal is given by

$$u = \operatorname{sign} Y = \operatorname{sign} \{A \sin (t - t_0)\} = \operatorname{sign} \{\sin (t - t_0)\}.$$

This means that $u(t)$ is the function of period 2π, which is -1, $+1$ in the intervals $t_0 - \pi < t < t_0$ and $t_0 < t < t_0 + \pi$, respectively. The suspected optimal trajectories are thus again made up of arcs on which u is one of the constants ± 1. We can write the differential equations of these arcs in the complex form

$$\dot{z} = -iz, \quad \text{where} \quad z = x - u + iX, \qquad u = \pm 1.$$

The solution is

$$z = re^{-i(t-\gamma)},$$

where γ and $r > 0$ are constants. The arcs thus lie on concentric circles, whose center $z = 0$ is the point $(u, 0)$ of the x-axis. We shall have two systems of such arcs, corresponding to the values ± 1 of the control u, and we pass from an arc of one system to one of the other wherever u changes sign. The arcs are described clockwise, and the time t on each arc differs only by a constant from the angle subtended at the center.

Our problem of finding the suspected optimal trajectories is thus reduced to fitting together suitable circular arcs of the two sets of circles. We shall work backward from the terminal time $t = 0$, at which the oscillator reaches the prescribed energy level, $\frac{1}{2}R^2$, say. This means that at $t = 0$ the phase point is required to be on the circle.

$$x^2 + X^2 = R^2, \tag{10.1}$$

or, in particular, to be at the origin, if $R = 0$. The terminal position is thus that of a phase point Q given by

$$x + iX = Re^{i\alpha} \qquad -\pi \leq \alpha < \pi.$$

If $R \neq 0$, the transversality condition, according to (3) and (9.3) of Section 9, requires the vector (y, Y) to be directed along the inward radial direction at Q, unless $\dot{x}$ is tangent there to the target (10.1). This last can only occur when (10.1) touches a circle of center $(\pm 1, 0)$ at the point Q, i.e., when Q is on the x-axis; we shall exclude this for the moment. Moreover, by symmetry, we may then suppose $0 < \alpha < \pi$. Thus

$$y + iY = -ce^{i\alpha} \qquad (c > 0)$$

at $t = 0$. The case $R = 0$ can now be included also without affecting this result. The constant t_0 in our expression for $Y(t)$ evidently reduces to α, and we have

$$u(t) = \operatorname{sign} \{\sin (t - \alpha)\}.$$

This expression for $u(t)$ remains valid in the excluded case $\alpha = 0$, since Y then vanishes for $t = 0$; it is also valid for $-\pi \leq \alpha < 0$, by symmetry, but we shall restrict ourselves again, by symmetry, to the case in which $0 \leq \alpha < \pi$. In that case, at $t = 0$ (or, if $\alpha = 0$, at all small negative t) $u(t)$ is clearly -1. This means that the final circular arc of our suspect, ending at Q, has its center at $0' = (-1, 0)$.

We describe this arc backward from Q to the nearest phase point Q' prior to Q at which $u(t)$ changes sign. This means that we describe anticlockwise an arc subtending at O' the angle $\pi - \alpha$. Now Q' can be obtained more simply by a geometrical construction. To this effect, we denote by Ω' the point $-R - 1$ of the x-axis. The triangles OQO' and $\Omega'O'Q'$ have equal angles at Q and O', respectively, and the pairs of adjacent sides are equal too. Therefore they are congruent. This means

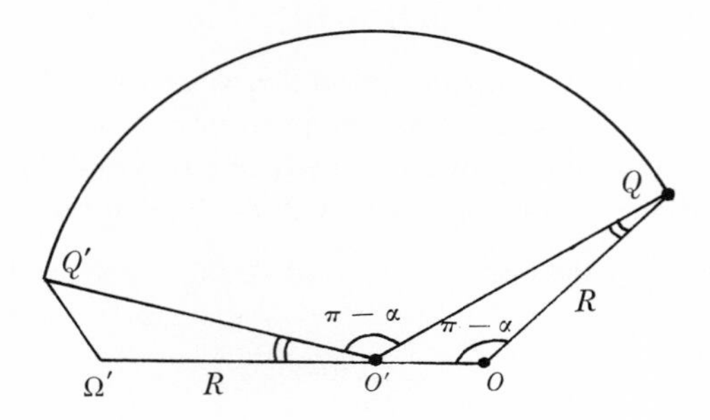

that Q' is on the unit circle of center Ω', and that the angle at Ω' made by the direction $\Omega'Q'$ with the x-axis is again $\pi - \alpha$. As we continue to trace our trajectory backwards from Q', the arcs described are now semicircular arcs, with centers alternately at

$$O'' = (1, 0) \quad \text{and} \quad O' = (-1, 0).$$

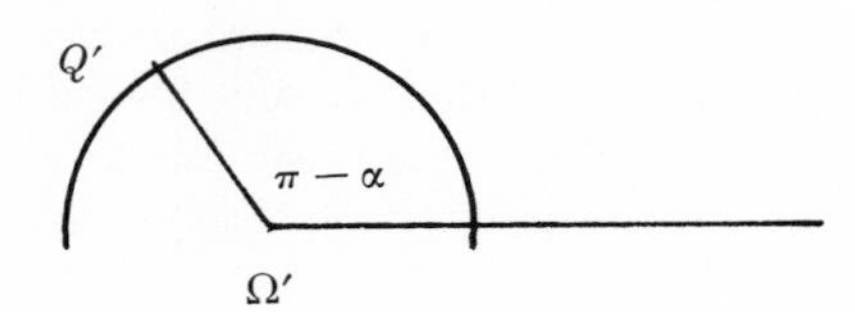

The first such arc takes us back to a point Q'' at the other end of a diameter through O''. By reflection in O'', we see that Q'' is on the lower half of a unit circle of center $\Omega'' = (R + 3, 0)$, and that the radius $\Omega''Q''$ now makes an angle $-\alpha$ with the positive x-axis, counterclockwise.

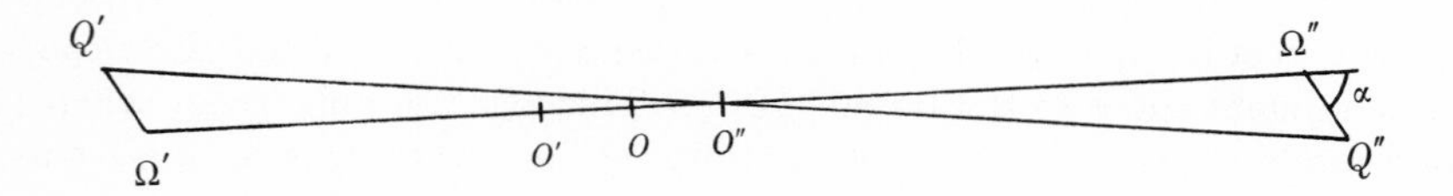

Let now Γ denote the disc $x^2 + X^2 \leq R^2$, and let Γ' and Γ'' denote, respectively, the arcs in the second and fourth quadrant, consisting of the upper halves of unit circles of centers at the points of the x-axis:

$$-R - 1, \ -R - 3, \ldots$$

and of lower halves of unit circles of centers at the points

$$R + 1, \ R + 3, \ldots$$

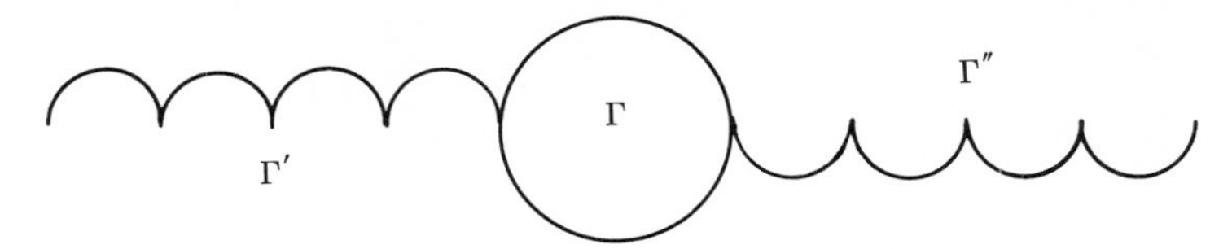

Our constructions show that on any suspected optimal trajectory, that ends on the rim of Γ, the control $u(t)$ is always -1 above $\Gamma' + \Gamma + \Gamma''$, and $+1$ below it. The circular subarcs of center O' are thus all above this set, and those of center O'' are all below it. We shall speak of them as the upper and lower circular subarcs.

It is now easy to see that there is just one suspect through a given phase point P. We simply trace from P the clockwise upper or lower circular arc to its intersection with $\Gamma' + \Gamma + \Gamma''$, and we note that this intersection coincides, for an appropriate α subject to $0 \leq \alpha < \pi$, with one of the points $Q, Q', Q'', \ldots$ constructed above, or else, for a corresponding α subject to $-\pi \leq \alpha < 0$, with one similarly obtained by the symmetrical construction.

Proof of Optimality in Problem B. We shall again calculate the suspected optimal time T, or more precisely, we shall determine T modulo 2π, which will suffice for our purposes. To this effect, we first suppose Q, the terminal phase point, to be on the upper half of the rim of Γ.

If now P is below $\Gamma' + \Gamma + \Gamma''$, we denote by θ the angle subtended at O'' by the lower circular arc from P to the intersection Q^* with Γ'. While if P is above $\Gamma' + \Gamma + \Gamma''$, we denote by $-\theta$ the angle subtended at O' by the upper circular arc

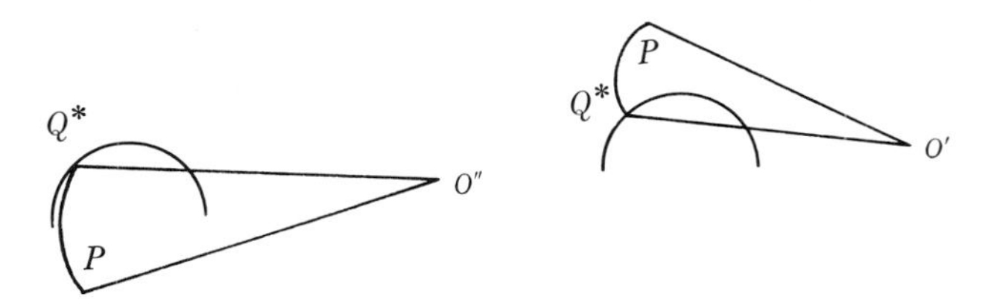

not from P along the trajectory to $\Gamma + \Gamma''$, but from P along its backward extension, to Γ'. Thus $-\pi < \theta \leq \pi$; we write $O_s = (u_s, o)$ for O' if $\theta \leq 0$, and for O'' if $\theta > 0$. We denote further by Ω^* the center of the unit circle, whose upper half is an arc of Γ' containing Q^*, and by ω_s the distance from Ω^* to O_s.

Between Q^* and the last intersection Q' with Γ', our trajectory, or its extension back to Q^*, consists of an even number of semicircles; then comes the final arc $Q'Q$, which subtends at O' the angle $\pi - \alpha$. Our trajectory itself is now obtained by adding or taking away the circular arc Q^*P, which subtends the angle $\pm\theta$. The suspected optimal time is the sum of these various angles; thus

$$T = \theta + \pi - \alpha \qquad (\mathrm{mod}\ 2\pi).$$

We can construct this angle geometrically. The unit radius Ω^*Q^* makes with

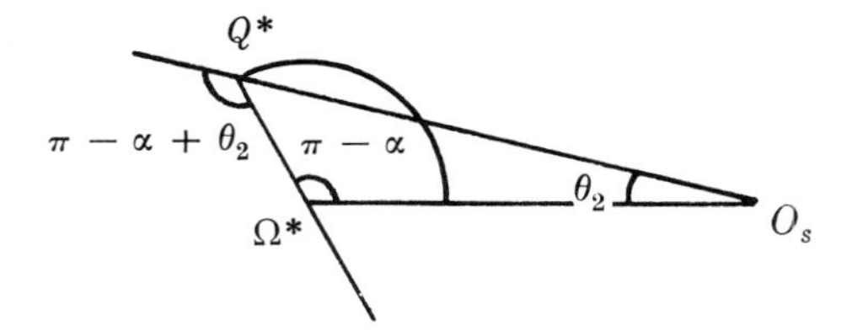

the x-axis the angle $\pi - \alpha$. We denote by θ_2 the angle at O_s in the triangle $\Omega^* O_s Q^*$; then, for this triangle, the exterior angle at Q^*, made by the extension of $O_s Q^*$ with $Q^*\Omega^*$, is $\pi - \alpha + \theta_2$. The further addition of the angle $\theta_1 = \theta - \theta_2$ is quite simple too.

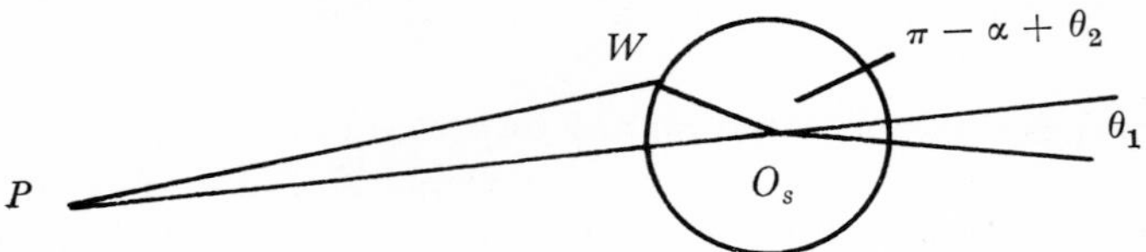

On the unit circle of center O_s we mark off the angle θ_1, made with the x-axis by the extension through O_s of the segment PO_s. By the above we add $\pi - \alpha + \theta$, if we take a model of our previous triangle $\Omega^* O_s Q^*$, placing the side $O_s Q^*$ over the equal segment PO_s; the third vertex Ω^* becomes a point W of our unit circle about O_s, and of the two possible positions of W, we must choose the one for which the angle $\pi - \alpha + \theta_2$ between the extension of PO_s and the radius $O_s W$ is clockwise. In that case, this radius makes with the x-axis the desired angle $\theta + \pi - \alpha$.

The point W, which determines this angle, is at the distance ω_s from P, and the angle at W of the triangle PWO_s is $\pi - \alpha$. It is therefore easily found, apart from the ambiguity already discussed. From this construction, it follows that if we take for P any phase point (x, X) outside Γ, and write T for $T(x, X)$, we have, since the distance WP is ω_s,

$$(x - u_s - \cos T)^2 + (X - \sin T)^2 = \omega_s^2. \tag{10.2}$$

The corresponding equation, when the final point Q is on the lower part of the rim of Γ, is derived by reversing the axes and the signs of the u_s. It may be written

$$(x - u_s + \cos T)^2 + (X + \sin T)^2 = \omega_s^2. \tag{10.3}$$

In the equations (10.2), (10.3), u_s, ω_s remain constant in corresponding (x, X)-domains, and the latter constitute two systems of domains which together cover the exterior of Γ. As we move out from Γ, we first have two zero-angled triangles

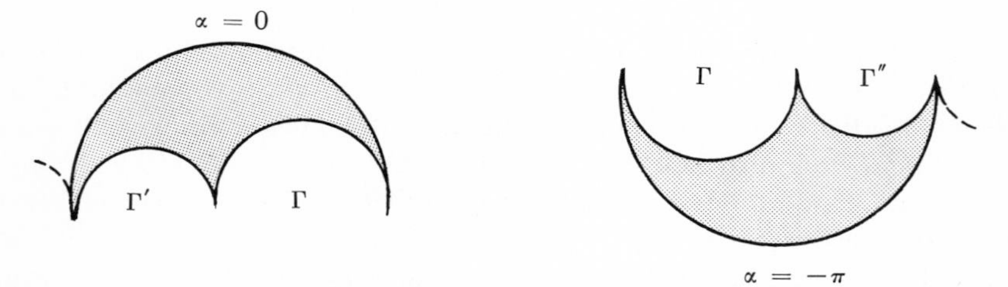

bounded by circular arcs as shown; then two series of zero-angled quadrilaterals bounded by circular arcs. We show the first of these.

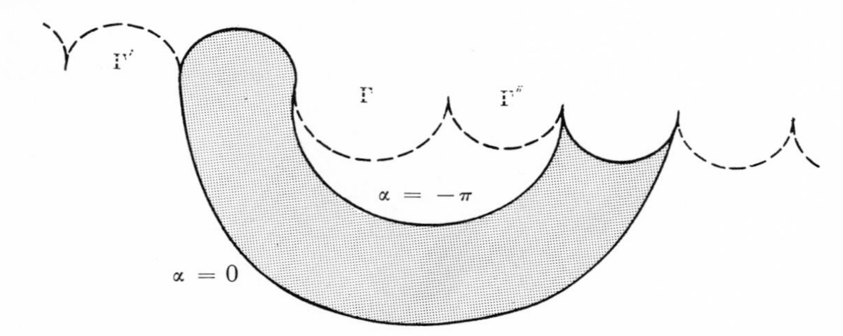

In each of these domains, we can differentiate in t the relevant equation (10.2), or (10.3), along any trajectory arising from an admissible control $u(t)$. Thus in the case of (10.2), we obtain

$$(x - u_s - \cos T)(X + \dot{T}\sin T) + (x - \sin T)(u - x - \dot{T}\cos T) = 0.$$

If we set $g = 1 + \dot{T}$, we find, when (10.2) holds,

$$\textbf{(10.4)} \qquad g = (u_s - u)\frac{\sin T - X}{X\cos T - (x - u_s)\sin T}$$

similarly, in a domain in which (10.3) holds, we have

$$\textbf{(10.5)} \qquad g = (u_s - u)\frac{\sin T + X}{X\cos T - (x - u_s)\sin T}.$$

Here g can be written, instead of $1 + \dot{T}$, in the form

$$g(x, X, u) = 1 + XT_x + (u - x)T_X.$$

In order to discuss the expressions found for g, we first suppose (10.2) holds in the domain considered. This means that the suspected optimal trajectory, which starts from $P = (x, X)$, terminates at a point Q on the upper rim of Γ. The denominator in (10.4) may then be interpreted, except for sign, as twice the area of our triangle PWO_s, formerly considered. This area is that of the congruent triangle $O_s\Omega^*Q^*$, and it vanishes if and only if Q^* lies on the x-axis, i.e., if $\alpha = 0$. Thus the denominator in question has a constant sign, and by setting $P = \Omega^*$ we see, in the case of a domain below $\Gamma' + \Gamma + \Gamma''$, that the sign is positive, since T is then $\pi - \alpha + \theta_2$, which is between O and π, and since then $X = 0$, $-(x - u_s) > 0$. In the case of a domain above $\Gamma' + \Gamma + \Gamma''$, the same is true, since the expression does not vanish on Γ'.

The fact that the area of PWO_s remains positive, and indeed constant, as P moves along its circular arc to Q^*, ensures also, by continuity, that the cyclic order of the vertices is unchanged, and therefore that the triangle is congruent, by translation and rotation alone, to the corresponding one when P is at Q^*, and therefore also to the triangle $O_s\Omega^*Q^*$. In particular, if PW is horizontal, then, since the corresponding side of $O_s\Omega^*Q^*$ is also horizontal, we see that PO_s is parallel, and so coincident with, Q^*O_s, i.e., P is on Γ'. It follows at once that the numerator $\sin T - X$, which vanishes if and only if PW is horizontal, can only vanish when P is on Γ'. It is also easy to see that it changes sign when P crosses Γ', and is positive below it. Since $(u_s - u)$ changes sign also, we see that $g \geq 0$.

Similarly, we find that this last is the case for the domains in which (10.3) holds. Further, $g = 0$ only when $u = u_s$, or when (x, X) lies on $\Gamma' + \Gamma''$.

We can now argue as in problem (A), but with a slight difference: g vanishes on $\Gamma' + \Gamma''$ and is $+\infty$, or undefined, on the trajectories $\alpha = 0$, $\alpha = -\pi$. This last might be inconvenient. However, if we consider, on any trajectory C arising from an admissible control $u(t)$, the function

$$Q = (x - c)^2 + X^2$$

where c is constant, we find that along C

$$\tfrac{1}{2}\dot{Q} = (x - c)X + X(u - x) = (u - c)X.$$

By taking $c = u_s$, we see that in that case $\dot{Q} \geq 0$, and therefore C cannot cross the circles $Q =$ const., except outward, when X has the sign of $u - u_s$. In particular, it cannot so cross the circular arcs of the trajectories corresponding to $\alpha = 0$, or $\alpha = \pi$. These arcs therefore constitute one-way barriers. Again, by taking $c = \omega$ where ω is the x-coordinate of a center of a semicircular arc of Γ' or Γ'', we not only find that this arc is likewise a one-way barrier, but also that C cannot be tangent to it except when $X = 0$ or when $u = c = \pm 1$; this last is excluded unless $R = 0$, in which case it holds only for the final arc of the suspected optimal trajectory $\alpha = 0$, or $\alpha = -\pi$.

It follows that C can be decomposed into a finite number of arcs, each of which is either an arc of a suspect, or an arc wholly contained in the interior of one of our domains, except perhaps for its end-points. On any such arc, the difference of $t + T$ is the integral of g and therefore ≥ 0; by addition, this difference is ≥ 0 on C, and by taking C to end on Γ, we see that T is optimal.

Chapter I

Naive Optimal Control Theory

§11. INTRODUCTION

We qualify as "naive" any parts of the calculus of variations or of optimal control that deal with alleged necessary conditions, unsupported by any general existence theory. In principle, they run counter to Perron's paradox, so their status is purely heuristic unless supplemented, as in the examples studied in the Preamble to this second Volume, by an actual proof that they lead to the desired solutions. This basic weakness is sometimes obscured by an analogy to the case of discrete problems. In the calculus of variations this analogy has been the main source of serious errors, because it takes no account of the lack of compactness.

In optimal control, the ideas that we term naive took a long time to clarify, after Lagrange's initial error. They now center around Pontrjagin's maximum principle or its many variants and analogues, which are due to Valentine, Hestenes, and McShane or to Bellman, Kuhn-Tucker and others. Still more recent forms are, for instance, the abstract formulations of Gamkrelidze and Neustadt, and the "Theory of Max-Min" of Danskin's book. While we qualify all such investigations as naive, we remind the reader that the same qualification applies, on the one hand, to the approach to Euler and Lagrange, whose great significance to analysis we stressed in the Preamble to Volume I; and that it applies also, nowadays, to the epoch-making ideas of Georg Cantor, which constitute what is termed "naive" set theory.

The naive variational approach mostly provides us with no more than suitable suspects. However, in the present Chapter, we shall mainly limit ourselves to problems in which these suspects are, automatically, the actual unique solutions. This nice and simple state of affairs is almost unheard of in the calculus of variations. Corresponding results in Chapter V of Volume I, for favorable problems, were only obtained with the very beautiful deformation arguments of the Carathéodory-Tonelli unicity theory, using Hilbert's existence theory and conjugate points. Now, on the contrary, we are just beginning optimal control, and we are limited in our methods. Of course we shall need restrictions—one does not get the utmost by flogging an ancient horse. The restrictions will be somewhat drastic and also rather annoying; one may feel that they should not be there. However, surprisingly, we can solve certain types of problems.

The most important case, and the one to which we shall limit ourselves, is that of certain so-called "linear" problems, in which the differential equations are linear in the space variables and controls. They correspond, in the calculus of variations proper, to the problems with a quadratic Lagrangian (quadratic problems); the latter played a part in Chapter III of Volume I, in the secondary Jacobi theory. In our argument here, even linearity is not quite enough. We shall require a general position assumption, without which the solutions would exhibit a strange indeterminacy, something like a speed-wobble in an old car. This assumption we may at least expect to find satisfied in most problems, but this is not all: in addition, we shall require the target to be a so-called equilibrium point. This last requirement is, in practice, never truly satisfied. It leaves a gap between what is mathematically postulated and what is physically feasible, since no actual physical target can be a mathematical point. Moreover, in problems such as moonshots, we cannot even pretend that the target is a point.

With these unpleasant limitations, the problems are formally still rather complicated, and we shall consider only the simplest case, which is that of a time-optimal problem subject to autonomous constraints. This means that the coefficients in our linear differential equations are independent of t; i.e., they are constants. We shall apply our results to a few of the simplest examples that one finds in virtually every book that covers linear control problems with continuous time. These examples, which go back to Fel'baum and Bushaw, are again quite intricate, and the solutions are best visualized with the help of the beautiful diagrams that one finds in *Optimal Processes* and elsewhere, diagrams whose beauty, certainly, at least rivals the classical ones of fluid mechanics.

§12. DISCRETE TIME AND PROGRAMMING

In Volume I we had no need to include any material dealing with the elementary theory of maxima and minima of functions of a finite number of real variables. Now, however, we shall touch on it briefly, mainly in order to clarify some of the technical jargon the reader may meet in the literature and help him to see the basic concepts behind it.

Many of those who study optimal control have come to it from problems in computing, engineering, economics, investment and similar studies, in which time may be measured only in integer units. These units may be millionths of a second, or they may be months, or even years. On an investment, for instance, it may happen that dividends are paid only once a year. Conversely, it often happens that computing machines, with a discrete time, are used to solve approximately the everyday problems of optimal control where time is a continuous variable.

A typical control problem with discrete time may be derived from our basic problem of optimal control by giving the obvious interpretations of derivative and of integral, with respect to discrete time. A derivative $\dot{x}(t)$ stands for $x(t + 1) - x(t)$, where t now only takes integer values; the integral of a function $F(t)$ becomes the sum of the values of F for the appropriate set of integers t.

The formal similarity between such a problem and the corresponding problem with continuous time often causes persons to argue by analogy and to use the discrete model to draw inferences in regard to the similar problem with continuous time. Similarly, in the calculus of variations proper, Euler and Lagrange did not hesitate to argue by analogy from the theory of maxima and minima of functions of a finite number of real variables. These analogies might be perfectly correct, if we had, in problems with continuous time, the same degree of compactness that one experiences in discrete cases. Unfortunately, as explained in Section 4 of the Preamble to this Volume, we have no such compactness, at least not in our present naive setting. Therefore the analogies may well lead us astray, as they did Euler and Lagrange. In order to reinstate them we need a generalized theory similar to that of Chapter VI of Volume I.

The discrete time problem that we have described is now generally referred to as one of "dynamic programming." It is easy to see that it can be expressed as a problem of minimum for a function of a finite number of variables, subject to equality and inequality constraints. Such a problem is referred to in computing circles as a "programming problem" or simply as a "program," although doubtless these terms will be less restricted in the future, as more general discrete problems, such as those of max-min, come to be considered. Of course, a problem of maximum is included since it becomes one of minimum by change of sign; however, a max-min problem is more general.

We shall not comment on the special methods currently used in dynamic programming, but only on those derived from them, by analogy, for treating problems with continuous time. As regards the latter, it will suffice to say here that a detailed criticism is given in *Optimal Processes.* The methods are neither necessary nor sufficient, and they depend on assumptions of smoothness that are, in practice, never satisfied. This is an instance of the misleading character of such analogies.

The more general programming problems differ in a relatively minor way from the classical Euler-Lagrange problems of the constrained minimum of functions of a finite number of real variables. The difference lies in the presence of inequality constraints in addition to, or in place of, equality constraints. The corresponding slight modification of the variational Lagrange problem with constraints, and of the Lagrange multiplier rule for it, was made by Valentine some 30 years ago. It is clear, moreover, that Lagrange and his followers were well aware of the slight changes which result from the introduction of inequality constraints, since Lagrange applied his method of multipliers to problems of statics, in which the multipliers may be interpreted as the reactions of the constraints. In that case, the only difference that an inequality constraint $g(x) \leq 0$ makes at a point x at which $g(x) = 0$ is that the corresponding reaction is directed outward, and therefore that the relevant multiplier has the appropriate sign. There is, of course, no reaction from this constraint at a point at which $g(x) < 0$.

We mentioned in the Preamble to this Volume that the variational form of the Lagrange multiplier method does not take into account the phenomena of rigidity and anomaly. Actually, the corresponding difficulties in statics and in the constrained minima of functions of a finite number of variables are classical. They appear in overdetermined equilibrium states, as in the case of tables that stand on more than three legs. In such cases, the reactions of the constraints are indeterminate. In programming problems, it is usual to exclude all such possibilities, just as it is usual to do so in statics, by a special assumption concerning the nature of the constraints, which is termed the Kuhn-Tucker constraint qualification. We shall describe it below.

The basic programming problem is that of the minimum of a function $f(x)$ in the set $G \cap H$ of points x of Euclidean n-space, where G consists of the points that satisfy m inequalities $g_i(x) \leq 0$, and H of those which satisfy p equalities $h_j(x) = 0$, and where $i = 1, 2 \ldots, m, j = 1, 2, \ldots, p$. Let $x_0 \in G \cap H$, and suppose the functions g_i so ordered that $g_i(x_0) = 0$ $i = 1, 2, \ldots, m_0$, while $g_i(x_0) < 0$ $i = m_0 + 1, m_0 + 2, \ldots, m$. The point x_0 is then said to satisfy the Kuhn-Tucker constraint qualification, if the functions f, g_i, h_j are all continuously differentiable at x_0, and if, further, the gradients at x_0 of the functions h_j $j = 1, 2, \ldots, p$, and of those functions g_i for which $i = 1, 2, \ldots, m_0$, are linearly independent.

By slight changes in what can be found in a calculus book, with or without the proof, we thus have:

(12.1) Elementary Multiplier Rule. *Let x_0 provide a local minimum of f in $G \cap H$, and suppose that x_0 satisfies the Kuhn-Tucker constraint qualification. Then there* *exist reals* μ_i, λ_j $i = 1, 2, \ldots, m, j = 1, 2, \ldots, p$, *termed multipliers and subject to*

$$\mu_i \geq 0 \qquad i = 1, 2, \ldots, m_0; \qquad \mu_i = 0 \qquad i > m_0;$$

such that the function

$$\tilde{f}(x, \mu, \lambda) = f(x) + \sum_{i=1}^{m} \mu_i g_i(x) + \sum_{j=1}^{p} \lambda_j h_j(x)$$

has at x_0 *a vanishing gradient in* x.

We shall not prove this multiplier rule here, since we do not use it. However, proofs should certainly be given, in the future, in advanced calculus books. In the meantime, it is difficult to find a book dealing with discrete control theory or with programming that does *not* prove the rule.

What is perhaps more interesting than the rule itself, which, after all, represents only a necessary condition for a constrained minimum, is a discussion of some cases in which it is, at the same time, a sufficient condition, not only for a local minimum, but also for a global one. This again is to be found in many books:

(12.2) A Partial Converse of the Elementary Multiplier Rule. *Delete the hypotheses of* (12.1) *and suppose its conclusions satisfied. Suppose further that the functions* f, g_i *are convex, and that the functions* h_j *are linear. Then* f *assumes at* x_0 *its minimum in* $G \cap H$.

The proof of this converse is actually quite trivial. The function $\tilde{f} = f$ at x_0, and since $\tilde{f} \leq f$ in $G \cap H$, this proves our assertion.

Thus, subject to certain apparently rather natural assumptions, we have, for a programming problem, and in particular for the discrete time analogues of our problems of optimal control, some rather simple necessary and sufficient conditions for a minimum. Moreover, we get the impression that the sufficiency part is trivial.

There is only one drawback to this apparently ideal state of affairs: persons who come from it to the problems of optimal control with continuous time are unprepared for the totally different setup that they meet there, in which necessary conditions are illusory and the whole weight of the subject rests on questions of existence and sufficient conditions. Therefore, once again, the analogy with discrete problems turns out to be very misleading.

Methods based on (12.1) and (12.2) have a further weakness when we attempt to extend them to continuous time problems. It then turns out that the Kuhn-Tucker constraint qualifications exclude the phenomena of rigidity and anomaly, not only for the trajectories considered, but also for their subarcs. In practice these phenomena occur in many of the simplest problems, and one of the main advantages of the maximum principle is that it allows for them. For instance, in the oscillator problem of Section 10 of the Preamble to this Volume, a complete discussion is impossible without the anomalous trajectories, which are there the ones that touch the target at their terminal points.

Conceptually, the ideas at the back of (12.1) go back to Euler and Lagrange. Those implicit in the maximum principle represent a further evolution, which has taken over a hundred years, and which we describe to a certain extent in the Preamble to this Volume. It is this principle that is the starting point of our naive theory.

§13. SOME BASIC REMARKS ON LINEAR DIFFERENTIAL EQUATIONS

We find it necessary at this point to supplement the little knowledge of differential equations that we assume. We have already done so once, in Volume I, in Section 19 of Chapter I, and indeed a second time there in Section 28 of Chapter II. However, our present remarks are more directly concerned with the properties of solutions and are confined to the linear case. We shall apply them only in the case of constant coefficients, but it is convenient to give them here in the more general case where the coefficients vary with time.

In our remarks, it will be convenient to use some of the language and imagery of n-dimensional geometry. This is not always easy to visualize, and, in addition, our notation will be our own, so that the reader will need to remind himself frequently of its meaning. The basic facts that we describe are, however, really rather simple, and the best way to read this section may well be for the reader to rewrite it in the way that seems best for him. This, as a general rule, is a good way to study anything in mathematics.

In this section, a vector will usually be in n-space and will depend on t. The scalar product of two such vectors v_1, v_2 will be denoted by (v_1, v_2); it will also depend on t. We shall denote by A a fixed $n \times n$ matrix, whose elements are sufficiently often differentiable functions of t, and by A^*, its adjoint, derived by transposing rows and columns. In this section, most of the definitions will be relative to the fixed matrix A, or to its adjoint.

The symbols φ, ψ will be reserved for vectors which satisfy, respectively, the differential equations

$$\text{(13.1)} \qquad \text{(a) } \dot{\varphi} = A\varphi, \qquad \text{(b) } \dot{\psi} = -A^*\psi,$$

and where, moreover, ψ is not the constant 0. We shall write Ψ for the $(n-1)$-dimensional subspace, depending on t, which is formed by the vectors of n-space orthogonal to ψ.

We term continuously differentiable subspace a proper subspace of n-space, again dependent on t, whose points are the linear combinations of a system of continuously differentiable vectors. We reserve the letter Π for such a subspace, if it is $(n-1)$-dimensional for all values of t. We write $v \in \Pi$, and we say that v lies in Π, if, for each t, the vector v lies in Π.

We term Π covariant if for every continuously differentiable vector $v \in \Pi$ we have

$$\text{(13.2)} \qquad \dot{v} - Av \in \Pi.$$

(13.3) Characterization of Covariance. *Π is covariant if and only if it is a Ψ. This is the case if and only if it consists of the vectors of the form*

$$\text{(13.4)} \qquad v = \sum_{k=1}^{n-1} a_k \varphi_k,$$

where the a_k are scalars depending on t, and the φ_k are $n-1$ linearly independent solutions of (13.1)(a), *orthogonal to ψ at some $t = t_0$.*

PROOF. To see that any $\Psi^{\cdot}$ is covariant, we observe that, for differentiable $v \in \Psi^{\cdot}$, we have

$$0 = (d/dt)(v, \psi) = (\dot{v}, \psi) - (v, A^*\psi) = (\dot{v} - Av, \psi),$$

whence $\dot{v} - Av \in \Psi^{\cdot}$. Further, to obtain (13.4), we first note that, for any φ,

$$\text{(13.5)} \qquad \frac{d}{dt}(\varphi, \psi) = (A\varphi, \psi) - (\varphi, A^*\psi) = 0,$$

so that $(\varphi, \psi) = 0$ at t_0 implies $(\varphi, \psi) = 0$ for all t, and therefore implies $\varphi \in \Psi^{\cdot}$. Hence, for $n - 1$ linearly independent φ_k we have $\varphi_k \in \Psi^{\cdot}$, so that $\Psi^{\cdot}$ must consist of the vectors of the form (13.4). Conversely if the φ_k are so chosen orthogonal to ψ at $t = t_0$, the system of vectors (13.4) constitutes $\Psi^{\cdot}$.

Finally, if Π is covariant, and π is its unit normal,† we find, for differentiable $v \in \Pi$,

$$(\dot{v}, \pi) + (v, \dot{\pi}) = \frac{d}{dt}(v, \pi) = 0$$

$$0 = (\dot{v} - Av, \pi) = -(v, \dot{\pi}) - (Av, \pi) = -(v, \dot{\pi} + A^*\pi),$$

so that the vector $\dot{\pi} + A^*\pi$ is orthogonal to every differentiable $v \in \Pi$, and so to Π, and therefore it is a scalar multiple $q\pi$ of the normal. We can thus choose a scalar λ so that

$$\frac{d}{dt}(\lambda\pi) + A^*\lambda = (\dot{\lambda} + q\lambda)\pi = 0,$$

and this means that $\lambda\pi$ is a ψ, so that Π is then $\Psi^{\cdot}$. Thus (13.3) is established.

If the value at $t = t_1$ of a vector v, depending on t, lies in the corresponding position of the subspace $\Psi^{\cdot}$, we say that v intersects $\Psi^{\cdot}$ at $t = t_1$, and we write

$$v \in (t_1)\Psi^{\cdot}.$$

More generally, given a positive integer k, we say that v has a k-ple intersection with $\Psi^{\cdot}$, or has contact of order $k - 1$ with it, at $t = t_1$, and we write

$$v \in {}^k(t_1)\Psi^{\cdot},$$

if v is $(k - 1)$ times differentiable in t, and if the scalar product (v, ψ) and its first $k - 1$ derivatives in t all vanish at $t = t_1$. When T is a set of values of t, we write

$$v \in {}^k(T)\Psi^{\cdot},$$

if T consists of values t_α to which correspond positive integers k_α (≥ 1), such that

$$v \in {}^{k_\alpha}(t_\alpha)\Psi^{\cdot} \qquad \text{and} \qquad \Sigma_\alpha k_\alpha \geq k.$$

We shall say that an $n - 1$ times differentiable vector v, depending on t, is in general position if there is no value t_0 of t and no $\Psi^{\cdot}$ for which v has an n-ple intersection with $\Psi^{\cdot}$ at $t = t_0$.

(13.6) Characterization of General Position. *In order that an $n - 1$ times differentiable vector v be in general position, it is necessary and sufficient that, for each t_0, the*

---

† Except on this page, π has its usual meaning. (The rarer twin form was intended.)

values at t_0 of the vectors

(13.7)
$$\left(\frac{d}{dt} - A\right)^k v \qquad (k = 0, 1, \ldots, n-1)$$

be linearly independent.

PROOF. We have, for every ψ,

$$\left(\frac{d}{dt}\right)^k (v, \psi) = \left[\left(\frac{d}{dt} - A\right)^k v, \psi\right],$$

because this is clearly true when $k = 1$, and by an easy induction it holds generally. To derive (13.6) it is now sufficient to observe that, at t_0, linear dependence of the vectors (13.7) is equivalent to their being simultaneously orthogonal to the initial value at t_0 of some ψ.

(13.8) The Isolated Intersections Theorem. *If T is a bounded infinite set of values of t, the relation $v \in (T)\Psi$ cannot hold for a v in general position.*

PROOF. Suppose this false. There would then exist in T a sequence of values t_ν with a limit t^*. At the t_ν and therefore also at t^*, we would have $(v, \psi) = 0$. Between any two t_ν there would be a zero of the derivative $(d/dt)(v, \psi)$, so that, by continuity, the latter would vanish at t^*. Similarly, at t^*, the successive derivatives of (v, ψ), of orders $0, 1, \ldots, n-1$, would vanish, so that v would not be in general position.

(13.9) Sharper Result in a Special Case. *Let A be a constant matrix with real eigenvalues, and let v be a constant vector. Then the relation $v \in {}^n(T)\Psi$ cannot hold for any set T unless $v \in \Psi$, i.e., unless (v, ψ) vanishes identically.*

PROOF. We can arrange for A to be singular by replacing A and ψ by $A = \tilde{A} - \lambda I$ and $\tilde{\psi} = \psi e^{\lambda t}$, if necessary, where λ is an eigenvalue of A and I denotes the identity matrix, and by observing that

$$\left(\frac{d}{dt} + \tilde{A}^*\right)\tilde{\psi} = e^{\lambda t}\left(\frac{d}{dt} + A^*\right)\psi = 0.$$

The assertion is thus certainly evident when $n = 1$, and we suppose it true when n is replaced by $n - 1$.

Since A is now singular, there is a constant unit vector a such that $aA^* = 0$, and therefore $a\dot{\psi} = -aA^*\psi = 0$. By a rotation of axes, we may suppose a along the x_1 axis. We denote by $\hat{v}$ and $\hat{A}$ the $(n-1)$-dimensional vector and the

$$(n-1) \times (n-1)$$

matrix, derived from v and A by omitting, respectively, the first component, and the first pair of rows and columns. The vector $\dot{\psi}$ now lies in the $(n-1)$-dimensional subspace orthogonal to x_1, and we have

$$\left(\frac{d}{dt} + \hat{A}^*\right)\dot{\psi} = \left(\frac{d}{dt} + A^*\right)\dot{\psi} = 0.$$

Further, the expression $(\hat{v}, \dot{\psi}) = (v, \dot{\psi})$, regarded as function of t, has at least $n - 1$ zeros, each counted with its multiplicity since this expression is the derivative of (v, ψ). By the inductive hypothesis, this expression therefore vanishes identically, so that (v, ψ) can only be a constant, which is then clearly 0.

§14. SUSPECTED SOLUTIONS OF THE SIMPLEST TIME-OPTIMAL PROBLEMS

We consider in n-space a particle whose position x at the time t is subject to the linear differential equation, with constant matrix-coefficients,

(14.1) $$\dot{x} = Ax + Bu,$$

where A, B are $n \times n$ and $n \times r$ matrices, and u is an r-dimensional vector with values in a convex polyhedron, or polytope, of r-space, which contains the origin, and which we denote by U. Our problem is to determine a piecewise continuously differentiable control $u(t)$ for which our particle is transferred in least time from the given initial position x_0 to a target consisting of the origin of x.

Instead of the origin of x, we could take as target any equilibrium point, i.e., any point x_1 for which there exists a trajectory that reduces to this point for all t. This means that there exists a point $u_1 \in U$ such that $Ax_1 + Bu_1 = 0$; therefore, by writing x, u for $x - x_1$, $u - u_1$ and translating U so that u_1 becomes the origin of u, the problem reduces to the one with the origin of x as a target. Our main results would also remain valid if A, B were allowed to depend suitably on t, and if U were allowed to be a convex figure, instead of a convex polytope. The minor changes needed are indicated in *Optimal Processes*, with additional elucidations by the translator.

We shall require in the sequel a general position assumption, which is the following: each vector v, which has the form Bw, where w is the direction of an edge of U, is in general position. This condition, which affects only a finite number of vectors v, may in practice be fulfilled by slightly rotating U if necessary. However, it constitutes an essential restriction on our method. In accordance with the characterization (13.6) of the preceding section, the condition states that, for each such direction w, the vectors

(14.2) $$Bw, ABw, \ldots, A^{n-1}Bw$$

are linearly independent. The reason for this restriction will appear shortly.

In regard to our stipulation that $u(t)$ be piecewise continuously differentiable, this is the natural one in a naive theory, since the solutions will turn out to be so, and since we are not troubled at the moment by questions of existence or compactness. However, it goes without saying that this requirement can here be relaxed. In linear problems, which are, properly speaking, quadratic variational problems, a natural space of controls is that of square integrable ones, and this is the one used in *Optimal Processes*. We prefer not to commit ourselves to such a choice in what is, for us, a very special type of control problems, which we treat somewhat cursorily, whereas in *Optimal Processes* an actual existence theorem is proved at this stage using Hilbert space techniques. We have not thought it worthwhile to go into so much detail in problems that contain unpleasant restrictions.

We pass on to the study of our "suspects."

By definition, a suspected solution, i.e., a pair consisting of a suspected optimal trajectory $x(t)$ and a corresponding suspected optimal control $u(t)$, is one that obeys the maximum principle. The latter asserts the existence of a nonvanishing solution $y = \psi(t)$ of the adjoint equation

(14.3) $$\dot{y} = -A^*y,$$

where A^* is A transposed, such that the expression

$$H(x, y, u) = (y, Ax + Bu)$$

attains, when $x = x(t), y = \psi(t)$, its maximum in u at the value $u = u(t)$. (We use here our previous notation for the scalar product of two vectors; t is any point of the relevant time interval.) In addition, certain end-conditions are to be satisfied: at the initial time, which we denote by t_0, the vector $x(t)$ takes the value x_0, and at the final time, which we agree to make $t = 0$, we have, on the one hand, $x(t) = 0$, and on the other hand, the transversality condition in t, which states that $H \geq 0$ for the arguments $(x, y, u) = (0, \psi(0), u(0))$. (This last condition may be verified at any convenient time t instead of at the terminal time $t = 0$, for we remarked in the Preamble to this Volume that H is constant on a suspected solution, as a result of the maximum principle.)

Before proceeding any further, we need to verify that a suspected solution fulfills the condition that we laid down, that $u(t)$ be piecewise continuously differentiable. Actually we shall find that $u(t)$ is piecewise constant. We term switching time for a suspected solution one for which $u(t)$ is discontinuous in t.

We observe that for any fixed t, the maximum in u of $H(x(t), \psi(t), u)$ is attained when the scalar product $(\psi(t), Bu)$ is maximal, and since the latter is linear in u, its maximum is attained at a vertex of U. It is attained at this vertex only, unless there be, through the latter, at least one edge on which our scalar product is constant; in which case the direction w of such an edge satisfies, by subtraction, the relation

(14.4) $$(\psi(t), Bw) = 0.$$

By (13.8), this last can only occur at a finite set T of values of t between t_0 and 0, since Bw is in general position. By continuity of ψ, the subset of the complement of T, at which the maximum in u occurs at a same vertex, is relatively closed. Hence, only one such vertex can occur when t lies in a complementary interval of T, so that the switching times lie only in T.

If A has only real eigenvalues, (13.9) shows that there are at most $n - 1$ switching times at which the value of $u(t)$ switches from a vertex of U to another, and at which the edge joining these two vertices has a fixed direction w. The total number of switchings is thus at most $n - 1$ times the number of nonparallel edges of U. In particular if U is a cube, this is at most $r \cdot (n - 1)$. However, such estimates of the number of switching times in the case in which A has real eigenvalues generally appear to be much too large, and sharper estimates are not known.

§15. UNICITY AND OPTIMALITY

We pass on to the relationship of our suspected solutions to actual solutions. For this we require:

(15.1) Lemma. *Let $u(t)$ be a suspected optimal control and $\hat{u}(t)$ an arbitrary control such that both transfer our particle from the initial position x_0 at time t_0 to the origin at time $t = 0$. Then $\hat{u}(t)$ coincides with $u(t)$ almost everywhere in $t_0 \leq t \leq 0$.*

PROOF. We write $v(t)$, $\hat{v}(t)$ for $Bu(t)$, $B\hat{u}(t)$, and we denote by G an $n \times n$ matrix $G(t)$, which is the identity matrix for $t = t_0$, and which satisfies the adjoint differentiable equation

(15.2) $$\dot{G} = -GA.$$

We write further G^* for the matrix $G^*(t)$, which is also the identity matrix for $t = t_0$ and which satisfies the differential equation $\dot{G}^* = AG^*$. Then GG^* is the identity for $t = t_0$ and has the derivative

$$\dot{G}G^* + G\dot{G}^* = (-GA)G^* + G(AG^*) = 0.$$

It follows that G^* is the inverse G^{-1} of G.

Now any vector solution φ of $\dot{\varphi} = A\varphi$ has the form G^*x_0, where $x_0 = \varphi(t_0)$, and we can regard the differential equation (14.1) as obtained from the one for φ by adding the perturbation Bu, which is now v. Its solution, according to the old method of variation of constants, may thus be written

$$x = G^*\xi$$

where

$$\xi(t_0) = x_0, \qquad G^*\dot{\xi} = v.$$

This last equation, multiplied by G, becomes $\dot{\xi} = Gv$, and hence we find that the solutions of (14.1) have the form

$$x = G^{-1} \cdot \left(x_0 + \int_{t_0}^{t} Gv\, dt\right). \tag{15.3}$$

In our lemma we suppose the two trajectories concerned to agree at both ends in regard to position and time. We apply to each the equation (15.3) with $t = 0$, after multiplying by G and subtracting x_0. Hence

$$\int_{t_0}^{0} Gv(t)\, dt = \int_{t_0}^{0} G\hat{v}(t)\, dt.$$

If we multiply this scalarwise, by a constant vector y_0, and recall that any vector function $y = \psi(t)$ subject to (14.3) has the form $y = y_0G$ where y_0 is its initial value at $t = t_0$, we find that

$$\int_{t_0}^{0} \{yv(t) - y\hat{v}(t)\}\, dt = 0. \tag{15.4}$$

However, since $u(t)$ is subject to the maximum principle, we can choose y for the conjugate vector along the trajectory $x(t)$ so that at $x(t), y(t)$ the function $H(x, y, u)$ of u attains its maximum at $u = u(t)$. The integrand of (15.4) which can be written as the difference

$$H(x, y, u(t)) - H(x, y, \hat{u}(t))$$

at $x(t), y(t)$, is thus non-negative, and consequently, 0 almost everywhere. Further, in the set of t for which this difference vanishes and $u(t) \neq \hat{u}(t)$, the maximum of H in u is not uniquely attained, so that a relation of the form (14.4) then holds, as in the preceding section, and this is only possible at a finite set of t. Hence $u(t) = \hat{u}(t)$ almost everywhere, as asserted.

(15.5) Theorem. *Let $u(t)$ be a suspected optimal control which transfers our particle from the initial position x_0 at time t_0 to the origin at time $t = 0$, and suppose that the corresponding function $x(t)$, which defines the trajectory described by the particle, is not constant in any time interval terminating at $t = 0$, i.e., that the final arc of the trajectory does not reduce to a single point, consisting of the origin. Then $u(t)$ is an optimal control, and the only one to make this transfer.*

In the above statement, it is understood that we identify two controls which differ only in t-measure 0. We observe further that the case in which a final arc of the trajectory reduces to the origin need not be specially excluded unless the origin of u is a vertex of U.

PROOF OF (15.5). Let $\hat{u}(t)$ $t_0 \leq t \leq t_1$, where $t_1 \leq 0$, be any control which transfers, in the same time or less, our particle from x_0 to the origin. By setting $\hat{u}(t) = 0$ for $t_1 < t \leq 0$, we obtain a control which effects the transfer in the same time as the given $u(t)$. By Lemma (15.1), we then have, almost everywhere, $\hat{u}(t) = u(t)$, and hence also $t_1 = 0$.

Similarly, in the excluded case all trajectories joining x_0 to 0 are identical except for final arcs of constancy.

For a fuller account of linear problems, we refer the reader to *Optimal Processes*, where both the existence of a solution and the "synthesis" of the optimal controls are considered.

§16. TWO DIMENSIONAL PROBLEMS: SWITCHING TIMES AND BASIC CONSTRUCTIONS

In the rest of this Chapter, we treat the case in which A, B are nonsingular 2×2 matrices and U is a parallelogram with the origin as center. (If B is singular, we can control the system with a single parameter, and such problems were illustrated in the Preamble to this Volume.) Moreover, we shall, for simplicity, treat only the case in which the eigenvalues of A have negative real parts. This means that the trajectories with $u(t) = 0$ approach the origin for large t; we then say that the system is stable. The eigenvalues may be complex or real.

Accordingly, by choice of unit of time, we may suppose that these eigenvalues are either $\lambda \pm i$, or λ, $\lambda - 1$, where $\lambda < 0$. By elementary changes of coordinates, given by affine transformations of the x and u planes, indicated in *Optimal Processes*, we may suppose that B is the unit matrix, and that A is one of the matrices

(16.1)
$$\text{(a)}\ \begin{pmatrix} \lambda & -1 \\ 1 & \lambda \end{pmatrix}; \qquad \text{(b)}\ \begin{pmatrix} \lambda & 0 \\ 0 & \lambda - 1 \end{pmatrix}.$$

Here $\lambda < 0$ is assumed, and we shall need also a general position assumption. As we shall see below, the latter will affect only case (b), and it then excludes the case in which the parallelogram U, after our affine transformation, has a side parallel to a coordinate axis. To solve our problem completely and uniquely, with these assumptions, we have only, by Theorem (15.5), to find a suspected optimal control which transfers a given x_0 to the origin. We shall use the complex notation for a vector in the plane.

To determine the suspected optimal controls and trajectories, according to the maximum principle, we must first solve the adjoint equation $\dot{y} = -A^*y$, where A^* is the transpose of (a) or (b) in (16.1). The solution is $y = ce^{-\lambda t}\eta$, where η is

$$e^{i(t+\alpha)}, \quad \text{or} \quad \cos\alpha + ie^t \sin\alpha,$$

according to whether we are in case (a) or (b); here α, c are constants of integration, and we have $c > 0$. We have to determine the directions of y orthogonal to the sides of U, and so the values of t at which $u(t)$ switches from one vertex to another. This is most easily done by determining the corresponding intersections of the curves $\eta(t)\ -\infty < t \leq 0$, with the lines ℓ_1, ℓ_2 through the origin, perpendicular to the sides of the parallelogram U. The η-curves in case (a) are counterclockwise unit circle arcs, and the intersections occur in four sets of periodic values of t, of period 2π; in case (b) they are vertical segments going from the horizontal diameter of the unit circle to the circumference, upward in the upper half of this circle, downward in

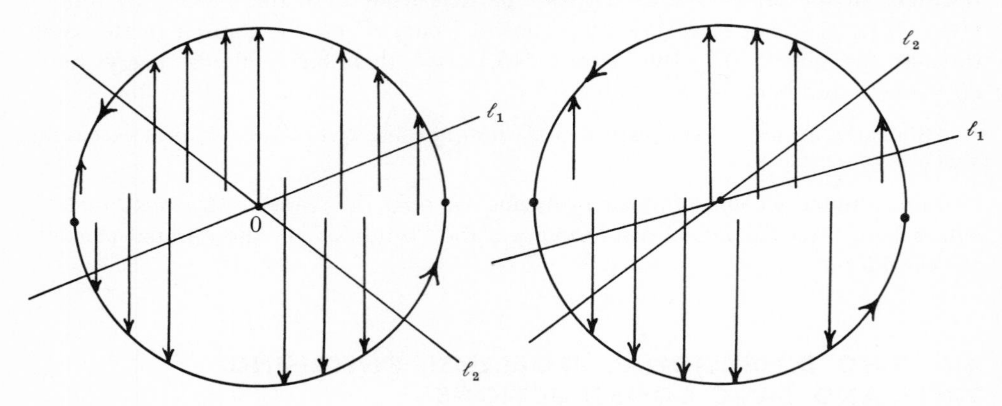

The intersections of the lines ℓ_1, ℓ_2 with the η-curves in cases (a) and (b), when ℓ_1, ℓ_2 are in different quadrants

The corresponding figure with the lines in a same quadrant

the lower half; so that in case (b), if the lines ℓ_1, ℓ_2 lie in different quadrants, each η curve has one such intersection, unless it is too short, while if they lie in the same pair of quadrants, as in our second figure, some η-curves have two intersections with the pair of lines, and the others have one or none. We note further that, in case (b), the η-curves that reduce to the single points $\eta = \pm 1$, and also the two η-curves situated on the upper and lower halves of the imaginary axis, respectively, coincide with a whole segment of a possible position of one of the lines ℓ_1, ℓ_2, unless we specifically exclude this possibility by requiring U to have no side parallel to a coordinate axis. This is the general position exclusion we forecast earlier, and it is clearly the only such exclusion we need to make.

For simplicity, we suppose ℓ_1 in the first and third quadrants. This is no loss of generality. Moreover, we denote by α_k $(k = 1, \ldots, 4)$ the angular sectors into which

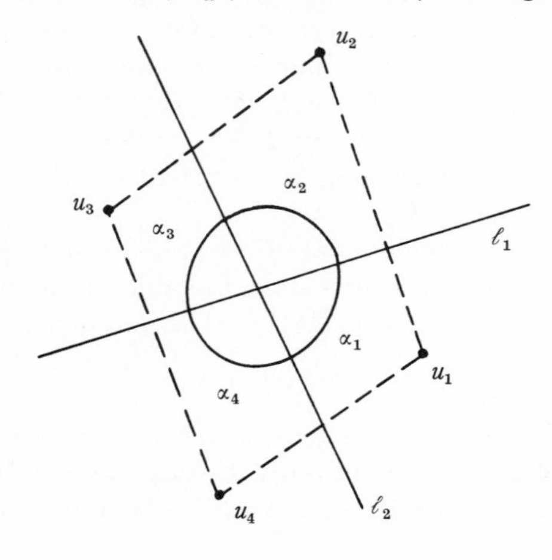

the pairs ℓ_1, ℓ_2 divide the plane, and we use the same symbols for the corresponding angles. We write further u_k ($k = 1, \ldots, 4$) for the vertices of U. The indices are chosen, for definiteness, so that as we proceed counterclockwise around the origin, starting from the real axis, we pass successively from α_1 to α_2 by crossing ℓ_1, then from α_2 to α_3 by crossing ℓ_2, and so forth, as shown in the figure. Moreover, u_k is, for each k, the vertex of U in α_k. We note that when $\eta(t)$ is in the sector α_k, the control $u(t)$ along our suspected optimal trajectory takes the value u_k.

We term sojourn time at u_k, or in α_k, the time that elapses between consecutive switches, and for which $u(t) = u_k$, or what comes to the same, $\eta(t)$ is in the angular sector α_k. In case (a), this sojourn time is simply α_k, the measure of the angle itself; it does not depend on the time and place at which the former of the switches occurs. In case (b), a sojourn only takes place when ℓ_1, ℓ_2 lie in the same pair of quadrants, and it is then in α_2; we calculate the corresponding sojourn time τ. We denote to this effect, by t^* and $t^* + \tau$, the initial and final times of the sojourn, and by γ_1, γ_2 the angles made by ℓ_1, ℓ_2 with the real axis. Since the point $\eta(t)$ lies on ℓ_1 for $t = t^*$ and on ℓ_2 for $t = t^* + \tau$, we find that

$$\tan \gamma_1 = e^{t^*} \tan \alpha, \qquad \tan \gamma_2 = e^{t^*+\tau} \tan \alpha,$$

and hence that $\tau = \log (\tan \gamma_2/\tan \gamma_1)$, which again does not depend on the time and place at which the former of the switches occurs.

We still have to determine the trajectories. To this effect we denote by x_k ($k = 1, \ldots, 4$) the vertices $-A^{-1}u_k$ of the parallelogram derived from U by the affine transformation $u \to x$ given by setting $Ax + u = 0$, i.e., $x = -A^{-1}u$. The trajectories for which the control is u_k are then subject to

$$\frac{d}{dt}(x - x_k) = A(x - x_k).$$

They are obtained by translation of the origin to the point x_k, from the corresponding solutions of $\dot{x} = Ax$, i.e., from the curves $x = \varphi(t)$. The latter have the form $ae^{\lambda t}\xi(t)$, where ξ is similar to our previous η, and is given by the expression

$$e^{i(t+\beta)}, \quad \text{or} \quad \cos \beta + ie^{-t} \sin \beta,$$

according as we are in case (a) or (b); here a and β are constants of integration, and

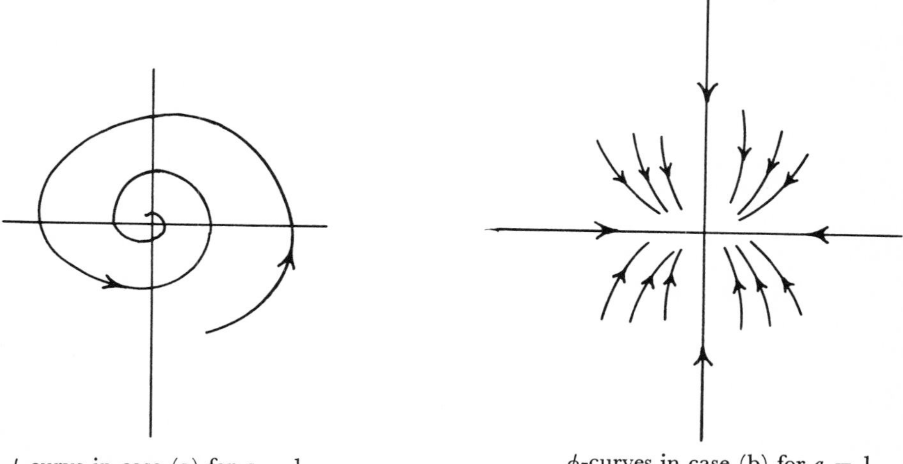

ϕ-curve in case (a) for $a = 1$

ϕ-curves in case (b) for $a = 1$

we have $a > 0$ except for the trivial solution $\varphi = 0$. We sketch the φ-curves for $-\infty < t < +\infty$ in the case $a = 1$, from which the general case follows by a magnification a. The origin is reached for $t = +\infty$. We may remark that the ξ-curves and our previous η-curves coincide, except that in case (b) they are reversed. The φ-curves are derived by multiplying by the factor $ae^{\lambda t}$, which deforms them toward the origin.

We have to fit together suitable translations of these φ-curves, for which the origin has been shifted, in turn, to the appropriate vertex x_k.

For this purpose, just as in the examples treated in the Preamble to this Volume, we proceed from the target, backward along the relevant trajectories. Each of these must contain a final arc on which controls are not switched, by Section 14. There are four trajectories on which this final arc can lie, those with the control at one of the four vertices u_k. We denote by C_k the final suspected optimal part, if any, of such

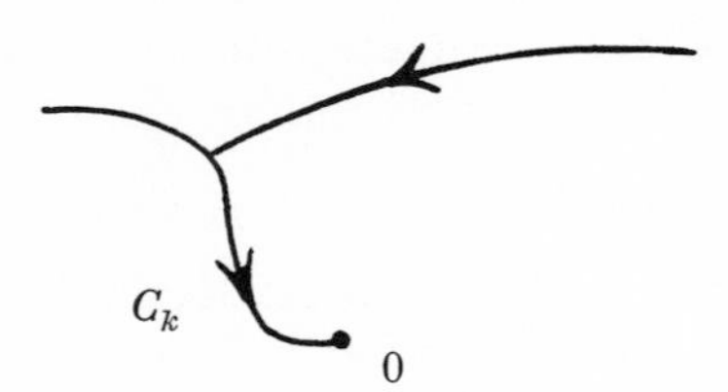

a trajectory ending at the origin, and by $C_{k\ell}$ the subset, if any, of C_k on which the control may switch to u_k from u_l. From a point of $C_{k\ell}$ we may now proceed backward along the trajectory through that point for which the control is u_ℓ, and so on. We note that on this new arc, the previous switching position, if any, is completely determined by the sojourn time at u_ℓ. In fact, as we shall see, the switch must occur on a rather simple locus, derived from $C_{k\ell}$ by an affine transformation.

§17. DISCUSSION OF CASE (a)

The curve C_k $k = 1, \ldots, 4$ is here an arc $-\alpha_k \le t \le 0$ of the translation by $-x_k$ of the φ-curve terminating, for $t = 0$, at $\varphi(0) = x_k$. By choice of x, the switch to u_k can occur anywhere on C_k, but only from u_{k-1}. (If $k = 1$, $k - 1$ is understood (mod 4) and so is 4.) Further, for any point x of C_k, if we denote by $\hat{x}$ the preceding switch-point on the trajectory through x with control u_{k-1}, and by $\hat{t}$, $\hat{t} + \tau$ the times at which $\hat{x}$ and x are reached on this trajectory, we find that, for appropriate constants a, β,

$$\hat{x} - x_{k-1} = ae^{\lambda \hat{t}} e^{i(\hat{t}+\beta)},$$

and that $x - x_{k-1}$ has a similar expression with $\hat{t} + \tau$ in place of $\hat{t}$. Hence

$$x - x_{k-1} = (\hat{x} - x_{k-1}) e^{\lambda \tau} e^{i\tau}.$$

Moreover, τ is the sojourn time α_{k-1}, which is the same for all $x \in C_k$. Thus the locus of the switches immediately preceding those on C_k is derived from C_k by a magnification $e^{-\lambda\tau}$ and a rotation $-\tau$, about x_{k-1}, where $\tau = \alpha_{k-1}$. Further, the initial point of this locus is clearly the final point of C_{k-1}.

By forming in this way the successive images of the four curves C_k and joining them together, we thus obtain four curves which contain all possible switches. The curves cannot cross, since we have no multiple switches. They tend to infinity, since the successive arcs forming them are magnified in a ratio $e^{-\lambda t} > 1$ from the corresponding arcs of the preceding stage on their neighbors. Hence they divide the plane into four domains, all extending to infinity, in which the control $u(t)$ remains constant on our suspected optimal trajectories.

In other words, we can now replace $u(t)$ by a corresponding function $u(x)$, which takes only the four values u_k $k = 1, \ldots, 4$. This is the solution to the so-called synthesis problem.

At the same time we see, since our construction provides a continuous deformation of the arcs C_k into their successive images, that the suspected optimal trajectories thus constructed cover the whole plane. This automatically implies, by Theorem (15.5), that our problem is solved uniquely for each initial position x_0. All this, and also case (b) below, is very beautifully illustrated by diagrams in *Optimal Processes*. In this connection, the reader may note that the final diagram, containing the optimal control curves, which thus cover the plane, can be obtained quite simply by suitably translating the domains bounded by pairs of switching curves onto appropriate portions of the elementary diagram giving the φ-curves, and then cutting out these portions and pasting them back together, with the domains in their original positions. This construction illustrates the use to which one can put the solution of the synthesis problem.

We pass on to case (b), which we subdivide into case (b_1) when ℓ_1, ℓ_2 lie in different pairs of quadrants, and case (b_2), when they lie in the same pair, namely the first and third quadrants.

§18. DISCUSSION OF CASE (b_1)

We refer the reader to our η- and φ-diagrams, which give the η- and φ-curves. The latter are also the same in case (b_2), but the derived constructions will depend on the positions of U, which are different. We note that the φ-curves are not affected by our setting $a = 1$, except as regards the time t along them. There is only one φ-curve through a given point other than the origin.

We refer also to our definition of the curves C_k and of their switching subsets $C_{k\ell}$. Each of the C_k is here an infinite arc, since there is, in each α_k, at least η-curve permanently in it for $t \leq 0$. However, it is only for $k = 2$ or 4 and $l = 1$ or 3 that there is a subset $C_{k\ell} \neq 0$ at which the control was switched from u_ℓ to u_k, since an η-curve which crosses one of the lines ℓ_1, ℓ_2 must start for $t = -\infty$ in α_1 or α_3 and end up for $t = 0$ in α_2 or α_4. We see further that $C_{k\ell}$ then coincides with the whole of C_k.

We now denote by D_1 and D_3 the domains, which contain C_1 and C_3 respectively, into which $C_2 + C_4$ separates the plane. We shall solve the synthesis problem by setting $u = u_2$ on C_2, $u = u_4$ on C_4 and $u = u_1$, $u = u_3$ in D_1, D_3, respectively. We note, incidentally, that each C_k, when prolonged as a trajectory for positive t, ends at the corresponding x_k. This implies that we can distinguish the domains separated by $C_2 + C_4$, specifying that D_1 contains the point x_3, and, equivalently, because of symmetry, that D_3 contains the point x_1.

The verification of this geometrically rather intuitive remark, for the various positions and shapes of the parallelogram U, would be very tedious if done by computation. Instead we can make use of the unicity theorem (15.5). We have only to show that C_2 and C_4 are not met a second time by the prolongation of C_1 for $t > 0$. We shall suppose there is such an intersection. If it occurs for $t = +\infty$, i.e., at x_1 itself, then by altering slightly the position of u_1 we would obtain a problem in which x_1 is in D_1, so that the crossing of C_2 or C_4 occurs for a finite t.

In that case, since our problem does not contain the time explicitly, we can readjust the time on C_1 to agree with that on C_2 or C_4 at the intersection. We can thus form a trajectory C by following C_1 prolonged as far as this intersection, and then

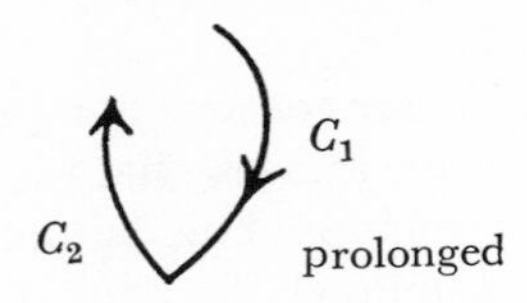

the final arc of C_2 or C_4. In that case, the initial and terminal points of C both coincide with the origin. By Theorem (15.5), C cannot then satisfy the maximum principle. On the other hand, by choosing the curve $\eta(t)$ in the η-diagram, so that it crosses ℓ_1 or ℓ_3 for the value of t at which we switch from C_1 prolonged to C_2 or C_4 respectively, we find that C, by our previous analysis, does satisfy the maximum principle. This contradiction completes the proof.

On our suspected optimal trajectories, we shall solve the synthesis problem by setting $u = u_2$ on C_2, $u = u_4$ on C_4 and $u = u_1$, $u = u_3$ in D_1, D_3, respectively. We obtain a picture of these trajectories in D_1 and D_3 by simply translating D_1 by the vector $-x_1$, and D_3 by $-x_3$; they are then the corresponding parts of φ-curves.

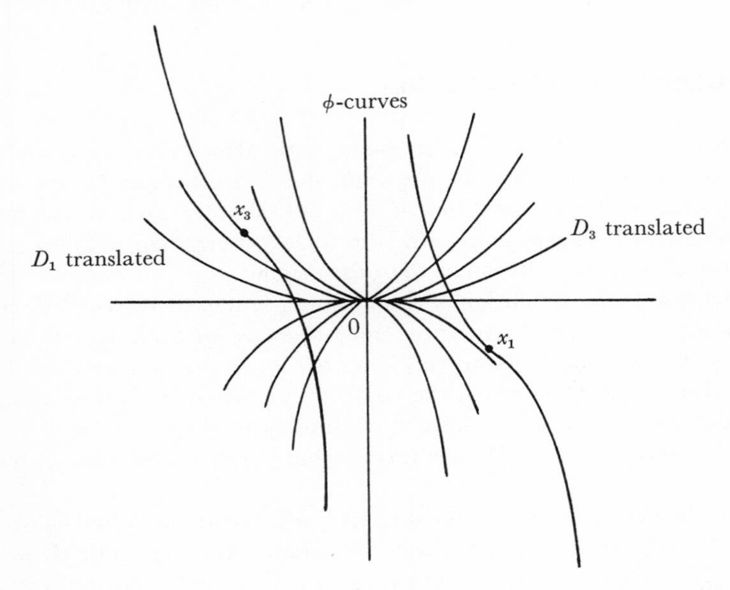

What mainly matters is that the composite picture obtained by translating the domains back is then completely covered by suspected optimal trajectories, which are understood to be completed by final arcs of C_2 or C_4, so as to terminate at the origin. By Theorem (15.5), these trajectories, therefore, constitute the unique solution of our problem.

Here again, so as not to depend too much on our drawings, and partly to provide methods applicable to equations whose coefficients vary with t, and to the higher dimensional cases, we give an alternative analytical proof that our suspected optimal trajectories cover the plane. To this effect, given any positive number h, we define in D_1 or D_3 a certain deformation Γ^* of $C_2 + C_4$, obtained as follows: let x be any point of $C_2 + C_4$, and let t be the corresponding time. We follow backward from x for a time h the suspected optimal trajectory which switches controls from u_1 or u_3. Let x^* be the point so reached, which thus corresponds to the time $t^* = t - h$. The locus of such points x^* in D_1 or in D_3 will be denoted by Γ^*. In order to show that

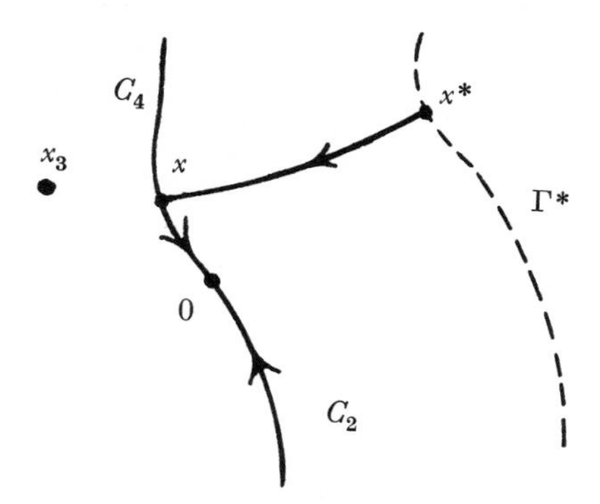

our suspected optimal trajectories cover the whole of D_1 and the whole of D_3, it is enough to show that as $h \to \infty$, the curve Γ^* in each of these domains approaches infinity, i.e., that given any finite disc in the plane, there is a value h_0 such that Γ^* lies wholly outside the disc when $h > h_0$.

This last is, however, rather easy to establish, because, as we shall see, Γ^* is derived from $C_2 + C_4$ by a very simple transformation Λ. Thus, if we consider the deformation in D_3, the differences $x - x_3$, $x^* - x_3$ have the form

$$ae^{\lambda t}(\cos \beta + ie^{-t} \sin \beta)$$

and that of the similar expression with t^* in place of t. In these two expressions the constants a, β are the same. Hence

$$x^* - x_3 = \Lambda(x - x_3)$$

where Λ is the matrix $\begin{pmatrix} 1 & 0 \\ 0 & e^h \end{pmatrix}$ multiplied by the factor $e^{-\lambda h}$. Thus Γ^* results from $C_2 + C_4$ by an affine transformation, which magnifies both coordinates, and since its origin is the point x_3 *outside* D_3, it follows that Γ^* approaches infinity for large h, as required.

§19. DISCUSSION OF CASE (b_2)

This case is more complicated than the preceding one because in it we attain the number 2 of switches on a same trajectory. This is the maximum number possible here, according to Section 14.

We again refer to our diagram of η-curves. C_1 and C_3 will now be infinite arcs, because in α_1 and α_3 there are η-curves which remain from $t = -\infty$ to $t = 0$. The other η-curves which terminate in α_1 or α_3 cross both ℓ_1 and ℓ_2; they start in α_3 or α_1, respectively, and their sojourn time in α_2, or in α_4, is the previously introduced constant τ. Finally, there are η-curves terminating in α_2 or α_4; they start in α_1 or α_3, and their time in α_2 or α_4 is at most τ. (Indeed, by the argument used earlier, this time would be exactly τ if we prolonged them for positive t.) Thus C_2, C_4 are now finite arcs which correspond to a time interval τ. We see further that $C_{k\ell} = C_k$ for $\ell = k - 1$, and $C_{k\ell} = 0$ otherwise. Each C_k is thus a switching curve.

There are, however, two further switching curves C_2', C_4': they consist of the points at which a suspected optimal trajectory switches its control from u_1 to u_2, or from u_3 to u_4, prior to switching later from u_2 or u_4, to u_3 or u_1, respectively. The curves C_2' and C_4' lead from the free end of C_2, and that of C_4, respectively, to infinity. They are constructed most simply in terms of the operation Λ defined in case (b_1), where we now set $h = \tau$. They are, respectively, the affine transforms resulting from Λ when the origin is taken at x_2 or x_4 of the curves C_3 and C_1. In fact, to reach the switch point on C_2' or C_4', we proceed backward for a time τ along the portion of a suspected optimal trajectory which precedes its final switch point on C_3 or C_1. Thus the same construction as in our discussion of case (b_1) applies here, with the indices changed around and with τ for h.

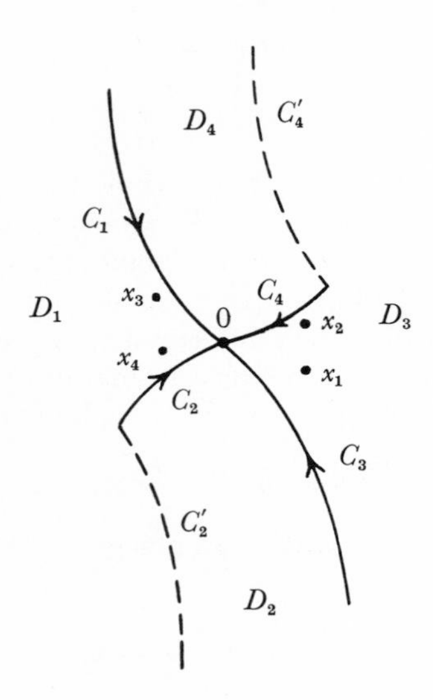

We denote by D_1, D_2, D_3, D_4 the four domains into which the plane is separated by the switching curves. They are indicated in the figure. We observe† that D_1 contains the points x_3, x_4 and that D_3 contains x_1, x_2. We shall solve the synthesis problem by setting $u = u_k$ in D_k $k = 1, \ldots, 4$. By translating the domains D_k by $-x_k$, we obtain a picture‡ of our suspected optimal trajectories in each of them, simply by again taking the corresponding parts of the φ-diagram. In this way, or by a modification of the alternative argument used in case (b_1), we find that these trajectories, completed by the final parts of the C_k, cover the whole plane. As before, it then follows from Theorem (15.5) that they solve our problem uniquely.

† The proofs are similar to that of the corresponding statement in case (b_1).
‡ We leave the reader to draw this for himself.

Chapter II

The Application of Standard Variational Methods to Optimal Control

§20. INTRODUCTION

After the naive theory, which is still the subject of contemporary research in optimal control, the next stage corresponds to the variational methods to which we introduced the reader in Chapter I of Volume I. These are the standard methods of the calculus of variations, the solid everyday machinery for solving problems. They aim at sufficiency without flaws or frills. They are based on geodesic coverings of domains, on Hilbert's independence integral and on the Weierstrass formula. They do not yet involve the more refined concepts, such as conjugate points, Morse numbers and generalized curves and flows. In optimal control they are applied effectively for the first time. The Chapter comprises work not previously published, based on researches circulated only in the form of a Mathematics Research Center report.†

It is very important in optimal control that we have methods that really work in practice. Basically the naive methods do not; their scope is too limited if we restrict ourselves to the linear case of the preceding Chapter, but if we extend them they run counter to Perron's paradox. They force us to accept either restrictions that are never honestly satisfied or else assumptions of existence that are, in the naive context, unverifiable. The claim is sometimes put forward that these assumptions are either obvious on physical grounds or else are justified by some empirical agreement of the results derived from them with what one somehow expects. This is logically on a par with the former claim of clerics that the earth is an immovable flat disc.

Thus we clearly need a standard theory. Its methods, as we remarked in Volume I, actually go back to the work of Huygens in optics, in relation to Fermat's principle of least time. Unfortunately, classical assumptions of very smooth one-to-one coverings were gradually introduced into them in the course of the development of the calculus of variations. These assumptions are not satisfied in optimal control, and we shall free ourselves from them. In a sense, this brings us closer to the spirit of the original optical context, all the more so because we limit ourselves to time-optimal problems in this Chapter. *Plus ça change, plus c'est la même chose.*

---

† MRC report no. 654, jointly sponsored by the MRC, U.S. Army, Madison, Wisconsin, under Contract No. DA-11-022-ORD-2059; by the National Aeronautics and Space Administration, under Contract No. 50-002-040 (U.W. listing 144-6184); and by the National Science Foundation, under Contract No. GP-5712 (U.W. listing 144-4773).

In optimal control, just as in the calculus of variations proper, the standard methods consist largely of formalizing the procedure used to solve some special problems. Here these problems will be mainly the ones treated in the Preamble to this Volume; however, we must use our imagination to try and visualize much more general cases, and we shall carry out the formalization with them in mind. For this reason, we consider a very general setting, which can later apply in the generalized context, and we leave the control space quite unspecified; control values will simply be certain labels denoted by u, whereas t, x denote, as previously, time and a variable Euclidean point. Also, in contrast to the lavish assumptions, of twice, or more, continuous differentiability, which appeared in our classical version of the standard methods, no function in the present Chapter will be assumed to be more than once continuously differentiable. A function will be termed smooth if it is continuously differentiable; a set will be termed smooth if it is defined by inequalities of the type $f(x) \geq 0$, where the functions f which occur are smooth and their number is finite. Actually most of our assumptions of this nature will concern only partial, piecewise or local forms of smoothness, and some quite basic quantities will not even be supposed continuous.

We shall limit ourselves to the autonomous case of a problem of least time. We seek a trajectory that leads in least time from a given position of the initial point to a given target. This target may be either a point or a locally smooth set of points, not necessarily connected. In this problem, it may well happen that the initial positions from which it is possible to reach the target at all occupy a set R, which need not be the whole space outside the target, nor a domain. In quite simple cases, R is of lower

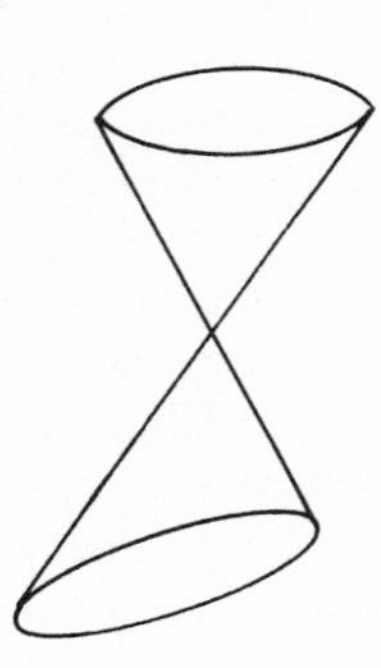

dimension, or its structure may be even more complicated. One case that should not be ruled out is that in which R consists of the two portions of a cone joined by the vertex. Clearly such a set cannot be covered simply by a family of trajectories that have extremities in the two portions. This is why, in applying standard variational methods, we must free them of the classical restrictions.

Actually, the case in which R consists of two portions of a cone is not unlike what one meets in practice, in the case of a simple moonshot, when only the initial conditions are controlled. There is then, according to astronomers, a quite small piece of phase space through which the projectile must pass in order to hit the moon. In multistage rockets, we have greater freedom, but even then the state of affairs is rather similar, and this accounts for a number of near-misses.

At any rate, the reader should realize that the generality of the definitions and methods of this Chapter is largely dictated by practical considerations. Actually, our theory is still not quite as general as we would wish, even in the context of an autonomous problem of least time; it contains an undesirable multiplier restriction.

The latter, according to the experience of virtually everyone who has worked in the field, may well be unavoidable in a sufficiency theory. It is the same restriction which originally spoiled Lagrange's multiplier method, and which goes, in the discrete case, by the name of Kuhn-Tucker constraint qualification. It does not appear in the maximum principle; however, the maximum principle is not a sufficiency theory. It almost seems that the extension of the standard classical method to problems with constraints necessitates this restriction. Generally speaking, an extension of a theory in one direction often necessitates a restriction in another; it must be, so to speak, paid for.

Here we really have to do with three such extensions: we reduce smoothness and drop the restriction to one-to-one coverings of domains, and we allow for constraints. The first will force us to forego a few luxuries and the second to work harder, but the third will be downright inconvenient and render necessary a separate discussion of the corresponding multiplier restriction every time we apply our theory. This is the price we must pay.

§21. TRAJECTORIES AND LINES OF FLIGHT

We denote by $g(x, u)$ a smooth function of x depending (as on a label) on the control value u in any manner. Further, we term admissible control a function $u(t)$ that is defined on a relevant time interval and belongs to an arbitrarily preassigned class of such functions, with values in the control space. We term admissible trajectory, associated with a definite admissible control $u(t)$, an absolutely continuous function $x(t)$ defined on the same time interval with values in x-space such that the pair $x(t)$, $u(t)$ satisfy the differential equation

$$\dot{x} = g(x, u), \tag{21.1}$$

almost everywhere in t; the relevant time interval will, for convenience, be taken to end at $t = 0$, and the corresponding terminal value $x(0)$ of $x(t)$ will be supposed to lie on the given set, which we term the target. As explained in the preceding section, this target is taken to be a sufficiently elementary configuration without interior points.

Since $x(t)$ is absolutely continuous, its derivative $\dot{x}$ is measurable in t. This reduces, in practice, the class of utilizable controls $u(t)$ and the possible functions $g(x, u)$, but we need not make such restrictions explicitly.

Our problem is to determine, if possible, the least time from a given position to the target, along admissible trajectories. We wish to show how to adapt the standard variational methods to this problem. We shall extend the methods at the price of certain restrictions.

In the classical setting, the standard method of geodesic coverings, described in Chapter I of Volume I, for a problem in which the Weierstrass condition is everywhere satisfied, consisted in seeking a one-to-one covering of a simply connected domain by a family of curves subject to a condition of exactness. We then analyzed this exactness rather fully, assuming a high enough order of differentiability. The curves had to be extremals for which certain square brackets vanish initially.

The extension of this part of the analysis does not seem practicable when we reduce smoothness assumptions, as we must in optimal control. However, it is not needed: we are not looking for necessary conditions, but for sufficient ones which work in practice. Proofs of necessity are a luxury. We shall concentrate on sufficiency.

In the classical setting, there is then little lost in supposing at the outset that the family considered consists of extremals satisfying the stated initial condition of the vanishing of square brackets.

Similarly, here in our time-optimal problem we drop all pretense of necessity. We limit ourselves to a family of trajectories that we suspect, rather arbitrarily and high-handedly, of providing the solution to our problem, between their initial points and the target. These suspected trajectories we term lines of flight. The class of these lines of flight takes the place of the family of curves considered in the classical context. The classical theorem, according to which this family could consist only of extremals, becomes a hypothesis to be combined with the Weierstrass condition and transversality. Its analogue is then the maximum principle. Therefore, we shall not suspect all admissible trajectories indiscriminately, but only those subject to this principle: every line of flight is to obey the maximum principle. This has become a hypothesis; it is not even a definition, since there will be further conditions to satisfy.

The first such additional condition consists in rather arbitrarily strengthening the maximum principle, and this is the unpleasant restriction to which we referred in the preceding section. In this stronger form, the maximum principle now states that along a line of flight $x(t)$, with control $u(t)$, there exists a conjugate vector function $y(t)$, absolutely continuous in t and with values in a space isomorphic with x-space, such that

$$\textbf{(21.2)}\quad \begin{cases} \text{(a)}\ \dot{y}(t) = -y(t)g_x[x(t), u(t)], \\ \text{(b)}\ y(t)g[x(t), u] \leq 1 \text{ for all } u, \text{ with equality when } u = u(t), \\ \text{(c)}\ \text{for } t = 0, \text{ the vector } y(t) \text{ is normal to the target at } x(t), \\ \text{(d)}\ \text{for all } t, \text{ we have } y(t) \neq 0. \end{cases}$$

This differs from the actual maximum principle of Pontryagin in that in the inequality (21.2)(b) the right hand side is unity, instead of a quantity $H \geq 0$ which is constant in t. By replacing H by unity, i.e., y/H by y, we do not affect our trajectories, except for excluding the case where $H = 0$. Thus our strengthening of the maximum principle amounts to requiring that H should not vanish. In terms of the Hamiltonian $\mathscr{H}$, which is here $y_0 + H$, and which vanishes along trajectories that obey the maximum principle, this requirement becomes $y_0 \neq 0$, and, according to Section 8 of the Preamble to this Volume, $y_0 = -\kappa_0$. Thus, by stipulating that $H \neq 0$ or that $H = 1$, we are, in effect, requiring κ_0 to be unity. This means that $\tilde{L}$ is to be simply $L + \lambda(\dot{x} - g)$, i.e., that the multipliers are as in Lagrange's original rule, and this corresponds in the discrete case to the Kuhn-Tucker constraint qualification. We have said that this rule is faulty when stated as a necessary condition. This does not prevent our using it to get sufficient conditions, and the general consensus among workers in the calculus of variations has long been that we cannot hope to obtain sufficient conditions without it. This is because if we set $H = 0$, i.e., $\kappa_0 = 0$, our equations do not change if we replace L by another Lagrangian, for instance by $-L$. Any conclusions drawn would apply to every other problem with the same constraints.

The additional requirement $H = 0$, which we have thus imposed on our suspects, may be interpreted, in the language of the police court, as follows. "On the basis of information received" (the maximum principle), suspicion is attached to certain trajectories. However, in some of these cases the grounds for suspicion hardly seem to be relevant. In a crime mystery, an overeager policeman, anxious to round up every conceivable suspect, is liable to include all persons whose behavior attracted his watchful eye, and in particular any unusual persons such as poets, mathematicians and chess players. If one of these normally innocuous individuals is brought in for questioning, an embarrassed magistrate will be profuse with apologies. Nevertheless, such an apparently harmless person is often chosen as the culprit in a crime mystery.

In optimal control, a trajectory for which $H = 0$ is simply an unusual trajectory subject to the constraints. This is not a valid reason for suspicion, since the Lagrangian is not involved at all. Nevertheless, it may turn out that such a trajectory is the desired solution. This is certainly so in the rigid case, which we met in Section 4(a) of the Preamble to this Volume. It happens also, for appropriate initial values, in the oscillator problem B of Section 10, where H vanishes along the two solutions which touch the target. Any such unusual solutions require a special discussion, as in the problem in question. In order to take them into account, we shall allow ourselves, at a later stage, the option of referring to our present lines of flight as standard ones, and of adding to them, if we see fit, certain weak lines of flight, along which $H = 0$.

For the time being, however, we shall suppose that a suitable class of trajectories has been singled out, and that its members obey the strengthened maximum principle. These members will be termed lines of flight. The class to which they belong will be subject to further conditions, which we shall state in due course.

A line of flight $x(t)$ will usually be associated with a definite corresponding admissible control $u(t)$ and, for brevity, we shall speak of the line of flight

$$x(t),\, u(t).$$

Here t ranges in the appropriate time interval ending at $t = 0$. Further, we term canonical line of flight, a trio of functions

$$x(t), y(t), u(t)$$

such that $x(t)$, $u(t)$ defines a line of flight, and that $y(t)$ is the corresponding vector-valued conjugate function, subject to (21.2). An open arc of a line of flight or a canonical line of flight will be termed an arc of flight or a canonical arc of flight, respectively; at times the words arc of flight will be shortened simply to flight.

We remark that, in general, the conjugate function $y(t)$ is not uniquely determined by the line of flight $x(t)$, $u(t)$, but may depend on auxiliary parameters ρ, which represent, for instance, initial or terminal conditions. Thus a line (or an arc) of flight is in general the projection of a whole family of canonical lines (or arcs) of flight, which depend on the additional parameters ρ. This is one of the basic facts that our discussion has to allow for, and we note that when lines of flight merge or separate, so do the corresponding sets of values of ρ.

From the practical point of view, which has constantly to be borne in mind in a standard theory, our discussion may be said to start with the determination of all the trajectories, terminating on the given target, which obey the maximum principle. This happens to be exactly the same as the procedure we adopted in the naive approach and also in each of the examples treated. From the trajectories so obtained, we then exclude, at least temporarily, those for which $H = 0$, and we single out those that we wish to call lines of flight by laying down further conditions that we shall describe in the following sections.

So far, in this Volume we have not needed to make use of this singling out procedure. However, it was what we had to use in the Preamble to Volume I, in the brachistochrone and in the minimal surface of revolution.

§22. THE SYNCHRONIZATION CONDITION AND THE NOTIONS OF STANDARD PROJECTION AND DESCRIPTIVE MAP

So far we have only restricted our lines of flight to consist of trajectories which obey the strengthened maximum principle. In the calculus of variations proper, this corresponds to considering a family of extremals which satisfy the transversality conditions at their final points. In Volume I, we found, both in the examples of the Preamble and in the theory of conjugate points of Chapter III, that we had to impose the further requirement that the family cover a domain one-to-one. In optimal control, even in the simple problems treated so far, this further requirement is not applicable. We must find a way of replacing it by others, which are verified in practice.

The most obvious further condition for reducing the class of what we wish to term lines of flight would be the following: if two such trajectories, which obey the strengthened maximum principle, lead to the target from the same initial point, in different times, we discard the one with the longer time. Actually, we shall not proceed quite in this way, which has practical difficulties; instead we merely discard one of the two. This means that we can lay down the following synchronization rule: if two lines of flight have the same initial point, they lead to the target in the same time from this point. In that case it is clear that some further conditions are still needed. These conditions will not be formulated in quite such a simple-minded way; they will be based on various new concepts and theorems, which occupy most of this Chapter.

Given a set Q^* of pairs $q^* = (q, c)$, where q, c denote points of two Euclidean, or metric, spaces (say), the operation of projecting Q^* onto the corresponding set Q of the values of q which occur in it will be termed a standard projection if the following condition is satisfied:

(22.1) *Given any point $q_0^* = (q_0, c_0) \in Q^*$, and any small enough curve $\gamma \subset Q$, which issues from q_0, there exists on γ a continuous function $c(q)$ such that $c(q_0) = c_0$ and that all points of the form $[q, c(q)]$ for $q \in \gamma$ lie in Q^*.*

We shall need such a projection to deal with certain irrelevant parameters ρ that occur in connection with a family of arcs of flight; as indicated in the preceding section, these parameters serve to distinguish corresponding canonical flights. The intrusion of these parameters is in part responsible for basic differences between our present discussion and that given in Volume I. It prevents our using not only one-to-oneness, but also a related local condition whereby certain smooth maps in Volume I were required to possess nonsingular Jacobian matrices. The following definition will help to free us from these conditions.

A map f from a set Q to a set $P = f(Q)$, where Q, P lie in two Euclidean or metric spaces will be termed descriptive if, for each $q \in Q$,

(22.2) *Given any rectifiable curve $C \subset P$ issuing from $f(q)$, there exists a rectifiable curve $\Gamma \subset Q$ issuing from q such that every small arc of C issuing from $f(q)$ is the image under the map f of a small arc of Γ issuing from q.*

The term "descriptive" has here been chosen after some thought. It is intended to imply that a certain type of information about the image P enables us to derive corresponding information about the original set Q. This is, in practice, what maps are for. A short route on a map should refer to at least one short real route.

It is convenient to illustrate the above definition in two ways, first by considering the effect of the intrusion of an irrelevant parameter, and second by giving an example of a map that fails to be descriptive.

Given a set I of values of c, let f^* be a map of the Cartesian product $Q^* = Q \times I$, where, for each $q^* = (q, c)$ subject to $q \in Q$, $c \in I$, the value $f^*(q^*)$ coincides with $f(q)$. Here c may be termed an irrelevant parameter. Further, we suppose that Q, I lie in Euclidean or metric spaces. In that case we see that if the map f is descriptive, so is the map f^*.

An example of a map f that is not descriptive is obtained by choosing, in the complex plane, the function

$$f(q) = \begin{cases} q + 1 & \text{if} \quad \mathscr{R}q < -1, \\ q - 1 & \text{if} \quad \mathscr{R}q > 1, \\ q - \mathscr{R}q & \text{if} \quad -1 \leq \mathscr{R}q \leq 1. \end{cases}$$

A curve C that crosses the imaginary axis of p corresponds to a curve Γ that crosses the strip $-1 \leq \mathscr{R}q \leq 1$.

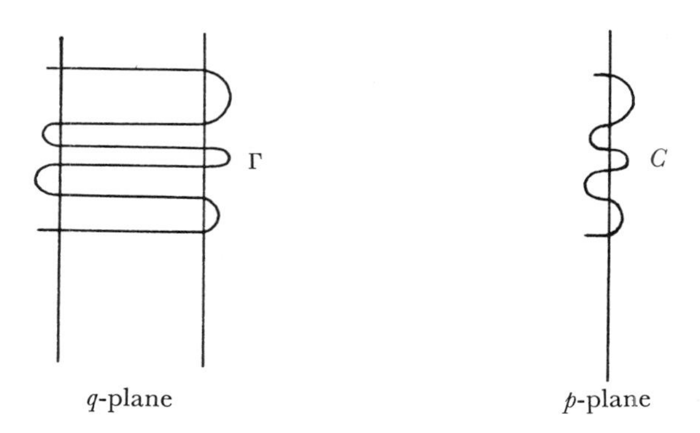

§23. THE NOTION OF A SPRAY OF FLIGHTS

In each of the examples in this Volume treated so far, we were able to decompose the set covered by our lines of flight into subsets, in which the corresponding portions of our lines of flight provided a smooth covering. We therefore begin by considering a family of arcs of flight that satisfies certain conditions of smoothness.

Suppose defined, on an open Euclidean set whose points we denote by σ, a pair of extended real-valued functions

$$t^-(\sigma), t^+(\sigma) \quad \text{where} \quad -\infty \leq t^-(\sigma) < t^+(\sigma) \leq 0.$$

The points σ at which $t^-(\sigma) \neq -\infty$ are to constitute an open set and the two functions are to be continuous, except, in the case of $t^-(\sigma)$, at any points where the value $-\infty$ is taken. Further, we shall suppose that the local restriction of the function $t^+(\sigma)$ to small segments parallel to the σ-axes is of bounded variation on each such segment.

We suppose further that the open set of σ is the projection of a certain set of (σ, ρ), situated in a higher-dimensional Euclidean space. Of this set of (σ, ρ) we need not assume that it is open; instead we shall suppose that the operation of projecting it is standard in the sense of the preceding section.

We shall denote by S^-, S, S^+ the sets of (t, σ) for which σ is as before, and t is subject to the corresponding condition

$$-\infty < t^-(\sigma) = t, \quad \text{or} \quad t^-(\sigma) < t < t^+(\sigma), \quad \text{or} \quad t = t^+(\sigma).$$

We denote by $[S]$ the union of these three sets. Similarly, we denote by S^{*-}, S^*, S^{*+} the sets of (t, σ, ρ) for which t is subject to these respective conditions, and (σ, ρ) is as before. We write $[S^*]$ for the union of the three sets.

This being so, we consider a family Σ of arcs of flight with corresponding controls, given by functions

$$x(t, \sigma), \; u(t, \sigma) \quad (t, \sigma) \in S.$$

Here σ is the label, which distinguishes a member of the family, i.e., σ remains constant on an arc of flight of Σ, and this arc then corresponds to the open time interval $t^-(\sigma) < t < t^+(\sigma)$. We shall denote further by Σ^* a family of canonical arcs of flight which correspond to the arcs of Σ and which are obtained by giving, with the preceding functions, a further conjugate vector-function

$$y(t, \sigma, \rho) \quad (t, \sigma, \rho) \in S^*.$$

The definition of the functions $x(t, \sigma), y(t, \sigma, \rho)$ will be supposed extended to the sets $[S]$, $[S^*]$. This means defining them for $t = t^+(\sigma)$ and for $t = t^-(\sigma) > -\infty$ where the values of x, y correspond to the end points of our arcs. The sets of values of $x(t, \sigma)$ in the (t, σ) sets S^-, S, S^+, $[S]$ will be written E^-, E, E^+, $[E]$, and those of the pair $x(t, \sigma), y(t, \sigma, \rho)$ in the (t, σ, ρ) sets S^{*-}, S^*, S^{*+}, $[S^*]$ will be E^{*-}, E^*, E^{*+}, $[E^*]$.

Finally, we write, when $(t, \sigma) \in S$ and when x is a point of E sufficiently near to $x(t, \sigma)$,

$$h(t, \sigma), \quad g(x, t, \sigma), \quad g_x(x, t, \sigma)$$

for the expressions

$$g[x(t, \sigma), u(t, \sigma)], \quad g[x, u(t, \sigma)], \quad g_x[x, u(t, \sigma)].$$

We now suppose the following conditions satisfied:

(23.1)

(i) The function $h(t, \sigma)$ and for each fixed $x \in E$ the function $g(x, t, \sigma)$ [when (t, σ) is near to the values at which $x(t, \sigma)$ assumes the value x], are smooth in S and satisfy at $x = x(t, \sigma)$ the relation

$$\frac{\partial h}{\partial \sigma} = \frac{\partial g(x, t, \sigma)}{\partial \sigma} + g_x(x, t, \sigma) x_\sigma.$$

(ii) The function $y(t, \sigma, \rho)$ is continuous in $[S^*]$.

(iii) The function $x(t, \sigma)$ is smooth in $[S]$.

(iv) The maps $S^- \to E^-$, $S \to E$ defined by the function $x(t, \sigma)$ are descriptive.

These conditions, together with those in the definition of the functions $t^-(\sigma)$, $t^+(\sigma)$ and the stipulations about the corresponding sets of (t, σ, ρ), play a basic part in our discussion. When they are satisfied, we term Σ a spray of flights from E^- to E^+, and Σ^* a canonical spray of flights from E^{*-} to E^{*+}. We term E^- or E^{*-} the source, and E^+ or E^{*+} the destination, of Σ or Σ^*, while E or E^* will be termed the corresponding flight-corridor. This terminology must not make us forget that some arcs of Σ do not originate in E^-; they are the ones that start at $t = -\infty$. All arcs of flight of Σ terminate in E^+, but only those that start at a finite time originate in

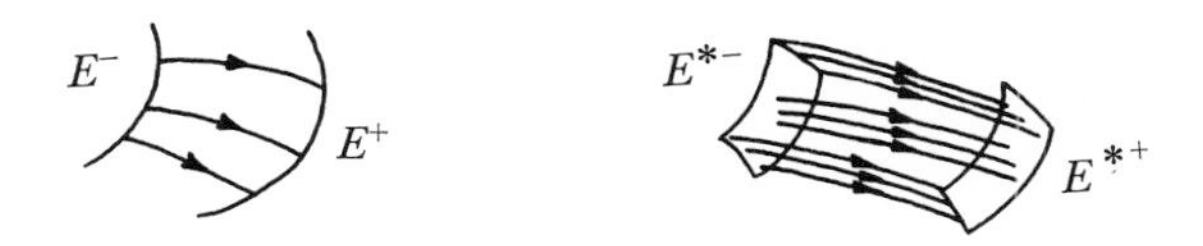

E^-. It should also be emphasized that we attach to each spray Σ a definite corresponding canonical spray Σ^*; i.e., we distinguish formally between two sprays defined by a same family of arcs of flight, associated with different families of canonical arcs. We also wish to emphasize the possibility of degeneracy in a spray. For instance, Σ may consist of subarcs of a given arc of flight.

We shall use the notion of spray of flights in much the same way as we use that of a geodesic covering in the calculus of variations proper.

§24. THE HILBERT INDEPENDENCE INTEGRAL

The basic tool for studying a spray of flights, and ultimately for establishing the main results of this Chapter, will be the same one we used for geodesic coverings in Volume I, namely the Hilbert integral. The remaining sections will largely be devoted to proving its independence under suitable hypotheses. However, the integral will now be very different in character from the one we encountered in the calculus of variations proper: formally it is the natural analogue; conceptually it constitutes a new departure. The same quantities appear in the integrand, but they are now many-valued, and this is absolutely essential to our method in problems with constraints. This means that the independence of our integral will here be a much stronger one; it must apply not only in the previous sense, used in Volume I, but also in regard to the many-valuedness. All this indicates clearly that our main difficulties will be conceptual ones. We shall not merely prove results, but also develop relevant concepts. This is often the case in modern mathematics, and such difficulties can no longer be shirked.

We denote by R, at least for the time being, the set actually covered by our lines of flight. This set may thus be smaller than the one denoted by the same symbol in the introduction to this Chapter. Further, for an arbitrary point $x \in R$, we denote by $T(x)$, and term flight-time from x, the length of the time interval along a line of flight issuing from the point x. By our synchronization condition, this flight-time depends only on x. A subset of R in which $T(x)$ is bounded will be termed a set of bounded flight-time.

Given a subset A of R, we shall term canonical set corresponding to A the set $A^\#$ of the points (x, y) of $2n$-space. Each point (x, y) lies on a canonical line of flight such that its projections x lie in A. By a canonical set $A^\#$ of bounded flight-time we mean the canonical set, corresponding to a subset A of R of bounded flight-time. We shall denote further by

$$\mathscr{Y}(x),$$

for $x \in R$, the set of the values of the conjugate vector y for which (x, y) lies in the canonical set $R^\#$ corresponding to R.

Thus $\mathcal{Y}(x)$ is a function, whose values, for $x \in R$, are sets. In other words, it is, basically, what we call a many-valued function. However, since the processes of analysis are normally restricted to single-valued functions, we shall operate, not on $\mathcal{Y}(x)$ directly, but on certain associated single-valued functions $y(x)$. By a function

$$y(x) \in \mathcal{Y}(x) \qquad x \in R,$$

we shall mean a single-valued function $y(x)$ defined in R, whose value at each point x lies in the corresponding set $\mathcal{Y}(x)$ at this point. We may speak of the function $y(x)$ as being a branch of the many-valued function $\mathcal{Y}(x)$. We term any such branch a momentum in R, and we term $\mathcal{Y}(x)$ the momentum range at the point x.

The notion of branch of a many-valued function is here not at all the same as in the theory of analytic functions. We impose here no smoothness or continuity conditions on $y(x)$, nor even any sort of measurability. For instance, if $\mathcal{Y}(x)$ is the constant set consisting of two vectors $\pm y_0$, its branches would be all functions of the form $\varepsilon(x)y_0$, where $\varepsilon(x)$ is any function taking only the values ± 1, or else one of these. The introduction of so many different branches will not, however, complicate our analysis appreciably.

In relation to a given spray of flights Σ, we shall need an analogous but more restricted notation. The symbols S, E and so on, being as in the preceding section, we write

$$\mathcal{Y}_\Sigma(x),$$

to mean, for $x \in [E]$, the set of the values of $y(t, \sigma, \rho)$ at those points $(t, \sigma, \rho) \in [S^*]$, for which $x(t, \sigma)$ takes the given value x. We shall write

$$y_\Sigma(x) \qquad x \in [E],$$

to mean a function defined in $[E]$, whose value at each point x lies in the corresponding set $\mathcal{Y}_\Sigma(x)$ at this point. We shall refer to $\mathcal{Y}_\Sigma(x)$ as the momentum range for Σ at the point x.

On any rectifiable curve C of bounded flight-time in R, we define the curvilinear integral

(24.1)
$$\int_C y(x)\, dx = \int y(x) \frac{dx}{ds}\, ds$$

for any momentum in R such that $y(x)\, dx/ds$ is a measurable function of the arc length s along C. The functional, defined by this integral for the class of curves C and momenta $y(x)$ $x \in R$ specified above, will be termed the Hilbert integral. Our task is to study its independence, and this in its turn will necessitate still further definitions and concepts.

Although the integrand in (24.1) involves the choice of a momentum $y(x)$, i.e., of a particular branch of the many-valued function $\mathcal{Y}(x)$ $x \in R$, there is one case in which the Hilbert integral will not be affected by this choice: this is the case in which the component of $y(x)$, in the direction of the tangent dx/ds to C, happens to have the same value for all such choices. It is convenient to give a name to such a direction, if it exists.

At a point $x \in R$, we term direction of univalence a direction θ such that all the vectors $y \in \mathcal{Y}(x)$ have the same projection $y\theta$ on this direction. Further, we term curve of univalence a rectifiable curve $C \subset R$ such that, at almost all points of C, the direction of the tangent to C is a direction of univalence. Finally, we term set of univalence a subset A of R such that all rectifiable curves $C \subset A$ of bounded flight-time are curves of univalence.

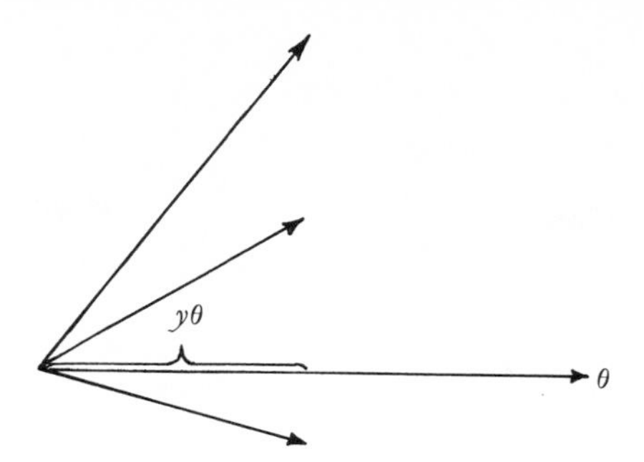

A direction θ of univalence corresponding to a set $\mathscr{Y}$ consisting of three vectors y.

For instance, if for each $x \in R$ the vectors $y \in \mathscr{Y}(x)$ all have the same projection in a certain plane Π, then every rectifiable plane curve situated in Π will be a curve of univalence; the plane Π, or any set which lies in a parallel plane, is then a set of univalence.

The notion of univalence has an obvious bearing on the study of the Hilbert integral. For any rectifiable curve C of bounded flight-time situated in a set A of univalence, we express the Hilbert integral in terms of the arc length s along C by writing

$$\int_C y(x)\, dx = \int y[x(s)]\theta(s)\, ds,$$

where $x(s)$ is the representation of C in terms of its arc length, and where

$$\theta = \theta(s) = dx/ds$$

is almost everywhere on C a direction of univalence at the point $x(s)$. The integral does not depend on the choice of the function $y(x) \in \mathscr{Y}(x)$ $x \in R$.

A subset A of R will, further, be termed set of exact integrability, or simply an exact set, if it is a set of univalence, and if in addition, for every rectifiable curve $C \subset A$ of bounded flight-time, we have for each $y(x) \in \mathscr{Y}(x)$ $x \in R$,

$$\int_C y(x)\, dx = T(x_1) - T(x_2),$$

where x_1, x_2 are the initial and final points of C.

In addition to the above notions of univalence and exactness, we shall also require corresponding relative notions associated with our spray Σ. The relevant changes in our definitions are routine. At a point $x \in [E]$, we term direction of relative univalence a direction θ such that all vectors $y \in \mathscr{Y}_\Sigma(x)$ have the same projection $y\theta$ on this direction. We term curve of relative univalence a rectifiable curve $C \subset [E]$ such that, at almost all points of C, the direction of the tangent to C is a direction of relative univalence. We term set of relative univalence a subset A of $[E]$ such that all rectifiable curves $C \subset A$, of bounded flight-time, are curves of relative univalence. A subset A of $[E]$ will, further, be termed a set of relative exact integrability, or simply a relative exact set, if it is a set of relative univalence, and if, in addition, for every rectifiable curve $C \subset A$ of bounded flight-time, we have for each $y(x) \in \mathscr{Y}_\Sigma(x)$ $x \in [E]$,

$$\int_C y(x)\, dx = T(x_1) - T(x_2),$$

where x_1, x_2 are the initial and final points of C.

The discussion of relative exactness will partly depend on a more restricted form of the same condition. This arises when we consider only those curves C that are images of (t, σ) curves under the map $x(t, \sigma)$, and only those momenta that have the form $y(t, \sigma, \rho)$ along them. In that case, by (21.1) and (21.2)(b), the Hilbert integral takes the form

$$\int_\Gamma yx_t\, dt + yx_\sigma\, d\sigma = \int_\Gamma dt + \int_\Gamma yx_\sigma\, d\sigma$$

where Γ is a (t, σ) curve whose image is C, so that the relative exactness condition reduces to the vanishing of $\int yx_\sigma\, d\sigma$, or equivalently, to the vanishing of yx_σ. This is the reason why this last condition will play a part in the sequel.

§25. PRELIMINARY LEMMAS

In this section Σ is fixed. Our first lemma partly makes up for the lack of assumptions about $T(x)$, $y(x)$. The other two relate the vanishing of yx_σ to our other conditions. Here and in the rest of this Chapter, we denote for convenience by

$$y_\Sigma(x)$$

for $x \in [E]$ a momentum $y(x) \in \mathscr{Y}_\Sigma(x)$, and we term it a momentum relative to Σ.

(25.1) Lemma. *Let C be a rectifiable curve, situated, together with its end points, in E^- or in E. Then C is of bounded flight-time, and there exists along it a bounded, Borel measurable momentum $y_\Sigma(x)$ relative to Σ.*

(25.2) Lemma. *If E^+ is a relative exact set, then yx_σ vanishes in S^{*+}.*

(25.3) Lemma. *If yx_σ vanishes in S^{*-}, then E^- is a relative exact set. If it vanishes in S^*, then E is so.*

Proof of (25.1). By (23.1)(iv), we can attach to each point of C, including the end points, a neighborhood on C that is the image of a curve Γ. We can suppose t bounded on each such Γ, and it then follows from Borel's covering theorem that $T(x)$ is bounded on C. In proving the second assertion, we may suppose C so small that there is a corresponding (t, σ) curve, which we again denote by Γ, and we can choose on Γ a continuous, and therefore bounded, function of the form $y(t, \sigma, \rho(\sigma))$. To each point $x \in C$ we now attach the first point (t, σ) of Γ at which $x(t, \sigma) = x$. By substitution in $y(t, \sigma, \rho(\sigma))$, we obtain a Borel measurable $y_\Sigma(x)$ on C, which is also bounded, as asserted.

Proof of (25.2). Let Γ be the small rectifiable curve in S^+, which corresponds, by setting $t = t^+(\sigma)$, to a small segment parallel to one of the σ-axes. Let C be the image of Γ in E^+, and let $y_\Sigma(x)$ be a momentum relative to Σ. Since E^+ is a set of relative univalence and, further, a relative exact one, we may write

$$\int_C y_\Sigma(x)\, dx = \int_\Gamma yx_t\, dt + yx_\sigma\, d\sigma,$$

and further equate the common value of the two sides of this formula to the difference Δt of $t^+(\sigma)$ between the ends of Γ. Here y now stands for $y(t, \sigma, \rho)$, and ρ for a continuous function of σ, suitably chosen; moreover, by (21.2)(b) and (21.1), we have

$yx_t = 1$. Hence we find that

$$\int_\Gamma yx_\sigma \, d\sigma = 0.$$

This must now hold for Γ, however we choose the small segment parallel to a σ-axis through an initial σ_0, and however we choose the initial value $\rho_0 = \rho(\sigma_0)$ of a corresponding continuous function $\rho(\sigma)$ along Γ. Since yx_σ is continuous in $[S^*]$, we find that each of its components yx_β must vanish at the point $[t^+(\sigma_0), \sigma_0, \rho_0]$, i.e., at an arbitrary point of S^{*+}, as asserted.

PROOF OF (25.3). The two assertions are proved in the same manner, and we shall limit ourselves to the one concerning E^- and S^{*-}. We assume then that $yx_\sigma = 0$ in S^{*-}. We denote by C any small rectifiable curve in E^-, of bounded flight-time. (If no such curve exists, we have nothing to prove.) We represent C in terms of its arc length s, by a function $X(s)$, and we denote by $\theta(s)$ the direction of the tangent at the corresponding point, for almost every s. As origin for s, we choose a value at which $\theta(s)$ is approximately continuous, and we denote by $\hat{x}$, $\hat{\theta}$ the corresponding values of $X(s)$, $\theta(s)$. Further we denote by $\hat{y}$ any vector in $\mathscr{Y}_\Sigma(\hat{x})$ and by $(\hat{t}, \hat{\sigma}, \hat{\rho})$ a point S^{*-} for which $x(\hat{t}, \hat{\sigma}) = \hat{x}$, $y(\hat{t}, \hat{\sigma}, \hat{\rho}) = \hat{y}$.

Approximate continuity of $\theta(s)$ implies that, given $\varepsilon > 0$, there exists a closed set B of values of s such that for every sufficiently small interval I of the form $0 \le s \le \delta$, we have

(i) $|\theta(s) - \hat{\theta}| < \varepsilon$ whenever $s \in B \cap I$,

(ii) meas $(I - B) < \varepsilon \cdot$ meas (I).

We now denote by Γ a rectifiable curve in S^- such that small arcs of C issuing from $\hat{x}$ are, in accordance with (23.1)(iv), the images under the map $x(t, \sigma)$ of small arcs γ of Γ, issuing from $(\hat{t}, \hat{\sigma})$. We represent Γ in terms of its arc length λ by functions $t(\lambda)$, $\sigma(\lambda)$, so that the point $(\hat{t}, \hat{\sigma})$ corresponds to $\lambda = 0$. We can then define a continuous increasing function $s(\lambda)$, which vanishes at $\lambda = 0$, and which gives rise to the corresponding arc length along C, i.e., which satisfies the relation

$$X[s(\lambda)] = x[t(\lambda), \sigma(\lambda)].$$

We shall denote by Λ the set of λ for which $s(\lambda) \in B$.

This being so, let Δs, ΔT denote the difference in s and in $T(x)$ at the ends of a small arc of C. We wish to show that

$$\begin{cases} \text{(a) the ratio } \dfrac{\Delta T}{\Delta s} \text{ is bounded,} \\ \text{(b) for an arc of } C \text{, issuing from } \hat{x} \text{, which shrinks to this point,} \\ \qquad \operatorname{Lim} \dfrac{\Delta T}{\Delta s} = -\hat{y}\hat{\theta}. \end{cases}$$

We remark that (a) and (b) together imply the assertion of (25.3). In fact, (b) implies, on the one hand, that $\hat{\theta}$ is a direction of relative univalence at $\hat{x}$, and on the other hand, since $\hat{x}$ was any point of C at which $\theta(s)$ is approximately continuous, and so almost any point of C, that for every $y_\Sigma(x) \in \mathscr{Y}_\Sigma(x)$, $x \in [E]$, we have, almost everywhere along C,

$$\frac{dT[X(s)]}{ds} = -y_\Sigma[X(s)] \frac{dX}{ds}.$$

Moreover, (a) implies that we can integrate here in s, to obtain the relation which defines relative exactness. The proof of (25.3) is thus reduced to that of (a) and (b), and we now establish these two statements.

To this effect, let J be the interval of λ corresponding to an arc γ of Γ, and suppose γ mapped by $x(t, \sigma)$ onto our small arc of C. Clearly $\Delta T = -\Delta t$, where Δt is the difference of t at the ends of γ. On the other hand, we have along γ, by hypothesis, $yx_\sigma = 0$, and, by (21.2)(b) and (21.1), $yx_t = 1$. Hence

$$\Delta t = \int_J yx_t \, dt(\lambda) + yx_\sigma \, d\sigma(\lambda) = \int_J y\theta \, ds(\lambda).$$

Evidently this implies the boundedness of the ratio $\Delta t/\Delta s$, and so (a). Further, if we take γ to issue from $(\hat{t}, \hat{\sigma})$ and the corresponding arc of C to be small, γ and so J will be small. Moreover, in the expression found for Δt, the vector y is a continuous function of λ, obtained by taking $y = y(t, \sigma, \rho)$ along γ, while θ is the direction $\theta(s)$, where $s = s(\lambda)$. In terms of these functions, if we set $\varphi = \varphi(\lambda) = y\theta - \hat{y}\hat{\theta}$, we thus have

$$\frac{\Delta t}{\Delta s} - \hat{y}\hat{\theta} = \frac{1}{\Delta s}\int_J \varphi \, ds(\lambda) = \frac{1}{\Delta s}\int_{J\cap\Lambda} + \frac{1}{\Delta s}\int_{J-\Lambda}.$$

For small J these last two terms cannot exceed certain fixed multiples of an arbitrarily small positive ε: on the one hand, φ is bounded in $J - \Lambda$ and this set has $s(\lambda)$-measure less than $\varepsilon\Delta s$, by (ii) above; on the other hand, $J \cap \Lambda$ has $s(\lambda)$-measure at most Δs, while in it, by (i) above and by the continuity (and boundedness) of y, the absolute value $|\varphi|$ of the integrand is at most a fixed multiple of ε. This completes the proof.

§26. THE THEOREM OF MALUS

This theorem of geometrical optics was reformulated for the classical calculus of variations. We need to reformulate it again here, and to establish it under greatly reduced smoothness assumptions. We shall need the following:

(26.1) Lemma. *In a canonical spray, we have*

$$\frac{\partial}{\partial t}\left(y\frac{\partial x}{\partial \sigma}\right) = 0.$$

In this statement, x and y stand for the functions $x(t, \sigma)$, $y(t, \sigma, \rho)$, and the relation asserted is for $(t, \sigma, \rho) \in S^*$. The lemma asserts, incidentally, the existence of the left hand side, although we do not assume second derivatives to exist.

Proof of (26.1). We denote by $(\hat{t}, \hat{\sigma}, \hat{\rho})$ and $\hat{x}, \hat{y}, \hat{u}$, a point of S^* and the corresponding values of x, y, u; further, by β, any coordinate of σ and by c the value at $(\hat{t}, \hat{\sigma}, \hat{\rho})$ of

$$y\frac{\partial}{\partial \beta}\{h(t, \sigma) - g[x(t, \sigma), \hat{u}]\}.$$

By performing in different orders the operations of integration in t and differentiation in β, on the relation (21.1), and then differentiating in t, we obtain successively

$$x_\beta(t, \sigma) - x_\beta(\hat{t}, \sigma) = \int_{\hat{t}}^{t} \frac{\partial}{\partial \beta} h(\tau, \sigma)\, d\tau,$$

$$\frac{\partial}{\partial t} x_\beta(t, \sigma) = \frac{\partial}{\partial \beta} h(t, \sigma).$$

This last we multiply scalarwise by y, with $(\hat{t}, \hat{\sigma}, \hat{\rho})$ for (t, σ, ρ). We then add, at this same point, for $x = \hat{x}$, the relation

$$x_\beta(t, \sigma) \frac{\partial}{\partial t} y(t, \sigma, \rho) = -\hat{y} g_x(x, u) x_\beta(t, \sigma),$$

which follows from (21.2)(a). We thus find that

$$\frac{\partial}{\partial t}\left\{ y \frac{\partial x}{\partial \beta} \right\} = c$$

at $(\hat{t}, \hat{\sigma}, \hat{\rho})$. It only remains to prove that $c = 0$.

However c, by its definition and by (23.1)(i), is the value for $(t, \sigma) = (\hat{t}, \hat{\sigma})$ of

$$\frac{\partial}{\partial \beta} \hat{y} g(\hat{x}, t, \sigma),$$

and this vanishes by (21.2)(b), since the set of σ is open.

(26.2) Corollary. *On each arc of Σ^*, the quantity yx_σ is constant.*

In fact, the proof of (26.1) shows that x_β is, for constant σ, absolutely continuous in t, since its difference is an integral. The function y is also absolutely continuous in t by Section 21. It follows that yx_σ is absolutely continuous in t, and so constant by (26.1), for constant σ, ρ.

(26.3) Theorem of Malus. *Let Σ be a spray of flights with a relative exact destination E^+. Then Σ possesses a relative exact source E^-, and a relative exact flight-corridor E.*

PROOF. By (26.2), yx_σ is constant on each arc of Σ^*, and by (23.1) it is continuous in $[S^*]$. The constant value on each arc is 0 by (25.2), and the assertion (26.3) then follows from (25.3).

§27. CHAINS OF FLIGHTS

The relationship between the classical calculus of variations and geometrical optics, which shows itself in the classical form of the theorem of Malus, becomes particularly close in the least time problems of optimal control. In geometrical optics, the source E^-, and the destination E^+ of a spray of flights Σ would correspond to a pair of consecutive lenses or mirrors, and Σ to the family of light rays passing from one to the other. Such a system must then be studied as part of a whole complex of such families of rays, fitted together between parts of optical instruments. Just as we fit together such families of rays in geometrical optics, we shall here fit together different sprays of flights.

A finite or countable sequence of sprays of flights in R,

$$\Sigma_1, \Sigma_2, \ldots, \Sigma_N, \ldots$$

will be termed a chain of flights, and the corresponding sequence of canonical sprays a canonical chain, if, for $r = 1, 2, \ldots, N - 1, \ldots$, they "fit together" in inverse order, so that the source of each Σ_r^* contains the destination of Σ_{r+1}^*. It is thus the canonical sprays that must fit, not only their projections the Σ_r.

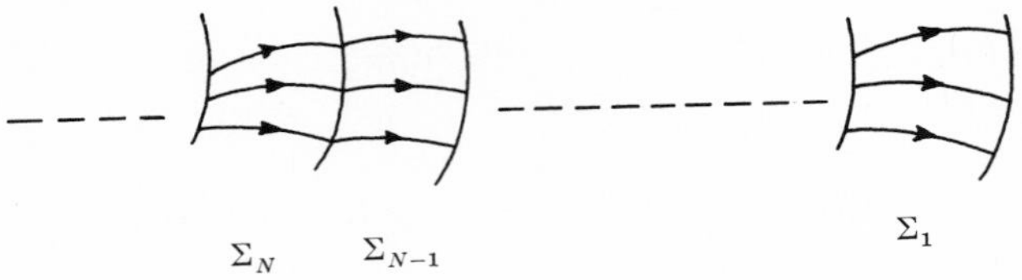

Σ_N Σ_{N-1} Σ_1

The destination of Σ_1 is termed the destination of the chain. A chain of flights whose destination is a subset of the target will be termed a chain of flights to the target. A finite chain consisting of N sprays has also a source; the latter is defined as the source of Σ_N. Generally, the sources and flight-corridors of the individual sprays of a chain of flights will be termed its constituent sets. We do not mention destinations: they are subsets of sources of succeeding sprays, except for the destination of Σ_1 which is that of the whole chain. If the source or flight-corridor of an individual spray Σ_r is a relative exact set for this spray, we term it a relative exact constituent set for the given chain. In the case of the source, this clearly implies that the destination of Σ_{r+1} is a relative exact set for Σ_r, and *a fortiori* for Σ_{r+1}, since the set $\mathscr{Y}_\Sigma(x)$ for an $x \in E_{r+1}^+$, contracts when Σ passes from Σ_r to Σ_{r+1}.

By an obvious induction, we thus conclude from Malus's theorem (26.3) that if the destination of Σ_1 is for Σ_1 a relative exact set, then all the constituent sets of the chain of flights are relative exact for the chain. This is in particular the case, by the transversality condition (21.2)(c), if the destination of Σ_1 lies in the target. Thus:

(27.1) Theorem. *For a chain of flights to the target, all the constituent sets are relative exact.*

§28. PIECING TOGETHER FRAGMENTS OF CURVES

Let $\mathscr{K}$ be the class of rectifiable curves in R, of bounded flight-time, and let R_ν, where ν describes a set of positive integers, be a finite or countable system of disjoint subsets of R whose union is R. A curve $C \in \mathscr{K}$ will be termed fragmentary or a fragment if its interior portion lies in some R_ν. The class of such fragments will be denoted by $\mathscr{K}_0$. More generally, subject to conditions described below, $\mathscr{K}$ could denote a given class of rectifiable curves in a metric space, and $\mathscr{K}_0$ a subclass. We wish to describe a situation in which $\mathscr{K}$ can be derived from $\mathscr{K}_0$ by simple operations of addition and subtraction of curves.

This very simple procedure will enable us to extend considerably the results of the preceding section. Therefore we ask the reader to have patience while we attempt to formulate it in a manner that we can use for this purpose. Addition and subtraction of curves are intuitive operations. We need to define them more precisely and restrict them so as to ensure that they lead from curves in $\mathscr{K}$ to curves in $\mathscr{K}$.

To this effect, we admit here only two forms of the addition of curves:

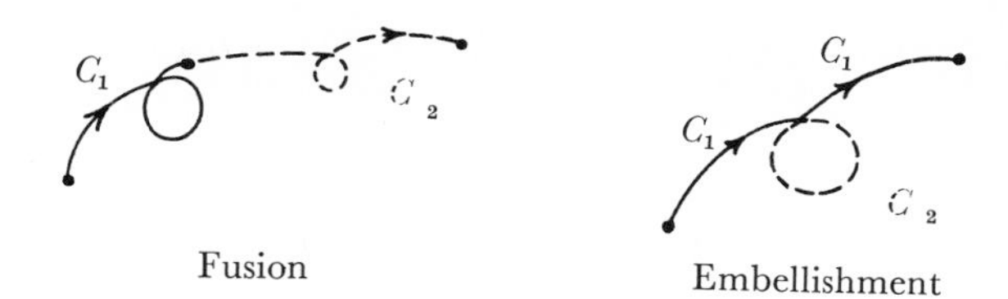

Fusion Embellishment

(i) If the final point of C_1 is the initial point of C_2, we term fusion of C_1, C_2 a curve C made up of two adjacent arcs, consisting of C_1 and C_2, in that order.

(ii) If C_2 is a closed curve which intersects C_1, we term embellishment of C_1 by C_2 a curve C that describes first an arc of C_1 up to an intersection, then C_2 and then the remaining arc of C_1. In each case, C_1, C_2, C are supposed to belong to the class $\mathscr{K}$.

We define correspondingly two subtraction operations, which we term, respectively, those of cutting and trimming C_2 from C. We term C_1 the result of this cutting or trimming, if C is expressible as the fusion of C_1, C_2, or as the embellishment of C_1 by C_2.

From the classical point of view, the above operations are not always uniquely defined. Thus, if C_1, C_2 have opposite pairs of extremities, we can form their fusion

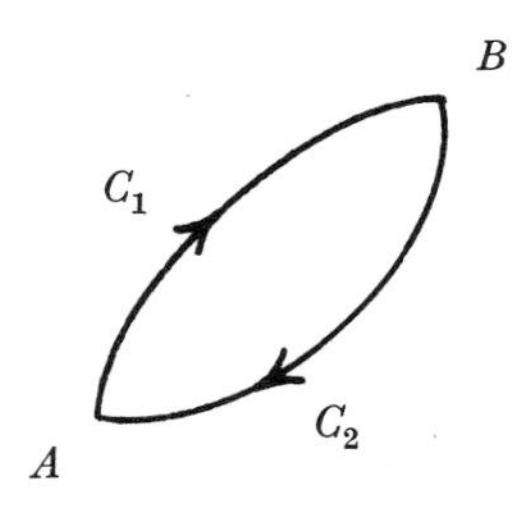

C in two ways: in one case C describes C_1 from A to B, and then C_2 from B to A; in the other, it describes first C_2 from B to A, and then C_1 from A to B. The two forms of C are, however, identified by regarding them as ways of describing the same closed curve, so that this classical convention removes all ambiguity here.

However, things are not so simple if we consider the embellishment of a curve C_1 by a closed curve C_2, where C_2 intersects C_1 in at least two points A, B. This embellishment can then be effected in two ways: the embellished curve C can consist of the arc of C_1 up to A then C_2, and then the arc of C_1 from A onward; or it can consist of C_1 up to B, then C_2, and then C_1 from B onward. In classical analysis,

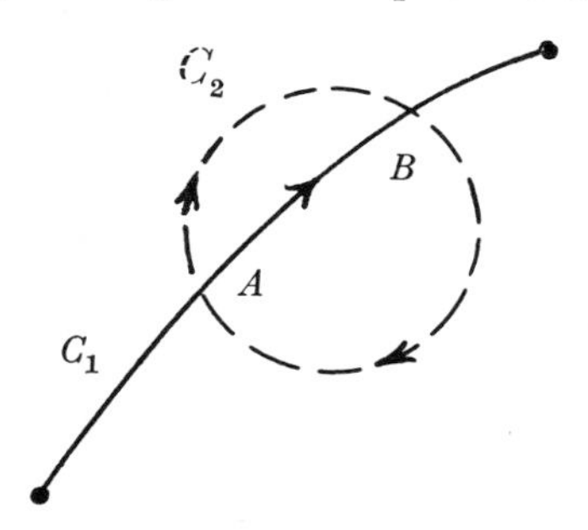

the two forms of C are not equivalent; in fact, in the sense of Fréchet, they are different. Nevertheless, we shall agree to identify them. This means that we discard the classical definition of curve; instead, we adopt that of Sections 63 and 64 of Chapter VI of Volume I: two curves are identified if they give rise to the same operation of curvilinear integration. This identification removes all ambiguity.

The same example illustrates the fact that by adding one embellishment and removing another, we can replace the arc AB of C_1 by the corresponding arc of C_2. It is sufficient to remove, from the embellished curve C, the closed curve that is the fusion of the arc AB of C_1 and the arc BA of C_2.

In the sequel, the classes $\mathscr{K}$ and $\mathscr{K}_0$ will be such that if a curve is a member, so is each arc, and also the inverse arc. Such classes of curves we term hereditary and reversible. In that case, the operation of cutting can be omitted; it can be carried out in two stages by fusion with an inverse arc, and by trimming by a closed curve consisting of an arc and its inverse. The operation of fusion is, moreover, associative, and we can define the fusion of a finite number of members of $\mathscr{K}$ whose end points agree in pairs where the definition requires this. We shall speak of this operation as finite fusion. On the other hand, we shall allow the two operations of embellishment and trimming to be carried out countably often, and we then speak of at most countable embellishment, and at most countable trimming. Each operation is, of course, restricted by the condition that, at each stage, it leads only from members of $\mathscr{K}$ to members of $\mathscr{K}$.

This being so, we apply to the class of fragmentary curves $\mathscr{K}_0$ the operations of finite fusion and countable embellishment. The resulting subclass of $\mathscr{K}$ will be denoted by $\mathscr{K}_1$ and its members will be termed reconstituted curves. From $\mathscr{K}_1$ we then define a subclass $\mathscr{K}_2$ of $\mathscr{K}$ whose members are obtained by at most countable trimming; we term these trimmed reconstituted curves.

In optimal control, we are concerned with an actual problem of minimum in the whole of a set R. So far, on the model of the classical calculus of variations and of the still older investigations of geometrical optics, we have discussed only what happens in certain subsets R_ν, whose union turns out to be R. This means that we have information about the class of fragments $\mathscr{K}_0$, and that we seek information about the class of our original curves $\mathscr{K}$. The method that we shall develop applies only in the case in which we can recover $\mathscr{K}$ from $\mathscr{K}_0$ by setting $\mathscr{K} = \mathscr{K}_2$. This is also basically what occurs in the optimal control problems so far treated.

However, the validity or nonvalidity of the relation $\mathscr{K}_2 = \mathscr{K}$ is entirely dependent on the manner in which R is decomposed into disjoint sets R_ν. Thus if R is the plane, and we decompose it into three sets R_1, R_2, R_3, consisting of its rational points, its irrational points and the points with exactly one rational coordinate, we find that $\mathscr{K}_0$ (and so also $\mathscr{K}_2$) is empty. On the other hand, if the class $\mathscr{K}$ is as stated previously and ℓ is a line on which $T(x)$ is bounded in bounded subsets of ℓ, the relation $\mathscr{K}_2 = \mathscr{K}$ does hold for the decomposition of the plane R into the three sets consisting of ℓ and the two open half-planes separated by ℓ. To see this, we verify that each $C \in \mathscr{K}$ belongs to $\mathscr{K}_2$, and in so doing we may suppose the end points of C to lie on ℓ. Then C meets each of the two open half-planes in at most countably many open arcs C_ν, and the line ℓ in a closed set. We denote by γ the directed segment with the same ends as C, by γ_ν the directed segment with the same ends as C_ν, by γ_ν^* the opposite segment of γ_ν, by Γ_ν the closed curve consisting of the fusion of γ_ν, γ_ν^* and by Γ the embellishment of γ by the finite or countable system of closed curves that are fusions of C_ν, γ_ν^*. Clearly all these curves are of bounded flight-time, and the length of Γ is at most three times that of C. Hence $\Gamma \in \mathscr{K}_1$, and by trimming off the Γ_ν we find that $C \in \mathscr{K}_2$.

Generally, if $\mathscr{K}_2 = \mathscr{K}$, we shall term $\mathscr{K}_0$ a repairable class of fragments and the decomposition of R into the disjoint sets R_ν a repairable decomposition. In that case we term R the unimpaired union of the sets R_ν. More generally, a class of subsets P of R, not necessarily disjoint or countable, will be said to have R as its unimpaired union, if it has the union R, and if further, there exists a repairable decomposition of R into at most countably many disjoint sets R_ν, such that each P is the union of those R_ν which are its subsets.

§29. THE FUNDAMENTAL THEOREM AND ITS CONSEQUENCES

We are now in a position to tackle the rather general situation to which, thanks to the various concepts we have introduced, the standard variational methods become applicable. At this stage, however, it is convenient to introduce an additional hypothesis, whose object is to ensure that a certain integral exists along each rectifiable curve C of bounded flight-time in R; we suppose that there exists in R a momentum $y(x)$ such that $|y(x)\ dx/ds|$ does not exceed along C some integrable function $K(s)$ of the arc length s of C. We shall term this the integrable momentum hypothesis. (Of course, we do not suppose $y(x)$ to be measurable along C in terms of arc length.)

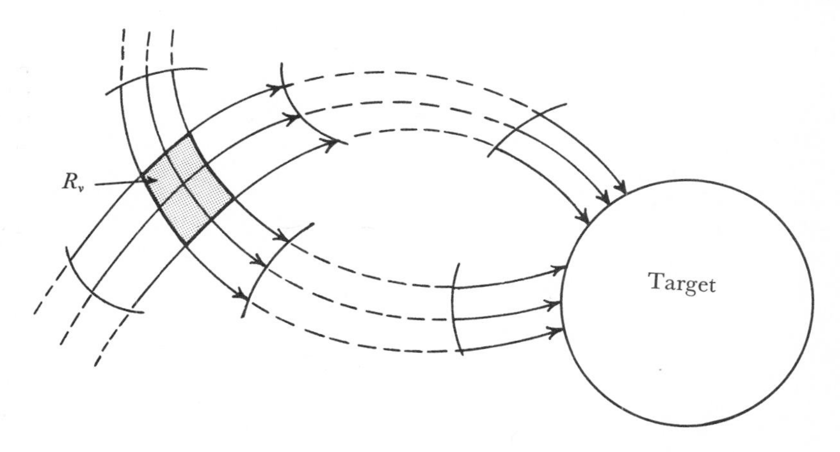

Intersecting sprays of flights

In practice, as we shall see in a moment, this strengthens only slightly the assumption already made, and made with some reluctance, according to which, as explained in Section 21, we exclude from our lines of flight the suspected optimal trajectories along which $H = 0$. In fact, the integrable momentum hypothesis can then be verified, in many cases, in a much stronger form. For the lines of flight issuing from a subset A of R, which is bounded and of bounded flight-time, normally remain, all the way to the target, in some bounded subset B of R, in which the function $g_x(x, u)$ is uniformly bounded for all relevant values of u. In that case, since the conjugate vectors along a line of flight obey (21.2)(a), we easily verify an inequality of the form

$$|y(x)| \leq e^{a|t|} = e^{aT(x)},$$

provided that $y(x) \in \mathscr{Y}(x)\ x \in R$, and that $y(x)$ is bounded on the target, i.e., for $t = 0$ at the terminal points of the lines of flight coming from A.

This being so, we recall that a chain of flights was defined in Section 27 in terms of sprays of flights, and that their sources and flight-corridors were termed its constituent sets; for brevity we shall term its canonical constituent sets those of the corresponding canonical chain.

We shall term concourse of flights a system, finite or countably infinite, of chains of flights to the target, such that R is the unimpaired union of their constituent sets, and that $R^{\#}$ is the union of their canonical constituent sets. The basic assumption on which the application of our standard methods is based will be the existence of such a concourse. The concept of unimpaired union is here fundamental, for there is nothing to prevent the various constituent sets from intersecting, and we do not desire to prevent this; it is all part of the general elimination of one-to-oneness from the classical form of our standard methods.

In any practical problem, we must thus begin by verifying the existence of a concourse of flights. The ideal would be for this to be implicit in the complete description of the lines of flight, and indeed, such a description will go a long way toward it. For in order to describe our lines of flight properly, there is really little that we can do except to group them into families, which correspond to our chains, and to divide these up into families of smooth arcs, which correspond to our sprays. Such a description may be thought of as the preliminary work of rounding up the suspects and of classifying them suitably, before calling in our reader as the expert prosecutor, who will really prove their guilt. His first task is then, naturally, to verify that they do in fact satisfy the conditions on which he intends to base his case.

In practice, the most troublesome condition to be verified is that R is indeed the unimpaired union of the relevant constituent sets. According to our definition, this necessitates expressing R as the union of certain disjoint sets R_ν, each of which is wholly contained in any constituent set in question, which it meets, and proving that the decomposition of R into these sets R_ν is repairable. The appropriate decomposition will not normally be hard to find, and the proof that it is repairable will normally follow the model of the proof, given in the preceding section, of the relation $\mathscr{K}_2 = \mathscr{K}$, in the case of the decomposition of a plane R by the line ℓ and the two open half-planes separated by ℓ. This type of proof is clearly of a routine nature.

We now come to our main result and to its corollaries:

(29.1) Fundamental Theorem. *Suppose that a concourse of flights exists. Then R is exact.*

PROOF. By hypothesis, there is a repairable decomposition of R into disjoint R_ν, each of which is a subset of every constituent set Q of the chains of flight of our concourse, such that Q meets R_ν. We define the classes of curves $\mathscr{K}_0$, $\mathscr{K}_1$, $\mathscr{K}_2$ accordingly, taking for $\mathscr{K}$ that of the rectifiable curves in R, of bounded flight-time.

Let now $C \in \mathscr{K}_0$, and let Σ be any spray of flights of one of our chains such that C meets either the source or the flight-corridor of Σ. It then follows from our hypothesis that C lies in some R_ν, wholly contained in this source, or flight-corridor. By Theorem (27.1), we therefore have

$$\int_C y_\Sigma(x)\, dx = T(x_1) - T(x_2), \tag{29.2}$$

where x_1, x_2 are the initial and final points of C. From this relation, applied to arcs of C, we deduce that $T(x)$, regarded as function of the arc length s along C, is absolutely continuous, and that its derivative in s is almost everywhere $y_\Sigma(x)\, dx/ds$.

This is true simultaneously for all relevant Σ, since there are at most countably many sprays, provided that we exclude at most countably many sets of s of measure 0. This means that the derivative in question has almost everywhere the stated value for every Σ, and so that almost every point of C is a point of univalence on C; this is because every $y \in \mathscr{Y}(x)$ has the form $y_\Sigma(x)$ for some Σ at the point x, since, by hypothesis, $R^\#$ is the union of the various canonical constituent sets. Hence we may rewrite our relation (29.2) in the form

$$\text{(29.3)} \qquad \int_C y(x)\, dx = T(x_1) - T(x_2),$$

where $y(x)$ is now any momentum in R. Moreover, the relation (29.3) is thus proved for every $C \in \mathscr{K}_0$. It extends at once, by addition, to the case where C is a finite fusion of members of $\mathscr{K}_0$, and in particular the left hand side then vanishes if C is closed. Hence the relation (29.3) is unaffected by at most countable embellishment of C, since its left hand side then continues to exist, on account of our integrable momentum hypothesis. Thus (29.3) holds for all $C \in \mathscr{K}_1$. For the same reason, the relation is also unaffected by at most countable trimming, and must hold for all $C \in \mathscr{K}_2$, i.e., for all $C \in \mathscr{K}$.

This completes the proof.

(29.4) Corollary. *With the same hypotheses, let C be any rectifiable curve in R of bounded flight-time, let x_1, x_2 be its initial and final points and let $y(x)$ be any momentum in R. Then*

$$\int_C y(x)\, dx = T(x_1) - T(x_2).$$

Further, if, in particular, C is a trajectory arc that starts at the time t_1 and ends at the time t_2, then

$$\int_C y(x)\, dx \leq t_2 - t_1.$$

Proof. We need only justify the last statement, and this follows from the fact that $y(x)\dot{x} \leq 1$ along a trajectory, by (21.1) and (21.2)(b).

In particular, if we set $x_1 = x$, and suppose x_2 on the target, we obtain as a further corollary:

(29.5) Sufficiency Theorem. *With the same hypotheses, let x be any point of R. Then the flight-time $T(x)$ is the least time for transferring the point x to the target along a trajectory in R.*

Chapter III

Generalized Optimal Control

§30. INTRODUCTION

Since the title of this final Chapter does not, perhaps, do justice to its practical character, we ask the reader to think of a really important practical project, such as a moonshot, in which the basic problem is one of control theory, and to imagine that we are jointly consultants on it, together with a distinguished experimental physicist or engineer and an eminent logician. In case this combination should seem incongruous, let us specify that this is no hit or miss project, but one in which it is essential that every eventuality be completely worked out beforehand to the smallest detail. In these circumstances, the cooperation of experimentalists with mathematicians and logicians can give tremendous power. It is similar to the combination that produced the atomic bomb. In that affair there was, perhaps, no actual logician, but the mathematician S. Ulam was very close to being a logician, since he was best known for his work on the role of the continuum hypothesis in certain questions of abstract measure theory.

The strength of this kind of collaboration lies in the certainty that fundamental issues will not be shirked. Indeed, the present generation has learned that the greatest progress is not made by evading main difficulties and main issues, but by honestly coming to grips with them. Therefore we have here avoided long enough the fundamental difficulties inherent in optimal control. This is precisely where the generalized methods of the last part of Volume I will help us. In any case, the hypotheses of both Chapter I and Chapter II of this Volume can only be verified when the control mechanism has been chosen, whereas in a really important project this mechanism is only selected as a result of the theoretical investigation.

The best way to adapt our generalized methods to control problems, and to other problems involving constraints, is still the subject of much research. For this reason, what we describe here is related only to the older form of the author's generalized theory, the form which uses generalized curves, but not generalized flows. It was first adapted to problems with constraints by McShane. The optimal control version is due to Filippov and Warga; however, we shall present this version rather differently here, in order to emphasize its practical nature.

As we have explained many times in these lectures, our basic difficulties, from the mathematical and logical point of view, are existential, and here they are aggravated by a lack of compactness and closure properties of solutions of differential equations. However, for the experimentalist, who will have much to say in the sequel, these existential difficulties are also a sign of hidden trouble of a practical nature, and this must be brought out into the open. It is from this practical side that we shall be led to a setting in which existence theorems are virtually automatic.

The practical nature of our setting shows itself again when we pass on to the necessary conditions expressed by Pontrjagin's maximum principle, in so far as the only relatively simple proofs of this principle rest on ideas that are basically equivalent to those leading to our generalized setting. The deeper significance of this lies in the necessary and sufficient condition (86.3) of Appendix II of Volume I and in the variational convexity principle from which this condition is deduced. However, to see this it would be necessary to adapt to optimal control the newer form of our generalized approach by linearizing constraints just as we linearized the notion of boundary. This suggestion, which the author of these lectures never fails to make, is now beginning to be applied in recent work, and the author's joint work with W. H. Fleming shows that it can also be used very effectively in multiple integral problems.

With the older form of generalized setting that we use here, the connection with necessary conditions appears rather as a coincidence of the kind one tends to expect in reward for good conduct. It would be nice if we could go further and point to the moral that crime does not pay. We would like to be able to say that it is actually easier to prove Pontrjagin's maximum principle in its more general form in our generalized setting, and also to prove existence, than to flout logic by proving only the principle by itself and assuming existence. Unfortunately this would be an exaggeration, and indeed, in these lectures it has never been our object to spare the reader by teaching only the minimum, but on the contrary to give him a broad insight into all relevant parts of mathematics. In this respect, our demands on the reader have progressively increased, and we now ask of him one final great effort, worthy of the seasoned veteran that he has now become.

This further effort is necessary mainly because, as our good friend the experimentalist will confirm, it is not enough to provide ordinary or generalized trajectories. We have to specify definite corresponding controls. This means going through the unpleasant process of defining appropriate implicit functions. This process was unpleasant enough in the classical calculus of variations; now we need it at a much more advanced level. The controls that we seek, as functions of the time, must for practical purposes satisfy suitable measurability conditions.

Some of the deepest questions in analysis are connected with just these matters, and an account of them is given in the famous book by Lusin on analytic sets. In our case, there is the further complication that in the generalized setup, the values of our control functions at a given time t are not just points of the control space U, but measures on U. In stochastic control theory, which we do not treat here, the state of affairs is even worse. It is clearly desirable that we should possess suitable tools for dealing with this. Fortunately, all our needs in this respect can be met by a single lemma, known as Filippov's lemma. The general form of this lemma, due to McShane and Warfield, itself uses powerful apparatus: it is based on the famous continuum hypothesis.

This is the second time that we mention this profound conjecture, which Cantor originally announced as a theorem, to be proved in the next issue. Since it now appears that it may simplify parts of our subject, we ought at least to dispel the aura of mysticism which has grown around it and the legend that it is beyond the understanding of man. A similar aura of mysticism once enveloped Euclid's axiom of parallels. What a particular generation considers beyond the understanding of man may later seem rather commonplace, and at some intermediate stage it is suddenly one of the softest and most popular of Ph.D. topics. This stage does not seem to have been quite reached in the case of the continuum hypothesis. However, the curiosity of our experimentalist is aroused: could we, very briefly, describe this hypothesis and the present knowledge relating to it?

In doing so, we shall partly paraphrase some remarks by Dr. Barkley J. Rosser during a recent informative Colloquium talk, which point to some similarities of the history of Cantor's conjecture with that of Euclid's axiom of parallels.

Nowadays what with non-Euclidean geometry and Einstein's relativity, the aura of mystery has gone from Euclid's axiom of parallels, and we realize that it is independent of Euclid's other postulates, whereas to the philosopher Kant, geometry was unthinkable without this axiom. Euclid himself based his "Elements" on five postulates, which we would now speak of as axioms, although this term had a different meaning in Euclid's time. Only the first four postulates were used to prove Euclid's first twenty-eight propositions, and the last of these propositions clearly implies that, given a line ℓ and a point P not situated on ℓ, one can construct through P in the same plane at least one line ℓ', not intersecting ℓ. It looks as if what

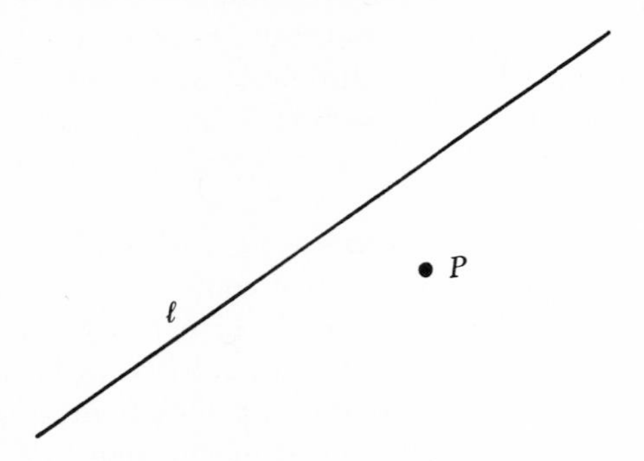

Euclid really wanted to prove with his four postulates was that there is exactly one such line ℓ', and, when he failed to do so, he rather lamely added a fifth postulate to his initial list to ensure this. At any rate, for two thousand years, many attempts were made to prove the fifth postulate, which we call the axiom of parallels, from the other four. In the Middle Ages, one monk seems to have gone so far as to draw a number of conclusions from the negation of this axiom, so that he was really doing what we call non-Euclidean geometry; however, he hoped only to reach a contradiction, and when he failed to reach one, he destroyed all his work. Finally Kant produced what he regarded as a philosophical proof of the postulate, the fact that *he* was incapable of conceiving the opposite. This final indignity may have been more than mathematicians could bear. At any rate, after a few more decades, the independence of the fifth postulate was established by a rather simple method, the method of models. Within the framework of Euclidean geometry, one constructs a model satisfying only the first four of Euclid's postulates. One of the simplest such models was that of Cayley: in it, the points are interpreted as points interior to a disc, and the lines as portions of lines situated in this disc. Clearly, several such lines through P do not intersect ℓ.

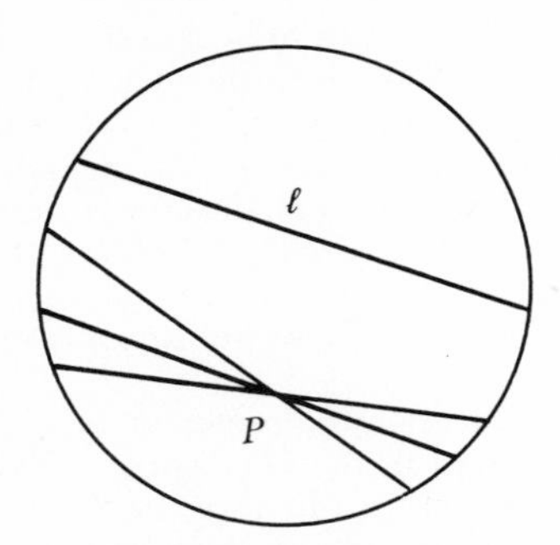

The story of the continuum hypothesis is similar, but shorter. Cantor's papers are written in a vivid and inspiring style, which still makes exciting reading. He was very conscious of the great power of his new concepts, and of his own deep insight. He must have been very confident of his ability to prove the highly plausible theorem that he announced, that the cardinal of the reals is the least cardinal greater than that of the integers, or, as we now usually write it, that

$$2^{\aleph_0} = \aleph_1.$$

All the available evidence pointed to this. In the first place, it was known that

$$2^{\aleph_0} > \aleph_0,$$

or, what amounts to the same, that

$$2^{\aleph_0} \geq \aleph_1,$$

and this important inequality had already had applications in analysis. In the second place, every set of points actually constructed on the line, or in Euclidean n-space, was known to be either at most countable, or of the same cardinal as the real line, and this evidence has been greatly strengthened subsequently.

After Cantor, others tried to prove his conjecture. In this way, a number of strange statements were found to be equivalent to or consequences of either the continuum hypothesis or its negation. They are treated in Sierpinski's book on the subject. A very different approach was attempted in the nineteen twenties by Hilbert, who claimed thus to establish the conjecture. This approach was perhaps most in accord with the basic simplicity of Cantor's own conception. However, it was generally considered only to have shown the need to lift the whole question out of mathematics proper into the realm of mathematical logic and metamathematics. This may not sound like a simplification to a physicist or to a practical analyst, but one must bear in mind that previously no one bothered to define a set. Sierpinski begins one of his books by saying: "Everyone knows what is meant by a set, for instance the set of persons in this room, the set of books in a particular library, and so forth." He then goes on to give a few further examples. This is what we now would call naive set theory. To clarify Cantor's conjecture, we place it instead in a setting consisting of formal set theory and Boolean algebra, properly based on axioms, just as the geometry of Euclid's "Elements" was based on his postulates. This is the only way to dispel the aura of mysticism.

In this axiomatic setting, the continuum hypothesis can now be considered as a fresh axiom. Two questions then arise: whether the continuum hypothesis is compatible with the other axioms of set theory, and whether it is independent of them. The answer to both these questions turns out to be affirmative, and to be provided, just as in the case of Euclid's axiom of parallels, by a suitable model. This model is constructed within set theory itself, just as Cayley's model was constructed within the Euclidean plane, and it is not too complicated. It is found that after satisfying the other axioms of set theory, there is still enough freedom, so that we can arrange for the cardinal

$$2^{\aleph_0}$$

to take the value $\aleph_1$, or, if preferred, the value $\aleph_2$, which is the next cardinal larger than $\aleph_1$. This clearly settles both our questions. For details, the reader should refer to the recent literature, for instance to work by Dana Scott. Older papers, for instance the classical work of Gödel, are more difficult.

Thus the status of the continuum hypothesis can now be regarded as reasonably cleared up; it is that of an independent axiom, just like the axiom of parallels in geometry. Therefore we need have no compunction in using it in analysis, just as we use the axiom of choice and various other axioms, which are convenient, and in this way, we shall be following the spirit of Cantor's original conception. Of course, we could try to avoid it, if we feel unhappy about it, just as Tonelli systematically avoids explicit use of the axiom of choice, at the expense of clumsier theorems and clumsier proofs. We prefer to use it.

§31. THE PREPROBLEM

In a moonshot, the differential equations of a trajectory depend on the relative positions of the earth and the moon during the motion, and so on the constants which specify the initial values of these positions. They depend also on the mass of the projectile to be landed on the moon, and this mass may also affect the controls indirectly, since it increases with the amount of controlling equipment. We have thus a problem of optimal control in which the constraints are further dependent on certain constant parameters. Such a problem is formulated in Chapter IV of *Optimal Processes*, as follows: we ask for the minimum of an integral

$$\int f(t, x, u, w)\, dt,$$

for trajectories $x(t)$, controls $u(t)$, and constants w, subject to

$$\dot{x} = g(t, x, u, w),$$

where $u(t)$, w range in given sets U, W, and appropriate end-conditions are specified.

We can at once eliminate the inconvenient constants w by regarding the pair (x, w) as a point of a higher space, and by adjoining the differential equation

$$\dot{w} = 0,$$

which ensures the constancy of w on a trajectory. We must then add to our end-conditions that the initial, or final, values of the projection w of (x, w) must lie in W. Thus the only effect of constant parameters on our basic problem is to alter the dimensionality and the end-conditions. Since the dimensionality has always been at our disposal, this only means that we must now consider rather more general types of end-conditions than formerly. Our problem is thus once again that of the minimum of

$$\int f(t, x, u)\, dt$$

for trajectories $x(t)$ and controls $u(t)$ subject to

$$\dot{x} = g(t, x, u),$$

where $u(t)$ ranges in U and $x(t)$ satisfies appropriate end-conditions.

It is convenient to introduce a further formal simplification, which reduces this to something like the time-optimal case. We introduce an additional coordinate x_0 subject to

$$\dot{x}_0 = f(t, x, u),$$

and we rewrite x and g for the pairs (x_0, x) and (f, g). Further, we add the end-condition $x_0 = 0$ at the final end of a trajectory, which, as in the preceding Chapters, may be supposed to correspond to the time $t = 0$. Our problem is then that of the minimum of $-x_0$ for trajectories $x(t)$ and controls $u(t)$ subject to

(31.1) $$\dot{x} = g(t, x, u),$$

where $u(t)$ ranges in U and $x(t)$ satisfies appropriate end-conditions. In regard to these end-conditions, we shall suppose, without loss of generality, that they specify only, on the one hand as usual the final value $t = 0$, and on the other hand that the initial and final values of $x(t)$, regarded as an ordered pair of points, belong to a certain preassigned subset B of the Cartesian product of x-space with itself. In other words, the initial value of t is not specified or restricted directly. (To see this, it is sufficient to set $t + t_0$ in place of t and to regard t_0 as a constant parameter, and, in addition, to introduce a new x-coordinate x_{n+1}, with the final value 0, subject to $\dot{x}_{n+1} = 1$.)

The problem of minimum, thus formulated for trajectories subject to (31.1) and to the above end-conditions, will be termed, in the sequel, the controlled preproblem. It is convenient also to consider a slightly different problem, which we term the uncontrolled preproblem. We denote by $G(t, x)$ the set of values taken for fixed (t, x) by the vector $g(t, x, u)$ as u ranges in U. We ask for the minimum of $-x_0$ for trajectories $x(t)$ subject to our previous end-conditions, and to

(31.2) $$\dot{x} \in G(t, x).$$

In this Chapter, we shall not be concerned with quite this preproblem, whether we take it in the controlled, or in the uncontrolled form, but with a rather different problem, which is really the practical problem associated with it.

§32. MORE SEMANTICS

What is stated as a problem or as a question often involves some basic assumption that may be incorrect. In such a case we have an improper problem or improper question. Examples abound: one finds them in examination papers, in questionnaires which begin with the words "This will only take a few minutes of your time," and of course in anything to do with politics or criminal proceedings, described in local papers. However, to avoid hurting anyone's feelings, we will mention only the most familiar instances of improper questions:

Do you still beat your wife?

Why is the moon made of green cheese?

The first is an insulting assumption, the second a tactful expression of disbelief. The most appropriate answers are counter-questions:

If you think everyone is so like you, why abuse people?

Would you rather have the moon made of candy?

Generally speaking, improper questions cannot simply be ignored, as they reveal something that needs correcting in the questioner's state of mind or in his sources of misinformation. The task of correcting this may be, in some cases, too great to be undertaken, but a proper answer would have to tackle it. However, before answering in this way, it is necessary to elucidate what the question really means, that is to say, what it is that needs correcting. This is where semantics may help.

We encountered semantics first in Chapter VI of Volume I. Now it comes up again, which shows once more how closely many parts of Mathematics are connected with Foundations. This is why we added a logician to our team. However, in this case, it is the experimentalist, at least as much as the logician, who will help us to reformulate our preproblem.

The fact is that our preproblem, which we worded the way in which it usually appears in books and papers on optimal control or on the calculus of variations, contains incorrect or misleading conventions and assumptions. We ask for a minimum when it need not exist. This reminds one of the footballer who was asked: "What do you know of the Peloponnesian War?" He answered correctly: "Nothing," and was duly flunked. If the minimum exists, we want, not just its value, but also at least one trajectory $x(t)$ and corresponding control $u(t)$, for which the minimum is attained. If the minimum does not exist, we want, instead, the corresponding infimum, and at least one sequence of such trajectories and controls for which the infimum is approached. After some 300 pages of text, these are conventions that one is inclined to take for granted, but which, the logician on our consulting team rightly insists, should be made explicit.

However, even when all this has been set down in black and white, to the last comma, with all the i's dotted and all the t's crossed, it involves, like prohibition, a basic assumption that is contradicted by the facts of life. To see this we need only a little common sense. The whole thing can be explained in terms of an anecdote. This is the way semantics should be used, in the traditional relaxed Socratic fashion, particularly if we are a bit tired after some 300 pages of a year's lectures.

We shall suppose this anecdote recounted by our friend the experimentalist during a coffee break, at a time when he is anxious to get his own back at the pure mathematicians by poking fun at them.

Two brothers, a mathematics teacher and an engineer, went into partnership to buy an old hunting lodge at the top of a small mountain, and they decided to build a road to it from the nearest railway station in the valley and to convert the lodge into a hotel. The mathematics teacher had once attended a course on the calculus of variations, so he studied his old notes of the course and applied them to the problem of finding the road along which a station wagon could drive from the railway station to the lodge in least time. Taking account of the fact that the station wagon doesn't pull too well up a steep hill, he formulated the appropriate variational problem, and by working hard managed to solve it. He found that there was exactly one solution, given by an ordinary curve, winding its way up all around the mountain, in and out of gorges, past waterfalls, and so on, and that the time it would take the station wagon to drive along this road, if it were built, would be just 36 minutes. He went to great trouble to prove that if the road were built along any other rectifiable curve leading from the station to the lodge, the driving time would be greater. Finally he made an estimate of the cost, and he found that building the road, including a couple of bridges, would cost two hundred thousand dollars, at the very least.

Meanwhile the engineer had proceeded routinely to map out the usual zigzag road up. He found that on his road the station wagon would take 37 minutes and that the cost of building the road would only be ninety thousand dollars. This shows—the experimentalist concluded—how misleading mathematics can be in practice, and why it is best to check it experimentally in any practical case.

Actually, the reader will have noted that the experimentalist's anecdote concerns Maxwell's problem, which we discussed in Chapter VI of Volume I, along with other problems in Section 61. The relevant case is here the one in which there is an ordinary solution, which the mathematics teacher found, and also a hidden solution, consisting of a generalized curve, which he did not find. What the engineer constructed was an approximation of this generalized solution by a finite zigzag. Therefore, what the anecdote really shows is the practical nature of generalized curves, even in the case of a problem that already possesses an ordinary solution, and the reason for this is the possibility that there may exist a hidden solution.

This possibility can, of course, also occur in the nonparametric form of a variational problem with fixed end-points. In other words, there exist a pair of integrands $f_1(t, x, \dot{x})$, $f_2(t, x, \dot{x})$, a fixed pair of points P, Q of (t, x)-space, an admissible curve C_0 in the nonparametric form, joining P, Q and a sequence of nonparametric admissible curves C_ν, with ends P_ν, Q_ν tending to P, Q, such that

$$\textbf{(32.1)}\qquad \begin{aligned} &\int_{C_0} f_1\,dt = 1, &\quad &\int_{C_0} f_2\,dt = 1,\\ &\int_{C_\nu} f_1\,dt \to 1, &\quad &\int_{C_\nu} f_2\,dt \to 0, \end{aligned}$$

and moreover such that, for every admissible nonparametric curve C joining P, Q and distinct from C_0,

$$\textbf{(32.2)}\qquad \int_{C} f_1\,dt > 1.$$

Further, without going into details, we can arrange that the above circumstances remain in effect when we specify in addition that, on the curves considered, the derivative $\dot{x}$ is to lie in some sufficiently large, fixed cube U. We can then introduce variables x_1, x_2 and control parameters u, subject to the differential equations

$$\textbf{(32.3)}\qquad \dot{x}_1 = f_1(t, x, u), \qquad \dot{x}_2 = f_2(t, x, u), \qquad \dot{x} = u;$$

we write further x^* for (x, x_1, x_2), and B_0 for the set of ordered pairs of points of (t, x^*)-space, with the initial point given by $(t, x) = P$, $x_1 = x_2 = 0$, and the final point restricted by $(t, x) = Q$, $x_1 \le 1$.

We now consider, for the fixed time interval which is the projection of the segment PQ, the minimum $\mu(B_0)$ of the value x_2 at the final extremity, for controlled trajectories of (t, x^*)-space, subject to (32.3) where $u \in U$, such that the pair of end points belongs to B_0. This minimum is 1, since the class of trajectories in question comprises only one member, and this is then the corresponding value of x_2. However, for trajectories whose pair of end points lies as close as we please to B_0, the corresponding values of x_2 can be chosen as the integrals of f_2 along the C_ν, which tend to 0. An entirely similar state of affairs can be arranged when the time interval is not fixed; to see this we need only introduce, as already explained, the additional variable x_0 subject to $\dot{x}_0 = 1$.

When this is pointed out to our experimentalist friend as the real significance of his anecdote, he at once exclaims: "But then the optimal control problem, which we took such pains to formulate, is all wrong! Why, I can't even distinguish between trajectories whose ends are in B_0 and those whose ends are infinitely near! Who ever heard of missing the moon by a billionth of an inch! And a soft moon landing at that!"

After coffee, the discussion of the preproblem is not considered worth resuming, the main progress having been made during the break, as often happens. The experimentalist, as the most practical in the group, sums this up: "It seems to me that our mathematicians have shown the need for ideas similar to that of generalized curve. Why not ask them to prepare a report on this, and we can then meet to discuss it?"

§33. CONVENTIONAL AND CHATTERING CONTROLS IN DIFFERENTIAL EQUATIONS

In our definition of generalized curve, which was given in the parametric case, we introduced a local turbulence that amounted to replacing the tangent vector $\dot{x}$ by a measure on the set of such vectors, such that the resultant vector was directed along the path described. The corresponding notion in the nonparametric case is a little simpler, and this is really what we should adapt to optimal control. The vector $\dot{x}$ in the nonparametric case is replaced by a measure such that the time derivative of the point $t, x(t)$ is the integral of $1, \dot{x}$ in this measure. In particular, the total measure is thus unity. We shall speak of the measure, which is of course here non-negative, as a unit measure or a probability measure.

For instance, in the case of an infinitesimal zigzag along the t-axis of the (t, x)-plane, for which the slopes are $\dot{x} = \pm 1$, the relevant probability measure at any point of the t-axis is obtained by attaching to each of these two slopes the weight $\frac{1}{2}$.

Now an admissible nonparametric curve may be regarded as a controlled trajectory, for which the moving point $x(t)$ is subject to the differential equation

$$\dot{x} = u.$$

This means that the velocity vector is controlled directly and coincides with the control value u. In the generalized case, we must therefore attach a probability measure to u. The actual velocity $\dot{x}(t)$ then becomes the integral of u with respect to this measure; probabilists would call it the expected value of u for this probability measure. In the case of the trajectory corresponding in (t, x)-space to our infinitesimal zigzag, we have as moving point $x(t)$, a controlled object, such as a ship or a submarine, in which the speed control is set at unity, corresponding to maximum speed, say, but the direction control is constantly shifted from forward to reverse, so that there is no actual motion. This may seem far-fetched, but in wartime evasive action at high speed with rapidly changing direction and very little motion is a closely related, standard nautical procedure.

By analogy with this case, we shall here regard, quite generally, control values $u \in U$ as special instances of the notion of a probability measure on U. Such a measure will be termed a chattering control value v, and we say that it reduces to a conventional control value u if the measure is wholly concentrated at u. We write V for the set of chattering control values v, i.e., for the set of non-negative unit measures of U.

In the sequel, we shall incorporate in our notation the fact that $U \subset V$, as follows. Given a continuous function $\varphi(u)$ defined in U, we shall write $\varphi(v)$ for its integral in the measure $v \in V$. Thus the symbol $\varphi(v)$ is an extension to V of the function originally defined in U. Evidently, if v reduces to a conventional control value u, the corresponding value of $\varphi(v)$ agrees with that originally defined as $\varphi(u)$. We shall use, more generally, a similar notation if φ is a function of other variables besides u. For instance, if $\varphi(t, x, u)$ is continuous in (t, x, u), the symbol $\varphi(t, x, v)$ is, for fixed (t, x), the integral on U of $\varphi(t, x, u)$ with respect to the probability measure v.

Just as the conventional notion of control is derived from that of control value, by making this value depend on the time, we shall here term chattering control a function $v(t)$, defined on a time-interval, and whose values lie in V, i.e., are probability measures on U. However, for practical reasons, we shall require that our conventional and chattering controls really do control something. There are far too many gadgets and so-called controls that do not: the starter that doesn't start, the television knob that produces only a blur, the temperamental tap that drips all day and yet only lets through a trickle of water when turned on. Here, a conventional control $u(t)$ is there for the purpose of controlling a conventional trajectory by means of a differential equation

$$\dot{x}(t) = g[t, x(t), u(t)]. \tag{33.1}$$

Similarly, a chattering control is no mere ornament, but something whose purpose is to control, by means of the analogous differential equation

$$\dot{x}(t) = g[t, x(t), v(t)], \tag{33.2}$$

a more general kind of trajectory $x(t)$ which we term "relaxed." If $u(t)$, $v(t)$ are honest controls, there must exist at least one trajectory $x(t)$ satisfying such a differential equation. Honest controls are controls that always work, not sources of revenue for a repair man. In our case, since $\dot{x}(t)$ is measurable, this implies that the right hand side must be measurable for each function g which is (say) continuous in (t, x, u). Thus honest controls, whether conventional or not, are not quite arbitrary.

The rest of this section will mainly be devoted to analyzing the very practical requirement that our controls be honest. It will turn out that this reduces to a very mild measurability requirement. This is the main reason why questions of measurability, which even analysts were inclined to disregard, are now relevant in optimal control.

In what follows, U will be, as usual, a bounded closed Euclidean set. For a much more general choice of U, we refer the reader to the papers of Warga and of McShane and Warfield. In the preceding Chapter, we allowed U to be very general, mainly because we wished to make possible the substitution for U of our present set V. Now we consider U and V together, and there is no need for such a substitution. We can therefore restrict again the generality of U, since, in practice, its points are simply given by positions on a finite number of dials.

In these circumstances, a conventional control $u(t)$ is termed measurable if the vector-valued function $u(t)$ is so in the ordinary sense, i.e., if its components are real, measurable functions. However, we can at once identify this requirement with another, which provides a more convenient definition: the conventional control $u(t)$ is measurable if for every polynomial $p(u)$ in u the composite function $p(u(t))$ is measurable. By taking for $p(u)$ a component of u, we see that this new requirement is sufficient; it is also necessary, since a sum or product of measurable functions is measurable.

We can now extend the definition: a chattering control $v(t)$ will be termed measurable if, for every polynomial $p(u)$ in (the components of) u, the function $p(v(t))$ is measurable.

From these definitions, it follows that if the conventional or chattering control $u(t)$ or $v(t)$ is measurable, and $g(t, u)$ is any real, or vector-valued, continuous function of (t, u), then the function $g(t, u(t))$ or $g(t, v(t))$ is measurable. We need only verify this when g is real and t is restricted to a finite interval T; and since in $T \times U$ the function $g(t, u)$ is the uniform limit of a polynomial, we may suppose without loss of generality that $g(t, u)$ is itself a polynomial, if we bear in mind that the limit of a sequence of measurable functions is always measurable. However, if $g(t, u)$ is a polynomial, $g(t, u(t))$ is a finite sum of terms of the form $t^{\nu} g_{\nu}(u(t))$, where $g_{\nu}(u)$ denotes a polynomial in u; these terms are measurable, and therefore so is their sum $g(t, u(t))$.

As in the case of measurable functions, we shall identify two measurable (conventional or chattering) controls, if they agree almost everywhere. Further, the differential equations (33.1) and (33.2) will only be required to hold almost everywhere; to make up for this, the function $x(t)$ is restricted to be absolutely continuous. If $g(t, x, u)$ is continuous, the existence of such absolutely continuous solutions $x(t)$ of (33.1) or (33.2), when $u(t)$ or $v(t)$ is a measurable conventional, or chattering, control, now follows by writing $f(t, x)$ for $g(t, x, u(t))$, or for $g(t, x, v(t))$, and by appealing to the following standard result:

(33.3) Existence of Solutions to the General Initial Value Problem for Ordinary Differential Equations. *Let $f(t, x)$ be a vector-valued function with values in x-space, and suppose that in some neighborhood of (t_0, x_0), $f(t, x)$ is continuous in x for each t, measurable in t for each x, and uniformly bounded in (t, x). Then there exists an absolutely continuous function $x(t)$, defined in some neighborhood of t_0, such that $x(t_0) = x_0$ and that, almost everywhere in that neighborhood,*

$$\dot{x}(t) = f(t, x(t)).$$

The proof of this general existence theorem for the initial value problem is obtained by combining a standard numerical technique with a rather simple application of equicontinuity; similar methods have become routine in partial differential equations. The theorem itself occurs, in a slightly different form, in Carathéodory's Real Functions, published fifty years ago; it is thus standard, and even classical. However, it always seemed a very lopsided affair, since continuity was assumed in x, but so much less in t, and it is only in terms of modern control theory that this becomes natural. It is thus, in a sense, very modern, and, until recently, the older existence theorem of Volume I, Chapter I, Section 19, was quite sufficient for applications, just as we ourselves had no occasion in Volume I to use any other. Similarly, until recently no one regarded a car as a necessity, and no one, even now, really needs a high-powered car to take him a few blocks; what is needed is the freedom to go further afield, for example, the security of being able to rush a child to a hospital in an emergency. In control theory, (33.3) is a high-powered tool of the same general nature; it is needed for stochastic control, which we do not treat; and it is needed here to attain the security provided by existence theorems for solutions of control problems. Incidentally, the methods of the present Chapter will, several times, come rather close to stochastic ones.

PROOF OF (33.3). By hypothesis, there is a constant M such that $|f(t, x)| < M$ throughout some neighborhood of (t_0, x_0). For small $a > 0$, this neighborhood contains the set E of the points (t, x) for which

$$\textbf{(33.4)} \qquad |t - t_0| \leq a, \qquad |x - x_0| \leq M\,|t - t_0|,$$

and for small $\delta > 0$, it contains (since E is closed) the set E_δ of the points distant $<\delta$ from E. Thus in E_δ we then have $|f(t, x)| < M$.

The interval $|t - t_0| \leq a$ will now be made into that of definition of the desired function $x(t)$. We have thus to construct in it a function $x(t)$, such that

$$\textbf{(33.5)} \qquad x(t) = x_0 + \int_{t_0}^{t} f(\tau, x(\tau))\, d\tau.$$

It will suffice to do so in the interval $t_0 \leq t \leq t_0 + a$.

Following the practice of numerical analysts, we first solve a similar problem for a finite grid, i.e., one in which our t-interval is replaced by a finite set of points t_ν where $\nu = 0, 1, \ldots, N$. We take these to be points of division of a subdivision of our interval into N equal parts $<\delta$, and we suppose them in increasing order, with

$t_N = t_0 + a$. We take as our finite problem that of determining values x_ν $\nu = 0, 1, \ldots, N$ corresponding to the t_ν and starting with the given value x_0, such that

$$x_\nu - x_{\nu-1} = \int_{t_{\nu-1}}^{t_\nu} f(\tau, x_{\nu-1})\, d\tau. \tag{33.6}$$

This is the finite difference analogue of our differential equation. To solve it, we suppose, by induction, that $x_{\nu-1}$ has been determined, and that $(t_{\nu-1}, x_{\nu-1}) \in E$. Then, in the integrand on the right $(\tau, x_{\nu-1}) \in E_\delta$, so that this integrand has absolute value $<M$, and is measurable in τ, since $x_{\nu-1}$ is a constant. Thus the integral exists, so that (33.6) defines x_ν. We verify that (t_ν, x_ν) lies in E, which justifies our induction.

From this solution of the finite problem, we see that, if $\varphi_N(t)$ is the step-function with the value x_N at t_N and x_ν for $t_\nu \le t < t_{\nu+1}$ $(\nu = 0, 1, \ldots, N-1)$, then for each t of $t_0 \le t \le t_0 + a$ the point $(t, \varphi_N(t))$ lies in E_δ. Hence the function $f(t, \varphi_N(t))$ is a measurable function with absolute value $<M$, and we can define

$$\psi_N(t) = x_0 + \int_{t_0}^{t} f(\tau, \varphi_N(\tau))\, d\tau. \tag{33.7}$$

The family of the functions ψ_N is clearly equicontinuous and uniformly bounded, so that there exists a uniformly convergent subsequence along which $N \to \infty$, and for which the limit is a Lipschitzian function $x(t)$. Clearly, by (33.6), $\psi_N(t) = \varphi_N(t)$ for $t = t_\nu$ $\nu = 0, 1, \ldots, N$. We can therefore write, for $t_\nu \le t < t_{\nu+1}$,

$$\psi_N(t) - \varphi_N(t) = \int_{t_\nu}^{t} f(\tau, \varphi_N(\tau))\, d\tau \tag{33.8}$$

so that the absolute value of the difference on the left is at most Ma/N.

This shows that $\varphi_N(t)$ tends, like $\psi_N(t)$, to $x(t)$, for our subsequence of N; thus—by continuity of f for constant t—the function $f(t, x(t))$ is the limit of the boundedly convergent sequence of measurable functions $f(t, \varphi_N(t))$, and is therefore measurable. Moreover, for the same reason we can make $N \to \infty$ along our subsequence, in (33.7), taking limits under the integral; we then obtain (33.5). This completes the proof, since the right hand side of (33.5) is absolutely continuous, has the initial value x_0 and possesses almost everywhere the derivative $f(t, x(t))$.

EXAMPLE. Taking for V the dashed topology in $C_0(U)$, show that measurability of $v(t)$, as defined above, is equivalent to the requirement that, for every $B \cdot \cdot i$-compact subset $Q \subset V$, the set of t such that $v(t) \in Q$ be measurable.

SKETCH OF SOLUTION. It should first be noted that the above requirement is equivalent to its special case for every closed dashed ball Q. If now $\mathscr{P}$ is the set of polynomials $p_\nu(u)$, with rational coefficients, such that the dashed norm of p_ν is ≤ 1, the requirement then means that for each $v_0 \in V$ and each $a > 0$, the sets of t for which $(v(t) - v_0)p_\nu < a$ have, for $\nu = 1, 2, \ldots$ i.e., for $p_\nu \in \mathscr{P}$, a measurable intersection. These sets are, however, measurable with our definition if $v(t)$ is measurable, and their intersection is then measurable also.

Second, the requirement in question implies, whenever $f(v)$ $v \in V$ is a continuous real function in the dashed topology of V, measurability in the usual sense of the composite function usually denoted by $f(v(t))$. This is then so, in particular, when we restrict $f(v)$, as we have been doing here, to be the integral, in the measure v, of a continuous function $f(u)$ $u \in U$.

§34. THE HALFWAY PRINCIPLE AND THE FILIPPOV LEMMA

Thus our practical requirement for a chattering or, in particular, a conventional control to be "honest," is the same as to be measurable. Now an ordinary analyst would be inclined to leave it at that, since nonmeasurable functions are met rather rarely, if at all. However, practical demands are often the hardest to satisfy, because no two persons can quite agree as to what they should be. At any rate, not everyone will agree offhand that what we called an honest control really deserves the name. We asked of $v(t)$ that, for each continuous $g(t, x, u)$, there exist a solution $x(t)$ of the corresponding differential equation (33.2). There will be two classes of objectors.

The "hawks" will object that an $x(t)$, which merely exists for a given chattering control $v(t)$, but which is not, in some sense, unique, may be termed compatible with this control, but is not really controlled by it at all. In other words, our control is not really a control, and, consequently, not an honest one. We deal with this objection in the next section, before coming to the relation of all this to our preproblem.

The "doves," on the other hand, may object that our "honesty" is quite unnecessarily strict: instead of concerning ourselves with the solubility of the differential equations arising from all possible continuous functions of the form $g(t, x, u)$, we should only make requirements which relate to the particular function $g(t, x, u)$ that actually occurs in our problem. In other words, what this criticism attacks is the universality of our requirement, as when an administration imposes the same building code or the same standard of dress in the tropics and at the North Pole as in Washington, D.C. or in London. Of course, no administration does this, but we are all too familiar with instances as arbitrary, and as callous, of bureaucratic red tape. We might mention the case of British soldiers in the desert at Tobruk, who had to fetch every drop of water under enemy fire, but were still required to shave daily. With such awful examples of human stupidity in mind, the criticism of universality of our requirement becomes most pertinent, and the present section is devoted to our reply, which may come as a surprise: oddly enough, and this is the gist of the Filippov lemma, honesty in our sense turns out to be no hardship whatsoever.

We shall begin with an important principle. In it P, Q will denote topological spaces, and R a measurability space, subject to conditions that we shall state below. By a measurability space we mean a set given with a σ-ring (or additive family) of subsets, termed measurable subsets. A map from such a space to a topological space is termed measurable if the inverse image of each $B \cdot \cdot i$-compact set is measurable.

We shall consider Q to be in some sense "halfway" from R to P. The principle is then as follows:

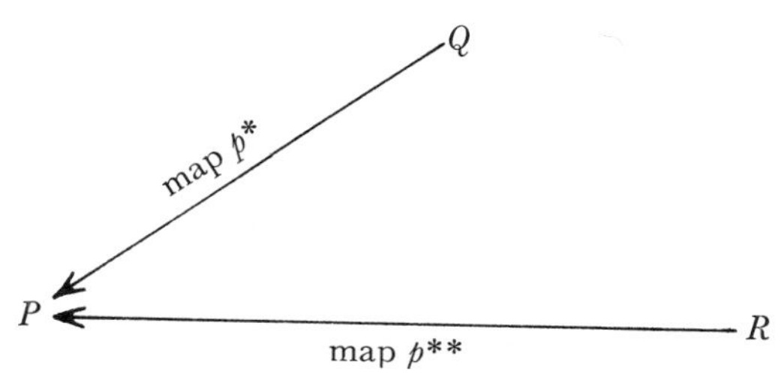

(34.1) Halfway Principle of McShane and Warfield. *Suppose given a continuous map p^* from Q to P, and a measurable map p^{**} from R to P, such that*

$$p^{**}(R) \subset p^*(Q) \subset P.$$

Then there exists a measurable map q^* from R to Q such that $p^{**} = p^* q^*$.

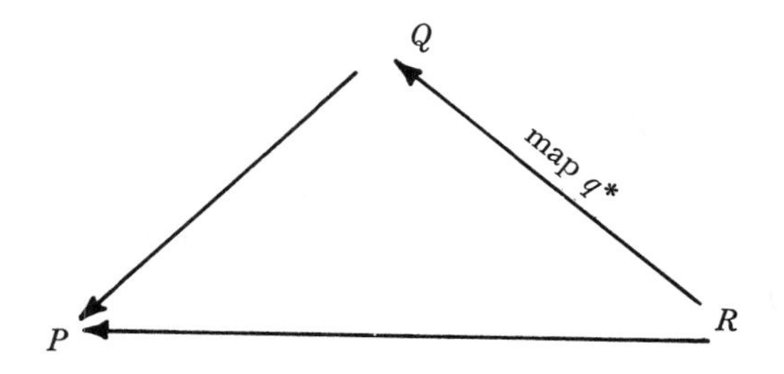

In regard to the conditions on the spaces P, Q, R, we shall need only the case in which P is Euclidean n-space and R is an interval of the real line, with measurability in the sense of Lebesgue. However, it costs nothing to take, instead, for P any Hausdorff space, and for R any measurability space; this we shall suppose throughout. It remains to specify our conditions on Q, and in this respect we shall consider three different cases:

(a) *Q is a $B \cdot \cdot i$-compact metric space.*

(b) *Q is a separable metric space.*

(c) *Q is a closed subset of the non-negative reals.*

We shall refer to our principle, subject to (a), (b) or (c), respectively, as (34.1a), (34.1b) or (34.1c). For our purposes, only (34.1a) will be required. However, the proof will proceed via (34.1c). As regards (34.1b), this is the most convenient form of the principle, but it is subject to the continuum hypothesis, and we refer the reader to McShane and Warfield for the proof and for certain slight extensions of (a) and (b). We need hardly point out that (34.1b) is a very remarkable theorem, which is of interest even in such special cases as that in which P and R coincide and p^{**} is the identity map. The reader should make a point of studying the way in which McShane and Warfield use the continuum hypothesis to obtain such a strong, and tangible, result in analysis. However, the proof of (34.1a), or rather its reduction to (34.1c), is of interest also, and in order to tackle it we shall recall the definition and a basic property of Cantor's famous ternary set.

Most readers will be familiar with Cantor's set, since it is usually given as an illustration very early in set theory. However, it is strange how much depth may be found even in the most elementary construction originated by Cantor. From the unit interval of the real line, we remove the open subinterval consisting of its middle third, from $\frac{1}{3}$ to $\frac{2}{3}$. From each of the two intervals remaining, we remove their open middle thirds. At the n-th stage, we are similarly left with 2^n closed intervals of length 3^{-n} and we remove their middle thirds. If we carry out this process indefinitely, the set H of the points remaining is termed Cantor's ternary set, or the Cantor discontinuum. It consists of the points of the form

$$t = \sum_{\nu=1}^{\infty} a_\nu 3^{-\nu} \quad \text{where} \quad a_\nu = 0 \text{ or } 2.$$

By associating to such a point, the sum

$$g(t) = \sum_{\nu=1}^{\infty} (\tfrac{1}{2}a_\nu) 2^{-\nu}$$

we obtain a continuous map g from H onto the unit interval. The function g has a unique monotone extension to the unit interval, and is then continuous on that interval and, moreover, constant in each subinterval complementary to H; in particular since H is found, by a simple subtraction of the lengths removed from the unit interval, to have measure 0, our extension of g has derivative 0 in the intervals removed, and so almost everywhere. This is relevant in the calculus of variations in so far as such functions have to be excluded in the notion of admissible curve, as explained in Chapter V of Volume I, Section 55, (*b*).

As might be expected, the Cantor set is the source of many counterexamples in analysis, often far from obvious ones. For instance, when a theorem suggested by the present author was included in Saks' *Theory of the Integral* with a faulty proof (due to Saks), the present author was at least able to clarify matters by such a counterexample, and incidentally to devise, in so doing, a method later used by Mulholland to solve the so-called Geöcze problem.

However the most interesting way of using the Cantor set is to derive positive results, rather than counterexamples, and this depends on less immediate properties of H. One such property will be helpful here, and was found by Urysohn. By combining the map g of H with the map of the unit segment onto the unit square, due to Hilbert, we obtain a map of H onto this unit square, and by a similar method we can map H onto the infinite-dimensional Hilbert cube. Now every separable metric space can be regarded as a subset of the Hilbert cube; it is therefore the continuous image of a subset of H. In the case of a $B \cdot\cdot i$-compact metric space, more than this is true. In standard topology books, e.g., the one written by J. G. Hocking and G. S. Young (Theorem 3.28) it is shown that:

(34.2) Urysohn's Property of the Cantor Set. *Every $B \cdot\cdot i$-compact metric space is a continuous image of the Cantor set H.*

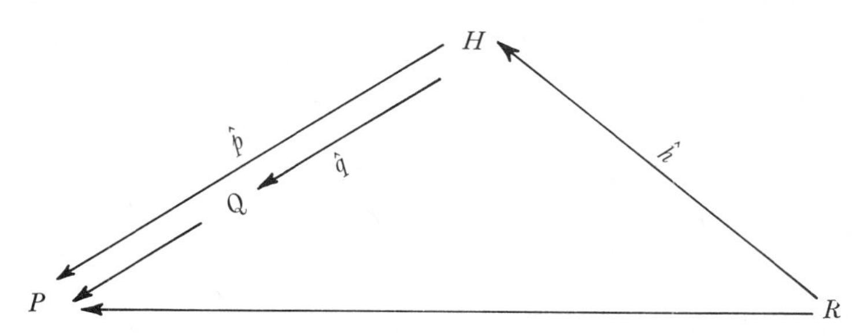

Proof That (34.1c) Implies (34.1a). We denote by $\hat{q}$ a continuous map onto Q from the Cantor set H, and by $\hat{p}$ the map $p^*\hat{q}$. Since $Q = \hat{q}(H)$, we have

$$p^{**}(R) \subset p^*\hat{q}(H) = \hat{p}(H).$$

Thus (34.1c) with H in place of Q has its hypotheses satisfied, and so implies the existence of a measurable map $\hat{h}$ from R into H, such that $p^{**} = \hat{p}\hat{h}$. Writing $q^* = \hat{q}\hat{h}$, we verify, on the one hand, that

$$p^{**} = (p^*\hat{q})\hat{h} = p^*q^*,$$

and on the other, that q^* is measurable, since the inverse under it of a $B \cdot\cdot i$-compact set $\tilde{Q}$ may be written

$$\hat{h}^{-1}(\tilde{H}) \quad \text{where} \quad \tilde{H} = \hat{q}^{-1}(\tilde{Q}),$$

so that $\tilde{H}$ is $B \cdot\cdot i$-compact.

We see here the power of (34.2) as a tool.

Before passing to the proof of (34.1c), we remark that in the case of a map f from R to a closed set Q of reals, the real function $f(r)$ $r \in R$ defined by this map is measurable on R in the usual sense (i.e., the set of r for which $f(r) \leq a$ is measurable for every real a), if and only if the map f is measurable in the sense of this section. This remark will simplify verifications of measurability. To justify it, we observe that if the map f is measurable, so is the set $f(r) \leq a$, since it is the countable union of sets of the form $-v \leq f(r) \leq a$. Conversely, if the set $f(r) \leq a$ is measurable for real a, we verify first by countable union the measurability of the set $f(r) < b$, and, by passing to the complement, that of the set $a < f(r)$, and consequently, by intersection, that of the set $a < f(r) < b$; by countable union and passing to the complement, there then follows the measurability of the inverse image of any closed (and in particular any $B \cdot\cdot i$-compact) subset of Q.

Proof of (34.1c). We term truncation of Q at the point $\ell 2^{-k}$, and denote by

$$[Q]^{k\ell},$$

where k, ℓ are integers, the set of points $q \in Q$ such that

$$q \leq \ell 2^{-k}.$$

We write further

$$P_{k\ell} = p^*[Q]^{k\ell} - p^*[Q]^{k,\ell-1}, \qquad Q_{k\ell} = (p^*)^{-1}P_{k\ell}, \qquad R_{k\ell} = (p^{**})^{-1}P_{k\ell}.$$

Here some sets may be empty, and of course so are then their images, or inverse images. We note also the identity

(34.3) $$P_{k\ell} = P_{k+1,2\ell} \cup P_{k+1,2\ell-1};$$

this follows from the fact that the right hand side is a union of differences $p^*A - p^*B$ and $p^*B - p^*C$ where $A \supset B \supset C$, and therefore may be written $p^*A - p^*C$; here A, B, C are the truncations of Q corresponding to the indices $(k + 1, 2\ell)$, $(k + 1, 2\ell - 1)$, $(k + 1, 2\ell - 2)$.

We remark further that an inverse map of a difference is always the difference of the inverse maps; e.g., if A, B now denote subsets of P, the set $(p^{**})^{-1}(A - B)$ is the set of $r \in R$ such that $p^{**}(r) \in A$ while $p^{**}(r) \notin B$, or equivalently, such that $r \in (p^{**})^{-1}A$ while $r \notin (p^{**})^{-1}B$, and this is the set $(p^{**})^{-1}A - (p^{**})^{-1}B$. From this it follows that the sets $R_{k\ell}$ are differences of measurable sets, and so are measurable. Clearly also, for fixed k, the sets $R_{k\ell}$ $(\ell = 0, 1, \ldots)$ are disjoint; similarly the sets $P_{k\ell}$ are disjoint, and the sets $Q_{k\ell}$ are so.

We now set, whenever $Q_{k\ell}$ is not empty,

$$q_{k\ell} = \inf Q_{k\ell},$$

and we define a measurable function $q_k(r)$ $r \in R$ by setting

$$q_k(r) = q_{k\ell} \quad \text{when} \quad r \in R_{k\ell} \qquad (\ell = 0, 1, \ldots).$$

Clearly the only relevant k, ℓ are those for which $R_{k\ell}$ is not empty, and then $P_{k\ell}$, $Q_{k\ell}$ are not empty. Also, on account of (34.3) and of corresponding identities in Q, R, the sets $R_{k\ell}$ containing a given point $r \in R$, and also the corresponding sets $P_{k\ell}$, $Q_{k\ell}$, all shrink as k increases. Hence, on the one hand, $q_k(r)$, as the infimum of a shrinking set, will increase with k monotonely; and on the other hand, its values never exceed the supremum of the relevant initial set $Q_{0\ell}$. Thus the functions $q_k(r)$ $r \in R$ form an ascending sequence with a limit function $q^*(r)$ $r \in R$, which is evidently measurable and takes only values in Q.

It remains to show that the map q^* from R to Q, defined by this function, satisfies the identity $p^{**} = p^*q^*$. We shall suppose the contrary, and we must then derive a contradiction. To this effect, we fix a point $r_0 \in R$ for which

$$p^{**}(r_0) \neq p^*(q^*(r_0)).$$

For each k, there is just one ℓ such that $r_0 \in R_{k\ell}$, and we shall omit the index ℓ from our sets when it has this value. We denote further, for this ℓ, by Δ_k the closed interval of reals with the extremities $(\ell - 1)2^{-k}$, $\ell 2^{-k}$. From the difference formula

$$p^*A - p^*B \subset p^*(A - B),$$

when $A \supset B$, we deduce that

(34.4) $$P_k \subset p^*(Q \cap \Delta_k).$$

Moreover, we observe that the Δ_k (because of the relation in R similar to (34.3), which governs the way in which ℓ changes with k) form a nested sequence of intervals with lengths tending to O, and since they meet Q they have a single point $q_0 \in Q$ as their common intersection. We write $p_0 = p^*(q_0)$, and we denote by O any neighborhood of p_0. For all large k, it follows from (34.4) and the continuity of p that

(34.5) $$\bar{P}_k \subset O;$$

here the bar above denotes the closure, and the relation takes account of the fact that the set on the right of (34.4) is closed.

From (34.5) it follows, on the one hand, since $r_0 \in R_k$ and $p^{**}R_k = P_k$, that $p^{**}(r_0) \in O$, and, since O is arbitrary, that $p^{**}(r_0) = p_0$. On the other hand, since $q_k(r_0)$ is the infimum of Q_k, we have $q_k(r_0) \in \bar{Q}_k$, and therefore $p^*(q_k(r_0)) \in \bar{P}_k \subset O$, for all large k. However, $q_k(r_0)$ has the limit $q^*(r_0)$, and O is arbitrary; thus, by continuity of p^* we find that $p^*(q^*(r_0)) = p_0$. Thus $p^{**}(r_0) = p^*(q^*(r_0))$, contrary to our hypothesis. This completes the proof.

We now return to our optimal control problem, after this remarkable theorem, and we denote again by $g(t, x, u)$ a fixed continuous vector-valued function. The domain U of u is a bounded closed Euclidean set, and V is as before the space of probability measures v on U. We write again $G(t, x)$ for the set of the values of the function $g(t, x, u)$ when (t, x) is kept fixed and u allowed to vary in U. We denote further by $\tilde{G}(t, x)$ the set of the values of $g(t, x, v)$ when (t, x) is kept fixed and v allowed to vary in V. According to Theorem (79.1) of Appendix I of Volume I, Section 79, the set $\tilde{G}(t, x)$ is the closure of the convex hull of $G(t, x)$. It therefore reduces here to the convex hull itself, since the convex hull of a closed Euclidean set is actually closed. However, we shall not need these facts about $\tilde{G}(t, x)$ in the sequel.

From (34.1a) we now derive the following results:

(34.6) First Corollary. *Let $x(t)$ be continuous in the finite time interval T, and let $z(t)$ be a measurable vector-valued function in T such that $z(t) \in G(t, x)$, or else $z(t) \in \tilde{G}(t, x)$. Then there exists a measurable conventional, or else chattering, control, $u(t)$ or $v(t)$, such that $z(t) = g(t, x(t), u(t))$ or else $z(t) = g(t, x(t), v(t))$.*

(34.7) Second Corollary (the Filippov Lemma). *If, in particular, $x(t)$ is an admissible (uncontrolled) conventional trajectory, subject to $\dot{x}(t) \in G(t, x)$ [or else an admissible (uncontrolled) "relaxed" trajectory, subject to $\dot{x}(t) \in \tilde{G}(t, x)$] almost everywhere then there exists a measurable conventional, or chattering, control, $u(t)$ or $v(t)$, so that $x(t)$ coincides with the corresponding controlled trajectory, satisfying the differential equation*

$$\dot{x}(t) = g(t, x(t), u(t)) \quad [\text{or else } \dot{x}(t) = g(t, x(t), v(t))]$$

almost everywhere.

The second corollary follows from the first by simply remarking that $x(t)$ is then, by hypothesis, absolutely continuous, so that its derivative $\dot{x}(t)$ is measurable, and so fulfills almost everywhere the conditions for $z(t)$.

To prove (34.6), it is sufficient to take, in (34.1a), P to be (t, x)-space, R to be T, and Q to be $T \times U$ or else $T \times V$; the maps p^*, p^{**} are those defined by the functions $t, g(t, x(t), u)$ or $t, g(t, x(t), v)$ and $t, z(t)$. The measurable map q^* then defines a function of the form $t, u(t)$, or else $t, v(t)$, with the stated properties.

We may interpret (34.7) to mean that, if $u_0(t)$ or $v_0(t)$ is any conventional, or chattering, control, such that $x(t)$ is a corresponding trajectory subject to the differential equation $\dot{x} = g(t, x(t), u_0(t))$, or $\dot{x} = g(t, x(t), v_0(t))$, then there is a measurable control $u(t)$ or $v(t)$ such that the same differential equation arises if we replace $u_0(t)$ or $v_0(t)$ by $u(t)$ or $v(t)$.

§35. UNICITY AND A KEY LEMMA FOR APPROXIMATIONS

We have disposed of the "doves," and must now reply to the "hawks." Our answer to the latter is, in effect, that they are perfectly right, *but* · · · . They contended quite rightly that an honest control must mean one which actually determines a trajectory, subject to given initial conditions. This, however, involves not so much a restriction on the generality of $u(t)$ or $v(t)$, as one on the continuous function $g(t, x, u)$. It stands to reason that we must restrict the control mechanism g as well as the control $u(t)$ or $v(t)$, if we really wish to determine anything, just as in an accident we cannot blame the driver, if the manufacturer supplied a faulty steering wheel. We shall therefore impose a further condition on the function g.

We now suppose that the continuous function $g(t, x, u)$ in our differential equation satisfies, as function of x, a Lipschitz condition

$$\textbf{(35.1)} \qquad |g(t, x_2, u) - g(t, x_1, u)| \leq K \cdot |x_2 - x_1|$$

uniformly in (t, u). In that case, if we write

$$f(t, x) \quad \text{for} \quad g(t, x, u(t)) \quad \text{or} \quad g(t, x, v(t))$$

where $u(t)$, or $v(t)$, is a measurable, conventional or chattering control, the unicity of a trajectory controlled by the differential equation (33.1) or (33.2), subject to given initial conditions, is a consequence of the following standard result:

(35.2) Unicity Theorem for the Initial Value Problem of an Ordinary Differential Equation $\dot{x} = f(t, x)$. *Suppose, in addition to the hypotheses of* (33.3), *that for some constant* K, *the function* $f(t, x)$ *satisfies, whenever* (t, x_1) *and* (t, x_2) *lie in some neighborhood* N *of* (t_0, x_0), *the Lipschitz condition*

$$|f(t, x_2) - f(t, x_1)| \leq K \cdot |x_2 - x_1|.$$

Then in some neighborhood of t_0 *there exists one and only one absolutely continuous function* $x(t)$ *such that*

$$x(t) = x_0 + \int_{t_0}^{t} f(\tau, x(\tau))\, d\tau.$$

Proof. In view of the existence theorem (33.3), we have only to establish unicity. We suppose, if possible, that there are two such solutions, and we have to obtain a contradiction. By writing $x + x_0(t)$ and $f(t, x)$ in place of x and

$$f(t, x) - f(t, x_0(t)),$$

where $x_0(t)$ is a solution, we may suppose $x_0 = 0, f(t, 0) = 0$ and moreover set $t_0 = 0$. By hypothesis, then, some solution $x(t)$ of the integral equation

$$x(t) = \int_0^t f(\tau, x(\tau))\, d\tau$$

does not vanish identically in any interval of the form $|t| \leq \delta$. We choose $\delta < 1/K$, and we denote by $A > 0$ the maximum of $|x(t)|$ for $|t| \leq \delta$. Then

$$|f(\tau, x(\tau))| = |f(\tau, x(\tau)) - f(\tau, 0)| \leq K \cdot |x(\tau)| \leq KA$$

and hence $|x(t)| \leq KA\delta < A$, contrary to the definition of A as a maximum.

This completes the proof.

From the point of view of analysis and the classical theory of differential equations, this standard unicity theorem is an even more lopsided business than the standard existence theorem (33.3) that it supplements, which dates from the same period; we assume even more smoothness in x, but only measurability in t. However, what was formerly regarded as a defect has become a virtue, since it exactly fits the needs of control theory where the differential equation of a trajectory involves a given control, which is rarely taken to be continuous. In fact, Theorem (35.1) ensures that a conventional, or a chattering, measurable control really does serve to control such a trajectory satisfactorily, subject to given initial conditions; therefore these controls must be regarded as honest ones, just as much as if they were smooth or otherwise restricted, and in fact they will play an important part, as we shall see in the course of this Chapter.

In applying (35.2) to the differential equations (33.1) and (33.2), where g is now subject to (35.1), we can eliminate all reference to the neighborhood N; moreover, by subdivision, unicity applies in any given time interval. Actually, we do not need the full force of (35.1), but only that it should hold along our trajectories. In many problems, trajectories that meet a given bounded subset of (t, x)-space and correspond to a given finite time interval are automatically uniformly bounded. This is, for instance, evidently the case if $g(t, x, u)$ is uniformly bounded, since

$$x(t) = x(t_0) + \int_{t_0}^{t} g(\tau, x(\tau), v(\tau))\, d\tau,$$

and the right hand side cannot then exceed $|x(t_0)|$ by more than a constant multiple of $|t - t_0|$. In practice, g is continuously differentiable, so that if our trajectories are uniformly bounded, (35.1) holds along them, with, for K, the supremum of $|g_x|$ in some bounded set of (t, x, u).

This remark again does not use the full force of the boundedness assumption on g, but only that g be bounded along our trajectories. It is interesting to note that this last is, conversely, deducible from (35.1) in the following sense: suppose g subject to (35.1), and let $\mathscr{F}$ denote the family of trajectories subject to (33.1) or to (33.2), which meet a given bounded subset of (t, x)-space, and which correspond to a given finite time interval; then the members of $\mathscr{F}$ are uniformly bounded, and g is so on them.

The proof uses the same trick as does our unicity theorem, and a very nice trick it is: there is a kind of pleasing circularity in arguments in which a quantity to be estimated reappears on the right hand side with a constant factor <1.

Since g is bounded, by continuity, on any bounded set of (t, x, u), it is enough to show that the trajectories $x(t)$ of $\mathscr{F}$ are uniformly bounded, and by subdivision we may suppose (say) that the time interval is of length at most $1/(2K)$ where K is the constant in (35.1). Writing t_0 for the value of t at which the trajectory $x(t)$ meets the given bounded set, or the first such value, we have either

$$x(t) - x(t_0) = \int_{t_0}^{t} g(\tau, x(t_0), u(\tau))\, d\tau + B$$

where

$$B = \int_{t_0}^{t} \{g(\tau, x(\tau), u(\tau)) - g(\tau, x(t_0), u(\tau))\}\, d\tau,$$

or else similar formulae with $v(\tau)$ in place of $u(\tau)$. From the second of these formulae, we see from (35.1) that $|B|$ is at most $|t - t_0|\, KA$ where A is the supremum in t of $|x(t) - x(t_0)|$, and hence that $|B| \leq \frac{1}{2}A$. On the other hand, the first of the two formulae shows that A cannot exceed the corresponding supremum of $|B|$ by more than the uniformly bounded quantity

$$M = \int |g(t, x(t_0), u(t))|\, dt,$$

where the integration extends over the given time interval and $u(t)$ may have to be replaced by $v(t)$. Thus

$$A \leq M + \tfrac{1}{2}A,$$

so that $A \leq 2M$, which proves our assertion.

As a consequence we see, incidentally, with our assumptions, that the members $x(t)$ of our family $\mathscr{F}$ are equicontinuous. For since $g(t, x(t), u)$ is uniformly bounded, the absolute value of the difference

$$x(t+h) - x(t) = \int_t^{t+h} g(\tau, x(\tau), u(\tau))\, d\tau$$

is at most some constant multiple of $|h|$, and the same applies with $v(t)$ in place of $u(t)$.

In the sequel, when we wish to stress the dependence on a function $g(t, x, u)$, subject to (35.1), of the trajectories determined by (33.1) or (33.2), for given controls and initial conditions, we shall term them conventional or relaxed g-trajectories. We shall, in particular, compare them with f-trajectories, which will be similarly determined when $g(t, x, u)$ is replaced by a continuous function of the form $f(t, u)$ independent of x. This will be done in the following key lemma, whose proof again rests on the nice basic trick.

(35.3) Lemma on Equivalent Approximations. *Let $f(t, u) = g(t, x_0(t), u)$ where $x_0(t)$ is continuous on the time interval T, and for $\nu = 1, 2, \ldots$ let $x_\nu(t)$ and $\xi_\nu(t)$ $(t \in T)$ denote relaxed g- and f-trajectories determined by the same initial values x_ν and the same measurable chattering controls $v_\nu(t)$. Then as $\nu \to \infty$, $x_\nu(t)$ tends uniformly in T to $x_0(t)$, if and only if $\xi_\nu(t)$ does so.*

PROOF. We may suppose, by subdivision, that the length $|T|$ of T is $\leq 1/(2K)$, where K is the constant in (35.1). We write

$$a_\nu = \operatorname*{Sup}_{t \in T} |x_\nu(t) - x_0(t)|, \qquad b_\nu = \operatorname*{Sup}_{t \in T} |\xi_\nu(t) - x_0(t)|.$$

By (35.1), and by integrating in the unit measure $v_\nu(t)$,

$$|g(t, x_\nu(t), u) - g(t, x_0(t), u)| \leq K a_\nu,$$

where we can substitute $v_\nu(t)$ for u. Now, since

$$x_\nu(t) - \xi_\nu(t) = \int_{t_0}^{t} \{g(\tau, x_\nu(\tau), v_\nu(\tau)) - g(\tau, x_0(\tau), v_\nu(\tau))\}\, d\tau,$$

it follows that

$$|x_\nu(t) - \xi_\nu(t)| \leq K a_\nu |T| \leq \tfrac{1}{2} a_\nu.$$

Hence

$$|a_\nu - b_\nu| \leq \operatorname*{Sup}_{t \in T} |x_\nu(t) - \xi_\nu(t)| \leq \tfrac{1}{2} a_\nu,$$

so that b_ν lies between $\frac{1}{2}a_\nu$ and $\frac{3}{2}a_\nu$, and from this our assertion evidently follows.

We must here interrupt our discussion to present some auxiliary material.

§36. CONTROL MEASURES

As a result of our key lemma, the main questions to be discussed next, viz., the relation of all this to the preproblem and the establishing of automatic existence theorems, will turn out to reduce to matters largely covered in Volume I, in the theory of generalized curves of Chapter VI, Section 67. The actual material now needed is, however, simpler than this, and, as usual in control theory, it is related to the nonparametric form rather than to the parametric form treated there. Therefore, we now interpolate a section in which we treat this material in the form best adapted to our present needs, even though this entails some repetition of arguments in Volume I.

Our notation will be, in part, temporary. In particular, instead of vector-valued functions $f(t, u)$, used in the previous section, we shall here have real-valued ones: our later applications will take for granted any trivial extensions of the results of this section to the case where the values are Euclidean vectors. We thus denote here by f an element of the function space $\mathscr{C}_0(T \times U)$ of continuous real functions $f(t, u)$ defined on $T \times U$, where U is, as before, the set of our control values u, and where T is some fixed time interval. We write Δ for a variable subinterval of T.

For such f, Δ, we now consider the function w of f, Δ defined by the integral

(36.1) $$w(f, \Delta) = \int_\Delta f(t, v(t))\, dt,$$

where $v(t)$ $t \in T$ is a measurable chattering control, or in particular a conventional one. As previously, we here understand the integrand $f(t, v(t))$ as a shorthand notation for an integral of f, for constant t, with respect to the probability measure $v(t)$ on U. Just as in the case of Riesz measures, we may regard w as a measure and identify $w(f, \Delta)$ with the integral

$$\int_{\Delta \times U} f\, dw.$$

It is then natural to write

(36.2) $$w = v(t)\, dt,$$

bearing in mind that in (36.1) we really have a repeated integral in $v(t)$ and in dt. Strictly, w is not a Riesz measure, but a slight extension of one, enabling us to form the integral of the product of a continuous function $f(t, u)$ with the characteristic function $\Delta(t)$ of a time interval Δ in T. We shall term w, in this section, a control measure. Thus every control measure is determined by a measurable chattering control $v(t)$. However, since we operate on functions $f(t, u)$ it is a little more convenient to make use of w, rather than $v(t)$.

The control measure w will be termed simplicial if it is defined by (36.1), where $v(t)$ reduces to a conventional piecewise constant control $u(t)$. In that case, if we use the formula (36.2), we must reinterpret this $u(t)$ as a unit measure on U concentrated at the one point $u(t)$. This will be understood in the sequel.

The set of all control measures w, or as we shall say, the space of control measures, will be denoted by W. We can think of it as a subset of the set of Riesz measures on $T \times U$ if these are given the slight extension already mentioned. The notion of convergence, to which we may again sometimes refer as fine convergence, is, however, slightly affected by this extension: a sequence of control measures w_ν $\nu = 1, 2, \ldots$ will be termed convergent if, for each f, the values $w_\nu(f, \Delta)$ tend to a limit $\omega(f, \Delta)$ uniformly in Δ. We shall see below that the limit always has the form $w(f, \Delta)$ where $w \in W$ [we term this the property of sequential completeness of W (36.3)(i)]; we say accordingly that w_ν tends, in that case, to w.

(36.3) Theorem. (i) *The space W is sequentially complete.* (ii) *In order that a real function $\omega(f, \Delta)$ be of the form $w(f, \Delta)$ where $w \in W$, the following system of conditions is both necessary and sufficient:*

(36.4) $$\begin{cases} \text{(a) } \omega(f, \Delta) \text{ is linear in } f \text{ and additive in } \Delta; \\ \text{(b) } f(t, u) \geq 0 \text{ in } \Delta \times U \text{ implies } \omega(f, \Delta) \geq 0; \\ \text{(c) } f(t, u) = 1 \text{ in } \Delta \times U \text{ implies } \omega(f, \Delta) = |\Delta|. \end{cases}$$

(36.5) Theorem. (i) *The space W is sequentially compact.* (ii) *Simplicial control measures are dense in W.*

PROOF OF (36.3). We need only prove (ii), since the limit of functions $\omega(f, \Delta)$ subject to (36.4) itself satisfies (36.4). Moreover, in (ii) we need only prove sufficiency, the necessity being evident. Suppose then that $\omega(f, \Delta)$ satisfies (36.4).

If $m \leq f \leq M$ in $\Delta \times U$, where m, M are constants, (36.4) implies that $\omega(M - f, \Delta)$ and $\omega(f - m, \Delta)$ are ≥ 0, and hence that

$$\textbf{(36.6)} \qquad m\,|\Delta| \leq \omega(f, \Delta) \leq M\,|\Delta|.$$

If we write $\omega(f, \Delta)$ as the difference, for fixed f, of the function $\varphi(t) = \omega(f, \Delta_t)$, where Δ_t is the set of times $\leq t$ in T, it follows that $\varphi(t)$ is Lipschitzian, and so has almost everywhere in T a derivative $\dot{\varphi}(t)$ such that

$$\textbf{(36.7)} \qquad \omega(f, \Delta) = \int_{\Delta} \dot{\varphi}(t)\, dt.$$

This being so, let E_f denote the set of the points t, if any, at which the derivative $\dot{\varphi}(t)$ does not exist, and let E be the union of the sets E_f corresponding to these functions f which are polynomials with rational coefficients. Then the measure $|E|$ of E vanishes, since it is that of a countable union of sets of measure zero. We shall show that outside E, the derivative $\dot{\varphi}(t)$ exists for each f. In fact, if $\lambda(t, f)$ denotes at t the difference of the upper and lower derivates of φ for a given f, we have, on the one hand, by (36.6),

$$\lambda(t, f) \leq 2M(f)$$

where $M(f)$ is the maximum in $T \times U$ of $f(t, u)$, and, on the other hand, for any t not in E and any polynomial P with rational coefficients

$$\lambda(t, P) = 0,$$

and, consequently, $\omega(f, \Delta)$ being linear in f,

$$\lambda(t, f) = \lambda(t, f - P).$$

Since, however, we can choose P so that $M(f - P)$ is as small as we please, these relations, which imply that

$$\lambda(t, f) \leq 2M(f - P),$$

require $\lambda(t, f) = 0$, i.e., that $\dot{\varphi}(t)$ exists. We now set, for each f,

$$\dot{\varphi}(t) = \mathrm{v}(f, t) \qquad t \in T - E,$$

and we complete the definition of v by writing, for $t \in E$, for instance

$$\mathrm{v}(f, t) = f(t, u_0),$$

where u_0 is some fixed point of U.

Clearly, from (36.6), $\mathrm{v}(f, t) \geq 0$ if $f(t, u) \geq 0$ at the same t for all $u \in U$. Further, by considering the differences $f_1 - f_2$ and $f_2 - f_1$, we see that $\mathrm{v}(f, t)$ takes the same value at t, for two functions that agree for this value of t. Hence, further, by (36.4)(c), we see that $\mathrm{v}(f, t) = 1$ when f is the constant unity as function of u at the given value of t. Finally, it is evident that $\mathrm{v}(f, t)$ is linear in f. From these facts, it follows that v is a Riesz measure, depending on t, applied to functions $f(t, u)$ for constant t, and that this measure is a probability measure $v(t)$. We can then write

$$\mathrm{v}(f, t) = f\big(t, v(t)\big).$$

Finally, by construction, this last expression can be substituted for $\dot{\varphi}(t)$ in (36.7), and in particular is measurable for each f. This means, according to our definitions, that $v(t)$ is measurable and at the same time that $\omega(f, \Delta)$ is then identical with the function $w(f, \Delta)$ defined by (36.1) in terms of $v(t)$. This establishes our assertion.

Proof of (36.5). (i) Given a sequence w_ν $\nu = 1, 2, \ldots$ of control measures, we have to produce a convergent subsequence. By the diagonal method, we choose a subsequence along which $\nu = \nu_1, \nu_2, \ldots,$ for which the numbers $w_\nu(f, \Delta)$ have a finite limit for the countable set of pairs (f, Δ) made up of polynomials $f = P$ with rational coefficients, and of rational intervals $\Delta = I$. We shall show that the subsequence w_ν $(\nu = \nu_1, \nu_2, \ldots)$ is convergent.

To this effect, we define $M(f)$ as the maximum of $|f(t, u)|$ and we note that by (36.1)

$$w_\nu(f, \Delta) \leq |\Delta| \cdot M(f).$$

This ensures equicontinuity in Δ and in f. From the latter, in f, it follows that for our subsequence, the numbers $w_\nu(f, I)$ converge to a limit for each (f, I), since the polynomials P are dense. Similarly, from equicontinuity in Δ, for fixed f, we find that the numbers $w_\nu(f, \Delta)$ converge uniformly in Δ. This was our assertion.

(ii) This corresponds to the sufficiency part of Theorem (67.1) of Volume I, Chapter VI, Section 67, and the proof proceeds by similar constructions, which may be visualized in terms of moving pictures, or sound reproduction. There are two stages, the first being a restriction to a grid, as on a television screen or a musical scale. The second stage provides a separation in time of the elementary parts of each grid picture, or of the notes of each musical chord (as in an arpeggio) so that only one part, or note, appears at any one time, although the succession of elementary parts of pictures, or of single musical notes, may well be so rapid that the human brain tends to coordinate them.

We make use of a division of U into sets U_j determined by dividing (t, u)-space into half open cubes of side $2^{-\nu}$; a finite number of the cubes will intersect $T \times U$, and the intersections have the form $T_i \times U_j$, where the T_i are half open time intervals. We choose in each U_j a point u_j, and we denote by $\eta(u)$ the piecewise constant function that maps each U_j into the corresponding point u_j. This is the first stage of our construction. The second stage, in which we shall define, for a given $w \in W$, an approximating simplicial w_ν, will make use also of certain shifts in time, described in terms of a certain map of the time scale into small portions of itself, by means of a certain function $\tau(t, u)$ depending on u. We shall arrange that the point (t, u) always lies in the same cube of our grid as its image (τ, η), and we shall verify, for any time interval Δ expressible as a sum of T_i, the formula

(36.8) $$w_\nu(f, \Delta) = \int_{\Delta \times U} f_\nu(t, u)\, dw,$$

where f is any continuous function on $T \times U$, and where for each T_i not reducing to a point

(36.9) $$f_\nu(t, u) = \frac{1}{|T_i|} \int_{T_i} f(\tau(t, u), \eta(u))\, dt.$$

Since this implies that $f_\nu \to f$ uniformly in (t, u), and therefore that

$$w_\nu(f, \Delta) \to w(f, \Delta)$$

for each f and for each Δ expressible, for large ν, as the sum of T_i, it would then follow, as in the proof of (i), such Δ being dense, that $w_\nu \to w$. Thus to prove (ii) we have only to construct a simplicial control measure w_ν so as to satisfy (36.8) for the appropriate $\tau(t, u)$.

Let $v(t)$ be the chattering control corresponding to w, and let $\lambda_j(t)$ denote the $v(t)$ measure of U_j. Since $\lambda_j(t)$ is a difference of $v(t)$ measures of closed sets, and these are limits of $v(t)$ integrals of continuous functions of u, it follows from our definition of measurability for $v(t)$ that $\lambda_j(t)$ is measurable. Clearly also, since $v(t)$ is a unit measure on U, $\lambda_j(t) \geq 0$, $\Sigma_j \lambda_j(t) = 1$. We may therefore write

$$\lambda_{ij} = \int_{T_i} \lambda_j(t)\, dt \quad \text{where} \quad \lambda_{ij} \geq 0, \qquad \Sigma_j \lambda_{ij} = |T_i|,$$

and, except when T_i reduces to a point, we can divide T_i into a finite number of half-open subintervals T_{ij} such that $|T_{ij}| = \lambda_{ij}$. We denote by $v_\nu(t)$ the simplicial control defined by a piecewise constant function $u_\nu(t)$ equal to u_j in T_{ij} for each i, j. We write w_ν for the corresponding simplicial control measure.

We have still to verify (36.8), and it is enough, by additivity, to do so when $\Delta = T_i$. We define $\tau(t, u)$ by stipulating that, in each of the sets $T_i \times U_j$, it is the increasing linear function of t only that maps T_i on T_{ij}. In that case, for $u \in U_j$, the formula (36.8) is equivalent to

$$f_\nu(t, u) = \frac{1}{|T_{ij}|} \int_{T_{ij}} f(\tau, u_\nu(\tau))\, d\tau,$$

so that, since this is constant,

$$\int_{T_i \times U_j} f_\nu(t, u)\, dw = \frac{\lambda_{ij}}{|T_{ij}|} \int_{T_{ij}} f(\tau, u_\nu(\tau))\, d\tau.$$

Here $\lambda_{ij} = |T_{ij}|$, so that, by summing in j, we get

$$\int_{T_i \times U} f_\nu(t, u)\, dw = \int_{T_i} f(\tau, u_\nu(\tau))\, d\tau,$$

which is (36.8). This completes the proof.

§37. A PROPER SETTING FOR OPTIMAL CONTROL PROBLEMS

We resume our discussion and revert to our previous notation. The function $g(t, x, u)$ is again subject to (35.1) for simplicity, although the alternative conditions mentioned in Section 35 would do equally well. We shall term bundle of relaxed, conventional or simplicial trajectories the family of these trajectories which meet a given bounded closed subset of (t, x)-space, and which correspond to closed time intervals, possibly degenerate ones, all situated in a fixed finite time interval.

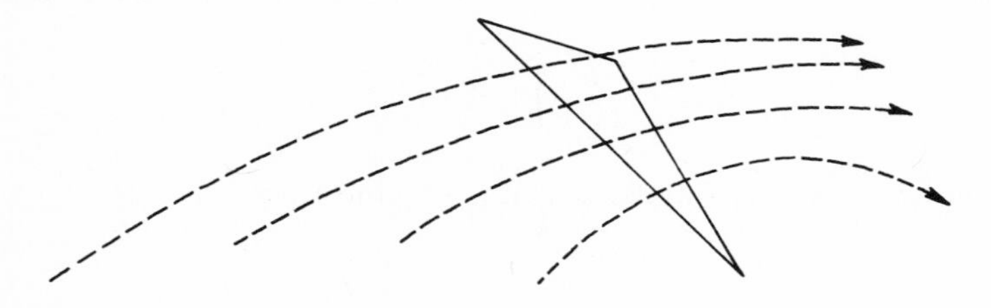

Some trajectories in a bundle and the set they all meet

In dealing with trajectories on possibly different time intervals, we need a slight modification of the notion of uniform convergence, and we shall use the same name for it. A sequence of functions

$$x_\nu(t) \quad t \in T_\nu \qquad (\nu = 1, 2, \ldots),$$

where the T_ν are closed time intervals all contained in some fixed time interval, will be said to converge uniformly to

$$x_0(t) \quad t \in T_0,$$

if, first, T_0 is a closed time interval whose extremities are the limits of those of T_ν, and, second, for some choice of a closed time interval T containing T_0 and all but a finite number of the T_ν, there exist, for large ν, extensions of our functions of the form

$$x_\nu(t) \quad t \in T,$$

which tend uniformly to a corresponding extension to T of $x_0(t)$. (Here T_0 may reduce to a single point.)

The following theorem provides, for optimal control, the setting that we are looking for. It is thus of great practical and theoretical importance, as our discussion will show.

(37.1) Theorem. *A bundle of relaxed trajectories is sequentially compact and complete, and the corresponding bundle of simplicial trajectories is dense in it.*

In this statement, it is understood that the sequential notion of convergence is that of uniform convergence in the sense just explained. This notion is not derivable from a distance, as the ordinary notion of uniform convergence is, and this is why we speak of sequential compactness and completeness, rather than $B \cdot \cdot i$-compactness.

Proof of (37.1). We first prove sequential compactness and completeness; i.e., we prove that, given a sequence

$$x_\nu(t) \quad t \in T_\nu \qquad \nu = 1, 2, \ldots \tag{37.2}$$

of trajectories of our bundle, there exists a uniformly convergent subsequence, whose limit

$$x_0(t) \quad t \in T_0 \tag{37.3}$$

is a trajectory of our bundle. We denote by T a closed time interval containing all the T_ν, and we continue the trajectories $x_\nu(t)$ onto the interval T. By what we saw in Section 35, the functions

$$x_\nu(t) \quad t \in T \tag{37.4}$$

are equicontinuous and also uniformly bounded. They therefore have a uniformly convergent subsequence, with a limit

$$x_0(t) \quad t \in T. \tag{37.5}$$

We can thin the subsequence to correspond to values of ν along which the extremities of the T_ν tend to those of some closed time interval T_0 (possibly reducing to a point). In that case, the corresponding subsequence of (37.2) will converge uniformly in our sense to the limit (37.3).

We must still show that this limit is a relaxed trajectory of our bundle. Since it clearly meets the given bounded closed set of (t, x), and since it is a part of (37.5), we need only show for this that (37.5) defines a relaxed trajectory, i.e., that there exists a measurable relaxed control $v_0(t)$ $t \in T$ such that, almost everywhere on T,

(37.6) $$\dot{x}_0(t) = g(t, x_0(t), v_0(t)).$$

For simplicity of notation, we shall now identify (37.4) with its uniformly convergent subsequence.

We denote by $f_0(t, u)$ the vector-valued function $g(t, x_0(t), u)$. We choose a point $t_0 \in T$, we write x_ν for $x_\nu(t_0)$, x_0 for $x_0(t_0)$, and $v_\nu(t)$ $t \in T$ for the measurable relaxed control corresponding to the trajectory (37.4), and we set

(37.7) $$\xi_\nu(t) = x_\nu + \int_{t_0}^{t} f_0(\tau, v_\nu(\tau))\, d\tau \qquad t \in T.$$

By the key lemma (35.3), the $\xi_\nu(t)$ converge uniformly to $x_0(t)$ on T. However, by (36.3)(i) and (36.4)(i), there is a subsequence of ν and a measurable relaxed control $v_0(t)$, such that, uniformly in $t \in T$, we have, for each continuous real function $f(t, u)$,

(37.8) $$\int_{t_0}^{t} f(\tau, v_\nu(\tau))\, d\tau \to \int_{t_0}^{t} f(\tau, v_0(\tau))\, d\tau.$$

This relation remains valid when f is a vector-valued continuous function, and in particular when $f = f_0$. In the limit, for this subsequence of ν, (37.7) then becomes

$$x_0(t) = x_0 + \int_{t_0}^{t} f_0(\tau, v_0(\tau))\, d\tau \qquad t \in T,$$

which implies (37.6) almost everywhere on T.

Finally, we show that simplicial trajectories in the bundle are dense in it. To this effect, we now denote by $x_0(t)$ $t \in T$ any trajectory of the bundle, and by $v_0(t)$ its corresponding (measurable relaxed) control. Further, we determine, in the given bounded closed set of (t, x), a point (t_0, x_0) such that $x_0(t_0) = x_0$. By (36.4)(ii) there exists a sequence of simplicial controls

$$u_\nu(t) \quad t \in T \qquad \nu = 1, 2, \ldots,$$

for which (37.8) holds uniformly in t for every f, and so, once more, for the function f_0 given by $f_0(t, u) = g(t, x_0(t), u)$. If we define $\xi_\nu(t)$ as in (37.7), now with $x_\nu = x_0$, it follows that $\xi_\nu(t)$ tends uniformly to $x_0(t)$ on T. Hence, by our key lemma (35.3), $x_0(t)$ is also the uniform limit of the trajectory $x_\nu(t)$ determined by the control $u_\nu(t)$ on T, subject to $x_\nu(T_0) = x_0$. This completes the proof.

(37.9) Corollary. *Suppose the set $G(t, x)$ of the values of $g(t, x, u)$ for fixed (t, x) is convex. Then any bundle of conventional trajectories is sequentially complete and compact, and the corresponding bundle of simplicial trajectories is dense in it.*

In fact, the sets $G(t, x)$ and $\tilde{G}(t, x)$ then coincide, so that by (34.7) every relaxed trajectory is a conventional one.

In practice, except when $g(t, x, u)$ is linear in u, the hypotheses of this corollary are rarely satisfied, since the conclusions run counter to the sad fact of life discussed in Section 4(c) of the Preamble to this Volume. However, for us, thanks to Theorem (37.1), this is really a sad fact no longer, since we are fully equipped to meet it by admitting relaxed, as well as conventional, trajectories.

We have stated earlier that these relaxed trajectories constitute a proper setting for optimal control problems, and we are now in a position to explain why. For convenience, we reserve temporarily x_0 to denote the additional coordinate that we foisted on the variable x, and we suppose that our preproblem concerns the minimum of the difference of x_0 for trajectories joining two closed (t, x) sets A and B. To make a sensible problem out of this, we must enlarge A and B slightly, if our trajectories are taken in the conventional sense, or more precisely, we must ask for a lower limit of the difference of x_0 for trajectories whose extremities approach A and B. In practice, the relevant trajectories will still meet a given fixed bounded closed set of (t, x), and they may be supposed to correspond to uniformly bounded time intervals. Our lower limit is unaltered if we admit relaxed trajectories, since these can be approximated uniformly by simplicial ones. However, this admission of relaxed trajectories then allows us to revert to the original formulation, according to which we merely ask for the minimum of the difference of x_0 for trajectories joining A to B. For if S is a sequence of relaxed trajectories for which the lower limit in question is approached, there is a uniformly convergent subsequence of S with the same property, and the limit is a relaxed trajectory joining A to B, for which the lower limit is attained.

In the relaxed problem of minimum thus obtained, it often happens in practice that a solution turns out to be conventional, and even elementary—sometimes even simplicial. For this reason, one might be inclined to think that relaxed trajectories are not really helpful; however, this is based on a vicious circle. In the same way, in many practical problems of ordinary maxima and minima, the solution may turn out to be a rational number, but the notion of irrational number is used in finding it. Or, in a murder mystery, the culprit may be one of the few persons the author has previously introduced, but we cannot take this for granted until we have proved that all others can be excluded. Moreover, even if there is a conventional solution, and we succeed in proving this without introducing relaxed trajectories, we have not excluded the possibility of a second solution, which would then be missed because it would be a relaxed one. This is precisely what happened in the anecdote about the two brothers, where the hidden solution turned out to be so much cheaper.

§38. HILBERT'S PRINCIPLE OF MINIMUM

The notion of relaxed trajectory may be considered in the spirit of Hilbert's famous dictum, which we quoted in the introduction to Chapter V of Volume I. The same applies, of course, to the notion of generalized curve. Existence theorems should be automatic; all that this costs is that we reinterpret suitably the notion of solution. If we have done our work properly in reformulating our problem, the following basic principle should be an automatic consequence.

(38.1) Existence Theorem for Relaxed Solutions. *Let Q be a bounded closed set of (t, x)-space, P a closed set in the Cartesian product of (t, x)-space with itself and T a closed finite interval of t. We denote by Σ the set of relaxed trajectories $x(t)$, defined on closed subintervals of T, which meet Q and possess a pair of extremities situated in P. The function $g(t, x, u)$ which occurs in the differential equation of our trajectories is supposed continuous and subject to the Lipschitz condition in x, (35.1). Then either Σ is empty, or there exists in Σ a relaxed trajectory for which the difference at the end points of the coordinate x_0 of x assumes its minimum.*

Is this an automatic consequence? Certainly it is. For, on the one hand, Σ is clearly a sequentially closed subset of a bundle of relaxed trajectories; on the other, Σ contains a minimizing sequence of trajectories

$$x_\nu(t) \quad t \in T_\nu \qquad \nu = 1, 2, \ldots,$$

for which the difference of x_0 approaches its infimum μ in Σ. By Theorem (37.1), there is a uniformly convergent subsequence whose limit, by sequential closure, lies in Σ. Evidently for this limit-trajectory, the infimum μ is the difference of x_0 at the ends. This completes the proof.

Remarks. We have followed Warga in assuming throughout that $g(t, x, u)$ satisfies the Lipschitz condition (35.1). We needed this to justify the relationship of the new setting to the preproblem, but the existence theory, once this setting was accepted, could have been established, subject only to continuity of the function $g(t, x, u)$. For this we refer the reader to McShane's papers. These deserve a detailed study, all the more so because their point of view is a little different from that of the present lectures. Indeed, in several respects their treatment is both more complete and more general than ours here. In regard to Filippov's lemma, further reference should be made to Jacobs and to Castaing.

§39. PONTRJAGIN'S MAXIMUM PRINCIPLE

Our final sections are mainly devoted to this famous principle, due to Pontrjagin and his associates Boltyanskii, Gamkrelidze and Mishchenko, and we shall follow to a large extent a recent version, somewhat more general, due to Gamkrelidze. For this we require rather different assumptions about the vector-valued function $g(t, x, u)$ (or more precisely, about its extension $g(t, x, v)$, which takes its place now that the preproblem has been abandoned). For greater generality, we suppress completely the dependence on the variable chattering control $v(t)$ by writing $g(t, x)$ for $g(t, x, v(t))$.

We have then to consider a convex family $\mathscr{G}$ of such functions $g(t, x)$, i.e., a family such that every convex combination

$$\sum \alpha_i g_i,$$

of a finite number of members $g_i \in \mathscr{G}$ with constant coefficients $\alpha_i \geq 0$ where $\sum \alpha_i = 1$, is itself a member of $\mathscr{G}$. (In the chattering case, which primarily interests us, the family $\mathscr{G}$ consists of functions g of the form $g(t, x, v(t))$, and convexity holds in a stronger sense, in which the coefficients α_i are allowed to be measurable functions of t instead of constants.) In addition, we lay down that every function $g(t, x)$ in $\mathscr{G}$ is to be continuously differentiable in x for fixed t and measurable in t for fixed x, and also that each g and its partial derivative g_x are to be bounded functions of (t, x), or, more generally, majorized in absolute value by some integrable function of t only. These various assumptions, and indeed the definition of the functions $g \in \mathscr{G}$, will only be required in a certain bounded open set O of (t, x)-space. We need not comment again on the lopsidedness of such assumptions: this is entirely natural in our context. In the chattering case all these assumptions are satisfied if we make the very natural stipulation that $g(t, x, u)$ is continuously differentiable. Gamkrelidze makes clear that other, equally natural special cases can arise, but we shall not go into this.

The dropping of the dependence on u, or rather on $v(t)$, occasions a corresponding change in the notion of Hamiltonian, which is suggested in Section 8 of the Preamble to this Volume. Just as we now have a family $\mathscr{G}$ of functions g, we shall have also a family

$$\mathscr{H} = y\mathscr{G} \tag{39.1}$$

of Hamiltonian functions $h(t, x, y) = yg(t, x)$, where y is a variable vector and each $g \in \mathscr{G}$ gives rise to a corresponding $h \in \mathscr{H}$.

We shall here be concerned only with points (t, x) that lie in a sufficiently fine neighborhood of the set described by a given fixed trajectory C of the form $x(t)$ $t_1 \leq t \leq t_2$. In terming C a trajectory, we imply that the function $x(t)$ is, almost everywhere in its interval, a solution of the differential equation

$$\dot{x}(t) = g(t, x(t)), \tag{39.2}$$

for some fixed corresponding member $g \in \mathscr{G}$; moreover $x(t)$ is to be absolutely continuous. We shall term ordinary point of C a point at which (39.2) holds; in particular, we say that C has ordinary end points if the derivatives $\dot{x}(t_i)$ exist and have the values $g(t_i, x(t_i))$, $i = 1, 2$. Finally, we shall suppose the function $x(t)$ continued outside its interval of definition, when convenient, subject to the same differential equation and to absolute continuity. We recall that, in virtue of the unicity theorem (35.2) of this Chapter, the function $x(t)$, and any such extension are uniquely determined by (39.2), once we fix the member $g \in \mathscr{G}$ and an initial condition of the type $x(t_0) = x_0$.

We shall write q for the ordered pair of end points of C, and P for a small neighborhood of q. Thus P lies in the space of such ordered pairs p, i.e., in the Cartesian product of (t, x)-space with itself, or equivalently, of O with itself. We denote by Q the subset of P consisting of ordered pairs $\hat{q}$ of end points of trajectories $\hat{C}$ in O, sufficiently close to C. Any such trajectory $\hat{C}$ has the form $\hat{x}(t)$ $\hat{t}_1 \leq t \leq \hat{t}_2$, where $\hat{x}(t)$ is absolutely continuous and satisfies, for almost all t of its interval of definition, a differential equation similar to (39.2), with g replaced by some member $\hat{g}$ of $\mathscr{G}$.

In P we shall suppose given further a smooth variety, or manifold, $\mathscr{M}$, with q as a boundary point. We may think of $\mathscr{M}$ as given locally (in terms of local coordinates)

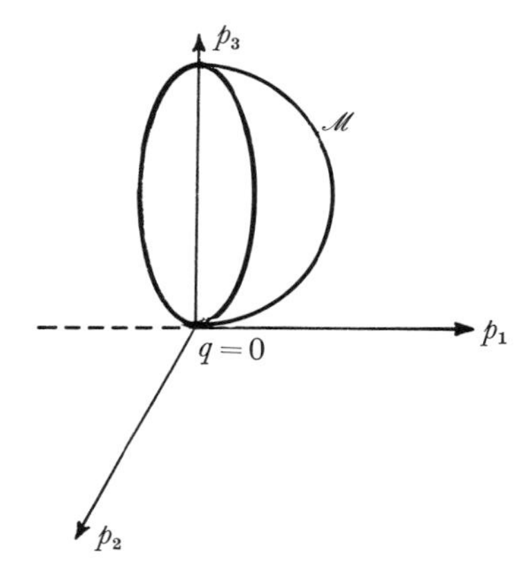

as a smooth one-to-one image of a nice Euclidean domain together with its frontier. We shall speak of the interior of $\mathscr{M}$, and the frontier of $\mathscr{M}$, to mean corresponding images of the interior, and the frontier, of this domain. We suppose the dimension of $\mathscr{M}$ to be ≥ 1, so that $\mathscr{M}$ does not reduce to a point.

We suppose further that the frontier of $\mathscr{M}$ has, at q, a tangent subspace, which is itself the frontier of a tangent half-subspace to $\mathscr{M}$, just as in the figure the half-plane $p_3 = 0, p_2 \leq 0$ is tangent to the hemisphere shown. (We get a tangent half-subspace by considering the half-lines tangent to $\mathscr{M}$ at q.) The tangent half-space will play an important part in the sequel. We shall suppose that a neighborhood of q in $\mathscr{M}$ has a continuous one-to-one map onto a neighborhood of q in this tangent half-subspace such that q corresponds to itself, and that, if $q + \delta p$ denotes the image of $p \in \mathscr{M}$, we have

$$p = q + \delta p + o(p - q)$$

where $o(p - q)$ is small compared with $p - q$ as $p \to q$. In particular, local coordinates can be thought of as coordinates on the tangent half-subspace. Further, a vector $\theta \neq 0$ in the underlying $(2n + 2)$-dimensional Euclidean space will be termed an inward normal of $\mathscr{M}$ at the point q, if it is, first, orthogonal at q to the frontier of $\mathscr{M}$, i.e., to a hyperplane through q that contains the tangent subspace of this frontier, and, second, directed toward the side of this hyperplane that contains the tangent half-subspace of $\mathscr{M}$.

The general principle that concerns us here will make no direct use of any property of minimum. Instead, we define a notion of extremality relative to $\mathscr{M}$. This has the advantage, incidentally, of preserving the symmetry of the variables. A trajectory C is an $\mathscr{M}$-extremal if Q contains no interior point of $\mathscr{M}$. Further, we term conjugate vector along C an absolutely continuous and nowhere vanishing, vector-valued function $y(t)$ with values in n-space, defined on the same t-interval as $x(t)$. If h is the Hamiltonian function corresponding to the member $g \in \mathscr{G}$ that enters into the differential equation (39.2) satisfied by $x(t)$, we term corresponding momentum and denote by $\eta(t)$ the $(n + 1)$-dimensional vector derived from $y(t)$ by the adjunction of the initial component

(39.3) $$-h\big(t, x(t), y(t)\big) = \eta_0(t).$$

We term corresponding transversality vector for C, the $(2n + 2)$-dimensional vector

(39.4) $$\big(-\eta(t_1), \eta(t_2)\big).$$

(39.5) Integrated Form of Pontrjagin's Maximum Principle. *Let $g \in \mathscr{G}$, let h be the corresponding Hamiltonian function $yg(t, x)$, and let C be an $\mathscr{M}$-extremal of the form $x(t)$ $t_1 \le t \le t_2$, which satisfies (almost everywhere) the corresponding differential equation* (39.2), *which we now write $\dot{x} = \partial h/\partial y$. If C has ordinary end points, or else $\mathscr{M}$ consists of pairs with the same t-coordinates as q, then there exists a conjugate vector $y(t)$ along C such that the pair $\big(x(t), y(t)\big)$ satisfies the following three conditions* (a), (b), (c):

(a) *The canonical Euler equations:*

$$\dot{x} = \frac{\partial h}{\partial y}, \qquad \dot{y} = -\frac{\partial h}{\partial x}.$$

(b) *The Weierstrass condition (Pontrjagin's version—integrated): as function of $\hat{h} \in \mathscr{H}$, the quantity*

$$\int_{t_1}^{t_2} \hat{h}\big(t, x(t), y(t)\big)\, dt$$

assumes its maximum when $\hat{h} = h$.†

(c) *The transversality condition.*

Then the transversality vector (39.4) *is an inward normal of $\mathscr{M}$. (Here q denotes the pair of end points of C.)*

This is the formulation recently given to Pontrjagin's maximum principle by Gamkrelidze, except for two relatively minor changes in the hypotheses. Instead of our assumption of convexity of $\mathscr{G}$, Gamkrelidze has an assumption of quasiconvexity that makes the principle directly applicable also to conventional controls by themselves. This elaboration would be uncalled for here, since it would now be a retrograde step to consider conventional controls by themselves, instead of as a special case of chattering controls. The other change we have made concerns transversality: Gamkrelidze assumes continuity of $g\big(t, x(t)\big)$ at the ends, while we assume less than this. However, this last assumption is not really natural either, since the condition concerns the momenta $\eta(t)$ and not the values of $\dot{x}$. In fact, it should be possible to remove altogether the assumption that the ends of C are ordinary, at least in the case of interest to us here, where we have chattering controls. We shall see below that in this case the momentum $\eta(t)$ is continuous, although $\dot{x}$ need not be so. It ought to be possible to use this fact.

We observe that (39.5) provides necessary (but in general insufficient) conditions for an attained minimum. This is because every minimizing trajectory C subject to smooth boundary conditions is *ipso facto* an $\mathscr{M}$-extremal, for a suitable $\mathscr{M}$: we can take for $\mathscr{M}$ the set of the pairs p of points (t, x), which bound arcs of curves subject to

† This maximizes the "total performance," the integral of our instantaneous one.

the given boundary conditions, and for which the difference of the first spatial coordinate is never less than for the pair q. (We recall that our problem of minimum was formulated for this difference.)

However, the main innovation in our formulation of Pontrjagin's maximum principle in this section, as compared with those of previous Chapters, lies in the new form of the Weierstrass condition (Pontrjagin's version). Before passing on to the proof, we wish to show that in the chattering case, which is mainly of interest to us, this "integrated" version is equivalent to a condition that holds at each point of C. As already stated, we suppose the basic function $g(t, x, u)$ continuously differentiable.

We first show that in this case the "integrated" version of (b) in (39.5) is equivalent to an "almost everywhere" version; the latter requires that for almost every t, the quantity

$$\hat{h}(t, x(t), y(t))$$

assume, as function of $\hat{h} \in \mathscr{H}$, its maximum when $\hat{h} = h$. This "almost everywhere" version clearly implies the "integrated" one; we have to verify the converse. Let

$$g_\nu(t, x) = g(t, x, u_\nu) \qquad \nu = 1, 2, \ldots,$$

where the u_ν describe a countable dense subset of U. We denote by $\mathscr{G}_0$ the countable subfamily of $\mathscr{G}$ consisting of the g_ν, and by $\mathscr{H}_0$ the corresponding subfamily of $\mathscr{H}$. The members of $\mathscr{H}_0$ will be h_ν $\nu = 1, 2, \ldots$.

This being so, we denote by T the set of points t of the interval $t_1 \leq t \leq t_2$ such that, for all ν,

$$h_\nu(t, x(t), y(t)) \leq h(t, x(t), y(t)). \tag{39.6}$$

It is easy to see that in T, we have, for every $\hat{h} \in \mathscr{H}$,

$$\hat{h}(t, x(t), y(t)) \leq h(t, x(t), y(t)). \tag{39.7}$$

In fact, $\hat{h}(t, x, y)$ is the integral in u, with respect to some unit measure $\hat{v}(t)$ on U, of a corresponding Hamiltonian arising from the constant control u. Therefore we need verify (39.7) only in the case in which $\hat{h}$ is the function $yg(t, x, u)$ for constant u; however, (39.7) is then an immediate consequence of (39.6), by continuity in u.

To obtain the desired "almost everywhere" version of (b), we verify that T consists of almost all t in $t_1 \leq t \leq t_2$. It is sufficient to show that the set E_ν, in which (39.6) is false, has measure 0 for each ν. Now each side of (39.6) represents a measurable function of t; in fact, since $y(t)$ is (absolutely) continuous, every function of the form $y(t)g(t, x(t), \hat{v}(t))$ that corresponds to a measurable chattering control $\hat{v}(t)$ is measurable. It follows that the set E_ν is certainly measurable. If now the measure of E_ν were positive, then by choosing $\hat{v}(t)$ to be u_ν in E_ν, and to coincide outside E_ν with the control $v(t)$ along C, we would obtain a Hamiltonian $\hat{h} \in \mathscr{H}$, for which (39.7) would be false throughout E_ν and would reduce to equality outside E_ν, so that by integrating in t we would find that (39.5)(b) is false.

The alternative "almost everywhere" version of (b), thus derived from (b), can, however, be strengthened further. To this effect, we show next that when this condition holds, the function $\eta_0(t) = -h(t, x(t), y(t))$ is equivalent to a continuous function. It is enough to verify uniform continuity in T, and indeed we shall verify also absolute continuity.

Let t', t'' be any two points of T. The differences

$$\Delta' = (-\eta_0(t')) - y(t')g(t', x(t'), v(t''))$$
$$\Delta = (-\eta_0(t'')) - y(t'')g(t'', x(t''), v(t'))$$

are then non-negative, since each of them has the form $h - \hat{h}$. Moreover, the absolute values of the differences

$$\delta' = (-\eta_0(t')) - y(t'')g(t'', x(t''), v(t'))$$
$$\delta'' = (-\eta_0(t'')) - y(t')g(t', x(t'), v(t''))$$

are uniformly small with $|t' - t''|$, and, in fact, since $g(t, x, u)$ is continuously differentiable, they cannot exceed an expression of the form

$$a\,|t' - t''| + b\,|x(t') - x(t'')| + c\,|y(t') - y(t'')|,$$

where a, b, c are constants. Hence the relations

$$-\delta'' \leq \Delta' - \delta'' = \eta_0(t'') - \eta_0(t') = \delta' - \Delta'' \leq \delta'$$

show that η_0 is uniformly and absolutely continuous in T. We note that the absolutely continuous function, to which η_0 is thus equivalent, can now be identified with η_0 itself: it is enough to substitute for $v(t)$, outside T any weak limit of $v(t')$ as $t' \to t$ for $t' \in T$. If we suppose such a change in $v(t)$ made from the outset in measure 0, this will not affect the trajectory C, but will result in the sets E_ν now being empty, since both $\eta_0(t)$ and $y(t)g(t, x(t), u_\nu)$ are continuous in t. Thus T is then the whole interval $t_1 \leq t \leq t_2$. In other words, in the chattering case we can arrange, if (39.5)(b) is satisfied, to substitute for $v(t)$ an equivalent control such that the quantity $\hat{h}(t, x(t), y(t))$, considered as function of $\hat{h} \in \mathscr{H}$, assumes, for each fixed t in $t_1 \leq t \leq t_2$, its maximum when $\hat{h} = h$. This is what may be termed the local form of the condition (b) along C, and it is in this form that the condition was stated in the maximum principle in our earlier Chapters. Incidentally, the condition now makes the momentum vector $\eta(t)$ continuous along C, since the components other than $\eta_0(t)$ are those of the absolutely continuous function $y(t)$; in fact, $\eta(t)$ will be absolutely continuous. We can show further that the component $\eta_0(t)$ satisfies, like the others according to (a), a simple differential equation; in fact we find that, almost everywhere,

(39.8) $$\dot{\eta}_0(t) = -y(t)g_t(t, x(t), v(t)).$$

This last need only be established in a perfect subset whose complement in $t_1 \leq t \leq t_2$ has small measure, and we can choose the subset so that various relevant measurable functions of t have continuous restrictions to it: the relevant functions will be $\dot{x}$, $\dot{y}$, $\dot{\eta}_0$, and those obtained by taking as arguments t, $x(t)$, $v(t)$ in

$$g(t, x, u), \quad g_t(t, x, u), \quad g_x(t, x, u).$$

The differential equation (39.8) then follows from the relations found above, connecting the difference of η_0 with the expressions $-\delta'$, δ''. It is sufficient to choose in them t'', in our perfect set, so that it tends to a point $t' = t$ distinct from it, and to verify, by a simple calculation based on (39.5)(a) and on all this continuity, that each of the quantities $-\delta'$, δ'' differs at most by a quantity that is small compared with $t'' - t'$, from the expression

$$-(t'' - t')y(t')g_t(t', x(t'), v(t')).$$

§39A. THE PERTURBATION

The one weakness of Theorem (39.5) is the unpleasant but minor additional hypothesis it assumes under (c). This weakness cannot be avoided as long as we make use, as we shall here, of the traditional idea of first variation in the proof. To apply this traditional idea to the context of Theorem (39.5), with its highly lopsided assumptions, characteristic of modern control theory, is already a strain on classical conceptions. We shall require for this a routine perturbation lemma, which amounts to the calculation of a first variation of the pair q of ends of C. The linear approximations provided by it will be used in conjunction with a separation argument for convex Euclidean sets. This should be compared with the line of argument of Appendix II of Volume I, where linearization and the separation of convex sets were effected in the setting of dual functional spaces, but with a similar object.

One perturbation lemma will make no actual use of $\mathscr{M}$-extremality. Therefore C is, for the present, simply a trajectory

$$x(t) \quad t_1 \leq t \leq t_2$$

subject to (39.2), where $g \in \mathscr{G}$. We embed C, for $\alpha = 0$, in a family of trajectories C_α of the form

$$x(t, \alpha) \quad t_1(\alpha) \leq t \leq t_2(\alpha),$$

which are supposed defined for small $\alpha \geq 0$. Two cases only will be considered: the one in which $t_1(\alpha)$, $t_2(\alpha)$ are independent of α, and the one in which C has ordinary end points. We shall state our results for this second case only; the other is merely a little simpler, and the necessary changes are obvious.

We shall suppose, where necessary, that the function $x(t)$ is suitably continued, subject to (39.2), outside its interval of definition. We denote by t_0 some fixed value of t in that interval, and initial conditions will be understood to refer to values at $t = t_0$. We write x_0, x_1, x_2 and $x_0(\alpha)$, $x_1(\alpha)$, $x_2(\alpha)$ for the values $x(t)$ and $x(t, \alpha)$, at t_0, t_1, t_2 or t_0, $t_1(\alpha)$, $t_2(\alpha)$, respectively. We write $q(\alpha)$ for the pair of end points of C_α.

We regard as determining the trajectory C, in accordance with Theorem (35.2), the quartet

$$w = (x_0, t_1, t_2, g)$$

consisting of its initial condition, the ends of its t-interval, and the function $g \in \mathscr{G}$ that appears in its differential equation (39.2). Similarly, C_α is determined by a quartet $w(\alpha)$. To make up for lopsidedness and lack of smoothness in some of our assumptions, we assume the simplest possible dependence on α, namely a linear one

$$w(\alpha) = w + \alpha\omega,$$

where ω is a quartet that we shall denote by δw and term the first variation of w. Generally the derivative for $\alpha = 0$ of a quantity depending on α is termed the first variation of its value at $\alpha = 0$. Thus

$$\omega = (\xi_0, \tau_1, \tau_2, \gamma)$$

where

$$\xi_0 = \delta x_0, \qquad \tau_i = \delta t_i \quad (i = 1, 2), \qquad \gamma = \delta g.$$

The trajectory C_α is thus determined by the initial condition $x = x_0 + \alpha\xi_0$ when $t = t_0$, in a t-interval of ends $t_i(\alpha) = t_i + \alpha\tau_i$ $(i = 1, 2)$, subject to the perturbed differential equation

(39A.1) $$\dot{x} = g(t, x) + \alpha\gamma(t, x).$$

Of course, we must ensure that $g + \alpha\gamma \in \mathscr{G}$; this we do by requiring

$$g + \gamma \in \mathscr{G},$$

and we denote by $\delta\mathcal{G}$ the family of functions $\gamma(t, x)$ subject to this requirement. Since $\mathcal{G}$ is a convex family, the function $g + \alpha\gamma$ then belongs to it because this function can be written $(1 - \alpha)g + \alpha(g + \gamma)$. Convexity of the family $\mathcal{G}$ thus plays an important part: it is what permits us to embed C in families of trajectories C_α, determined linearly in terms of α. In control problems, this state of affairs results, as a kind of bonus, from the introduction of chattering controls.

We shall refer to the quartet δw as the "data." They now determine the family C_α for small α. A set Ω of such data will be termed bounded if some fixed bound exceeds the absolute values of ξ_0, τ_1, τ_2, and some fixed integrable function of t exceeds those of $\gamma(t, x)$ and its partial derivative in x, for all $(t, x) \in O$ and for all $(\xi_0, \tau_1, \tau_2, \gamma) \in \Omega$. (The absolute value of a vector or a matrix is understood to mean the square root of the sum of the squares of its components or elements.)

We shall seek a suitable first order approximation to the solution $x(t, \alpha)$ of the perturbed equation (39A.1). This will partly reduce to solving a linear differential equation, with initial condition, of the type

(39A.2) $$\dot{\xi} = A(t)\xi + \chi(t), \qquad \xi(t_0) = \xi_0,$$

where $A(t)$ is the matrix and $\chi(t)$ the vector given by

$$A(t) = g_x\big(t, x(t)\big), \qquad \chi(t) = \gamma\big(t, x(t)\big).$$

We therefore give, as in the proof of Lemma (15.1) of Section 15 of Chapter I of this Volume, an explicit solution of (39A.2). Let Φ, Ψ denote absolutely continuous $n \times n$ matrix functions of t, which reduce, for $t = t_0$, to the identity, and which satisfy, almost everywhere in t,

(39A.3) $$\dot{\Phi} = A(t)\Phi, \qquad \dot{\Psi} = -\Psi A(t).$$

Then a solution $\xi(t)$ of (39A.2), and the only one by (35.2), which is absolutely continuous and satisfies the differential equation almost everywhere, is

(39A.4) $$\xi(t) = \Phi(t) \cdot \left\{\xi_0 + \int_{t_0}^{t} \Psi(s)\chi(s)\, ds\right\}.$$

(In fact, this reduces to ξ_0, for $t = t_0$, and by differentiation we find from (39A.3) that its derivative is almost everywhere the quantity $A\xi + \Phi\Psi\chi$. This will turn out to be $A\xi + \chi$; we need only observe that $\Psi\Phi$ is the identity at $t = t_0$ and has almost everywhere, by (39A.3), the vanishing derivative $\Psi\dot{\Phi} + \dot{\Psi}\Phi$; whence $\Psi\Phi$, and therefore also $\Phi\Psi$, is the identity for every t.)

We shall require a slightly sophisticated form of an error-estimate principle: let $X(t)$ $0 \le t \le T$ be an absolutely continuous vector-valued function subject to $|X(0)| \le a$ and to $|\dot{X}(t)| \le k(t)\, |X(t)| + r(t)$, where $k(t)$, $r(t)$ are integrable and non-negative, and where they satisfy

$$\int_0^T k(t)\, dt \le \tfrac{1}{2}, \qquad \int_0^T r(t)\, dt \le a;$$

then $|X(t)| \le 4a$. The proof may be based on our previous argument with the "pleasing circularity." We denote by M the maximum of $|X(t)|$. Then from

$$|X(t)| \le |X(0)| + \int_0^t k(\tau)\, |X(\tau)|\, d\tau + \int_0^t r(\tau)\, d\tau$$

we deduce

$$M \le a + \tfrac{1}{2}M + a,$$

which gives the desired inequality $M \leq 4a$. More generally, if the hypotheses are the same, except that the value of the integral of $k(t)$ is less than or equal to $\frac{1}{2}N$, in place of $\frac{1}{2}$, we find, by subdivision into intervals in which this integral does not exceed $\frac{1}{2}$, that $|X(t)| \leq 4^N a$. Moreover, the interval of t may be replaced by any other if we make the appropriate verbal changes in our statement.

We apply this error-estimate to the quantity

$$X = x(t, \alpha) - x(t) - \alpha\xi(t),$$

where the data determining the family C_α will be allowed to range in some bounded set Ω. By the mean value theorem, applied to each component of the vector-valued functions concerned on the segment joining the relevant pair of points of the triangle Δ with the vertices

$$\big(t, x(t)\big), \quad \big(t, x(t, \alpha)\big), \quad \big(t, x(t) + \alpha\xi(t)\big),$$

we find, for some integrable function $k(t)$ depending only on Ω, that

$$|[g + \alpha\gamma]_{x(t)+\alpha\xi(t)}^{x(t,\alpha)}| \leq k(t)\ |X(t)|,$$

$$|[\gamma]_{x(t)}^{x(t)+\alpha\xi(t)}| \leq \alpha k(t).$$

Similarly, we find that the expression

$$\rho(t, \alpha, \xi_0) = [g]_{x(t)}^{x(t)+\alpha\xi(t)} - \alpha\xi(t)g_x\big(t, x(t)\big)$$

satisfies, for bounded ξ_0, an inequality

$$|\rho(t, \alpha, \xi_0)| \leq \alpha k(t).$$

In addition, we see from the form of $\xi(t)$, obtained in (39A.4), that $\rho/\alpha \to 0$, uniformly with respect to ξ_0 for bounded ξ_0, at each relevant t, as $\alpha \to 0$. It follows by term by term integration that, given $\varepsilon > 0$, we must have for all small α, of smallness depending only on Ω, ε,

$$\int |\rho(t, \alpha, \xi_0)|\ dt \leq \varepsilon\alpha.$$

Strictly, all this is valid only as long as no part of the triangle Δ can escape from O. Integration may thus have to be restricted to a smaller interval, containing t_0, than the one on which $x(t, \alpha)$ is defined. The following argument should be thought of, as applied in the first instance to this smaller t-interval, if need be. However, it then shows easily enough that in the small relevant range of α such an escape cannot take place.

We have now $X(t_0) = 0$, and we shift the t-origin in our error-estimate principle to t_0. By combining in the obvious way the differential equations satisfied by $x(t, \alpha)$, $x(t)$, $\xi(t)$ and then making use of the inequalities found above, we derive that

$$|\dot{X}(t)| \leq k(t)\ |X(t)| + r(t),$$

where $r(t)$ is now the quantity

$$\alpha^2 k(t) + |\rho(t, \alpha, \xi_0)|,$$

and α is sufficiently small. By the error-estimate principle, $|X(t)|$ is then at most a certain constant multiple of $\varepsilon\alpha$. This implies, uniformly for data in Ω, a relation of the form

(39A.5) $$x(t, \alpha) = x(t) + \alpha\xi(t) + o(\alpha),$$

where $o(\alpha)$ is small compared with α as $\alpha \to 0$; the relation is now valid in a t-interval whose interior contains t_1, t_2.

(39A.6) Perturbation Lemma. *Suppose that C has ordinary end points, i.e., that (39.2) holds for $t = t_i$ $(i = 1, 2)$, or alternatively, that $\delta t_i = 0$ $(i = 1, 2)$. Then we have, as $\alpha \to 0$,*

$$x(t_i + \alpha\,\delta t_i, \alpha) = x(t_i) + \alpha\,\delta x_i + o(\alpha)$$

where $i = 1, 2$ and where [in terms of the function $\xi(t)$ of (39A.4)]

$$\delta x_i = \xi(t_i) + g\big(t_i, x(t_i)\big)\,\delta t_i.$$

Moreover, the term $o(\alpha)$ is small compared with α, uniformly for data which lie in a bounded set. In other words, if $q(\alpha)$ denotes the pair of end points of C_α, and we set

$$\delta q = (\delta t_1, \delta x_1, \delta t_2, \delta x_2),$$

we have (uniformly for bounded data)

$$q(\alpha) = q + \alpha\,\delta q + o(\alpha).$$

Proof. The lemma is an immediate consequence of the relation (39A.5), applied to the point $t_i + \alpha\,\delta t_i$, in conjunction with the relation

$$x(t_i + \alpha\,\delta t_i) = x(t_i) + \alpha g\big(t_i, x(t_i)\big)\,\delta t_i + o(\alpha),$$

which follows from the definition of ordinary end point.

The lemma shows, roughly speaking, that our somewhat lopsided assumptions do not seriously affect the approximate form of our end points, as given by the classical first variation.

§39B. REDUCTION TO A SEPARATION THEOREM

We now revert to the hypotheses of (39.5). As a result of our perturbation lemma, we have a certain linear function δq of our data δw. The values of δq are points of Euclidean $(2n + 2)$-dimensional space; we shall denote by δQ the set of these values for all possible data. It is easy to see that δQ is a convex cone with vertex at the origin; this is because the function δq of our data is linear and homogeneous, while the set δW of the data δw is the Cartesian product of the spaces of δx_0, δt_i $(i = 1, 2)$ with the convex cone $\delta\mathscr{G}$, i.e., the Cartesian product of Euclidean $(n + 2)$-dimensional space with a convex cone. Thus δW is a convex cone and so is its linear image δQ.

In the same $(2n + 2)$-dimensional Euclidean space, we shall denote by $\delta\mathscr{M}$ the set of tangential vectors to $\mathscr{M}$ at the point q. These can be regarded similarly as the first variations of difference vectors $p - q$ where $p \in \mathscr{M}$. Thus $\delta\mathscr{M}$ lies in the linear subspace through the origin, which is parallel to the tangent subspace to $\mathscr{M}$ at q; however, because q is a boundary point of $\mathscr{M}$, the set $\delta\mathscr{M}$ is only half of this subspace.

This being so, let θ be a unit vector in $(2n + 2)$-dimensional Euclidean space, with the variable p, and let Θ denote the hyperplane $\theta p = 0$ through the origin. We say that Θ separates (in the loose sense) two given sets A, B if the points p of one set all satisfy the relation $\theta p \leq 0$, and those of the other $\theta p \geq 0$.

We shall show that the maximum principle (39.5) is equivalent to the following statement (which will be established in the next sections, in an equivalent form):

(39B.1) Variation Separation Lemma. *Subject to the hypotheses of* (39.5) *and to the notation just introduced, there exists through the origin a hyperplane* Θ *which separates* (*in the loose sense*) *the sets* δQ, $\delta\mathcal{M}$.

EQUIVALENCE OF THE CONCLUSIONS OF (39.5) AND (39B.1). We again follow, in the main, the argument of Gamkrelidze. The idea of the lemma is to some extent suggested by McShane's discussion of Lagrange multipliers, in 1938. The conclusion of (39B.1) asserts the existence of a nonvanishing vector θ in $2n + 2$ dimensions such that, for all pairs of vectors $\delta q \in \delta Q$ and $\delta p \in \delta\mathcal{M}$,

(39B.2) $$\theta\, \delta q \leq 0 \leq \theta\, \delta p.$$

Here θ is an ordered pair of $(n + 1)$-dimensional vectors

$$(\sigma_i, \rho_i) \qquad i = 1, 2,$$

where σ_i is a real component and ρ_i is an n-dimensional vector, just as δq, for instance, is the pair

$$(\delta t_i, \delta x_i) \qquad i = 1, 2.$$

The first half of (39B.2) may therefore be written

(39B.3) $$\sum_{i=1,2} \sigma_i\, \delta t_i + \rho_i\, \delta x_i \leq 0.$$

If we substitute for the δx_i their values as linear functions of the data, the left hand side of (39B.3) takes the form

$$A_1\, \delta t_1 + A_2\, \delta t_2 + B\, \delta x_0 + L(\delta g)$$

where the last term is a linear expression in δg. Since the signs of δt_i, δx_0 are at our disposal, and since 0 is a possible value of the function δg, it follows that (39B.3) is equivalent to the pair of relations

(39B.4) $$\begin{cases} A_1\, \delta t_1 + A_2\, \delta t_2 + B\, \delta x_0 = 0, \\ L(\delta g) \leq 0. \end{cases}$$

The terms in δt_1, δt_2 fall away unless C has ordinary end points; however, in any case, the first equation (39B.4) implies $B = 0$, and by referring back to (39A.6) and to (39A.4) for the values of the δx_i, remembering that $\delta x_0 = \xi_0$, we find that

$$B = \rho_1 \Phi(t_1) + \rho_2 \Phi(t_2)$$

$$L(\delta g) = \left(\rho_1 \Phi(t_1) \int_{t_0}^{t_1} + \rho_2 \Phi(t_2) \int_{t_0}^{t_2}\right) \Psi(s) \chi(s)\, ds,$$

where $\chi(s) = \gamma(s, x(s))$, and γ is the function δg. If we set $B = 0$ and

(39B.5) $$y(t) = \rho_2 \Phi(t_2) \Psi(t)$$

we therefore have

(39B.6) $$L(\delta g) = \int_{t_1}^{t_2} y(t)\, \delta g(t, x(t))\, dt,$$

and, moreover, $y(t_2) = \rho_2$, $y(t_1) = -\rho_1$.

From (39B.5) it follows that $y(t)$ satisfies

$$\dot{y} = -y g_x(t, x(t))$$

so that $y(t)$ is a conjugate vector along C. We verify further that (39B.1) implies $y(t) \neq 0$. In the case of a problem for the fixed time interval $t_1 \leq t \leq t_2$, it is easy to see that $\sigma_i = 0$ for $i = 1, 2$. In the case of a variable time interval, our hypotheses include the assumption that C has ordinary end points; the coefficients A_i in the first equation (39B.4) then vanish, and by (39.6) they are

$$\sigma_i + \rho_i g(t_i, x(t_i)).$$

Thus, in either case, ρ_1, ρ_2 cannot both vanish, so that neither of them can vanish (on account of $B = 0$), and therefore $y(t) \neq 0$, by (39B.5), as we asserted.

It is evident further that if we write $g + \delta g = \hat{g}$ and $\hat{h}(t, x, y) = y\hat{g}(t, x)$, the relation $L(\delta g) \leq 0$ becomes, on account of (39B.6), identical with (b) of (39.5). Thus (39B.3) implies (a) and (b) of (39.5), and we easily see that the reverse is also true, with our hypotheses. It remains to discuss the transversality condition (c) of (39.5) and to relate it to the second half of (39B.2). It will suffice to treat the case where C has ordinary end points, the other being even simpler.

The vanishing of the coefficients A_i is equivalent to the relations

$$\sigma_i = (-)^{i+1} y(t_i) g(t_i, x(t_i)) \qquad i = 1, 2.$$

Since $yg(t, x) = h(t, x, y)$, it follows from (39.3) that $\sigma_i = (-)^i \eta_0(t_i)$ $i = 1, 2$, and therefore that θ coincides with the transversality vector (39.4). Hence the second half of (39B.2) is equivalent to (c) of (39.5), so that we have established the asserted equivalence of (39.5) and (39B.1).

§39C. AN EQUIVALENT FORM OF THE SEPARATION

It is our separation lemma (39B.1) which constitutes the real geometrical kernel of our principle. However, before proving it we wish to give to it yet another form, and once again we can only remind the reader that seemingly endless minor preparations are often just as necessary for a mathematical proof as they are for a decisive battle, or, for that matter, for a moonshot.

What we shall need here is to express the separation of the sets δQ, $\delta\mathcal{M}$ by a hyperplane in another way, as a property of being what we shall term non-overlapping. The discussion will be geometrical, and we shall consider sets in a fixed underlying Euclidean space. However, for such a set, the notions of interior, frontier, interior point and frontier point, will always be understood to be relative to the (smaller) space consisting of the linear completion of the set.

We denote by $\langle E \rangle$ the linear completion of a set E, and by $\langle A, B \rangle$ that of the union of two sets A, B. Two sets A, B will be termed strictly overlapping if they have a common interior point, and if further $\langle A, B \rangle$ is the fixed underlying Euclidean space. Two sets not strictly overlapping will be termed loosely non-overlapping.

In the sequel, a cone refers to one with vertex at the origin, and has at least one point (the origin). We term it degenerate if it reduces to a subspace or to a half-subspace. We shall need only the following special case of a corresponding statement in which no degeneracy is assumed:

(39C.1) Lemma. *Let A, B be convex cones, and suppose that B is degenerate. Then in order that there exist, through the origin, a hyperplane Θ which separates, in the loose sense, the sets A, B, it is necessary and sufficient that A, B be loosely non-overlapping.*

PROOF. Since we are nearing the end of our preparations, we prove only the lemma as stated. Moreover, we prefer to turn the statement around and say that in order that there exist no such hyperplane, it is both necessary and sufficient that A, B be strictly overlapping. In this form sufficiency is obvious. We may therefore suppose that there is no such separating hyperplane. Clearly $\langle A, B\rangle$ is then the whole space, so that we have only to show that A, B have a common interior point. This last is trivial (by degeneracy of B) in the case in which $\langle A\rangle = \langle B\rangle =$ the whole space, since if there is no common interior point, B cannot be the whole space and must be a half-space, in which case it is separated from A by its bounding hyperplane, contrary to hypothesis. We shall show that the general case reduces to this trivial special case.

To this effect, we denote by Π the intersection of $\langle A\rangle$ and $\langle B\rangle$, and we write

$$\langle A\rangle = \Pi \times \Pi_1, \qquad \langle B\rangle = \Pi \times \Pi_2$$

where Π_1, Π_2 are subspaces with only the origin in common. Now Π must contain an interior point of A; otherwise $\Pi \times \Pi_2$ would contain at most frontier points of A, so that $\Pi \times \Pi_2$ would have to lie in a hyperplane Θ, also containing only frontier points of A. Since Θ would then contain B, it would separate it in the loose sense from A, contrary to hypothesis.

This being so, we can now observe that every interior point of $\Pi \cap A$ is an interior point of A; otherwise we could, through the point, find a landing hyperplane for A in the subspace $\langle A\rangle$. The intersection of this hyperplane with Π could not be the whole of Π, since Π contains an interior point of A; it is therefore, in Π, a landing hyperplane of $\Pi \cap A$ through the point, which is impossible.

Similarly, every interior point of $\Pi \cap B$ is an interior point of B. This means that we need only show that the sets $\Pi \cap A$, $\Pi \cap B$ have a common interior point. This, however, reduces at once to the trivial special case treated.

§39D. PROOF OF THE MAXIMUM PRINCIPLE

It only remains to prove (39B.1). Following Gamkrelidze, we suppose it false, and we have to derive a contradiction. By (39C.1) the sets δQ, $\delta\mathscr{M}$ have a common interior point $\delta_0 q$, and the linear completion $\langle \delta Q, \delta\mathscr{M}\rangle$ is the whole $(2n + 2)$-dimensional space. We denote by k, m the dimensions of $\langle\delta Q\rangle$, $\langle\delta\mathscr{M}\rangle$, and by K, M two simplices of these dimensions, which contain $\delta_0 q$ in their interiors, and which are themselves interior, respectively, to δQ, $\delta\mathscr{M}$.

Now we can find a simplex Δ of dimension k in the space of data δw, such that the restriction to Δ of the linear map of δW onto δQ is a one-to-one linear map of Δ onto K. It is sufficient to choose $k + 1$ values in δW which are mapped into the vertices of K, and to denote by Δ the simplex with these $k + 1$ values as vertices. By combining the inverse linear map $K \to \Delta$ with the restriction to Δ of the map $q(\alpha)$ of (39A.6), regarded as a map of δW into Q, we obtain a map $\kappa(\alpha)$ of $K \to Q$, given by a function

$$\kappa(\alpha, \delta q) \qquad \delta q \in K,$$

such that

$$\kappa(\alpha, \delta q) = q + \alpha\, \delta q + o(\alpha)$$

where the term $o(\alpha)$ is small compared with α, uniformly for $\delta q \in K$. At the same time, it follows from our original hypotheses of smoothness for $\mathscr{M}$ that there exists a map $\mu(\alpha)$ of $M \to \mathscr{M}$, given by a function

$$\mu(\alpha\, \delta p) \qquad \delta p \in M$$

such that

$$\mu(\alpha\, \delta p) = q + \alpha\, \delta p + o(\alpha),$$

where again $o(\alpha)$ is small compared with α, and uniformly so for $\delta p \in M$. Moreover, the point $\mu(\alpha\, \delta p)$ is then interior to $\mathscr{M}$.

To prove our theorem it will suffice to show that there exist, for each small enough α, vectors $\delta q \in K$, $\delta p \in M$ for which

(39D.1) $$\kappa(\alpha, \delta q) = \mu(\alpha\, \delta p).$$

This relation implies that there exist points $\kappa(\alpha, \delta q) \in Q$ arbitrarily close to q which are interior to $\mathscr{M}$, and this contradicts $\mathscr{M}$-extremality. Thus everything now depends on our proving (39D.1). It is convenient, however, to subject this relation first to elementary transformations.

We denote by K^*, M^* the translations of K, M for which $\delta_0 q$ becomes the origin. We write

$$\delta^* q = \delta q - \delta_0 q, \qquad \delta^* p = \delta p - \delta_0 q$$

$$\kappa(\alpha, \delta q) - q - \alpha\, \delta_0 q = \alpha\kappa^*(\alpha, \delta^* q)$$

$$\mu(\alpha\, \delta p) - q - \alpha\, \delta_0 q = \alpha\mu^*(\alpha, \delta^* p).$$

Thus we now have, for $\delta^* q \in K^*$, $\delta^* p \in M^*$,

(39D.2) $$\kappa^*(\alpha, \delta^* q) = \delta^* q + o(1)$$
$$\mu^*(\alpha, \delta^* p) = \delta^* p + o(1),$$

where the terms $o(1)$ tend uniformly to 0 as $\alpha \to 0$, and the relation to be proved is

(39D.3) $$\kappa^*(\alpha, \delta^* q) = \mu^*(\alpha, \delta^* p)$$

for some $(\delta^* q, \delta^* p) \in S^*$, where $S^* = K^* \times M^*$. We write

$$s^* = (\delta^* q, \delta^* p), \qquad f_0^*(s^*) = \delta^* q - \delta^* p,$$

and for all small $\alpha > 0$

$$f_\alpha^*(s^*) = \kappa^*(\alpha, \delta^* q) - \mu^*(\alpha, \delta^* p).$$

On account of (39D.2), we have uniformly in S^*

(39D.4) $$f_\alpha^*(s^*) = f_0^*(s^*) + o(1);$$

while (39D.3), the relation to be proved, becomes

$$f_\alpha^*(s^*) = 0 \text{ for some } s^* \in S^*,$$

or, as we prefer to write it

(39D.5) $$0 \in f_\alpha^*(S^*).$$

On the other hand, since $\langle \delta Q, \delta\mathscr{M} \rangle$ is the whole $(2n + 2)$-dimensional space, the same is true of $\langle K, M \rangle$ and of $\langle K^*, M^* \rangle$. Evidently 0 is thus interior to $f_0^*(S^*)$ in the ordinary sense, $\langle f_0^*(S^*) \rangle$ being the whole space. From this fact, coupled with (39D.4), we can derive (39D.5) in several ways from various applications of the

Brouwer fix-point theorem. We shall derive it from the particular application which we made of that fix-point theorem in Volume I, Chapter I, Section 19, as a lemma, (19.5), used in a distortion theorem.

Since the map f_0^* is linear, we can determine in $f_0^*(S^*)$ a simplex S of dimension $2n + 2$ and with the origin in its interior, and in S^* a corresponding simplex of the same dimension Σ such that the restriction of f_0^* to Σ is one-to-one and maps Σ onto S. We denote by B a ball in S with center at the origin and radius ρ, and we define a map f_α from B into $f_\alpha^*(S^*)$ by the composition $f_\alpha^*(f_0^*)^{-1}$. On account of (39D.4), we have then, uniformly for $s \in B$,

(39D.6) $$f_\alpha(s) = s + o(1)$$

as $\alpha \to 0$. Hence for each small enough α, there exists, by the lemma referred to above, an $s \in B$ for which $f_\alpha(s) = 0$. In other words, we have then

(39D.7) $$0 \in f_\alpha(B).$$

However, by construction, $f_\alpha(B) \subset f_\alpha^*(S^*)$, so that (39D.5) must hold. This as we know is equivalent to (39D.1) and completes the proof.

§39E. EPILOGUE

With the establishment of a proper setting for optimal control and of satisfactory existence theorems, supplemented by the necessary conditions for a minimum, which are contained in the maximum principle, we have attained a satisfactory basis for the study of individual problems, such as moonshots and many others. This is, of course, only a beginning.

References

Banach, S.: Théorie des Opérations Linéaires. Monografie Matematyczme, Warsaw, 1931.

Bliss, G. A.: Lectures on the Calculus of Variations. University of Chicago Press, Chicago, 1946.

Bolza, O.: Vorlesungen über Variationsrechnung. Teubner, Leipzig & Berlin, 1909.

Carathéodory, C.: A letter to Tonelli. Bollettino dell' Unione Matematica Italiana (1923).

Carathéodory, C.: Variationsrechnung. Teubner, Berlin & Leipzig, 1935. (English trans. R. B. Dean and J. J. Brandstatter: Calculus of Variations and Partial Differential Equations of the First Order. Holden-Day, San Francisco, 1965.)

Gamkrelidze, R. V.: On some extremal problems in the theory of differential equations with applications to the theory of optimal control. J. SIAM, Ser. A, Control 3 (1965), 106–128.

Hardy, G., Littlewood, J., and Polya, G.: Inequalities. University Press, Cambridge, England, 1936.

Hestenes, M. R.: Calculus of Variations and Optimal Control Theory. John Wiley & Sons, New York, 1966.

Jacobs, M.: A generalization of Philippov's† lemma (Abstract). Amer. Math. Monthly, *73* (1966), 927.

McShane, E. J.: Generalized curves. Duke Math. J., *6* (1940), 513–536.

McShane, E. J. and Warfield, R. B., Jr.: On Filippov's implicit functions lemma. Proc. Amer. Math. Soc., *18* (1967), 41–47.

Morse, M.: The Calculus of Variations in the Large. American Mathematical Society, Providence, R. I., 1934.

Pontryagin,‡ L. S., Boltyanskii, V. G., Gamkrelidze, R. V., and Mishchenko, E. F.: The Mathematical Theory of Optimal Processes. K. N. Trirogoff (Tran.), L. W. Neustadt (Ed.), Interscience Publishers, New York, 1962.

Saks, S.: Theory of the Integral. Monografie Matematyczme, Warsaw, 1936.

Tonelli, L.: Fondamenti di Calcolo delle Variazoni. Vols. I and II, Nicola Zanichelli, Bologna, 1921, 1923.

Young, L. C.: Generalized curves and the existence of an attained absolute minimum in the calculus of variations. C. R. de la Sociéte des Sciences et des Lettres de Varsovie, classe III, *30* (1937), 212–234.

Young, L. C.: A Variational algorithm. Riv. di Mat. Univ. di Parma, *5* (1954), 255–268.

---

† Also spelled Filippov.

‡ Also spelled Pontrjagin.

Additional References

Balakrishnan, A. V.: Conference on Computing Methods on Optimization Problems. Los Angeles, 1964, Academic Press, New York, 1964.

Bellman, R. E.: Dynamic Programming. Princeton University Press, Princeton, N.J., 1957.

Bishop, E., and de Leeuw, K.: The representation of linear functionals by measures on sets of extreme points. Ann. Inst. Fourier Grenoble, *9* (1959), 305–331.

Botts, T. A.: Sufficient conditions for a generalized-curve problem in the calculus of variations. Duke Math. J., *11* (1944), 373–403.

Bourbaki, N.: Eléments de Mathématique. 3rd ed. Hermann, Paris, 1962. (English trans., Elements of Mathematics. Addison-Wesley Publishing Co., Reading, Mass., 1966.)

Cantor, G.: Ueber Unendliche, Lineare Punktmannich-faltigkeiten. Math.-Ann., *23* (1884), 453–488.

Cesari, L.: Existence theorems for weak and usual optimal solutions in Lagrange problems with unilateral constraints. I, Trans. Amer. Math. Soc., *124* (1966), 369–412.

Cesari, L.: Existence theorems for weak and usual optimal solutions in Lagrange problems with unilateral constraints. II, Trans. Amer. Math. Soc., *124* (1966), 413–430.

Courant, R., and Hilbert, D.: Methoden der Mathematischen Physik. Vols. I and II, J. Springer, Berlin, 1924, 1937. (English trans., Methods of Mathematical Physics, Vols. I, II, Interscience Publishers, New York, 1953, 1962.)

Danskin, J. M.: The Theory of Max-Min and its Application to Weapons Allocation Problems. Springer-Verlag, New York, 1967.

DeRham, G.: Variétés Différentiables. Hermann, Paris, 1960.

Filippov, A. F.: On certain questions in the theory of optimal control. J. SIAM, Ser. A, Control 1 (1962), 76–84.

Fleming, W. H., and Young, L. C.: A generalized notion of boundary. Trans. Amer. Math. Soc., *76* (1954), 457–484.

Fleming, W. H., and Young, L. C.: Representation of generalized surfaces as mixtures. Rend. Cir. Mat. Palermo, (2) *5* (1956), 117–144.

Frechet, M.: Sur quelques points du calcul fonctionnel. Rend. Cir. Mat. Palermo, *22* (1906), 1–74.

Gelfand, I. M., and Fomin, S. V.: Calculus of Variations. R. A. Silverman (Trans.), Prentice-Hall, Englewood Cliffs, N.J., 1963.

Hadamard, J. S.: Leçons sur le Calcul des Variations. Herman, Paris, 1910.

Hahn, H.: Über die Lagrangesche Multiplikatorenmethode. Akad, Wiss. Vienna, Math. Natur. Kl. Sitzungsber., II a, *131* (1922), 531–550.

Hausdorff, F.: Grundzüge der Mengenlehre. Chelsea Publishing Co., New York, 1949.

Hestenes, M. R.: On variational theory and optimal control theory. J. SIAM, Ser. A., Control 3 (1965), 23–48.

Hilbert, D.: Über das Dirichletsche Prinzip. Math. Ann., *59* (1904), 161–186.

Hocking, J. G., and Young, G. S.: Topology. Addison-Wesley Publishing Co., Reading, Mass., 1961.

Kowalewski, G.: Einführung in die Determinantentheorie. Viet & Comp., Leipzig, 1909.

Kuratowski, K.: Topologie. Monografie Matematyczme Warsaw, 1948–50. (English trans. J. Jaworowski: Topology. Academic Press, New York, 1966.)

Lebesgue, H.: En Marge du Calcul des Variations. Enseignement Math, (2) *9* (1963), 209–326.

Lee, E. B., and Markus, L.: Foundations of Optimal Control Theory. John Wiley & Sons, New York, 1967.

Lusin, N.: Leçons sur les Ensembles Analytiques. Collection Borel, Gauthier Villars, Paris, 1926.

McShane, E. J.: On multipliers for Lagrange problems. Amer. J. Math. *61* (1939), 809–819.

McShane, E. J.: Necessary conditions in generalized curve problems of the calculus of variations. Duke Math. J., *7* (1940), 1–27.

McShane, E. J.: Existence theorems for Bolza problems in the calculus of variations. Duke Math. J., *7* (1940), 28–61.

McShane, E. J.: Curve-space topologies associated with variational problems. Ann. Scuola Norm. Super Pisa, (2) *9* (1940), 45–60.

McShane, E. J.: A metric in the space of generalized curves. Ann. of Math., (2) *52* (1950), 328–349.

McShane, E. J.: Relaxed controls and variations problems. J. SIAM, Ser. A, Control 5 (1967), 438–485.

Minkowski, H.: Gesammelte Abhandlungen von Hermann Minkowski. Teubner, Leipzig & Berlin, 1911.

Moigno, F., and Lindelöf, L.: Lecons de Calcul des Variations. Mallet-Bachelier, Paris, 1861.

Morrey, C. B., Jr.: Multiple Integral Problems in the Calculus of Variations and Related Topics. University of California Press, Berkeley and Los Angeles, 1943.

Pallu De La Barriére, R.: Optimal Control Theory. W. B. Saunders Co., Philadelphia, 1967.

Phelps, R. R.: Lectures on Choquet's Theorem. D. Van Nostrand Co., Princeton, N. J., 1966.

Rado, T.: On the Problem of Plateau. J. Springer, Berlin, 1933.

Riemann-Webers: Differentialgleichungen der Physik. Vols. I, II, Friedr, Vieweg and Sohn Akt.-Ges., Braunschweig, 1925, 1927.

Rudin, W.: Principles of Mathematical Analysis. McGraw-Hill Book Co., New York, 1953.

Schwartz, L.: Théorie des Distributions. Hermann, Paris, 1951. (Also new edition, Hermann, Paris, 1966, both are recommended. See also Reviews in Math. Rev., *8* (1947), 264, and *11* (1950), 101.)

Sierpinski, W.: Leçons sur les Nombres Transfinis. Collection Borel, Gauthier-Villars, Paris, 1928.

Sierpinski, W.: Cardinal and Ordinal Numbers. Monografie Matematyczne, Warsaw, 1958.

Valentine, F. A.: The Problem of Lagrange with Differential Inequalities as Added Side Conditions, Contributions to the Calculus of Variations, 1933–37. University of Chicago Press, Chicago, 1937, pp. 407–448.

Warga, J.: Relaxed variational problems. J. Math. Anal. Appl., *4* (1962), 111–128.

Warga, J.: Necessary conditions for minimum in relaxed variational problems. J. Math. Anal. Appl., *4* (1962), 129–145.

Young, L. C.: On approximation by polygons in the calculus of variations. Proc. Royal Soc., (A) *141* (1933), 325–341.

Young, L. C.: Necessary conditions in the calculus of variations, Acta Math., *69* (1938), 239–258.

Young, L. C.: Generalized surfaces in the calculus of variations. I., Ann. of Math., *43* (1942), 84–103.

Young, L. C.: Generalized surfaces in the calculus of variations. II, Ann. of Math., *43* (1942), 530–544.

Young, L. C.: Some applications of the Dirichlet integral to the theory of surfaces. Trans. Amer. Math. Soc., *64* (1948), 317–335.

Young, L. C.: Surfaces paramétriques généralisées. Bull. Soc. Math. France, *79* (1951), 59–85.

Young, L. C.: Contours on generalized and extremal varieties. J. Math. Mech., *11* (1962), 615–646.

Young, L. C.: Generalized varieties as limits. J. Math. Mech., *13* (1964), 673–692.

Young, L. C.: A theory of boundary values. Proc. London Math. Soc., (3) *14A* (1965), 300–314.

* * *

The following books may be consulted for more references to classical results.

Carathéodory C.: Variationsrechnung. Teubner, Berlin & Leipzig, 1935, pp. 389–397.

Contributions to the Calculus of Variations 1938–41. The University of Chicago Press, Chicago, 1942, pp. 499–516.

* * *

For further references on convexity and duality, Young's inequality, and the like, see the following sources.

Fenchel, W.: On conjugate convex functions. Canadian J. Math., *1* (1949), 73–77.

Hörmander, L.: Sur la fonction d'appui des ensembles convexes dans les espaces localement convexes. Ark. Mat., *3* (1955), 181–187.

Zygmund, A.: Trigonometric Series. 1st ed., Monografie Matematyczme, Warsaw, 1935; 2nd ed., University Press, Cambridge, England, 1959.

INDEX

accessibility, local, 144
accessory. See *secondary*
additive function of intervals, 118, 119
admissible trajectory, 263
algorithm, Euler-Lagrange, 16–23
  Huygens, 26
analytic continuation methods, 129
angle, 60, 63
angle theorems, local, 61
  small, 63
angular neighborhood, 63
anomaly, 219
approximations
  equivalent, 300
  to vector function, 190
  Weierstrass, 114
augmented index, 88–89
autonomous problem, 232
axiom, of choice, 103
  of rearrangement of double sum, 95

Baire classification, 116
Banach. See also *Hahn-Banach.*
Banach continuation lemma, 100
Banach insufficient radius lemma, 185
Banach separation theorems, 184, 187
Banach space, 117, 189
barycenter, 96
Beauvais joke, 152
B · · i-compact, 114
  dual unit ball, 117
  closure of convex hull, 192
  localizers, 188
  Reisz measure and vector integration on, 121, 189–192, 204–207
bidual, 105
Bishop example, 203
Boltjanskii. See *Optimal Processes.*
Bolza problem, 4, 227
Borel covering theorem, 43
Borel measure, 189
boundary, of polytope, 92
  of generalized flows, 167
Bourbaki, Zorn lemma and, 102
Bourbaki compact, 114
Bourbaki measure, 121
brachistochrone, 8
brackets, Lagrange, 31, 32
broken secondary, 90
  solution, 16
Brouwer fix point theorem, 43, 321
bundle, of trajectories, 304

calibrated rising curve, 130
canonical coordinates, 47
canonical Euler equation, 48
  parametric, 52, 53, 54
canonical neighborhood, 56
canonical point, 56
canonical set, 269
Cantor, concepts of, 101–105, 283 et seq.
Cantor set, 294 et seq.
Carathéodory. See also *Tonelli-Carathéodory.*
  cheap extremals and, 150
  theory of conjugate points and, 39, 40
  variational algorithm and, 25
Carathéodory distortion lemma, 44, 58, 61
Carathéodory existence theorem, 291
catenary, 8
Cauchy characteristics, 32, 49
Cayley, Euclid's postulates and, 284
celestial mechanics, 34
center, of gravity, 95
  of measure, 192
chained neighborhood, 128
chattering controls, 155, 289
cheap extremals, 123
closure
  of convex hull, 192
  of set of curves, 168
  transfinite, 116, 185
combination, types, 95
compensated point, of vector space, 96
complete metric space, 114
complex vector, 76
cone, 99
  degenerate, 318
  positive dual, 116
conjugate points, 39
  parametric, 128
conjugate slope, 111
conservation, of energy, 56
consistent norm, 201
constant parameters, 285

constituent set, 276
  mixture, 203
continuation principle, Hahn-Banach, 26, 100
continuum hypothesis, 282, 283 et seq., 294
control measure, 300
conventional control, 218, 289
convergence, fine, 167
  intrinsic, 114
  weak*, 116
convergent sequences, space (c), 121
covering, geodesic, 26
convex combination, 96
convex figure, 105
convex hull, 96
convex minorant, 99
convexity, elementary, 10, 27–30
  geodesic, 67, 143
  variational principles, 197, 201
covariant subspace, 247
curve(s)
  η, 254
  fit, 124
  Fréchet, 161
  generalized, 167, 288
  internal, 144
  non-rectifiable, 149–151
  Peano, 58
  peripheral, 144
  ϕ, 256
  reconstituted, 278
  rectifiable, 152
  reversible, 278
  rising, 130
  without initial point, 12
  ξ, 256
cutting, of curves, 277
cycle, types, 92
cycloid, 8

data, 314
decidability, 186
deflected trajectory, markedly, 61
deformation, types, 133–135
  downward, 93
deformation lemma, main, 137
deformation lemma, small, 135
degenerate cone, 318
δ-pencil, 60
δ-trajectory, 60
dense set, 114
deRham currents, 155–156
descriptive map, 266–267
desirable closure properties, lack, 219
destination, 269, 276
diagonal method, 115
Dido, isoperimetric problem and, 215
differential equations
  existence of solutions, 291
  partial, 48
  unicity of solutions, 298
  with boundary values, 58–59
  with initial values, 40
digon, 195
Dirichlet principle, 4, 123

discontinuous nonparametric weak solutions, 148
discrete time, 244–246
dispersal identities, 98
dispersal zone, 95
distance
  Fréchet, 161
  function of, 105
  metric dashed, 116
  shortest, problem of, 7
  to set, 184
distinguished family, 78, 79
distinguished hyperplane, 76, 79
distortion lemma, 44
distribution, support, 118
divergent series, 160
drawing-pin surface, 161
dual, dutiful, 116
dual separation theorems, 187
duality
  of convex figures, 107
  of convex functions, 108
  of poles and polars, 50, 51
du Bois Reymond lemma, 18
dynamic programming, 233, 244

economy in smoothness, 111
eigenvalue, 93
elliptic case, 64
  totally, 123
embedding theorem, 57
embellishment, 277
enhancement, 130
enlargement principle, 199
envelope, in exactness theorem, 37
  in minimal surface of revolution problem, 14
envelope theorem of Jacobi, 38
equation of continuity, 194
equicontinuity, 115
ergodicity, 203
error estimate, 314
Euclid postulate, 283–284
Euler equation (s), 21, 222, 310
  canonical, nonparametric, 48
    parametric, 53, 54
  induced, 32
Euler example, 150
Euler formula, for homogeneous functions, 5, 25
Euler recipe, 5
Euler-Lagrange lemma, 17
Eulerian fluid representation, 170
exactness, 271
  set of, geometrical interpretation, 76
exactness theorem, 37
excess function. See *Weierstrass.*
existence theory, 122–154
  automatic, 147
  duality approach, 194–200
  generalized curve approach, 178
  global, 122, 124, 143
  Hilbert dictum and, 123
  local, 67

existence theory (*Continued*)
optimal trajectories and, 307
Perron's paradox and, 22–23
Tonnelli's approach, 151
extended real valued function, 108
extremal (s) , 6, 222
cheap, 123
favorable, 133
index of stability of, 88–89
$\mathcal{M}$, 310
Ω, 124
secondary. See *Jacobi equations.*
strictly internal, 144–145
well directed, 58, 62
extreme point, 193

factorizable neighborhood, 63
field, geodesic, 27
figuratrix, 51
Filippov lemma, 283, 292–297
fix-point theorem, Brouwer, 43, 321
flight
concourse of, 280
line of, 263, 265
arc of, 265
spray of, 267
chain of, 275–276
flight-corridor, 269
flight-time, 269
flow
generalized, 167
geodesic, 27
polygonal, 195
fluid analogy, 155, 170
focal points, 81
extraneous, 82
fragment, 276
Fréchet curves and surfaces, 161
function, support, 118
fusion, 277

game theory, 155
Gamkrelidze's variation of Pontrjagin's maximum principle, 243, 308–312. See also *Optimal Processes.*
general position, characterization of, 248
geoconvexity, 143
geodesics, 26–27
graded rising curve, 130
gradient, geodesic, 27

Hahn, spiraling of solutions and, 150
Hahn-Banach continuation principle, 26, 100
hairy square surface, 161
halfway principle, 292–297
Hamilton-Jacobi partial differential equation, 48
Hamiltonian(s), 94–121, 223, 227, 229, 308
non-parametric, global, 110
local, 47

Hamiltonian(s) (*Continued*)
parametric, admissible, 53
global, 110
local standard, 50
hanging polytope, 93
Hardy-Littlewood-Polya theorem, 38, 112–113, 234
hidden solution, 179, 288
Hilbert. See also *Courant-Hilbert.*
Hilbert anecdotes, 23, 123
Hilbert construction, 123
Hilbert cube, 295
Hilbert dictum, 123
Hilbert differential, 34
Hilbert independence integral, 27, 269
Hilbert principle, 307
Hölder inequality, 113
homogeneous function, 99
Euler formula, 5, 25
honest controls, 290
hull, 96
Huygens' variational algorithm, 25–27

implicit functions, 40, 42
improper questions, semantics and, 287
independence integral, 269
index of stability, 88–89
induced exactness, 31
inequalities, 112–113
insufficient radius lemma, 186
integrand, 164
exact, 166
integration, Stieltjes, 120
vector, 191
invariance, 35, 36, 37
of domain, 58
inward normal, 309
isolated intersections theorem, 249
isoperimeter, 215

Jacobi condition, parametric, 128
Jacobi envelope theorem, 38
Jacobi main theorem, 84
Jacobi secondary equations, 76
Legendre condition and, 88
Jacobi theory of conjugate points, 128
Jacobian, 10, 13, 42

Kuratowski procedure, 102

Lagrange. See also *Euler-Lagrange.*
Lagrange brackets, 31, 32
Lagrange problem, 215 et seq.
double curl identity and, 33
Lagrange representation, 209–212
landing function, 99
landing hyperplane, 99
landing point, 99

Lebesgue, Beauvais joke and, 152, 153, 156
Legendre condition, 52, 78, 88
Legendre transformation, 46–47
levels of parallels, geodesic, 26
Lichtenstein stability concept, 88
Lindeloef extremal theory, 39
line element, 56
  generalized, 169
  strong, 62
  turbulent, 169
  weighted, 169
linear form, 166
linear hull, 96
linear space, 95
linearity, 95
Lipschitz condition, 152
Littlewood. See *Hardy-Littlewood-Polya.*
longitudinal vibration, 170
Lusin, on analytic sets, 102, 283

Malus theorem, 32–34, 274–275
map proof, three, 57
maximum principle, 230, 231–233, 264 et seq., 308–312
Maxwell problem, 157
McShane
  and Warfield, halfway principle of, 293
  existence theory and, 308
  variation separation lemma of, 317
measurability, 175, 290, 292, 293
measure, support, 118
minimal surface of revolution, 8
minimax, 111, 123
minimizing sequence, Ω, 124
minimum, 143
Minkowski, convexity and, 30, 98
Minkowski inequality, 112
Mishchenko. See *Optimal Processes.*
mixed strategy, 155
mixture
  general, 202
  of finite set, 195
  Riesz, 202
  signed, 168
models, method of, 284 et seq.
momentum, 22, 30, 270
Morse theory, 70, 88–93
moving subset, 78
multiplier rule, 215–217
  elementary, 245–246

naive variational approach, 243
navigation problem, Zermelo, 156
neighborhood, 56, 63, 128
nominalism, 160
non-Euclidean geometry, 283 et seq.
non-overlapping property, 318
nonseparating hyperplane, 106
nonsingular property, 47, 48, 56
nontangency hypothesis, 34
norm, 114

"open" half-space, 106
optical instruments, 275
Optimal Processes (Pontrjagin) , 230, 233, 234, 244, 250, 253, 257
ordinary point, 308
overdetermined equilibrium states, 245
overlapping sets, 318

parameter
  admissible, 53
  geodesic, 25
  standard local, 47
partial order, 103
pencil, 82
  δ, 60
  local, 60
peripheral curve, 144
Perron paradox, 22–23
perturbation, 312, 316
Plateau problem, 8
Plato's cave, 164
Polya. See *Hardy-Littlewood-Polya.*
polygon, 195
polytope, 92
Pontrjagin, *Optimal Processes,* 230, 233, 234, 244, 250, 253, 257
Pontrjagin maximum principle, 243, 308–312
positive definite case, 28
positive extradefinite case, 124
preproblem, 285–286
programming, 244–246

quadratic form, 93

ray, 105
reconstituted curves, 278
refinement, of subdivision, 119
reflexive *z*-space, 105
reformulated variational theory, 110
regular refinement, 119
regular subdivision, 119
relaxed trajectory, 290
repairable decomposition, 279
representation, geodesic, 25
  of generalized curves, 171
resultant, of generalized line element, 169
reversal, local, of map, 42
reversible curves, 278
Riesz measure, 189
  restriction of, 205
Riesz mixture, 202
Riesz representation, 118
rigidity, 218
rising curve, 130

σ-index, 88–89
Saks, theory of integral and, 118, 294

satisfactory subsegment, 137
scalar, 95
scalar product, 76
Schwartz distributions, 3, 17–21
  generalized curves and, 155
  possible uses, 30
Schwarz inequality, 94
secondary equation, Jacobi, 75
secondary extremals, 75
secondary Hamiltonian, 74
selection principle, 127
semantics, 160, 287
semicontinuity
  of $|\delta g|$, 207
  of $|g|$, 207
  of Morse index, 91
  Tonelli's method and, 151, 183
seminorm, 184
separating hyperplane, 316
separation theorem, dual, 187
  of convex cone, 184
Sierpinski, definition of set, 285
significant set, 186
simplex, 92
simplicial boundaries space, 197
simplicial measures, 301
skater's curve, 161
slope, geodesic, 27
small sphere lemma, 66
sojourn time, 255
source (s) , 268
  sinks and, 196
spiralling and stretching, of solutions, 150
stability, index of, 88–89
standard parametric problem, 124
standard projection, 266
standard representation of $\langle Z_o, G \rangle$, 96
statics, 245
stick, of extremals, 82
Stieltjes integral, 119
stream, 203
streamlines, 40, 194
strengthened maximum principle, 264
strictly internal extremal, 144–145
stump-shaped functions, 18
subadditivity relation, 100
subbarycentric point, 98
subdivision, refinement, 119
submerged polytope, 92
sufficiency theory, 263
support, 118
surfaces, types of, 161
suspected solutions, 249
switching time, 251
synchronization, 266

target, 232, 244, 250, 262–266, 276, 281
test function, 18
thin triangle inequality, 132
thumbtack surface, 161
time optimal, 232
Tonelli, semicontinuity method, in calculus of variations, 151
Tonelli device, 84
Tonelli-Carathéodory unicity theory, 133
traffic, flow of, 195
trajectory, 60, 262, 263, 290
transfinite closure, 116, 185
transfinite induction, 103
transfinite numbers, 102
transition lemma, 55, 131
transversal, 26
transversality, 22, 222, 232, 310
transversality vector, 310
tubes, embedding in, 56–58
turbulence, 170

unicity, in small, 68
  optimality arch, 251–253
uniform convergence, on different intervals, 305
unimpaired union, 279
unit ball, 114
univalence, 270 et seq.
  relative, 271
Urysohn, property of *H* and, 294

variation
  bounded, 118, 119
  first, 21, 70
  permissible in Ω, 126
  second, 70
  total, 119
variational algorithm, of Huygens, 25
variational convexity principle, 197
  extended, 201
vector, complex, 76
vector integration, 184
vector space, 95
visibility lemma, 204

Warfield. See *McShane*.
weak maximal subset, 104
weak solution method, 123
weak* topology of dual, 116
Weierstrass approximation theorem, 114
Weierstrass condition, 222 et seq.
  convexity and, 28–30
  semicontinuity and, 154
Weierstrass excess function formula, 27, 222
  dual form, 49
well directed extremals, 58, 62
well-ordering, of arbitrary set, 103

Young (W. H.) inequality, 108
Young (W. H.) monotone sequence method, 189
Young (W. H.) visibility lemma, 204

Zermelo navigation problem, 156
Zermelo theorem, 103
zigzag, infinitesimal, 160
Zorn lemma, 102–104